Helen M. Martin

BIOLOGY

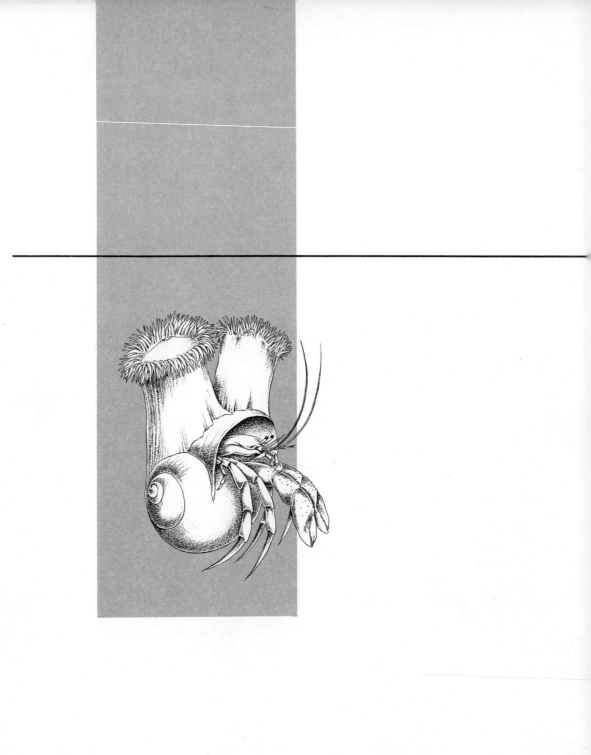

Biology

RELIS B. BROWN

Associate Professor of Biology

Lawrence College

D. C. HEATH AND COMPANY BOSTON

LIBRARY OF CONGRESS CATALOG NUMBER: 56–6544

Illustrated by R. Paul Larkin

PREFACE

THIS BOOK IS INTENDED to give its reader an insight into the science of living things. Such an insight will require some basic information, a grasp of the ideas that integrate this information, and an understanding of the work of biologists. How can these be provided?

Two classes of approach are standard — the types course and the principles course.

In the types course, the emphasis is on basic information — an acquaintance with kinds of living organisms which are the fundamental subjects of biology. This kind of course has the advantages of concreteness and ready verifiability. Disadvantages include the danger of presenting a catalog of facts which the student is unprepared to synthesize into a science. The course may become one of memorizing data and confirming laboratory manuals.

In the principles course, the stress is on the ideas which make biology a science. This kind of course unifies the story and points up the significance of understanding, but it has the danger that students may never become acquainted with whole organisms as individuals, but only those parts used to illustrate theories. A lack of abundant facts makes a good student unsure of the support for his ideas.

The course represented by this book combines these approaches in such a way as to gain the advantages of both. A survey of types is much more meaningful if it is undertaken with an understanding of principles. The student should acquire a grasp of how a living organism meets the demands of its environment before he surveys the variety of organisms. Learning the structure, physiology, and adaptations of an organism is easiest and best when the organism considered is both familiar and interesting. The obvious choice is the human organism.

Hence, the first part of this book is devoted to building a basis of understanding of morphological and physiological principles by a study of the world's best known and most exciting form of life. The reader plunges right into this study of humans without disjointed chapters on physics, chemistry, or cosmology.

From this background, the reader is prepared to investigate the variety of life. Three considerations influenced the choice of organisms to represent this variety. Forms described are presented as living wholes, not merely as reference frames for the illustration of principles. Secondly, these forms are available for direct observation and study by the reader. And thirdly, the number of organisms chosen is as small as practicable so that the reader has the opportunity to get the most out of each. Among the examples which satisfy these criteria, the ones chosen are not always the conventional ones, but the ones which illustrate the principles well with a minimum of those specializations which only divert the observer's attention from the ideas at issue.

In the last two parts of the book some of the principles and information previously accumulated are used in presenting broad evolutionary and ecological concepts. These parts of biology can be understood and appreciated only after the student has much biological information.

Two kinds of questions are included. The "Review Questions" are to stimulate the student to test his own grasp of the material presented. The "General Questions" are to encourage him to see beyond the material, to develop his scientific imagination and vision.

The glossary serves as a reference for the meanings of terms, their pronunciation if difficult or likely to be unfamiliar, and their derivation if the derivation is likely to be of help in recollection or understanding. The index is extensive.

This book, like many others, represents the work of thousands of people. In its content, there is little original except for selection and organization of material. If you were to trace to its source this observation or that interpretation recorded in the following pages, you would uncover a fascinating history involving a number of people through whose senses and minds the item has passed. The biography of an idea is frequently as exciting as the biography of a person. To those who preceded him and to the living universe they studied the author is indebted for the ideas and facts he has assembled.

But it takes more than an author and his predecessors to prepare a book. The effective participation of the editor, Dr. Richard T. Wareham, has been invaluable. The author is also profoundly indebted to the men who read the manuscript critically, Dr. Ray J. Nichols of the University of Mississippi School of Medicine and

Dr. Robert B. Gordon of State Teachers College, West Chester, Pennsylvania.

The careful work of the artists, R. Paul Larkin, Hugh Spencer, and Arthur Knapp, has contributed immensely to the interest and usefulness of the book. The skill of those responsible for the planning, format, printing, and other phases of production of this book present their results for the reader to see. And the author's family and colleagues, who have given their cooperation and priceless encouragement, are gratefully thanked. To all these the author expresses his deep appreciation.

RELIS B. BROWN

ACKNOWLEDGMENTS

Half-tones on the pages indicated are by courtesy or permission of the following:

American Museum of Natural History; 359, 373, 452, 453 (A, B), 499–500.
Armed Forces Institute of Pathology; 396.
Associated News Photo and Wide World Photo; 24.
Black Star; 378.
Cott, *Adaptive Coloration in Animals*, Methuen and Co. Ltd., 1940; 493.
Hartman and Wyeth; 77.
Johnson Cactus Gardens; 488.
John H. Owen; 271.
Schwarz and South Carolina Chamber of Commerce; 557.
Spartanburg Company; 577.
Hugh Spencer; 255, 315, 332.
Dr. W. M. Stanley; 248 (C).
United States Department of Agriculture; 254.
United States Forest Service; 321, 322, 558, 560, 562, 563, 564 (Above and Below), 566, 568, 570.

Dr. Williams; 248 (A).
Dr. R. Wyckoff; 248 (A, B, D, E, F).

Illustrations on the pages indicated were redrawn by permission, as follows:

Best and Taylor, *Physiological Basis of Medical Practice*, 5th Ed., Williams and Wilkins, 1950; 158.
Buchsbaum, *Animals without Backbones*, 2nd Ed., University of Chicago Press, 1948; 393, 403.
Darrah, *Textbook of Paleobotany*, Appleton-Century-Crofts, 1939; 523 (A).
Haupt, *An Introduction to Botany*, 2nd Ed., McGraw-Hill, 1946; 523 (B, C).
Hunter and Hunter, *College Zoology*, Saunders, 1949, there modified from Jennings; 262, 264.
Pauli, *The World of Life*, Houghton Mifflin, 1949; 418, in part.
Smith, *The Freshwater Algae of the United States*, 2nd Ed., McGraw-Hill, 1950; 286.
Winchester, *Genetics*, Houghton Mifflin, 1951; 218.

CONTENTS

BIOLOGY

Introduction

SCIENCE

Science is like housebuilding. Ten thousand years ago, when a man set out to build himself a shelter, he picked out a likely spot with raw materials nearby, and laboriously put together a house. By modern standards such a house would seem pretty crude, but it served his purposes.

Our ancient housebuilder must have first visualized the finished product. Then he thought about what materials would be needed, and how they could be worked up. Then he set to it.

If he was resourceful, he may have changed his plans as he went along. As a straighter tree or a smoother rock came to his attention, it was worked into the building. After he had the house built, and lived in it a while, he found leaks and chinks here and there. Perhaps a rafter broke under too great a strain. Repairing and remodeling were called for. But ordinarily the house satisfied his requirements, and he felt well rewarded for his efforts.

Similarly, in his attempts to understand and cope with his environment, man built theories to account for the things he observed. Occasionally a theory proved weak, and further experiences called for plugging the holes and perhaps modifying the explanation. But when a theory satisfied his sense of the rightness of things, he felt well rewarded for the thought put into it, and clung to it with an affection like that for his physical home.

Science is much like housebuilding. We now have the advantage of the ideas and experience of men for the last ten thousand years. Both our houses and our scientific explanations have become more elaborate through the years. In housebuilding men no longer work alone. Many men prepare the materials: lumber, bricks, cement, nails, fixtures, and so forth. Others shape them into partly finished products: doors, windows, rafters, floor boards. Still others draw up plans to follow in construction. Carpenters, brick-layers, plumbers, electricians, plasterers, painters, and other specialists work at their particular skills.

After the house is built and ready, the owner comes to live in it and use and enjoy it in the way he wishes. He may even alter parts of it here and there — change part of the base-ment into a playroom or add shutters to the windows.

So in science, some gather and prepare materials, like the patient astronomer who records the positions and intensity of stars night after night for a lifetime. Some are architects who visualize explanations of such starry phenomena. Some are specialists who take the explanations and the materials and put them together into the body of scientific knowledge available for each of us to use.

Uncounted numbers of such scientists have contributed to the structure of science, and this activity goes on today as vigorously as at any time in history. Results of this accumulation of fact and theory are woven into our daily lives. We use the practical, physical products of scientific development as naturally as we speak — electric current, automobiles, plastic utensils, vitamin-enriched foods, antibiotic drugs, and an endless number of other things which make our lives easier, happier, and more interesting. And even more significant than this, our thoughts, our beliefs, our motivations are influenced profoundly by the discoveries and theories of the men of science. Our understanding of the universe and of our place in it is affected by what has been said by the scientists of other days and of our day.

Each of us is to some degree a scientist. We observe events that occur about us. We draw conclusions, and use these conclusions in deciding on our own actions. As we find our conclusions inaccurate, we modify them in the light of further observations.

Contributions to science are not all the work of professional scientists. Many an amateur has made invaluable additions to our fund of knowledge and our theoretical concepts. Students in their first courses in biology have seen things never found before, and have brought new understanding of biological phenomena to men of much longer experience in science. So much remains to be discovered and explained that any alert and thoughtful mind may contribute an addition to science.

Two factors contribute to success in scientific activity: knowledge and workmanship.

Knowledge

Knowledge is acquired by study and experience. You study the results of other people's work, first in textbooks, then in original reports. When you have exhausted these sources, you pursue independent investigations as far as your opportunities and patience permit.

Dr. L. L. Woodruff set out to discover whether simple living organisms died of old age. He kept specimens of a tiny water animal, *Paramecium*, in his laboratory, watching for the animal to divide into two, as it did almost daily. Each time it divided, Woodruff separated the two so that there was no possibility of sexual reproduction. After many thousand such divisions of these animals, Woodruff came to the conclusion that they were potentially immortal, and in favorable environments might live indefinitely. One summer, Woodruff asked an older scientist, Dr. E. B. Wilson, if he had not adequately proved his point. He was getting tired of his constant vigil. The older scientist told him that he had undoubtedly proved his point, but that he should continue his work. "You can't keep an animal around the laboratory year after year without learning new things about him," Wilson said. The following spring, Dr. Woodruff discovered a new type of reproduction in *Paramecium*, a process he called "endomixis." Largely on the strength of this discovery, Woodruff was elected to the National Academy of Sciences, the highest official honor conferred on scientists in this country.

Workmanship

Workmanship is a matter of motivation and method.

Scientists are motivated by intense personal curiosity, by the desire to contribute to the knowledge and welfare of their fellows, and by anticipation of satisfactions to be derived from success in their work: the feeling of accomplishment, social esteem, and economic advancement.

Methods used vary widely, but successful methods have many traits in common. These may be illustrated by an example: Suppose you wanted to know whether characteristics you acquired during your lifetime might be inherited by your children. You would read the writings of those who had investigated the problem before you. Although most such references would deny the possibility, you might find some which said such inheritance might occur. So you decide to investigate the matter yourself.

Your first task is to plan an experiment which will bring out the answer. Humans are not easy to work on in this sort of study. Perhaps you will choose white rats.

Then you look for a characteristic which is clear-cut enough to be easily recognized. You think of cutting off the tails of rats to see if the next generation will have shorter tails.

After several generations of rats so treated, you find that some newborn rats have slightly shorter tails than the ones you started with, some the same length, and some slightly longer. On the average, no significant change has occurred.

Two considerations face you immediately. In the first place, rat tails may normally get longer generation after generation, so that your result of no change may actually be a shortening effect. You are thinking of alternative explanations of your results. To determine this point, you observe the length of tail in several generations of rats of which the tails have not been cut. This is called a control experiment, for the unoperated rats are controls which determine the normal situation in contrast to the situation of your experiment.

If this controlled experiment shows that rat tails average about the same length whether their parents' tails have been cut or not, you are ready for the second consideration: Have you carried on your experiment long enough and with enough animals to make your results significant? This is largely a matter of personal judgment, based on experience in other researches. You will be unable to test all of the white rats in the world for an infinite number of generations. You must satisfy yourself only that you have enough data to make your conclusion reasonably valid.

The next move will be to discuss or publish your results so that other scientists interested in the same problem may compare your findings with theirs, and criticize your methods and results in the light of their experience. By this community of effort generally acceptable principles are established.

BIOLOGY

Science is divided into sections according to the problems investigated. **Biology** (Greek: the study of life) is the science of living organisms. The processes carried on in and by living organisms are studied by methods developed in physics and chemistry. A knowledge of geology helps us understand the environment in which organisms live and upon which they depend for their necessities. Details of the living patterns of human organisms are the subject matter of the social sciences. How can we draw boundary lines around biology? A biologist must have some general information in all of the sciences to understand the problems in his own. Likewise, any person needs some experience in biological thought to pursue many other phases of human knowledge successfully.

Within the province of biology, other convenient divisions may be set up. We distinguish most living organisms as either plants or animals, indicating a division into **botany** and **zoology.** Yet, some organisms have characteristics of both plants and animals, and may be classified with either. Many of the ideas we derive from the study of one group are equally discoverable in and adaptable to the other, as we shall see later on in this book.

Morphology is the study of structure, and **physiology** the study of action, but either loses most of its meaning without the other. An understanding of gasoline combustion is of no value to an automobile mechanic if he doesn't know anything about the parts and organization of a car; and it is of no value to him to be able to recognize the names of the parts if he has no idea what they do.

Taxonomy is the study of classification and evolutionary relationships of living organisms. A student of **paleontology** investigates the past history of organisms. A student of **genetics** finds out about the inheritance of characteristics from one generation to another. **Ecology** is the science of the relations and adaptations between organisms and their environments.

All of these and many other subdivisions are merely viewpoints from which to investigate living organisms. As a beginning student of biology, you will want to get a general grasp of the whole field. Then, if some one approach excites more intense interest than others, you may pursue it with an understanding of its relation to other standpoints and to the whole field of knowledge.

LIFE

Biology, you have read, is the science of living organisms. It may seem simple to distinguish between something alive and something dead. But when you and I come to put the distinguishing features into words, we find difficulties. Humans and cows and sparrows which move from place to place under their own power are obviously alive. Trees and flowers with green leaves and a flourishing appearance are certainly living. But how about an oyster? Or a walnut? Or a poliomyelitis virus?

We have come to recognize certain qualities as being characteristic of life. One of these is complex organization. In an attempt to simplify a very complicated problem, we speak of the substance of which all organisms are made as **protoplasm.** The composition of protoplasm varies from one organism to another, and from one part to another of the same organism. But there are factors common to the make-up of all living things.

One such factor is that all protoplasm is colloidal. A colloid is a mixture of substances in which some particles, though too small to be seen with an ordinary microscope, are composed of more than one molecule of matter. To be more specific, we may try to set limits to the size of colloidal particles. A meter is an arbitrary unit of length approximately equal to 39.37 inches. A thousandth of a meter is a millimeter, and a thousandth of a millimeter is a micron. Colloidal particles may be defined as between five thousandths and two tenths of a micron in diameter. But in practice this seems too confining, for mixtures containing particles beyond these limits act as colloids do, so we are not yet prepared to be rigidly definite in our concept of colloidal particles.

Protoplasm is not only a mixture of colloidal particles in a continuous medium, but both the particles (dispersed phase) and the media (continuous phase) are diverse and changeable. Water is always a component of protoplasm, as are inorganic salts, fats, and proteins. Water and lipoid (Greek: fatlike) substances may both be continuous media in different parts or layers of the same lump of protoplasm, each containing a great variety of colloidal particles or droplets. When water is the continuous phase, lipoid droplets are dispersed in it, and vice versa.

The variety of components and their proportions which it is possible to find in protoplasm are tremendous. If we could understand the details of the composition of protoplasm more fully than we do now we should be much further along in our quest for biological knowledge. But students in this field face formidable difficulties.

In addition to the complexity of protoplasm, the relationships of the numerous components are constantly changing. Furthermore, most of the usual methods of chemical analysis cannot be applied to living protoplasm, for in the usual techniques of analysis the protoplasm is killed, changing its characteristics very greatly. Then the investigator is no longer studying protoplasm, but its decomposing remains. You cannot expect to get a complete understanding of the details of a wooden house by sifting its ashes after it has burned to the ground.

A second characteristic of life is its directional change. Protoplasm is dynamic. Within it physical and chemical actions are unceasing. Like a busy factory on twenty-four-hour duty, it operates on raw materials brought in, produces tools, uses them in making finished products, consumes the products or sends them to other factories, and gets rid of by-products and wastes.

The results of the activity of protoplasm are motion, growth, appearance and disappearance of structures and substances, and responses to external influences. The totality of this activity we call **metabolism,** derived from the Greek word for change. And, as stated in the previous paragraph, the change is directional, not random. The activities are meshed together as in a complicated machine, not a machine built by man, but an organism that builds and operates itself, perhaps reproducing itself, within limits set by its own "mechanism" and the nature of its surroundings.

A third characteristic of living organisms is individuality. Throughout the considerable changes occurring in a living organism we can recognize a stability, a conforming to pattern, that supports the scientist's faith in the orderliness of the universe. Rome has been in existence for many hundreds of years. Changes in its buildings, its trees, its inhabitants, its size, its activity are constantly going on. The majority of its characteristics in Caesar's day were very much different from those during Garibaldi's day, or now, but the individuality of Rome has survived all of these changes. Your friends will recognize you a year from now, even though much of the actual physical substance of you will have changed — new molecules coming in, old ones going out.

Another feature of this characteristic of individuality is that no two plants or animals are exactly alike. Even identical twins are carried in different parts of the mother's womb, and they are subjected throughout their lives to environments differing in at least some respects.

We shall later discuss the interaction of heredity and environment in living things, and find out that seldom is heredity and never is environment the same for two organisms. Since each organism is the product (not the sum) of the interaction of these two factors, it will be distinct from every other organism.

In one's social and political philosophy, this is probably the greatest lesson biology can offer. If no two humans are identical, why should we expect all people to conform to one pattern, to one culture, or to one philosophy? Isn't it our duty and privilege to use this knowledge of individual differences in planning our society? Shouldn't this idea give us a humility and a tolerance, and a realization that your criteria for truth, for beauty, for goodness may rightfully differ from mine?

A fourth characteristic of living things is reproduction. A living organism is usually capable of reproducing its kind either by itself or by cooperation with another organism. Each individual of some kinds of primitive plants and animals can produce new individuals by dividing into two. In most higher forms sexual reproduction is the rule, two organisms being required to produce new individuals.

The appearance of more and more new individuals would eventually exhaust the space and supplies available for life if it were not that many organisms die eventually. Individuals come and go; life continues.

In summary, then, living things are characterized by complex organization, by directional changes, by individuality, and by the capacity for reproduction.

CELLS

A single "lump" of protoplasm we call a **cell.** A group of cells of similar type and action is a **tissue,** as muscular tissue. Different tissues joined together and acting together constitute an **organ,** as the stomach. Several organs involved in one general metabolic process we may call a **system,** as the digestive system. Many systems work together in one organism. And yet there are many kinds of one-celled animals and plants, and in these organisms all of the activities of life take place within one cell.

The term "cell" was borrowed from a compartment in a prison. Robert Hooke (1635–1703), when he was preparator for the Royal Society of London, constructed a microscope, then a very new type of instrument. Among the things he examined with it was a thin slice of cork. He found numerous empty chambers which reminded him of prison cells. He pictured these chambers in his book of miscellaneous observations, *Micrographia*, published in 1665. Hooke called the chambers "cells."

It was almost two hundred years later that biologists clarified the idea that in life these hollow chambers contained protoplasm, and that the walls were but nonliving secretions of these living units. The term "cell" was then transferred to the protoplasm in one of the compartments.

Most cells, whether plant or animal, have the same fundamental organization. See Figure Int. 1. No matter whether the cell is an entire organism in itself, or only a small part of an organism, it has certain structures and certain metabolic capabilities.

For example, the **cell membrane** is a specialized structure at the periphery of the cell. This membrane has the characteristic of semipermeability. That is, through the membrane some things can pass into and out of the cell, but not others. Water, some inorganic salts, some simple organic compounds, and some gases in solution can pass through. More complex organic compounds, colloidal particles, and other larger particles may be stopped by the membrane.

Within the membrane, the protoplasm is usually divided

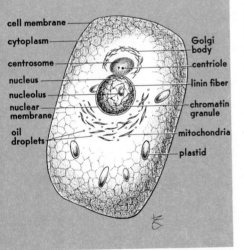

cell membrane
cytoplasm
centrosome
nucleus
nucleolus
nuclear membrane
oil droplets

Golgi body
centriole
linin fiber
chromatin granule
mitochondria
plastid

Fig. Int. 1 Diagram of a cell. Cells vary greatly in shape, size, and contents; but they have some structures and many activities in common. Most cells are too small to be seen without magnification.

into a central **nucleus** and peripheral **cytoplasm.** The nucleus has its own semipermeable **nuclear membrane** with characteristics slightly different from those of the cell membrane. The nucleus differs from the cytoplasm in both chemical make-up and physical structure.

In general it may be said that the nucleus seems to be the management or executive division of the cell; and the cytoplasm, the labor or manufacturing division. Much of the metabolic process goes on in the cytoplasm under the control of the nucleus.

In the cytoplasm are found such materials as fat droplets, starch grains, amino acids used in the manufacture of proteins, water, and dissolved salts. Oxygen enters and combines with some of the stored food, releasing the energy required for metabolism. The wastes of this reaction will be leaving.

The cytoplasm itself may contain certain differentiated structures. A **centrosome** often appears near the nucleus; it gets its name from the Latin *centrum*, center, and the Greek *soma*, body. This bit of cytoplasm contains one or two **centrioles** which will take a leading role in the division of the cell into two cells.

Mitochondria, named from the Greek for thread-grains, are small granules or rods of fatty-protein nature found in many kinds of cells. They seem to be prominent at locations of high metabolic activity, often of a secretory nature. Somewhat similar structures known as **Golgi bodies,** after the Italian histologist Camillo Golgi (1844–1926), are also associated with cell secretions. Mitochondria and Golgi bodies differ in their densities and in their reactions to certain dyes, and it is quite possible that each term designates many types of structures with different actions, but that we have not yet been able to distinguish these differences conclusively.

In many plant cells there are bodies called **plastids.** Some plastids contain stored food. The substance **chlorophyll** used by plants in the manufacture of food is usually carried in plastids called **chloroplasts.**

Certain nonliving structures are associated with cells. Particles of food such as oil droplets or starch grains may be contained in the cytoplasm. Most plant cells have a cellulose cell wall deposited outside the cell membrane.

Inside the nuclear membrane, the nucleus also has specific structures visible microscopically after certain preparations are made. A fine network of interlaced fibers known as **linin** (Latin for lint) **fibers** carries little beadlike knots known as **chromatin granules.** *Chromatin* comes from the Greek word for color, since these granules take the colored stains most deeply. At each cell division the chromatin granules are divided in such a way that each resulting cell usually gets a complete set. One or more objects called **nucleoli,** or little nuclei, may appear in the nucleus. These may be of different kinds. Sometimes chromatin granules cluster together and look like a nucleolus. Other nucleoli have chemical characteristics more like those of cytoplasm than like those of chromatin granules. Here again is a great need for further study, more experiments, and more analysis.

The occurrence of cells in nearly all living forms so far studied has given rise to the **Cell Theory,** which states that all living organisms are composed of cells and cell products. The last item is added to take care of such things as cellulose and the lime salts of bone which are deposited by cells and contain cells, but are not themselves cells. The universality of the Cell Theory is challenged by the discovery of viruses, which do not seem to have the complexity of structure found in, for example, human cells. But the question as to whether viruses are living organisms, organic molecules, or a transition between the two is still unsettled. If they are alive, it may be that nuclear and cytoplasmic material are both present in an arrangement different from that of human cells. See Chapter 13.

Accepting this Cell Theory as a working hypothesis, rather than as a certainty, we shall consider the biology of a sample organism, the human, as a product of the biology of its cells. Although we may speak of this tissue or that organ as performing a certain act, we shall remember that it is the cells of this tissue or that organ that we refer to. If we keep that principle in mind we shall avoid many of the pitfalls and unwise generalizations that afflict our thought not only in biology but in other fields.

SUMMARY

Science is an accumulation of fact and theory developed by people from many countries and many eras. It changes little by little as information is added and previously described phenomena are reinterpreted.

A scientist will visualize a problem — a question to put to the universe — and devise experiments and observations which may throw light on the problem. He examines the results of his experiments and observations critically to see if more than one logical explanation is possible. Then he tests the explanation which in his judgment is the best.

When he is satisfied that he has a contribution to make to the advance of science he submits it to the consideration of other people interested in his field of knowledge.

Biology is the science of living organisms. It may for convenience be divided into botany and zoology, and into morphology, physiology, taxonomy, paleontology, genetics, ecology, and other approaches to knowledge of living organisms.

Life is characterized by complex organization, by directional change, by individuality, and by reproduction. The protoplasm constituting living organisms is commonly organized into one or more cells, each normally delimited by a cell membrane and having a nucleus imbedded in cytoplasm. The cytoplasm contains several kinds of bodies, and carries on active metabolism. The nucleus also has distinctive structures, and seems to influence the activities of the cytoplasm. The widespread occurrence of cellular organization has given rise to the Cell Theory, which states that all living organisms are composed of cells and cell products.

REVIEW QUESTIONS

1. In what ways is science like housebuilding?
2. How does one acquire scientific knowledge?
3. What motivates people to undertake scientific investigation?
4. What is meant by a "controlled experiment"?
5. Name and define some of the sciences into which biology is divided.
6. What are the distinguishing characteristics of life?
7. Describe protoplasm.
8. What is metabolism?
9. What is the significance, to a scientist, of individual differences?
10. Define: cell, tissue, organ, system.
11. Describe the structure of a cell.
12. State the Cell Theory.

GENERAL QUESTIONS

1. Compare and contrast science with the composing of a symphony; with the playing of a symphony by an orchestra.
2. In Woodruff's experiment, how many generations of *Paramecium* should be required to prove his point? Is such a decision partly arbitrary, or supported by scientific considerations?
3. Which of the motivations of scientists mentioned on page 5 would appeal most strongly to you? Why?
4. Suppose you wished to find the answers to the following questions. Outline the procedure you would use in each case.

   (a) Is artistic talent inherited?

   (b) What causes cancer?

   (c) What causes gooseflesh in humans?

   (d) How does a hummingbird fly backwards?

   (e) How much of an oak tree is alive during the winter?

   (f) Can you cross apples with pears and get a hybrid?

   (g) Do snakes hypnotize birds?

   (h) How does a baby develop during the time before it is born?

   (i) Do earthworms know when birds are nearby?

   (j) How can a person know when he is in love?

5. What other branches of science would be particularly helpful to a person wishing to specialize in physiology? in taxonomy? in genetics? in ecology?

6. Express the size limits of colloidal particles in fractions of an inch.

7. Name five colloidal substances.

8. What evidence can you suggest to support the statement that changes in an organism are directional, not random?

9. What is there about you that is constant from year to year?

10. Why do we say an organism is the product, not the sum, of its heredity and environment?

PART I

HUMAN BIOLOGY

Tissues

A human has five fundamental kinds of tissues: epithelial, connective, muscular, nervous, and vascular. See Fig. 0.1.

Epithelial tissues are those which cover surfaces, such as the surface of the skin, or the lining of the stomach or of glands. Epithelial cells are tightly packed together and usually comparatively large with large nuclei. They have a high rate of metabolism. Epithelial cells protect surfaces, and secrete and absorb substances.

Connective tissues support the body and hold its parts together. The cells of these tissues secrete such structures as fibers, cartilage, and bone. Unlike the epithelial cells, the cells of connective tissue are scattered and not in close contact with each other, being separated by the solid secretions.

Muscular tissues are sheets or masses of contractile cells which bring about movements of some parts of the body with respect to other parts. These include not only such movements as those of the arms and legs, but also those of such organs as the stomach, heart, and blood vessels. The word "muscle" comes from the Latin *musculus*, little mouse, referring to the idea that a contracting muscle in the arm feels like a mouse wriggling under the skin.

Nervous tissues are made of cells with long processes connecting various parts of the body. Nerve cells help coordinate the varied activities of the body.

Vascular tissues include blood corpuscles of various kinds and the lymph nodes, spleen, and bone marrow cells from which the corpuscles arise.

Systems

These five kinds of tissues are organized into organ systems as follows:

The **skeletal system** consists of fibrous, cartilaginous, and bony connective tissues which support the body. Without the cartilaginous and bony tissues, a human would sink down into a flattened bubble, like a large bag of soft Jello. Without fibrous connective tissue, he would be draped on the bony skeleton like a circus tent with a center pole but no side supports.

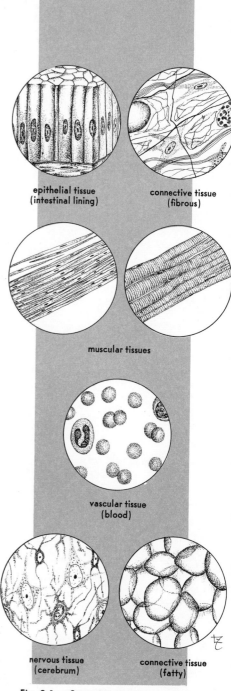

epithelial tissue
(intestinal lining)

connective tissue
(fibrous)

muscular tissues

vascular tissue
(blood)

nervous tissue
(cerebrum)

connective tissue
(fatty)

Fig. 0.1   Several kinds of human tissues.

The **muscular system** consists of muscle fibers encased in fibrous connective tissue and associated with the bony skeleton. It serves to move parts of the body. Of course the soft organs, such as the digestive and circulatory organs, contain muscle fibers, but these will be considered a part of the digestive and circulatory systems, and so forth.

The **digestive system** consists of the alimentary canal and its associated glands, and is lined throughout with epithelium, but includes connective tissues, muscles, nerve fibers, and vascular tissues as well. It changes insoluble food taken into the body into soluble products which are absorbed and used.

The **respiratory system** is lined with epithelial cells and includes in its make-up all of the other types of tissues as well. It makes oxygen available to the body, and gets rid of waste carbon dioxide.

The **circulatory system** likewise is lined with epithelium, supported by connective tissue, and operated by muscle fibers under the influence of nerve cells. It also manufactures and uses vascular cells. The circulatory system is the transportation facility of the body, moving substances from one part of the body to another.

The **excretory system** rids the body of waste materials. It uses all five tissues in the process.

The **nervous system** is primarily nervous tissue, conducting impulses throughout the body, but it, too, has an epithelial lining and connective tissue sheaths, besides being supplied with blood vessels.

The **endocrine system** is largely epithelial, with connective tissues in a supporting role, and nervous and vascular connections. It aids in coordinating the body's metabolism.

The **reproductive system** has all five tissues in its structure. It provides cells which bring about new individuals.

While we divide the human body into these nine systems for convenience in description, it is important to remember that none can exist without some of the others, and the interrelations are so complex that even in an elementary study it helps in understanding one to know something about many of the others.

Furthermore, there is nothing particularly significant about the number nine. Different methods of dividing the body could be used. For example, the skin, which is here included as part of the excretory system, could also be thought of as part of the skeletal system, since it supports tissues; or part of the nervous system, since it has many sense organs in which nerve impulses start; or a system by itself. The circulatory system may be divided into blood and lymph systems. Bones and muscles could be studied together in a locomotor system, which might include part of the nervous system, too.

So, with the understanding that classifications and names are man-made devices for facilitating description and memory, let us consider the systems listed above in the human as a sample living organism. From a study of man we should get ideas of a general nature on requirements of living organisms, and their methods of meeting these requirements. After that, we shall study in comparison some of the other groups of living things.

REVIEW QUESTIONS

1. Differentiate the five kinds of human tissues.
2. What are the contributions of the nine organ systems to the welfare of the human body?

GENERAL QUESTIONS

1. List the organ systems in the order of descending importance, explaining why you put each system where you do; that is, which system do you consider most important to the life of the body, which next, and so on.
2. Do you believe that all living organisms have the same set of organ systems as humans do? Why or why not?
3. Propose a division of the human body into six organ systems; into twelve.

CHAPTER 1

The Skeletal System

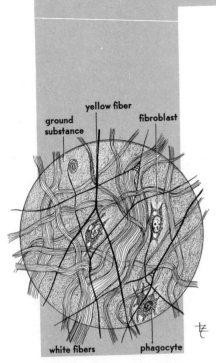

Fig. 1.1 Fibrous connective tissue. Note the fibroblast laying down a yellow fiber. The phagocytes, when active, have several branches; or they may round up and remain stationary for a while. This is loose connective tissue from beneath the skin.

PARTS OF THE SKELETAL SYSTEM

If by some as yet unknown chemical all of the tissues of the body except connective tissue were to be dissolved away, all of the structural features of the body could still be seen. Each skeletal muscle fiber, each digestive organ, each blood vessel would be outlined. Nerves, glands, even the fingerprints would be marked out in **connective tissue.** Such a framework allows for stability of organs without loss of suppleness and flexibility. The harder, more solid **cartilage** and **bone** give shape to the body and allow for efficiency of operation and locomotion. The high degree of economy and efficiency of the human body is shown by the hollowness of many bones, which provides lightness without sacrifice of strength. In this hollow space blood cells are manufactured.

FIBROUS CONNECTIVE TISSUE

Fibrous connective tissue (Fig. 1.1) consists of two kinds of fibers and several kinds of cells. The **white fibers** are more numerous, and are small, varying from one to ten or twelve microns in diameter. They are of indefinite length, since they interlace throughout an organ, forming an endless framework. Each fiber is made of several smaller **fibrils** firmly fastened together. The fibrils are very strong for their size, but are not particularly elastic.

The **yellow fibers** are about as large as the white ones, but are not composed of smaller fibrils, each fiber being a unit in itself. They are highly elastic; when stretched and released they return to their original length very readily. While the yellow fibers are not as numerous as white fibers, they are prominent in ligaments, arteries, the urinary bladder, and other structures where stretching is common. If a yellow fiber is stretched too far, it will break and recoil like a watch-spring.

The principal cells found in fibrous connective tissue are called **fibroblasts.** The Greek word *blastano* means to sprout or bring forth. Fibroblasts are angular cells, usually elongated along one side, where the fiber develops. It is not now certain whether a fibroblast secretes the fiber out of its own cytoplasm, or precipitates it out of the surrounding tissue fluid, or both. This problem is one of many biological problems still unsolved.

In addition to the fibers, fibroblasts secrete a **ground substance** which is very difficult to demonstrate structurally, but which seems to be found throughout the connective tissue. It may be that changes in the chemical and physical characters of this ground substance are important in the production and behavior of some cancers.

Vascular cells often leave the blood and lymph vessels and invade connective tissues. Some of these devour any foreign cells such as bacteria that accidentally get into the tissues; such scouts are known as **phagocytes** from the Greek words meaning eaters of cells. Other cells wander about or settle down and store or secrete substances.

Specialized cells occasionally found in fibrous connective tissue include the **fat cells** which store fat, and **pigment cells** such as give color to the sheath of the central nervous system. Freckles and other skin pigmentation in humans are in the epidermis, not in the connective tissue.

The compactness of connective tissue varies from the very dense tendons and ligaments to the very loose connective tissue under the skin.

CARTILAGE

Cells called **chondroblasts** deposit a solid substance about themselves. This solid substance, completely enclosing the cells which secrete it, is **cartilage,** or gristle. See Figure 1.2A. Cartilage is a very flexible, somewhat elastic, semi-transparent, bluish substance. Unlike the fibrous connective tissue, it lacks a good blood supply. Blood vessels may pass through cartilage because they were there before the cartilage was built around them, but there are no branches supplying blood to the chondroblasts. Since these cells, by encasing themselves, have cut themselves off from their sources of nourishment, they die when they have used up their stored materials.

Cartilage is tough and firm; it provides strength without absolute rigidity. In a human embryo in its early stages the skeleton is outlined in cartilage before the formation of bone. Some of this cartilage continues to grow and remains in the adult in such places as the front ends of the ribs, which, because they are flexible, allow breathing movements. Other locations of cartilage are at the joints, the nose, most of the larynx, the trachea, the bronchi, and the lower end of the breastbone. If you press gently on your nose or on the lower end of your breastbone, you may get some idea of the firmness and flexibility of cartilage.

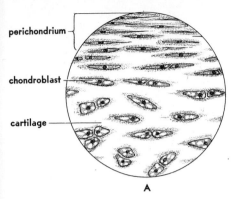

perichondrium

chondroblast

cartilage

A

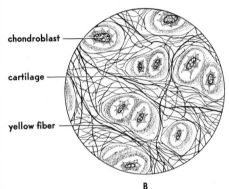

chondroblast

cartilage

yellow fiber

B

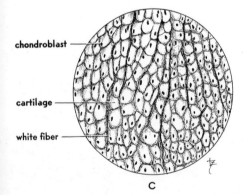

chondroblast

cartilage

white fiber

C

Fig. 1.2 Kinds of cartilage: **A**, Hyaline; **B**, Elastic; **C**, Fibrous. In what ways is each especially suited to the places in which it is found?

Cartilages are usually encased in a fibrous connective tissue sheath, the **perichondrium.** As the cartilage enlarges when the human grows, it envelops the inner fibers of the perichondrium, and more perichondrial fibers are laid down at the outer surfaces. These incorporated fibers are not ordinarily visible except with special techniques such as the use of polarized light, or of enzymes which digest away the cartilage but leave the fibers.

The cartilage we have been considering is called **hyaline cartilage** because of its semitransparency; *hyaline* comes from the Greek word for glassy. The connective tissue fibers it contains are not numerous enough to stand out. In some other cartilages, however, especially large numbers of fibers are included. For example, **elastic cartilage** (Fig. 1.2B) occurs in the external ear, in the Eustachian tube leading from the middle ear to the throat, and in some parts of the larynx. This cartilage has an abundance of yellow fibers in its make-up and allows a higher degree of flexibility than does hyaline cartilage. **Fibrous cartilage** (Fig. 1.2C) contains a very great number of white fibers and is in reality a mass of dense connective tissue in which some cartilage has been deposited. This is found where especially rigorous wear occurs, as in the pads between the vertebrae, at the jaw, shoulder, elbow, hip, and knee joints, and the juncture of the two halves of the pelvis.

BONE

Some fibroblasts deposit bone. These are called **osteoblasts.** Osteoblasts lay bone only on a solid base such as cartilage or white fibers.

The early skeleton of a human embryo is made of cartilage. As the body develops, some of the cartilage is replaced by bone. The cells of the perichondrium begin to dissolve away the adjacent cartilage. These cells are called **chondroclasts;** the Greek word *klasis* refers to breaking or pruning away. As the cartilage is eaten away, fibrous connective tissue from the perichondrium invades the opened space, bringing with it blood vessels and osteoblasts. The blood vessels branch into the space, and the osteoblasts deposit bone both on the dissolving spicules of cartilage and on the walls of the spaces surrounding the blood vessels.

As the osteoblasts deposit the bone they enclose the blood vessels in a sheath which grows until it envelops the osteoblasts themselves. Another group of osteoblasts lays down a second layer of bone inside the first, and still a third and a fourth and perhaps more layers may succeed. However, unlike the situation in cartilage, the bone cells retain contact with each other and with the branching blood vessels by means of tiny extensions of their cytoplasm, as is shown in Figure 1.3A.

Furthermore, the living bone is a very active structure, with changes in its construction constantly going on. As further subdivisions of the blood vessel network occur, some of the bone already deposited on cartilage or other vessels may be dissolved away by **osteoclasts;** after new vessels have penetrated the space, new osteoblasts may surround them with bone. Careful study of sections through bone will show how older, many-layered sheaths of bone have been eaten into, making room for newer sheaths. See, for example, Figure 1.3B.

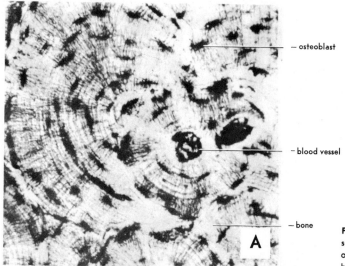

– osteoblast

– blood vessel

– bone

A

Fig. 1.3 Bone structure. Note the rings of bone surrounding each small blood vessel. Which of the osteoblasts are able to remain alive in the living bone? *Left* is at higher magnification than *below*.

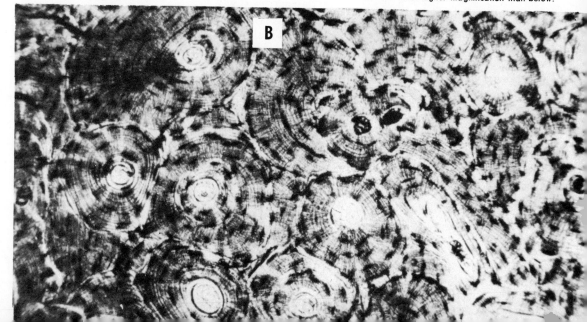

B

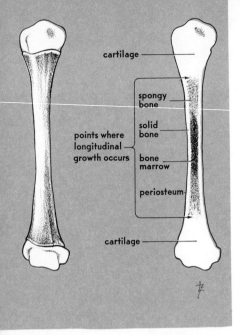

Fig. 1.4   Humerus of a young child. How does a bone grow in length?

Bone Development

In the replacement of cartilage by bone in a structure such as the humerus (upper arm bone), Fig. 1.4, the activity is not uniform throughout the element. In the finished product, the center of the bone is largely connective tissue and blood vessels. This is the **bone marrow;** it is a very active part of the body, engaged in the manufacture of enormous numbers of blood corpuscles. The marrow is bordered by a layer in which bone occurs in a sort of latticework called **spongy bone.** The outermost layer is the **solid bone,** which gives strength and rigidity to the whole. Outside the bone is the connective tissue sheath known as the **periosteum.**

When the humerus first starts to change from cartilage to bone, it is only about $\frac{1}{120}$ of its final length. In the process of growing without losing its stability, bone is developed in the middle first, extending toward the ends. When the child is born, it begins to use the arms and needs bone throughout the length of the humerus. Yet the humerus will increase three or four times in length before maturity. During the early years of infancy and childhood various other centers of bone formation are developed at the upper and lower ends of the humerus, particularly at the shoulder and elbow joints and where the more prominent muscles are attached. Finally at about the age of twenty years, all of these centers will have fused into one bone, but until that time the main shaft of the bone is separated from the ends of the bone by cartilage, which permits longitudinal growth. Growth in diameter is accomplished by depositing bone on the outer surface and dissolving bone on the inside, enlarging the marrow cavity.

The process of bone formation, illustrated by the humerus, is repeated in the formation of many other skeletal elements in the body. The exact time of fusion of the various ossification centers of a bone into one rigid structure varies slightly from bone to bone and from person to person, but in most people by the age of 20 or 21 years the bony growth in size is completed and the main shaft and ends are fused. See Table 1.1.

Because these fusions have not taken place earlier, there is some argument for restricting the athletic activity of high school students to sports which are less apt than wrestling, boxing, and high-pressure football to deform their incompletely ossified skeletons.

Interestingly enough, there seems to be a rule of thumb among mammals that the completion of bony fusion occurs at the end of the first fifth of the normal life span. This

TABLE 1.1

AGE AT WHICH FUSION OF
HUMAN BONES IS NORMALLY COMPLETED

Vertebrae	20–25 years
Breastbone	25–30 years
Skull	16 years
Hyoid bone	30 years
Shoulder blades	20–21 years
Collarbones	22–25 years
Humeri	15–25 years
Radii	15–25 years
Ulnae	15–25 years
Finger bones	21 years
Hip girdle	21–25 years
Femora	15–24 years
Tibiae	16–25 years
Fibulae	17–25 years
Heel bones	12–22 years
Toe bones	12–22 years

would indicate that, barring accidents and diseases, men should live about one hundred years.

Composition of Bone

The substance of bone is composed of both organic and inorganic material. The organic material is protein. The inorganic material consists chiefly of the phosphates and carbonates of calcium and magnesium. The bones of very young children contain more organic material than inorganic, and children's bones are weaker and more easily broken than the bones of adults, but they are also more easily healed. In youth and middle age the amount of inorganic material increases and the bones become strong and rigid. In older people, the organic material decreases in amount and suppleness, and the bones become more brittle and heal less readily.

Bone Nutrition

The use of phosphate in the manufacture of bone seems to be controlled by **vitamin D.** A small amount of the vitamin must be present to cause the deposit of sufficient phosphate to make the bones strong. The absence of this vitamin from the diet of an individual may lead to weak, rubbery bones and skeletal deformities, a condition known as **rickets.** Vitamin D, as we shall see later, may be manufactured by humans if they are exposed to direct sunlight.

The absence of the constituents of bone from the human diet would also prevent proper bone formation. However, in most normal human diets, this is not a serious problem.

During pregnancy, a mother must supply enough materials to form the bones of the embryo in addition to the amount needed for maintaining her own health. If there is not enough calcium in her diet to care for both of these needs, calcium is taken from her bones and deposited in the bones of the baby, and the mother may suffer from loss of strength in her bones and possible deformity. Therefore, special care is usually taken to include enough calcium, phosphorus, and vitamin D in her diet.

Endocrine Factors

In a later chapter we shall learn about the glands of the endocrine system and the hormones they secrete. Two of them are so important to the story of bones, however, that we shall mention them briefly here.

The **pituitary gland** in the head was so named because it was thought to secrete the mucus (Latin: *pituita*) for the nose. While the pituitary gland does not secrete mucus, it does secrete a **growth hormone** which regulates the growth in length of many of the bones of the body.

The more growth hormone there is in the body of a young human, the longer will his bones grow. Basketball players, particularly centers, are ordinarily those with an ample supply. Shorter individuals have less, and many of the dwarfs exhibited in circuses are people with a considerable deficiency of growth hormone, so that their arm and leg bones did not become very long. A pituitary dwarf is usually well proportioned, and is normal in most respects except for bone length and therefore size. See Figure 1.5.

The secretion of growth hormone is reduced after adolescence, although enough is produced to maintain a balance between wearing out and renewing cells.

In a few rare cases a diseased pituitary gland in an adult may secrete unusual quantities of growth hormone after normal development has been completed. This may result in an exaggerated growth of some bones such as those of the arms, legs, and lower jaw, producing a disproportionate figure with somewhat distorted features. Such a condition is known as **acromegaly** (Greek for enlargement of the extremities). If this condition is diagnosed early enough, treatment, usually surgical removal of the anterior part of the pituitary gland, may halt the onset of the disfigurement.

The other hormone involved in skeletal formation is **parathyrin,** secreted by the **parathyroid glands** in the throat. This hormone regulates the body's use of calcium. A normal amount of the hormone distributes the available calcium to the bones, teeth, blood, and other parts of the body in satisfactory proportions, allowing metabolism to proceed efficiently. An excess of the hormone causes withdrawal of calcium from bones and teeth and concentrates it in the blood. This produces softer bones, and tends to deaden or partially anesthetize the nervous system by exposure to the excess calcium in the blood supply.

A deficiency of the hormone causes deposition of calcium in the bones and teeth from the blood, making the bones and teeth harder and more brittle, and making the nervous system hypersensitive. In an animal or human in which this loss of parathyrin is extreme, the nervous system becomes so affected that convulsions result, and death will occur unless measures are taken to relieve the lack of parathyrin.

The story is told of the captain of a merchant vessel many years ago who found to his dismay that he seemed unsteady on his feet for reasons totally unknown to him. He would even fall down unexpectedly. Furthermore, he became very

Fig. 1.5 A man of average height stands between a giant and a dwarf. Explain these height differences.

lethargic. At his next stop in a large port he went to a hospital for examination, but nothing was found to indicate the cause of the trouble, and he went his way, supposing the trouble to be a passing event. However, the condition became aggravated, and he sought further medical counsel. After a variety of diagnoses and fruitless treatments extending over several months, his condition became so grave that he could not leave his hospital bed. At last, someone thought of the possibility of parathyroid oversecretion. And so the patient was prepared for surgical removal of some of the parathyroid tissue.

The parathyroid glands normally occur as four small patches buried in the thyroid tissue, two on either side of the trachea. One of these four glands was removed from the patient, but this didn't improve his situation. Another was taken, and still the symptoms persisted. The surgeons were puzzled, and hesitated to go too far, lest they remove so much that convulsions and death would result. But finally they removed a third gland — with no benefit to the patient. At last, armed with parathyroid extract to inject into the man if necessary, they removed the fourth gland. But still the patient was secreting too much parathyrin!

Further surgical exploration revealed a fifth gland and this was taken out, as was a sixth found later. Then, down at the base of the neck, a seventh parathyroid gland was found with a tumor on it. This had been the source of the trouble all along, but who would have looked for so many abnormal glands in such unusual places? The seventh gland was removed, and the patient died — of pneumonia. But the knowledge acquired by this unfortunate experience was valuable in saving the life of another patient with similar symptoms about a year later, and of many others since.

This story illustrates the practical value of the custom of scientists to publish new information, whether successes or failures. It also illustrates the far-reaching effects of changes in any one small part of the body on many others. And it emphasizes that bone is not a dead, permanent framework, but a living, changing, active tissue needing favorable conditions for its continued efficiency.

THE SKELETON

Although we usually think of the term "skeleton" as referring only to bones, the skeletal system includes connective tissue and cartilage as well. Connective tissue occurs all through the body. Its fibers form the framework for every organ in the body, and having once been described in general, need not for our purposes be described again.

Fig. 1.6 Human skeleton. The axial skeleton is shown in white, the appendicular skeleton in black. Rib cartilages are stippled.

Fig. 1.7 Human vertebral column, side view. The back is to the right in the figure. Note the curvatures and the differences among the separate vertebrae. The sacral region consists of five vertebrae fused and the caudal region of four vertebrae fused. How many vertebrae are there in each of the other regions?

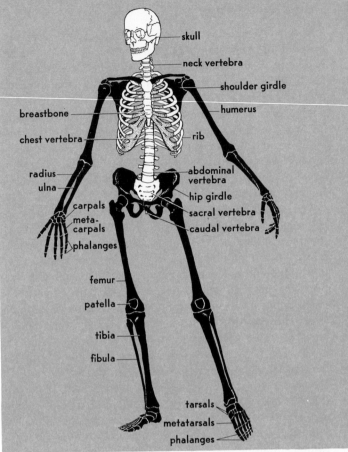

skull
neck vertebra
shoulder girdle
humerus
breastbone
chest vertebra
rib
radius
ulna
abdominal vertebra
hip girdle
carpals
meta-carpals
phalanges
sacral vertebra
caudal vertebra
femur
patella
tibia
fibula
tarsals
metatarsals
phalanges

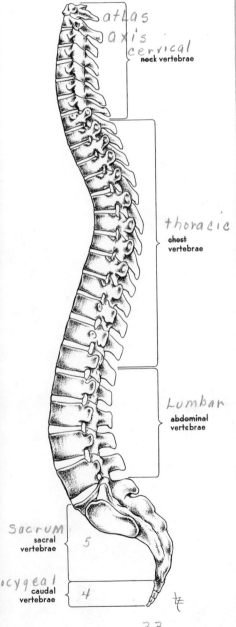

atlas
axis
cervical
neck vertebrae

thoracic
chest vertebrae

Lumbar
abdominal vertebrae

Sacrum
sacral vertebrae
5

ocygeal
caudal vertebrae
4

33

Cartilage is mostly replaced by bone, but those cartilages remaining may be described briefly in relation to structures with which they are associated, such as the respiratory tract.

But bones constitute an assemblage by themselves, associated closely with the muscular system, but distinct enough to be grouped into the concept of the **skeleton.** See Figure 1.6.

For convenience in description, we may divide the skeleton into **axial** and **appendicular** portions. The axial skeleton forms the axis of the trunk, and includes the skull, vertebrae (backbone), ribs, and breastbone (sternum). The appendicular skeleton forms the supports for arms and legs, and includes the shoulder girdle, hip girdle, and arm and leg bones.

AXIAL SKELETON

The basis of the axial skeleton is the **vertebral column** (Fig. 1.7). To it are jointed the skull, the ribs, and the hip girdle, and dependent upon it for support are the shoulder girdle and the breastbone. The adult human spinal column is made up of 26 vertebrae cushioned from each other by pads of fibrous cartilage. These pads act as shock absorbers.

At each step the vertebrae bounce on the pads and pound them flatter. Natural resilience and elasticity restore the thickness of the pad nearly to normal after the step. But during a day's time, if much walking, running, or jumping is done, the pads may be hammered down until the body is a fraction of an inch shorter at night than in the morning. During the sleeping hours, the pads regain their original size and are prepared to take another day's pounding.

A vertebra (Fig. 1.8) has a large, spool-shaped body, the **centrum,** with an **arch** projecting to the back and encasing the spinal cord, a part of the nervous system. Attached to the centrum and arch are various processes to which muscles are attached or other bones articulated. The vertebrae articulate with each other by projections from the arch. Each vertebra but the first has projections at the anterior end which meet the projections on the posterior end of the vertebra ahead of it. These articulations, strongly bound by tendons, prevent the vertebrae from bending very far away from each other, so that movement at any one articulation is only slight, giving a firmness and strength of support to the spinal column. But the number of vertebrae is enough to allow considerable arching of the column as a whole.

Projecting dorsally (toward the back) from each arch is a **spine.** In some vertebrae this is longer than in others, and

Fig. 1.8 Human vertebrae: **A,** Chest vertebra in side view; **B,** Chest vertebra from above; **C,** Abdominal vertebra in side view; **D,** Abdominal vertebra from above. How are these bones alike? How are they different from each other?

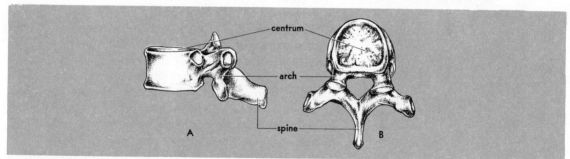

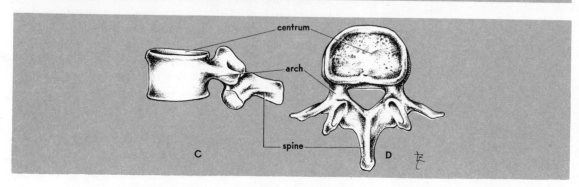

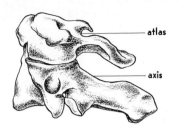

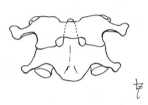

Fig. 1.9 Atlas and axis. Note the thumblike process of the axis projecting up through the atlas. Can you see how the atlas is able to rotate on the axis?

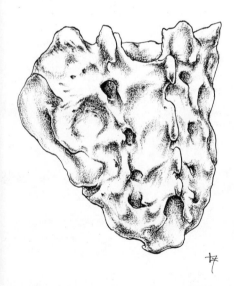

Fig. 1.10 Human sacrum. This is composed of five vertebrae fused. Can you distinguish the five vertebrae?

a few of these are particularly prominent in the vertebrae at the base of the neck and the top of the chest, where they may be felt below the skin. Others may be felt in the middle of the back, especially if the trunk be bent forward.

Again for convenience in description, we may divide the vertebral column into neck, chest, abdominal, sacral, and caudal sections.

The neck vertebrae, seven in number, support the neck region. The first two of these are especially modified. The first, or **atlas** (Fig. 1.9), supports the skull, and gets its name from the character in Greek mythology who supported the earth. It is ringlike in form with a saddlelike concavity on each side to receive the rounded projections at the base of the skull. The skull rocks forward and backward on these in nodding the head. The second vertebra, the **axis** (Fig. 1.9), has a larger centrum, from the anterior end of which a thumblike projection passes through the hole in the atlas and serves as a shaft on which the atlas may turn. Thus, when a person wishes to shake his head from side to side, the skull settles into the atlas saddles and the skull and atlas together rotate about the projection from the axis.

The chest vertebrae, twelve in number, follow after the neck vertebrae, and bear articulations receiving the ribs, a pair of ribs to each vertebra.

Below the chest vertebrae are the five abdominal vertebrae. These have the largest centra of any of the vertebrae in the body, but bear no ribs.

The **sacrum** (Fig. 1.10) is one mass, composed of five embryonic vertebrae which have fused together during early development, giving more solid support to the rest of the column. The weight of the head, arms, and trunk is transmitted to the hip girdle and legs through this fused group of vertebrae. Indications of the separate members of the sacrum are evident in the openings and in the spines and lateral projections.

Beyond the sacrum is the fused mass of four tail, or caudal, vertebrae. This is a much reduced structure, since humans do not ordinarily possess an external tail. Rarely, babies are born with a visible tail of six to eight inches length, but when this happens the physician in attendance usually cuts it off and preserves it to show his friends.

The Ribs and Breastbone

Each chest vertebra has two areas on each side articulating with a rib. One is on the centrum and one is on the arch. Together these articulations act as a hinge on which the rib can swing. The amplitude of the swing is quite limited, however, being controlled by the muscular and connective tissue attachments to the rib and by the articulation of many of the ribs with the breastbone. See Figure 1.11.

The breastbone is a long, flat bone extending along the midventral line of the chest. To it are articulated the cartilaginous ventral ends of the first seven pairs of ribs. The eighth rib cartilages, not quite reaching the breastbone, fasten to the posterior border of the seventh rib cartilages. Similarly, the ninth pair articulate with the eighth, and the tenth with the ninth. The eleventh and twelfth pairs of ribs do not articulate with other parts of the skeleton ventrally, but are held in place by muscles and connective tissue. These are sometimes called the floating ribs.

Because of the story in the Book of Genesis about the formation of Eve from Adam's rib, it was at one time thought that men always had one less rib than women, but when men began to substitute observation for acceptance of hearsay, this belief was found to be groundless.

The Skull

Unlike most other skeletal bones, in adults most of the skull bones are immovably joined to each other by **sutures.** The skull gets its name from the Icelandic for bowl. The skull protects the brain and is the basis for our facial features. When we are born, however, some of the separate bones of the skull can be moved with relation to each other, for the joints are of cartilage. This makes it easier for a baby's head to pass through the mother's birth canal at the time of birth. For some time after birth, the top of the skull remains cartilage, and only gradually do the bones fuse together to make a rigid box. See Figure 1.12.

Eight of the skull bones are primarily involved in the **cranium,** or brain box:

The **frontal bone,** named from the Latin for forehead, fits over the front and part of the underside of the brain, supporting the forehead, the eyebrow ridges, and the ceilings of the eye sockets.

The **ethmoid bone,** named from the Greek for sievelike, is below the frontal, forming a portion of the brain floor at the anterior end and part of the nasal septum separating the nose cavity into right and left chambers, and making part of the inner walls of the eye sockets. Posteriorly it is much perforated, like a sieve, and through the holes pass branches of the nerve of smell.

The **parietal bones,** named from the Latin for wall, make

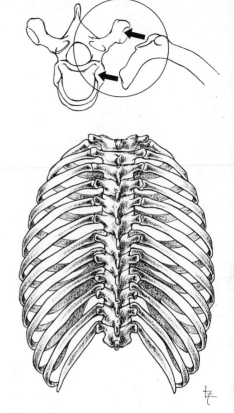

Fig. 1.11   Ribs from the back. The upper drawing gives detail of attachment of rib to the vertebra. Notice that it is attached at two places. What advantages are there to this arrangement?

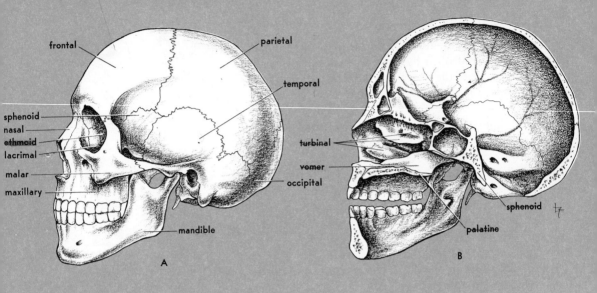

Fig. 1.12   Human skull: **A,** Side view; **B,** Skull cut through the middle to show inner bones.

the covering over the crown of the brain, roofing the greater part of it, and passing partway down the sides. The two parietals, right and left, meet in a very meandering suture weaving back and forth across the midline of the skull top.

The **temporal bones** are named from the Latin for time — hence a quarter of the heavens — hence a quarter of the dome of the skull. The right and left temporal bones make the side walls of the cranium and support the ear. The lower jaw is attached to the temporal bones. These bones may be felt above the ears, behind each ear as a protuberance, the **mastoid process,** and in front of the ear in the formation of part of the cheek bone. Internally the bone forms the lower side wall and part of the floor of the brain behind the frontal bone.

The **sphenoid bone** is named from the Greek for wedge-shaped. It forms the base of the braincase behind the ethmoid. It is wedged in between the two temporal bones. The pituitary gland, described earlier in this chapter, rests in a little concavity in the upper surface of the sphenoid bone. The lateral wings of the sphenoid bone form parts of the side walls of the eye sockets, and part of the floor of the cranial cavity.

The **occipital bone,** named from the Latin for against the head, forms the back wall of the cranium and bears the low mounds which rest in the saddles of the atlas. The occipital bone is pierced by an opening through which the brain continues as the spinal cord. The bone runs forward to overlap the sphenoid bone somewhat, thus contributing to the floor of the braincase as well as to the posterior wall.

The brain is surrounded, then, by the frontal bone in front, the two parietals on top, the occipital behind, the two temporals on the sides, and the ethmoid and sphenoid on the bottom.

The fourteen bones of the facial part of the skull are concerned with support of the nose, eyes, and mouth.

The two **nasal bones** form the support for the bridge of the nose, joining the frontal and maxillary bones. Toward the tip of the nose the bone gives way to hyaline cartilage. An occasional person may be found in whom this cartilage is never formed, and his nose may be pressed flat against his face without discomfort.

The two **turbinal bones** get their name from the Latin for whirlwind, because they are fantastically twisted. They are located within the nasal cavity and greatly increase the surface area of the interior of the nose. They are extremely delicate and fragile plates bearing the membranes which moisten and warm the air we breathe.

The **vomer** is named from the Latin for plowshare, indicating its shape. It divides the nose cavity into right and left parts in collaboration with the ethmoid.

The two **lacrimal bones,** pertaining to tears, are found in the front inner corners of the eye sockets, and are pierced by the ducts that drain tears from the surface of the eyes to the nose cavity. They are relatively small, thin bones forming part of the inner walls of the eye sockets.

The two **malar bones,** named from the Latin for cheek, form most of the cheek arches easily felt on the sides of the face below and behind the eyes.

The two **maxillary bones,** named from the Latin for jaw, form the support for the front of the face beside and below the nose, and carry the teeth of the upper jaw. They also form the support for most of the roof of the mouth. The teeth will be discussed more fully in connection with the digestive system, with which their action is associated.

The two **palatine bones** form the back end of the roof of the mouth, or palate, behind the maxillary bones. Like them the palatines also form parts of the floor and walls of the nose cavity.

The **mandible** forms the lower jaw, hinged to the temporals at its back ends, and bearing the teeth of the lower jaw. The mandible is two separate bones in the embryo, but these fuse into one firm jaw soon after birth, giving strength to the chin.

Contributing to the support of the nose, then, are the two nasals, the two turbinals, and the vomer; aiding in the support of the eyes are the two lacrimals and the two

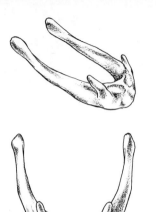

Fig. 1.13 Human hyoid bone. This forms the support for the base of the tongue. The front of the bone is shown at the right in the upper drawing, at the bottom in the lower drawing.

malars; and forming the walls of the mouth are the two maxillaries, the two palatines, and the mandible. Only the mandible is movably joined to the other bones of the skull.

The **hyoid bone** (Fig. 1.13) is named from the Greek for upsilon-shaped. It is entirely separate from the remainder of the skeleton. It is the horseshoe-shaped support for the tongue, the two ends being directed back toward the throat. By pressing under the chin on one side below the jaw articulation, the hyoid bone may be pushed over to the other side, and felt with the other hand. In fact, its entire curvature may be followed by the fingers. It is not joined to any other bone, but is suspended by muscles attached to it and to the mandible, and by muscles attached to it and to the breastbone. Tongue muscles also are attached to the hyoid bone.

In each middle ear of a human there are three very tiny bones, not joined with the rest of the skull, which assist in conducting sound waves to the receiving station. These are the hammer, anvil, and stirrup, which will be described more fully in the story of the ear, pages 160–161. See Figure 1.14.

Totaling the bones of the axial skeleton, we find 26 vertebrae, 24 ribs, 1 breastbone, 22 skull bones, 1 hyoid bone, and 6 ear bones, a sum of 80 bones.

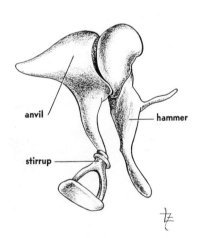

anvil

hammer

stirrup

Fig. 1.14 Bones of the middle ear. Can you tell their names from their shapes?

APPENDICULAR SKELETON

The skeletons of the upper and lower limbs are much alike in pattern. Each has a girdle in the trunk, a single long bone in the upper part of the appendage, two long bones in the next segment, and then a group of roughly cubical bones followed by a series of five cylindrical bones and five sets of bones supporting the digits.

The **shoulder girdle** (Fig. 1.15) is composed of two shoulder blades and two collarbones. The shoulder blades lie along the back of the shoulder buried in muscles. They can be felt especially at the top of the shoulder where a stout projection rises toward the surface of the body.

The collarbones run across the front of the body at the top of the chest, and may be felt reaching from the shoulder to the top of the breastbone. Once in a while a person may be born without collarbones. Such a person makes an excellent contortionist, for he may compress the shoulders to a much greater degree than a normal person, and thus crawl through openings too narrow for the average man. Many of the familiar animals have very small collarbones, as the dog or cat, or none at all, as the horse and cow.

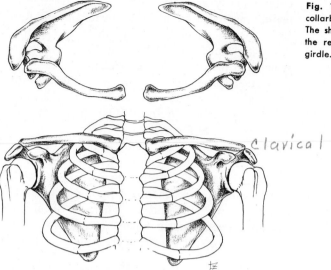

clavical

Fig. 1.15 Shoulder girdle from the front. The collarbones run from the breastbone to the shoulders. The shoulder blades lie behind the ribs. Compare the relative looseness of this girdle with the hip girdle.

The **humerus** (Fig. 1.16) is not the "funny bone" as some uninformed punsters like to think. It connects the shoulder and the elbow, but is rather deeply buried in muscles throughout its length, and can be felt only with some difficulty through the muscles. Its upper end is ball-like and fits into a socket in the shoulder blade, allowing for rotation through an entire hemisphere.

The bones supporting the forearm are the **radius,** named from the Latin for rod, and the **ulna,** the Latin cubit, or distance from the elbow to the end of the middle finger. The radius runs from the inside of the elbow to the thumb side of the wrist, and the ulna runs from the outside of the elbow to the little finger side of the wrist. These may be followed with the fingers by feeling along the arm. It will be noted that when the hand is placed palm down, the radius crosses over the top of the ulna in passing to the wrist. With the hand palm up, the two bones are about parallel.

The ulna has a hooklike projection, its concavity receiving the end of the humerus, and the end of the hook forming the "funny bone," which the Greeks called **"olecranon,"** or skull of the elbow. The elbow joint operates as a hinge, allowing movement of almost 180 degrees in one plane only; the olecranon prevents bending beyond the straightened arm.

The wrist bones, called **carpals,** are a series of eight bones in two rows of four bones each. These make a series of hinges giving great flexibility to the wrist. The separate carpals are somewhat irregular in shape, but all are more or less

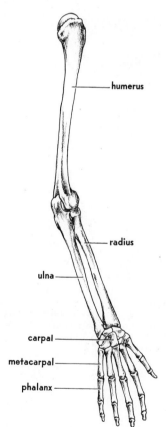

humerus

radius

ulna

carpal

metacarpal

phalanx

Fig. 1.16   Skeleton of the right arm.

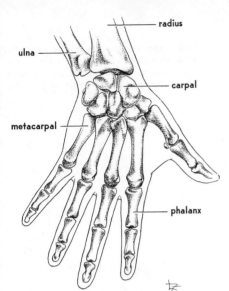

Fig. 1.17   Bones of the hand.

cubical. They are rather hard, solid structures, and this feature may have given rise to the idea of the Resurrection Bone, one bone of the body which was supposedly indestructible and from which the body would be reconstructed at the time of its resurrection.

The **metacarpal bones** are encased in the flesh of the hand. There are five of these in each hand, one leading to each of the fingers. They are nearly cylindrical, though enlarged at the joints. See Figure 1.17.

The fingers are supported by **phalanges** (a phalanx was a square battle formation used by the Greeks). Each thumb has two phalanges, the other fingers three apiece. They are cylindrical or spool-shaped bones, progressively smaller toward the tips of the fingers. The most distal and smallest phalanx in each digit is tapered, accommodating the nail.

Summing up, the skeletal elements of each arm are a

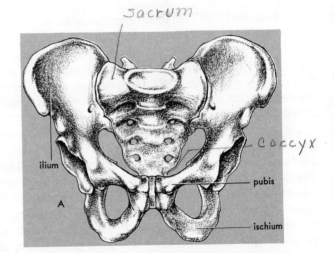

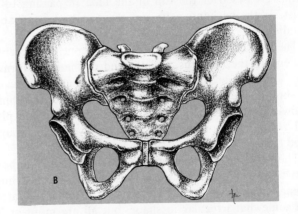

Fig. 1.18   A, Male human pelvis. B, Female human pelvis. Can you distinguish between them? Describe the differences.

shoulder blade, a collarbone, a humerus, a radius, an ulna, eight carpals, five metacarpals, and fourteen phalanges, a total of thirty-two bones.

In support of the leg we find bones somewhat comparable to those that support the arm. The **hip girdle** with the sacral and caudal vertebrae makes up the **pelvis** (Fig. 1.18). The hip girdle is composed of two bones joined to each other by fibrous cartilage in front, and joined with the sacrum at the back. Each of the two hip bones is a fusion of three embryonic structures, the **ilium** (Latin for flank), the **ischium** (Greek for hip), and the **pubis** (Latin for soft hair, hence groin). The ilium is the largest of the three, making the flaring plate projecting up the side of the abdomen. The ischium is the curved bar posterior to the ilium. The pubis is the curved bar in front of the ilium and ischium. The juncture of these three forms a socket into which fits the bent head of the thigh bone. The size of the opening between the two hip bones differs between the two sexes, being much larger in the female, who bears the children. This greater width of the pelvis contributes to the difference in bodily proportions between the two sexes.

The **femur** (Fig. 1.19), or thigh bone, is the longest and largest bone of the human body. It is somewhat hammer-shaped, with a long handle and a rounded head projecting at an obtuse angle from the upper end, where it fits into the socket in the hip bone. The hip joint is not quite as free as the shoulder joint, but when we watch acrobatic dancers in action we can detect little difference.

The **tibia,** or shin bone, and the **fibula** (Latin for buckle) are the two bones of the shank of the leg. The tibia is much the larger, and is located in the front of the leg where it may readily be felt. The fibula is a very slender bone deeply buried in the muscle of the calf of the leg, but its expansion may be felt projecting on the outer surface of the ankle.

The **patella** is a separate bone at the knee, the kneecap. In function it is somewhat comparable to the olecranon process of the ulna, but it is a separate entity, forming much later than most of the skeletal elements, and not becoming bone until the age of three or four years. The knee joint is a hinge joint like that of the elbow.

The **tarsals** supporting each ankle are seven in number. The name comes from the Greek for a mass of tangled roots, probably referring to the interweaving tendons of the region. The largest tarsal projects backward as the heel bone; the others contribute to the apex of the arch of the foot. The ankle is somewhat stronger and less supple than the wrist.

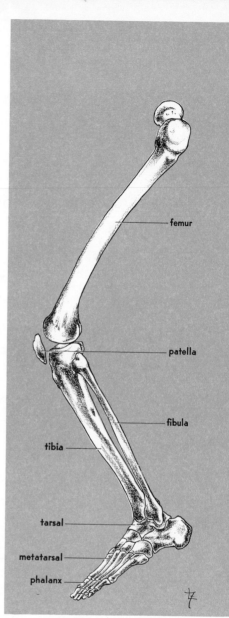

Fig. 1.19   Skeleton of the left leg.

TABLE 1.2   **36**   CHAPTER 1

BONES OF THE HUMAN SKELETON

AXIAL		80
Vertebrae		26
Neck	7	
Chest	12	
Abdominal	5	
Sacral	1	
Caudal	1	
Ribs		24
Breastbone		1
Skull		22
Cranial	8	
Facial	14	
Hyoid		1
Ear		6
APPENDICULAR		126
Upper		64
Shoulder blades	2	
Collarbones	2	
Humeri	2	
Radii	2	
Ulnae	2	
Carpals	16	
Metacarpals	10	
Phalanges	28	
Lower		62
Hip bones	2	
Femora	2	
Tibiae	2	
Fibulae	2	
Patellae	2	
Tarsals	14	
Metatarsals	10	
Phalanges	28	
TOTAL		206

The **metatarsals** are five in number, and make the base of the arch opposite the heel. They resemble the metacarpals somewhat in shape and relative position, except that there is no divergence comparable to that of the thumb metacarpal.

The **phalanges** are the bones of the toes and are like those of the fingers. The big toe has two phalanges, and each of the other toes three. As in the fingers, the end phalanges are modified in shape, supporting nails.

Summarizing the skeleton of the leg, there are a hip bone, a femur, a patella, a tibia, a fibula, seven tarsals, five metatarsals, and fourteen phalanges for a total of thirty-one bones. The two legs together total 62 bones, the arms 64, and the axial skeleton 80, making a grand total of 206 bones for the entire body. Variations in this number occur as in the absence of collarbones, radius, or some carpals, or extra fingers or toes. See Table 1.2.

HYGIENE OF THE SKELETAL SYSTEM

The development of a good posture is important in promoting the efficiency not only of the skeletal system, but of many other parts of the body as well. The fourfold curvature of the spinal column (see Figure 1.7) allows for the best carriage of the body in sitting, standing, or walking. The neck vertebrae are nearly vertical, curving to the back at the bottom of the group. The chest vertebrae continue this curve throughout the upper half of the chest, and begin to curve forward near the middle of the trunk. The abdominal vertebrae complete the forward bending and start to bend toward the back again. The sacrum curves toward the back and begins to curve forward in an arc that is continued by the caudal vertebrae. This combination of curves allows resilience and some flexibility in the spine without sacrificing the vertical support it gives to the body. Slouching, either in a sitting or standing position, puts stresses in unusual places in the column, and may lead to inefficient loading of muscles and tendons, eventually resulting in permanent malformations.

You will remember that bones are constantly undergoing change — tearing down and building up structures according to strains and stresses. Any unhealthful restriction or relaxation affects this renewal process, as is made painfully evident in malformations of the foot from wearing ill-fitting or unsuitable shoes. High heels, poorly formed arches, and shoes too soft to give proper support to the foot are among the methods used by humans to torture themselves unnecessarily. Frequent change from high to low heels and back is a particularly quick way to develop foot trouble.

With regard to children, it is well to remember that many bones are not fully formed until the age of twenty or twenty-one, and that cartilage is flexible. Serious bumps and falls, overvigorous contact sports such as football and basketball, and too heavy weights may cause some malformations.

Broken bones should be treated by a physician or surgeon. Because bones are supplied with blood vessels and nerves, and because other blood vessels and nerves often lie in the immediate vicinity of bones, an amateur's attempt to set a broken bone may greatly increase the damage already done. Moving the jagged edges of a bone in an attempt to unite the broken ends may tear to shreds all the tissues in the neighborhood of the break. However, if the ends of a broken bone are correctly set, a clot of tissue fluid and blood will make a temporary seal, and new bone will be formed by osteoblasts, knitting the broken ends together. For successful healing, bones should be held immobile in splints or casts during the knitting process. Properly set bones will heal, forming just as strong a support as the original unbroken bone formed, and there is no more likelihood of the bone breaking in the same place than in the case of the first fracture. If a broken bone is not properly set, however, there will be an area of weakness where it heals.

Aside from prevention of breaks and of malformations, the only hygienic consideration of importance in building and maintaining the skeletal system is in connection with diet. Diet is extremely important, however, and will be considered in Chapter 3.

We have seen that the skeletal system gives support and stability to the body. In the next chapter we shall see how the skeleton contributes to movement and locomotion.

SUMMARY

The human body is supported by three kinds of connective tissue: fibrous connective tissue, cartilage, and bone.

Fibrous connective tissue has cells called fibroblasts which produce white and yellow fibers and ground substance. Fibrous connective tissue may also have in it vascular cells, fat cells, and pigment cells.

Cartilage is firm and flexible, and may include white or yellow fibers.

Bone is rigid, yet active metabolically, changing its structure throughout its life, and contributing to the body not only support but also the manufacture of blood corpuscles. The healthy condition of living bone depends upon an adequate supply of building materials and vitamin D, and upon proper quantities of growth hormone and parathyrin.

The bones of the human body, considered as a group, make up the skeleton. The axial skeleton includes the bones of the skull, the vertebrae, the ribs, and the breastbone. The appendicular skeleton includes the shoulder and hip girdles and the bones of the arms and legs.

The structure and arrangement of the bones of the body largely determine the kinds of movement the body may make. Since the bones are living parts of the body, they are subject to change by stresses placed on them. Therefore, care should be taken to maintain a good posture and to avoid conditions which will produce malformations of bones. Broken bones, if properly set, will normally heal completely.

REVIEW QUESTIONS

1. Where may fibrous connective tissue be found in the human body?
2. Describe the structure of fibrous connective tissue.
3. Describe the structure and location of three kinds of cartilage.
4. How does the structure of bone differ from the structure of hyaline cartilage?
5. What is the importance to the skeleton of vitamin D? Of growth hormone? Of parathyrin?
6. Name and locate the 206 bones making up the human skeleton.
7. Describe a chest vertebra.
8. Explain the structure and actions of the atlas and axis.
9. Describe the relations of ribs to other bones of the body.
10. Compare, bone for bone, the appendicular skeletons of the arm and the leg.
11. How is efficient posture maintained?
12. Describe the best treatment for broken bones.

GENERAL QUESTIONS

1. Propose an experiment to test whether a connective tissue fiber is secreted out of a fibroblast's cytoplasm or precipitated from the surrounding tissue fluid or both.
2. Describe the activities now going on in the loose connective tissue under the skin of the back of your hand.
3. How does it happen that the external ear has elastic cartilage, whereas the knee has fibrous cartilage? What would happen if these were reversed?
4. Why may we speak of a bone as "living bone"?
5. Describe how a bone grows.

6. If an archeologist discovers a human skeleton hundreds of years old, how can he tell the age at death if the person died between the ages of 15 and 25?

7. Why are some people more likely to suffer broken bones than other people?

8. Suggest various examples in which publication of the results of experiments thought to be failures might be very helpful to the advance of science.

9. If, during one day, each intervertebral pad is pounded $\frac{1}{100}$ of an inch thinner than it was in the morning, how much shorter will the whole body be at night than it was in the morning?

10. Determine which portions of your spinal column can bend the most and which the least. Is the amount of bending allowed different in different directions — forward, sideways, backward?

11. What is the advantage of a meandering suture over a straight suture between the two parietal bones?

12. If you had to sacrifice one bone from the axial skeleton, which could you spare with the least disadvantage?

13. How does an anatomist tell whether a human skeleton was part of a man or of a woman?

14. How would tennis playing be changed if the shoulder and hip became hinge joints, and the elbow and knee became ball-and-socket joints?

15. Which bones of the body are chiefly long cylinders? Nearly cubical? Flat or curved plates?

CHAPTER 2

The Muscular System

When you examine a human or any other animal to see whether it is alive or dead, you look for movement. Does the face show movements? Does the heart beat? All of these "signs of life" are muscular contractions. The muscles of the body are responsible for effecting whatever movements the body or any of its parts may make.

TYPES OF MUSCLE

Three types of muscle may be distinguished by their structure and physiology: **visceral,** named from the Latin for pertaining to the entrails; **cardiac,** named from the Greek for pertaining to the heart; and **skeletal.** Visceral muscle is associated with the digestive tract, blood vessels, respiratory tract, excretory system, and reproductive system. Its fibers are small, spindle-shaped, with one nucleus approximately in the center of each fiber. Within the fiber are some long fibrils, which are hollow cylinders filled with liquid and with walls composed chiefly of a protein known as **myosin.**

Cardiac muscle, found in the heart, is a branched network of fibers with no definite separations between the cytoplasm of one fiber and that of the next. Nuclei are scattered down the middle of the cylindrical fibers, and no cell membranes mark off the cytoplasm into distinct cells. Furthermore, there are alternating light and dark bands in the fibrils which line up in such a way that the whole fiber looks transversely striated or striped. Since the cytoplasm is continuous from one part of the heart to another, a contraction started at one point sweeps over the whole network without cell membranes to hinder it.

Skeletal muscle (Fig. 2.1), found associated with the skeletal system, is also composed of cylindrical fibers, but these are unbranched normally, and do not form a continuous network. The nuclei are placed along the cylinder near the periphery rather than in the middle. Longitudinal myosin fibrils and transverse striations also occur in skeletal muscle.

Another marked distinction among these three types of muscle is found in their normal modes of contraction. Visceral muscle is relatively slow, and requires an impulse for contraction and another impulse for relaxation. These

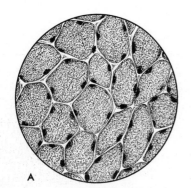

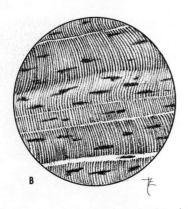

Fig. 2.1 Views of skeletal muscle through the microscope. **A,** Fibers cut across. Note the position of the nuclei at the edge of the fibers. **B,** Side view of the fibers showing striations.

impulses are involuntary; that is, in general they cannot be controlled at will. Cardiac muscle is faster, and rhythmic, beating without requiring a stimulus from the nervous system. Skeletal muscle is the quickest of all, and contracts upon nervous stimulation, relaxing when that stimulus ceases. Skeletal muscles are called voluntary muscles because in general they are the only ones which can be controlled at will.

CHEMISTRY OF CONTRACTION

(The myosin found in the muscle fibrils seems to be the actively contracting substance.) The myosin molecule (the smallest unit of myosin retaining the properties of that substance) seems to be a slender shaft about one micron long and $\frac{1}{200}$ of a micron in diameter, lying lengthwise in the fibril wall. (Upon adequate stimulation, the myosin molecule releases a part of itself as a phosphate molecule, and the remainder of the myosin molecule is thereby shorter. When this happens simultaneously to many or all of the myosin molecules in a fibril, and to the fibrils in one fiber, the whole fiber shortens. At least, this is one hypothesis to account for the mechanism of muscular contraction. The difficulties of investigation and confirmation of such a theory can be understood when you consider the delicacy of the materials used and the extreme complexity of the precautions necessary to maintain normal conditions during such a study.

The energy needed to bring about this breaking off of a phosphate molecule and consequent shortening of the myosin molecule is provided by the use of the food we eat and the air we breathe. Details of the provision of these materials will be discussed in the next two chapters, but we may anticipate a little here. Most of the energy the body uses is derived from the breakdown of a type of foodstuff called carbohydrate. The products of this breakdown combine with oxygen obtained from the air, the reaction giving off carbon dioxide, water, and energy. In the muscle the carbohydrate is in the form of a starch known as **glycogen.** Under suitable conditions glycogen may react with a phosphate to produce **glucose phosphate. Glucose** is a form of sugar, and is a simpler molecule than glycogen. Through a long series of chemical changes this glucose phosphate eventually breaks into a still simpler compound, **lactic acid.** These changes release some energy for muscular contraction, but the reactions are relatively so slow that they cannot provide energy fast enough for ordinary needs.

However, a sort of explosive compound is manufactured,

a substance known as **adenosine triphosphate.** Upon arrival of the stimulus for contraction, the adenosine triphosphate breaks down instantly, releasing one of its three phosphate portions, and giving off the energy requisite for the contraction. There is enough adenosine triphosphate available to keep up the contraction for a limited time.

Meanwhile some of the phosphate released is used in breaking down the glycogen, and the clumsy mechanism of energy release from glycogen is set into motion. Eventually this energy may be used to re-form adenosine triphosphate.

However, if prolonged contraction of the muscle occurs, another reaction fills the breach in time between the depletion of adenosine triphosphate and its restoration by breaking up of glycogen. **Creatine phosphate** is this "Peter at the dike." Creatine phosphate is used only in such emergencies, and may be dissociated into creatine and phosphate molecules with the release of enough energy to put the liberated phosphate back into the adenosine compound, reconstituting adenosine triphosphate. By the time the creatine phosphate shows signs of exhaustion, the glycogen-derived energy is available for rebuilding more creatine phosphate. Thus, as long as the glycogen supply holds out, energy will be available for muscle contraction.

The accumulation of lactic acid has a damaging effect on the contraction of muscle. To some extent this acid is counteracted by some of the substances normally present in muscle, and by the washing away of some of it as the blood courses through the muscle. But if too much accumulates, it will greatly hinder contraction and lower the muscle's efficiency. Normally some (about one fifth) of the lactic acid is broken down into carbon dioxide and water, providing energy for the rebuilding of the rest of it into glycogen. This process ordinarily proceeds most efficiently after the muscle has ceased contraction and is said to be at rest. Obviously the term "at rest" refers to the relaxed position of the muscle and not to a stoppage of all activity, for restoration of the supply of glycogen, adenosine triphosphate, and creatine phosphate continues during this time. The very elongation of fibrils which constitutes relaxation of the muscle is brought about by active addition of phosphate to the myosin molecules.

Since the blood stream bathes muscles with a continuous supply of glucose, oxygen, phosphate, and other materials, a "resting" muscle may restore its depleted stock readily. Furthermore, if some muscles in the body are in prolonged activity, as in hard manual labor or athletic competition, creatine phosphate may be transferred to them from muscles not in vigorous use at the time. This mobilization of supplies from muscles not directly involved in the activity contributes to the capacity of the body for great muscular effort.

A dehydrated form of creatine, called **creatinine,** is excreted in the urine in amounts depending on the amount of muscle in the body and not upon the degree of use or physical activity of those muscles. Any pronounced change in the rate of creatinine excretion indicates some extreme dietary change, a debilitating disease, or breakdown of muscle tissue.

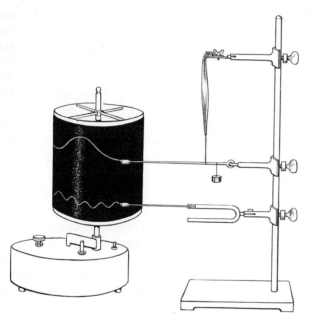

Fig. 2.2 A kymograph setup. If the muscle is stimulated, by electric shock, for example, the resulting contraction is recorded on the smoked paper by the lever attached to the lower end of the muscle. The wavy line at the base is drawn by a vibrating tuning fork, and it is used to time the duration of the contraction.

PHYSICS OF CONTRACTION

In order to study the physical characteristics of muscular contraction, physiologists use a device known as a **kymograph** (Fig. 2.2). A kymograph includes a cylinder on which is fastened a sheet of smoked paper and which may be made to revolve at predetermined speeds. One end of a living muscle is fastened to a rigid support, while the other end is attached to a hinged lever placed so that any contraction of the muscle will draw the end of the lever across the smoked paper, leaving a record of the contraction. Additional levers may be used to record on the paper the instant of application of the stimulus, and the passage of small units of time.

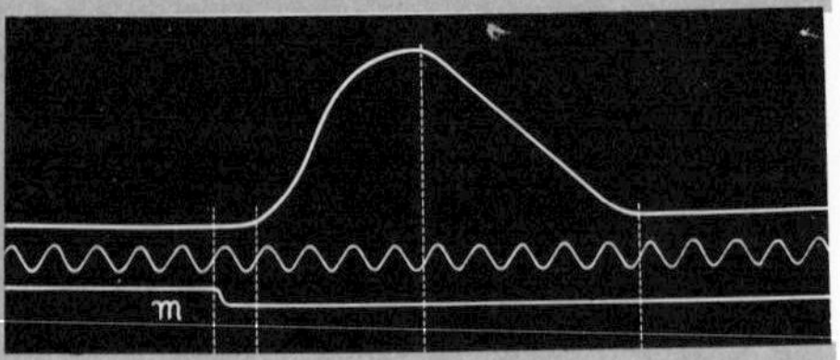

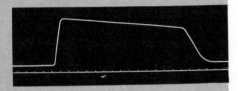

Fig. 2.3 A kymograph record of a single muscle twitch. If the middle line represents time, one-hundredth of a second from crest to crest, and the drop in the bottom line at m indicates the time the stimulus was given, determine the latent period, contraction period, and relaxation period for this twitch.

By means of this instrument it was found that a frog leg muscle may complete a single contraction in one tenth of a second. This includes about 0.01 second for the latent period — the time between the arrival of the stimulus and the first evidence of response indicated by change in the position of the lever attached to the muscle; 0.04 second for contraction — until the lever reaches the peak of its curve; and 0.05 second for relaxation — the dropping of the lever to its previous resting level. See Figure 2.3. Human muscles may be even faster than this, a single contraction being measured in a very few thousandths of a second.

If the stimulus is rapidly repeated ·or prolonged, contraction is maintained, and the lever remains longer at the top of the curve, only gradually dropping down as the muscle becomes fatigued. See Figure 2.4. Most muscle contractions in the body are of this prolonged nature rather than single twitches. In such a prolonged contraction the fibers of one muscle work in shifts, not more than a third of the fibers of one muscle being in contraction at one time. Some fibers may relax while others contract for a time, and then still others will contract as the second group relaxes. For any one fiber, however, contraction is at a maximum or not at all.

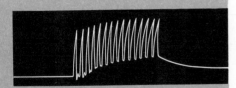

Fig. 2.4 Contraction maintained until fatigue sets in. Note that although stimuli continue to come in (notches on bottom line), the degree of contraction falls off gradually until the muscle is fatigued; and then it drops off rapidly.

Muscle Tone

In a muscle, only a very few fibers may be contracted for a weak effort, or more for a stronger effort. As a matter of fact, a muscle never has all of its fibers relaxed at one time unless it is diseased. A few fibers are always contracted, maintaining a state of readiness called **muscle tone.** Because of muscle tone, when a stimulus arrives for a sudden contraction the muscle is ready for practically instant action. Muscle tone is maintained by the cerebellum of the brain, which continually sends impulses to muscle fibers in rotation. The readiness is therefore continuous and no one set of fibers becomes exhausted.

Staircase Phenomenon

Another feature of muscular performance demonstrated by the kymograph is the "staircase phenomenon." This is familiar to every athlete as "warming up." If a muscle is stimulated to repeated contractions, the degree of contraction as indicated by the height to which the lever rises increases with each succeeding action until a plateau is reached. See Figure 2.5. This indicates an increased efficiency of muscular activity with exercise up to a maximum. This

Fig. 2.5 Staircase phenomenon. Each succeeding stimulus produces a slightly greater contraction than the last until a plateau is reached.

plateau is then maintained until the effects of fatigue become apparent.

An athlete preparing for participation in his sport knows by experience the value of exercising his muscles before entering active competition. Speaking of "warming up" in contrast to "going in cold" is not only a metaphorical way of expressing it, but a literal explanation of the advantage. About one fifth of the energy released in the chemical processes described before is used in contraction, and the other four fifths is dissipated as heat. A warmer muscle is capable of more rapid chemical changes and more efficient contraction; blood circulation is speeded up; breathing is faster; hence the quantity and ready availability of materials for providing muscular power is increased by the warming-up process.

Visceral Muscle

This account of the physical behavior of muscles is based on a study of skeletal muscles. As you read earlier in this chapter, visceral muscle contraction is very much slower, occurring in seconds rather than thousandths of a second. Visceral muscle contraction and relaxation are under the control of involuntary parts of the nervous system — we cannot regulate the movements of our stomachs by taking thought.

Cardiac Muscle

Cardiac muscle, we have seen, beats rhythmically, and will do so even if separated from its nerve supply. In fact, even skeletal muscle will beat rhythmically if put in a salt solution containing potassium salts, but from which all calcium salts have been removed; hence beating may be a fundamental property of all muscle, inhibited by certain concentrations of calcium salts. The normal concentration of calcium in the body fluids is sufficient to inhibit beating of visceral and skeletal muscle, but not enough to stop cardiac muscle. An excess of calcium perfused into the heart will cause it to stop beating in a contracted condition.

ANATOMY OF THE MUSCULAR SYSTEM

Muscular Anatomy

Most skeletal muscles are attached to parts of the skeleton (Fig. 2.6A). Each muscle fiber has its own thin connective tissue sheath; a bundle of such fibers is held together by a somewhat thicker connective tissue coat; and the entire muscle is enclosed in a still heavier connective tissue layer.

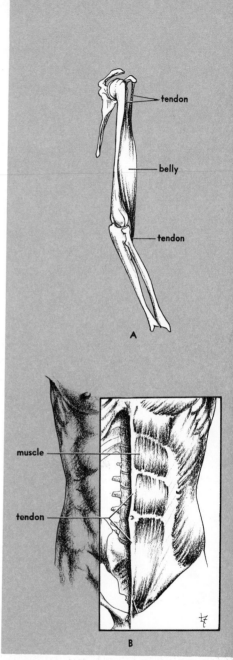

Fig. 2.6 Typical skeletal muscles: **A,** Biceps muscle in the arm; B, Muscles attached to the ventral abdominal tendon.

These various sheaths terminate in a tendon at each end of the muscle, and the tendon is usually fastened to a bone or to cartilage. Some tendons, as the great tendon along the front part of the abdomen, are attached to muscles at each side, so that the muscle may be thought of as interrupted by a tendon in its passage from one skeletal element to another.

The body of the muscle, between the terminal tendons, is spoken of as the **belly.** See Figure 2.6.

Muscles are designated by names referring to their location, shape, or action. On the basis of action we may distinguish between **flexors,** which bend a joint, and **extensors,** which straighten it out; between **abductors,** which pull a structure away from the axis of the body, and **adductors,** which pull the structure toward that axis; between **levators,** which raise a structure, and **depressors,** which lower it. A few of the muscles of the body are not easily classified as one of those six kinds, but most will fit into that scheme. See Figure 2.7.

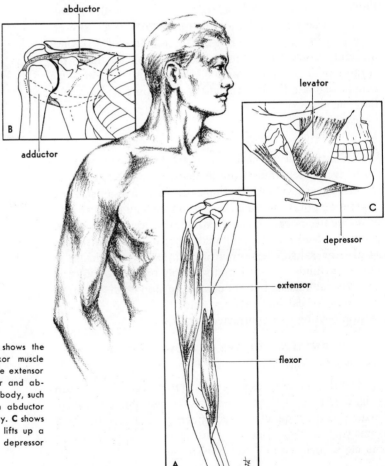

Fig. 2.7 Kinds of muscle action. **A** shows the flexor and extensor muscles. The flexor muscle bends a joint, such as the elbow; and the extensor straightens it out. **B** shows the adductor and abductor. An adductor pulls a part of the body, such as the arm, toward the body; and an abductor pulls it away from the midline of the body. **C** shows the levator and depressor. The levator lifts up a part, such as the lower jaw, and the depressor pulls it down.

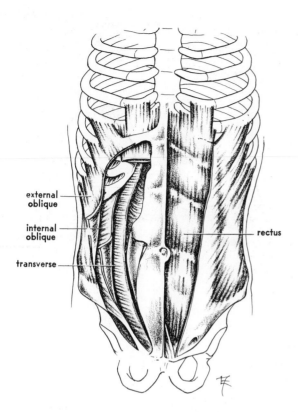

Fig. 2.8   Abdominal muscles. How are these supported without a skeleton in the front part of the abdomen?

external
oblique

internal
oblique

rectus

transverse

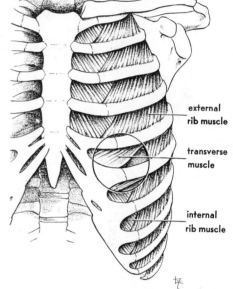

external
rib muscle

transverse
muscle

internal
rib muscle

Abdominal Muscles

The wall of the abdomen has four large sheets of muscle: the **external oblique, internal oblique, transverse,** and **rectus muscles.** The first three named attach dorsally to the lower ribs, the spinal column, and the ilium, and join in front with broad tendons. The rectus muscles run from the pubes to the lower rib attachments and to the breastbone. See Figure 2.8.

Fig. 2.9   Chest muscles. The external rib muscles overlie the internal rib muscles, and these in turn cover the transverse muscles of the chest. How does this compare with the arrangement of the abdominal muscles?

Chest Muscles

In the chest region similar muscles occur, but these are interrupted by ribs, so that the external oblique and the internal oblique muscles pass from one rib to the next instead of constituting a continuous sheet as they do in the abdomen. The transverse muscles in the chest run from the inner surface of the breastbone to the ribs. The breastbone occupies the front wall of the chest, and the rectus muscles do not extend above the lower part of the chest. See Figure 2.9.

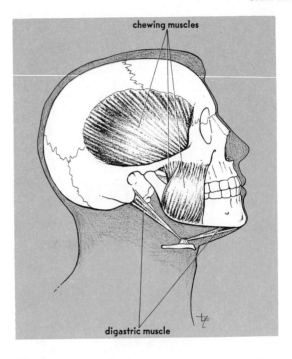

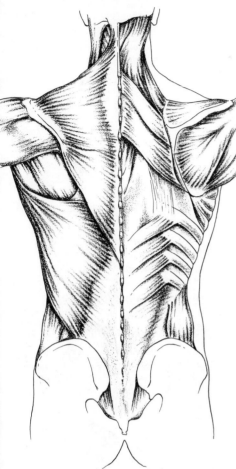

Fig. 2.10 Muscles of the back. Can you classify the muscles shown according to their action?

Fig. 2.11 Jaw muscles. Which are levators and which depressors?

Back Muscles

The muscles of the back (Fig. 2.10) are much more numerous, running between vertebrae and from vertebrae to the skull, the pectoral girdle, and the pelvic girdle.

Neck Muscles

Even more numerous are the muscles of the neck region, operating the mouth, pharynx, hyoid bone, and larynx.

Jaw Muscles

Likewise highly differentiated are the muscles of the head (Fig. 2.11), especially those which give expression to the face and which move the lower jaw. Of the latter may be mentioned the chewing muscles running across the cheek and behind the ear from the side of the skull to the lower jaw. These are powerful muscles used as levators to raise the lower jaw and aid in chewing.

The depressor of the jaw is a much weaker muscle, the **digastric,** so called because it has two bellies connected by a tendon. The upper belly runs from the mastoid process of the skull to a tendon which passes through a connective tissue loop fastened to the side of the hyoid bone. The tendon passes through this loop and into the lower belly of the muscle, which fastens to the front of the lower jaw.

When the two digastric muscles, right and left, contract, they pull the front of the jaw down, thus opening the mouth.

Arm Muscles

The muscles of the limbs are chiefly rather large and strong. The **breast muscles** run from the breastbone, ribs, and collarbone across the chest to the humeri, acting as adductors of the arms. The **deltoid** (Greek: Δ-shaped) **muscle** on each side runs from the shoulder blade and collarbone over the outer surface of the shoulder to the humerus, and serves as an abductor of the arm. Other muscles are used in rotating the head of the humerus in its socket.

The principal arm muscles are illustrated in Figure 2.12. In the upper arm are the muscles which operate the elbow joint. In the front side are the **biceps,** or two-headed, **muscle** and the **brachialis muscle,** which flex the elbow. The biceps runs from two places on the shoulder blade to the radius. and the brachialis from the humerus to the ulna.

Counteracting the effect of these muscles is the **triceps,** or three-headed, **muscle** on the back side of the arm. This muscle runs from one head on the shoulder blade and two on the humerus to a tendon fastened to the olecranon process of the ulna. When the triceps contracts it straightens the arm. It seems to be traditional for a boy wishing to make an impression to demonstrate the power of his biceps muscle, or to invite inspection of it in a contracted state. Actually, the triceps is a larger and more powerful muscle, but less accessible to notice.

In the forearm are the principal muscles operating the wrist, hand, and fingers. The bellies of these muscles lie along the arm, and the tendons extend down into the hand region. This arrangement allows considerable power and flexibility without concentrating bulk in the hand and fingers. A person unaccustomed to using his fingers vigorously, who types or plays the piano for some length of time, will find the feeling of fatigue in his forearm rather than in his fingers.

Running from the inner side of the elbow to the palm side of the hand are the flexor muscles which bend the wrist, hand, and finger joints, doubling the fist; on the opposite side are the extensor muscles, running from the elbow region to the back of the hand, and serving to straighten out the fingers and hand. In addition there is on the inner side a **pronator muscle** which rotates the radius across the ulna, turning the palm of the hand down, and

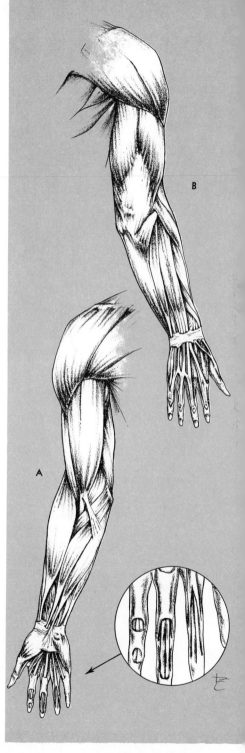

Fig. 2.12 Arm muscles: A, From the front; B, From the back. Point out the extensors and flexors of the shoulder, the elbow, the wrist, the fingers.

on the outer side of the arm a **supinator muscle** which rotates the radius across the ulna back to a position parallel with the ulna, turning the palm of the hand up. If you lay your forearm on a table so that the olecranon stays in one place, and then rotate your arm alternately palm up and palm down, you may observe the action of these muscles.

In the hand and the fingers there are some much smaller muscles used in delicate adjustments of the position of the fingers.

Leg Muscles

In the leg (Fig. 2.13) the muscles are similar in general to those of the arm, but larger and more powerful. There are abductor and adductor muscles of the thigh which draw the leg away from or toward its fellow. There are flexor and extensor muscles of the thigh which bend the hip joint, as in sitting down, or straighten it, as in standing up. Within the thigh are the flexors (back of the leg) and extensors (front of the leg) of the knee joint. In the shank may be found the flexor (back of the leg) and extensor (front of the leg) muscles of the ankle, foot, and toes. Long tendons run from these through the foot to the toes. As in the hand, there are some smaller muscles in the foot which adjust the positions of the toes, but the principal power operating the foot comes from muscles in the shank. Of these the flexors are much the stronger, for they are used in pushing the body along in walking or running. If you watch a person walking, you will see that the propulsion of the body involves bending the ankle so that the foot is pulled down and back; this is accomplished by the flexors in the calf of the leg. The extensors return the foot to its normal position for the next step.

HYGIENE OF THE MUSCULAR SYSTEM

Muscular exercise is satisfying in many ways. The exhilaration of bodily movement is a normal result of an active metabolism. Satisfaction in developing skill and deftness in a sport, social pleasures associated with participation in athletics, and the mental stimulus of competition contribute to a sense of well-being. And the increased efficiency of muscular action is of lasting benefit.

In choosing suitable exercises, you will want to consider your own physical capacity as well as the physical, mental, and emotional wants you wish to satisfy. These differ with each individual. But there are some general factors with which we are all concerned.

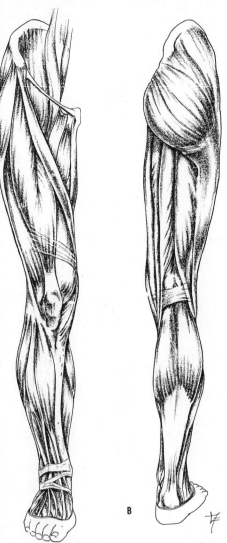

Fig. 2.13 Muscles of the right leg: A, Front of the leg; B, Back of the leg. Could the extensors and flexors both contract at once?

The bodily results of good exercise include an increase in the rate of circulation of blood and lymph; an increase in the efficiency of the heart and of the breathing apparatus; an increase in the rate of getting rid of waste materials, particularly through the skin, contributing to a healthy, glowing appearance; and an increase in the size and strength of muscle fibers.

Participation in vigorous sports is much better for you if you train up to them and train down afterward. The various increases mentioned in the previous paragraph do not arise at once. They develop gradually over a long period of increasing amounts of exercise. Similarly, the body makes a much more satisfactory adjustment to the cessation of such athletic activity if gradual training down is practiced. If a football player, for example, plays the last game of the season and then stops all vigorous exercise, his appetite tends to remain constant, but his use of the food intake is greatly curtailed, with the resulting deposition of fat. His circulation and breathing are now overtrained, and inefficiently used. His body would be much better able to adjust if he let down gradually over a period of a few months.

The effects of lack of exercise are vividly apparent to one who has had an arm or a leg in a cast for some time. The muscles degenerate in size and strength, and should be retrained as soon as possible. Massage of an immobilized muscle helps some in retaining its condition. A normally healthy person who has been confined to his bed for a week or more experiences a muscular weakness when he tries to resume his usual activities. This is a rather impressive demonstration of the sensitivity of the body, especially the muscles, to exercise or the lack of it.

A person unused to athletics who indulges in very energetic activity may manage well for a time, but later, perhaps the next day, he finds himself stiff and sore. This is due at least in part to the accumulation of waste materials in the muscles beyond the capacity of the muscles and blood stream to dispose of them. Some of this soreness may be prevented by stimulating circulation with showers and massage as soon as the exercise is over. If he trains, the efficiency of his muscles to reconvert the accumulated lactic acid and to store more glycogen, adenosine triphosphate, and creatine phosphate will increase. He will also find his circulatory rate speeded up; thus more waste products can be removed in a shorter time. The increased circulatory efficiency also has its effect on increased mental alertness and emotional satisfaction. The sedentary individual is often more easily tired and bored with his task than the active person. Good metabolism produced by suitable exercise promotes efficient mental work and enthusiastic interest in activities. Poor, sluggish circulation leads to early fatigue, inferior work, and acute dissatisfactions. A person confined to a task involving little physical effort will do well to use his muscles periodically, if only to stand and stretch. This will speed up the circulation temporarily, removing some of the wastes accumulated in the muscles which must be used in maintaining one position.

Of course, exercise may be overdone. The feeling of fatigue is a warning that it would be well to heed. Excessive use of muscles after they begin to show signs of distress may result in cramps due to stimulation beyond the capacity to respond. Or this may produce the soreness described earlier. If the muscle continues to be used, eventually the muscle fibers themselves will all be fatigued and incapable of further contraction. One cannot hang to a cliff by his fingers indefinitely.

One of the advantages of periodic physical examinations by a physician is the determination of the capacity for and need of muscular exercise. This is just as essential a part of healthy living as an adequate diet. Likewise periods of rest are important. If daily activity involves incessant use of certain muscles, these should be given a chance to rest, and less active ones exercised.

While temperaments and custom differ among individuals, in general the best work of a healthy person is done soon after he wakes. If he partakes of some physical exercise then, to "warm up his motor," he is in the best condition for both mental and physical work. As his work day progresses, his efficiency begins to lessen, and after a normal day's work, he would be wise to relax and not tax his physical and mental powers. Students who put off their studying until late in the evening find learning slower and retention poorer than those who study early in the day. Furthermore, enthusiasm and joy in studying and learning are more easily found when one is rested and full of energy. And for the greatest efficiency, periods of study should not be too long. A half hour or an hour of study should be followed by a few minutes of walking around, a game of ping-pong, or some other such bit of exercise.

Good posture is simply the efficient use of muscles. In addition to moving parts of the body, muscles hold parts of the body in place against the pull of gravity. Most of the organs, muscles, and bones of humans are built on the plan common to four-footed animals. This plan is based on the principle of a bridge, with double supports at each end of the arch. But the human is a drawbridge, standing on end. This creates an adjustment problem. Muscles keep the upright body from toppling over.

Efficient posture produces stability of position with the least possible expenditure of energy. This involves having the feet nearly parallel, slightly apart; legs about straight and parallel; four curves in the spinal column, as described in the previous chapter; head balanced on the atlas; and arms hanging at the sides. Such a position, if not stiffly held, may be kept for a long time without excessive fatigue. But a tendency for the arms to swing forward (round-shoulderedness), or the head to hang, or the toes to point in or out, or the hip to flex puts an added strain on some muscles, and may cause the person to tire much more readily.

Similarly, a seated posture in which the hip girdle and sacral vertebrae bear the weight of the trunk is very much superior to one in which the curvature of the lumbar vertebrae is reversed, and one "sits" on them instead of on the pelvis. Prolonged bending forward over one's work also puts undesirable strains on muscles and interferes with proper breathing movements.

A sprain, caused by a sudden stress upon a muscle for which it is not prepared, is a twisting or pulling of the muscle accompanied by the tearing of some tendon or muscle fibers. Rest and stimulation of circulation by hot or cold wet towels will relieve the pain and speed recovery.

SUMMARY

To summarize this account of the muscular system: Muscles are the organs of movement. Of the three kinds — visceral, cardiac, and skeletal — generally only the latter is subject to voluntary control. Muscular contraction involves shortening of the myosin molecules in the muscle fibrils. Energy for this is provided by exploding adenosine triphosphate. Breakdown of creatine phosphate provides for rapid rebuilding of the adenosine triphosphate, and maintains the supply of energy until the much slower breakdown of glycogen to lactic acid may be utilized.

The skeletal muscles of the body work in opposing sets: adductors versus abductors, levators versus depressors, and flexors versus extensors. The efficient use of these by a human being involves creating and maintaining a high level of efficiency through well-planned exercise carried on systematically, and development of good posture and wise use of muscles. Such a program not only provides for skillful and effective movement, but is also beneficial to mental activity and emotional satisfactions.

REVIEW QUESTIONS

1. Describe the three types of muscle.
2. Explain the chemistry of muscular contraction.
3. Describe a kymograph.
4. Explain muscle tone.
5. What is the staircase phenomenon?
6. Describe the structure of the biceps muscle.
7. Classify skeletal muscles according to their actions.
8. Describe the arrangement of muscles associated with the abdominal wall; the lower jaw; the arm; the leg.
9. What are the physiological effects of muscular exercise?
10. What is muscular fatigue?

GENERAL QUESTIONS

1. The limit of human vision with a good microscope is about $\frac{1}{10}$ of a micron. Can a myosin molecule be seen?
2. How would our lives be changed if muscular contraction obtained its energy directly from the change of glucose phosphate to lactic acid?
3. How do you account for the fact that the amount of creatinine in the urine is independent of the amount of muscular exercise?
4. Does the maintenance of muscle tone require energy?
5. Compare the list of chemicals present in a rested muscle with the list of chemicals present in a fatigued muscle.
6. How does parathyroid hormone deficiency produce convulsions?
7. How is the contraction of a muscle fiber translated into the movement of a bone?
8. Account for the fact that the human trunk has many more muscles in back than in front.
9. Which muscles contract and which relax when a pitcher throws a baseball?
10. Determine the places of attachment and the direction of the fibers in the pronator and supinator muscles of your arm.
11. Describe the contractions and relaxations of leg muscles in running.
12. Are the flexors of the toes on the top or bottom of the foot?
13. What are the advantages of "training down" after an athletic season?
14. In what ways do physical education courses contribute to success in other courses?
15. From the standpoint of wise use of muscles, what types of recreation would be most suitable for a city mail carrier? a switchboard operator? a watchmaker? a bank teller? a street sweeper? a professional football player? a housewife?

The Digestive System

Digestion

In the account of muscular contraction you read that a protein, myosin, contracted using energy provided by adenosine triphosphate, creatine phosphate, and glycogen. These and many other substances used by the body are made from foods acted upon first by the digestive system. The digestive system is a contorted and branched tube passing through the body from mouth to anus. Technically, the hollow of the tube is outside of the body and not part of the body itself. Food passes through the tube, is subjected to both physical and chemical forces, and most of that which can be made to dissolve is absorbed through the walls of the tube into the body. The remainder passes out of the tube without ever having entered the body. Thus the process of digestion is simply that of making parts of the food soluble and absorbable.

We may consider first the structure and arrangement of the tube and its parts, then the types of food worked on, and finally the process of digestion and its results.

ANATOMY OF THE DIGESTIVE SYSTEM

Teeth

The digestive system starts at the mouth (Fig. 3.1). The entrance is guarded by a pair of lips. A short distance behind the lips are the teeth, the upper ones projecting down from sockets in the maxillae, the lower ones projecting up from sockets in the mandible. Unlike some other animals in which an indefinite number of tooth replacements is possible, humans normally have two sets of teeth; if more are required, they must be paid for.

The first, or milk, set consists of twenty teeth. These are formed within the substance of the jaws, and push through the surface into the mouth cavity gradually.

In the discussion of the characteristics of living organisms, individuality was emphasized. This quality is conspicuously illustrated by the variation in the ages at which humans get their teeth. Some babies have one or more at birth. Some may postpone the event for a year or more. And it is an event — bringing joy and pride to the happy parents, and sometimes, though not always, pain and sorrow to the child.

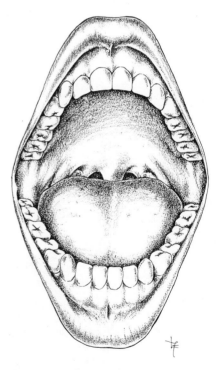

Fig. 3.1   Position of the teeth in the mouth.

Table 3.1 gives the time of appearance and shapes of the milk teeth. Remember that the times are approximate averages, and not rigid schedules.

TABLE 3.1·

MILK TEETH	TIME OF APPEARANCE	SHAPE OF CROWN	SHAPE OF ROOT
Incisors I	7 months	spadelike	conical
Incisors II	10–12 months	spadelike	conical
Canines	16–20 months	conical with rounded tip; one cusp on outer edge	conical, deep
Premolars I	12–15 months	flattened, with three cusps	two-branched
Premolars II	20–36 months	four cusps on uppers, five on lowers	three-branched

The incisors in the lower jaw usually appear slightly before those in the upper jaw. Incisors are used as chisels to cut through and break off pieces of food. Canines are used in grasping and pulling, and have a deeper root than other teeth, giving firm anchorage for such tasks as pulling meat off bones. The cusps on premolar and molar teeth provide a grinding surface. The divided root makes a very firm attachment and prevents rocking of the tooth in the socket when food is macerated by up-and-down and sidewise movement of the teeth.

The size of the jaws is increasing during these early years, and since the teeth do not grow in diameter after breaking through the gums, they would be separated by considerable spaces as the jaw grew to adult size if they were not replaced. Each member of the milk set is replaced by a permanent tooth which develops within the jaw internal to the temporary tooth. As time goes on, these permanent teeth press upon the temporary ones, and eventually push them out of their sockets, and take over their position. In addition, permanent teeth appear in the back part of the jaws in places where no milk teeth have preceded them. See Table 3.2.

TABLE 3.2

PERMANENT TEETH	TIME OF APPEARANCE	SHAPE OF CROWN	SHAPE OF ROOT
Incisors I	6–7 years	spadelike	conical
Incisors II	7–8 years	spadelike	conical
Canines	12 years	conical with rounded tip	conical, deep
Premolars I	8–9 years	two cusps }	{ conical, and slightly
Premolars II	9–10 years	two cusps }	branched at the tip
Molars I	6 years	{ square with rounded corners; four cusps (upper) or five (lower)	uppers three-branched; lowers two-branched
Molars II	12 years		
Molars III	17–20 years if at all	three cusps	conical or slightly branched at the tip

Because of the cramped quarters of the third molar tooth, there is sometimes difficulty with the third molars. If the room is inadequate, they may never reach the surface of the gum at all. Or, they may crowd in, causing pressure on the adjacent teeth and soft tissues, resulting in painful experiences.

The third molars are known as the "wisdom teeth," in harmony with the curious notion that wisdom appears at about the same time as do these teeth.

Aside from the external shape of the tooth, the structure is fundamentally alike for all human teeth, temporary or permanent. The outermost layer is a very hard, impenetrable substance known as **enamel.** Within this is a thick, bonelike layer, the **dentine.** In the center is the **pulp,** consisting of connective tissue, blood vessels, and nerves, as anyone who has suffered from toothache is well aware. If the enamel and dentine are eaten away by the action of acids, and bacteria gain access to the pulp, their secretions may cause pain. Such a tooth "cavity" may be cleaned out by a dentist, shaped up by drilling to hold a plug, and then "filled" with some substitute for the missing wall. Frequent thorough cleaning of teeth within fifteen minutes after eating retards the formation of the acids which destroy the enamel and dentine of teeth.

Here again great individuality is found. Some people have very resistant enamel, and few if any cavities develop. Others have weaker enamel, and visit the dentist much more frequently.

While there is a narrow space between the teeth and the lips and cheeks, most of the mouth cavity is located inside the rows of teeth. When the mouth is at rest, the molar teeth of the upper and lower jaws are opposite each other and nearly in contact, whereas the incisor and canine teeth of the lower jaw are behind those of the upper jaw. When the incisor teeth are to be used to bite off a piece of food, the lower jaw is thrust slightly forward bringing the upper and lower incisors into line with each other.

Tongue

The **tongue** (Fig. 3.2) is one of the most muscular organs of the body. It is coated, like the rest of the mouth wall, by an epithelium composed of several layers of cells, but under this epithelium skeletal muscles run in many directions. Contraction of these muscles produces a wide variety of movements. The tongue is capable of moving food about in the mouth from one group of teeth to another, and of

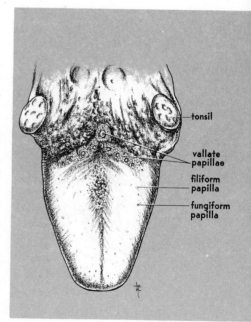

Fig. 3.2   Tongue, upper surface. Note the locations of the different kinds of papillae.

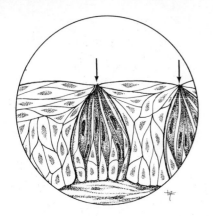

Fig. 3.3 Microscopic structure of a taste bud. The sensitive cells are below the surface. Only substances that dissolve and diffuse through the tiny pore to the taste bud are tasted.

lifting food back into the posterior part of the mouth from which it may be swallowed. The lower portion of the tongue is fastened to the floor of the mouth by a fold of tissue known as the **frenulum;** see Figure 3.4.

The upper surface of the tongue has tiny hillocks known as **papillae.** Some of the larger papillae possess special structures called **taste buds** (Fig. 3.3). These are clusters of banana-shaped cells sunk into pits in the surface of the papilla. Each taste-sensitive cell has a hairlike process at its exposed tip, and is in association with a nerve ending at the opposite end. In children taste buds are plentiful over the entire upper surface of the tongue, especially at the anterior end; in adults they occur chiefly on the back part of the tongue.

There are four different types of taste-sensitive cells in the taste buds, but these types are not uniformly distributed. The types are distinguished by the sensation they arouse when stimulated: sweet, sour, bitter, and salty. In general the sweet- and salty-sensitive cells are near the tip of the tongue, the acid-sensitive ones at the lateral borders, and the bitter-sensitive ones at the back. There is some overlapping of areas, however.

Some of the sensations commonly assigned to the sense of taste are in reality examples of the sense of smell. Many spices, for example, have relatively little taste, but affect the sense of smell powerfully. Odors may pass to the organs of smell through the nostrils or through the back of the mouth into the nose cavity. When one has a bad cold in the nose, so that access to the organs of smell is difficult, food is apt to appear "tasteless," whereas the sense of taste is actually unimpaired.

Salivary Glands

Associated with the mouth are three pairs of large **salivary glands** (Fig. 3.4). The **parotid gland** on each side is just in front of and below the external ear. Anyone who has endured the mumps will have little trouble in locating the gland, for it is the usual site of mumps infection. The parotid gland is a fairly large gland, about two or three inches in its greatest length. A duct runs from the gland to the inner wall of the cheek, opening into the mouth cavity about opposite the upper second molar tooth.

The **submaxillary gland** on each side is located just inside the posterior angle of the lower jaw. Its duct runs forward in the floor of the mouth, opening on the side of the frenulum of the tongue.

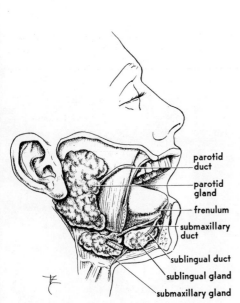

parotid duct

parotid gland

frenulum

submaxillary duct

sublingual duct

sublingual gland

submaxillary gland

Fig. 3.4 Human salivary glands. Can you point to the approximate location of these glands on your own face? Can you see in a mirror or in someone else's mouth where the ducts open?

The **sublingual gland** on each side lies under the tongue and along the inner surface of the anterior part of the lower jaw. Its duct runs to the side of the frenulum adjacent to that of the submaxillary gland.

The salivary glands secrete both **ptyalin** and **mucus.** Ptyalin is an enzyme that attacks carbohydrates; it will be discussed more fully later. Mucus is a protein substance, highly viscous, which serves to soften food and lubricate its passage through the digestive system.

The parotid gland secretes ptyalin, but no mucus. The submaxillary gland has approximately equal numbers of ptyalin-secreting cells and of mucus-secreting cells. The sublingual gland is composed largely of mucus-secreting cells, but has a few scattered ptyalin-secreting cells.

You might think of these salivary glands as outpouchings of the mouth cavity, highly subdivided like the branches of a tree, each terminal branch having at its tip a rounded fruit, and the whole structure hollow. The duct then represents the hollow trunk of the tree, its tributaries the branches, and the tiny spherical clusters of secreting cells the fruits. See Figure 3.5.

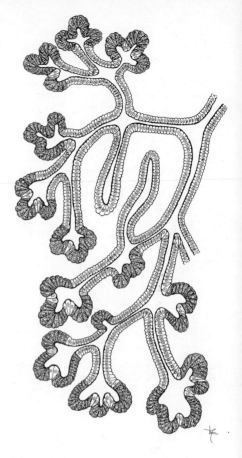

Fig. 3.5   Diagram of salivary gland structure. The secreting cells are stippled, the duct cells plain.

Mouth

Separating the mouth from the nose cavity above it is a shelf known as the **palate,** or roof of the mouth. The front part of it is supported by bone; this portion is the **hard palate.** Behind this is the **soft palate,** supported by connective tissue fibers, but containing no bone.

Pharynx

The mouth with its salivary glands is at the upper end of the digestive tract (Fig. 3.7). At the back of the mouth the nasal cavity and mouth cavity are both in communication with a chamber called the **pharynx.** This cavity has a lining similar to that of the mouth, composed of many layers of epithelial cells. Outside of this is a sheath of connective tissue, and beyond this several skeletal muscles which pull the pharynx open wider at the time of swallowing.

Esophagus

Beyond the pharynx is a long tube, the **esophagus.** In front of the opening of the pharynx into the esophagus is the opening of the pharynx into the trachea (through the larynx). Thus the pathway of air from nose to trachea crosses the route of food from mouth to esophagus. When

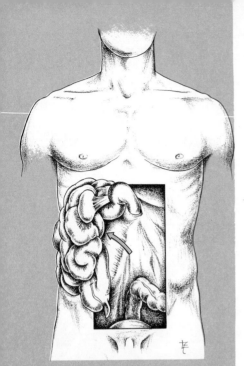

Fig. 3.6 The mesentery. This sheet of connective tissue suspends the abdominal organs.

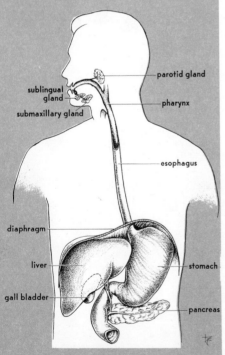

sublingual gland

submaxillary gland

parotid gland

pharynx

esophagus

diaphragm

liver

gall bladder

stomach

pancreas

Fig. 3.7 Human digestive tract from mouth to intestine. Only part of the liver is shown. Can you describe what happens to food in each chamber shown here?

swallowing occurs, however, the larynx is pulled forward and up under the base of the tongue, so that the opening into it is closed. If this isn't done speedily enough, food particles may get into the larynx or trachea, causing coughing and sputtering, but usually the mechanism is efficient enough to prevent this.

The esophagus leads from the pharynx down through the neck and chest, through the diaphragm which separates chest from abdomen, and into the abdominal cavity where it empties into the stomach. The esophagus is about ten inches long and about an inch in diameter. Its walls are constructed much as those of the pharynx, but part way down its length the muscular coat changes from skeletal to visceral muscle.

The part of the digestive tract in the trunk is fastened to the back of the chest and abdominal cavities by the **mesentery** (Fig. 3.6). The mesentery is a double sheet of connective tissue continuous with the lining of the body cavity and with the outer layer of the digestive tract. Between the two sheets of the mesentery pass nerves and circulatory vessels supplying the digestive tract.

Food passing into the upper end of the esophagus (Fig. 3.7) stimulates a wave of muscular contraction which pushes the food along toward the stomach. You may be able to visualize the process by putting a small marble in a flexible rubber tube, crooking your forefinger around the tube just behind the ball, and forcing the ball along through the tube by moving your flexed finger behind it. This wave of contraction in the muscular wall of the esophagus is known as **peristalsis,** which is derived from the Greek for contraction around. In the human the wave goes from the top to the bottom of the esophagus in about five or six seconds.

At the bottom of the esophagus is an especially prominent ring of visceral muscle, the **cardiac sphincter.** It is called cardiac only because it is near the heart; it has no direct connection with the heart. The cardiac sphincter remains closed except when the peristaltic wave reaches the bottom of the esophagus and pushes food into the stomach, or when pressure in the stomach becomes great enough to force the sphincter open, as in belching or vomiting. If one drinks a glass of water, the water will run down the esophagus ahead of the peristaltic wave, but since the sphincter is closed the water simply accumulates at the bottom of the esophagus until the wave arrives, opening the sphincter. The peristaltic wave accounts for the ability of people to swallow effectively when head downward, for if the food is manipulated into the top of the esophagus by the voluntary muscles of the tongue and pharynx, the esophageal muscles will close behind it and force it toward the stomach regardless of the direction of gravitational pull.

Stomach

The **stomach** is an enlargement of the digestive tube, having a capacity of about a quart to a quart and a half. The shape of the stomach varies with different individuals, and in the same individual at different times, but a typical form is illustrated in Figure 3.8. The entrance of the esophagus into the stomach is on the right side of the stomach near the top. The large, domelike portion of the stomach above the entrance is known as the **fundus.** This is normally distended with trapped gas. Below this is the slightly tapering, nearly vertical **body** of the stomach, curving to the right at the bottom, and passing into the narrowing **pylorus** which leads to the small intestine. *Pylorus* is the Greek word for gatekeeper. The junction between pylorus and intestine has walls thickened into a **pyloric sphincter.** The upper end of the fundus is at about the level of the lowest reach of the fifth rib, and the lowest part of the stomach is at about the level of the navel.

The lining of the stomach differs sharply from that of the esophagus. Instead of a many-layered. epithelium, there is only one layer of very tall epithelial cells. The epithelium is continued into literally millions of tiny deep pits, the **gastric glands.** The cells making up these glands are of two sorts — the **chief cells,** principally in the deeper parts of the gland, which secrete the enzymes of the stomach, and the **parietal cells,** mostly in the neck of the gland, which produce the acid of the stomach secretion.

Beneath the epithelium and packed around the glands is the connective tissue layer. Beyond this is the muscular coat consisting of three layers: an oblique layer, the innermost, particularly conspicuous in the region of the fundus; an intermediate circular layer, the thickest of the three, especially prominent in the lower half of the stomach; and an outermost longitudinal layer, most noticeable in the pylorus.

The inner wall of the stomach is thrown into folds which tend to flatten out as the stomach becomes filled. See Figure 3.9.

The contractions of the stomach occur principally in the lower half. The walls of an empty stomach are collapsed. Food that enters an empty stomach sinks down largely by

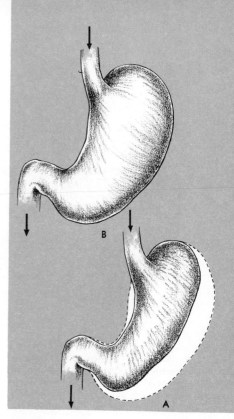

Fig. 3.8   Shape of the human stomach: A, When empty; B, When filled. Note that the length of the stomach is almost vertical, with a bend toward the right side of the body at the bottom.

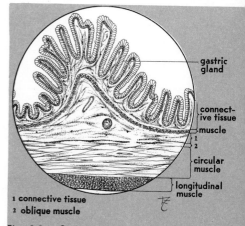

Fig. 3.9   Cross section through the wall of the stomach. The inner lining is up in the figure. It shows one of the many folds, and it is indented by long, narrow glands. The connective tissue runs up into the folds. The muscle layers are thick, and their contractions churn the food in the stomach.

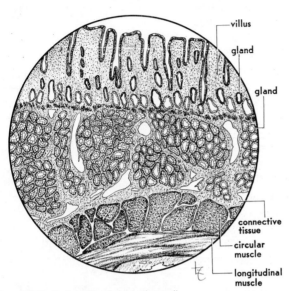

villus

gland

gland

connective tissue

circular muscle

longitudinal muscle

Fig. 3.10 Longitudinal section through the wall of the duodenum. Notice that the villi project up from the surface of the duodenum, and the deep, narrow glands project down. Notice also the different kind of glands in the connective tissue layer.

its own weight. When it reaches the middle of the stomach body, peristaltic movements of varying strength are initiated. There seems to be a period of strong contraction lasting from twelve to fifteen seconds, during which a wave may pass from the middle of the stomach to the pyloric sphincter. Then there is a period not quite half as long in which contractions are much weaker. These waves follow each other in rapid succession so that four or five waves are present at any one time. The strength of these contractions is influenced by the type of food — fats decreasing the strength very greatly, proteins somewhat less, and carbohydrates least.

Food leaves the stomach under pressure from the peristaltic contractions when the food is sufficiently softened. It enters the intestine a little at a time, having to wait for the intestinal contents to pass along to make room. Liquids may pass into the intestine as soon as they reach the pyloric sphincter, but more solid materials may take hours. Carbohydrates are nearly all out of the stomach by three hours after a meal; proteins are somewhat slower; and fats may be less than half out of the stomach at the end of three hours.

The position of the body makes some difference in the rate of emptying of the stomach. When the body is upright or on its left side, food leaves the stomach more slowly than when the body is lying on the right side. The old Roman custom of dining while reclining on a couch called gravity to the aid of digestion when the diner was lying on his right side.

Small Intestine

The **small intestine** is a much looped portion of the digestive tract, which would be about twenty feet long if it were straightened out. It is composed of three sections: the **duodenum** of about nine or ten inches; the **jejunum** of about eight feet; and the **ileum** of about twelve feet. The inner wall of the small intestine is feltlike because of its millions of tiny fingerlike projections known as **villi** (Fig. 3.10). In addition to these, glands somewhat like those of the stomach penetrate deeply into the intestinal wall. The entire surface, including the covering of the villi and the lining of the glands, is an epithelium of one layer of tall, narrow cells like those of the stomach. Outside of this layer is the connective tissue coat which surrounds the glands and forms the cores of the villi. Beyond this are the fairly thick band of circular muscle and the somewhat thinner band of longitudinal muscle. As in the stomach and the lower part of the esophagus these muscles are all visceral.

The duodenum is the site of greatest digestive activity, which continues as the food passes through the jejunum. The jejunum and the ileum absorb soluble products of food digestion.

Liver

Emptying into the duodenum about halfway down its extent are the ducts of two large glands. The **bile duct** receives **hepatic** (Greek for liver) **ducts** from the liver and the **cystic** (Greek for bladder) **duct** from the **gall bladder.** The **liver** is the largest gland in the body, a five-lobed mass occupying the upper end of the abdominal cavity, especially on the right side. Like the salivary glands it is made of the

Fig. 3.11   Human liver and gall bladder. The liver is pushed up to show some of the other organs. Trace the ducts from the liver, gall bladder, and pancreas to the duodenum. How does bile get into the gall bladder from the liver?

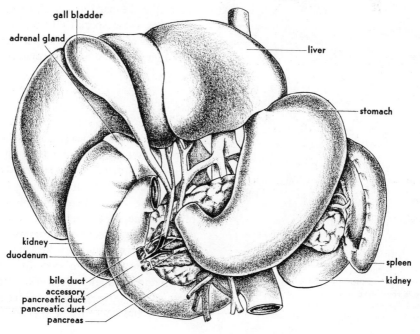

gall bladder
adrenal gland
liver
stomach
kidney
duodenum
spleen
kidney
bile duct
accessory pancreatic duct
pancreatic duct
pancreas

repeated branching of its duct, except that in the liver the terminal swellings make up a complex network of intercommunicating chambers and corridors. The gall bladder is a special outpouching of the bile duct enlarged into a hollow sac which stores some of the secretions of the liver before their passage into the duodenum. See Figure 3.11.

The gall bladder wall responds to irritation of foreign bodies by depositing a layer of cholesterol or calcium salts or both around the offender. Occasionally a precipitation of substances from the bile occurs. Any of these solid objects occurring in the gall bladder is known as a gallstone. If a gallstone becomes wedged in the bile duct, it may be the source of considerable trouble, perhaps calling for surgical removal. If gallstones form repeatedly, a surgeon may deem it 'wise to remove the entire gall bladder. This may be done without greatly disturbing normal bodily metabolism; liver secretions then pour into the duodenum continually rather than being stored up and released upon the usual stimulus. The control of gall bladder emptying will be discussed a little later.

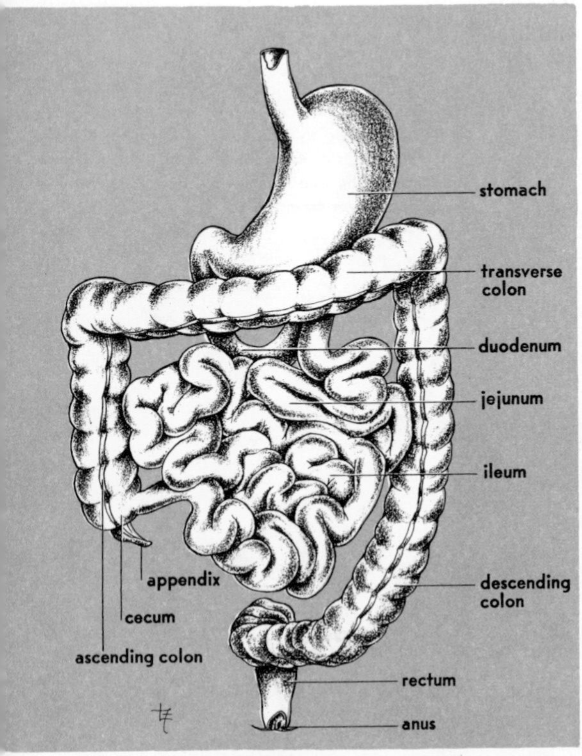

Pancreas

The **pancreas** opens into the duodenum by a **pancreatic duct** at the same point as does the bile duct. An accessory pancreatic duct may occur a short distance away. The pancreas is constructed much like the parotid gland, except that the pancreas has some special clusters of cells known as the **islands of Langerhans.** These are not concerned with digestion, and their characteristics will be considered further in Chapter 8.

Large Intestine

The end of the ileum (Fig. 3.12) is usually located in the lower right-hand corner of the abdominal cavity. It empties into the **large intestine** on the side of the latter. From this opening hangs a rounded pouch, the **cecum** (Latin for blind), which ends blindly except for the small **vermiform appendix** (Latin for worm-shaped attachment). The cecum and appendix show very little movement. The intestinal contents drop into the cecum from the ileum, and gradually are worked up into the other parts of the large intestine. Since stagnation may occur in the contents of the appendix, and since

Fig. 3.12　Human stomach and intestines. The small intestine is condensed in the figure so that it will not obscure the other parts. In life it occupies most of the front part of the abdominal cavity.

an abundance of bacteria is present throughout the large intestine, bacterial action may on occasion produce inflammation of the appendix, known as appendicitis. Removal of the appendix does not interfere with the normal activity of the remainder of the digestive system, and the appendix seems to be of very little use to the body. In some of the herbivorous mammals such as rabbits the cecum is as large as the stomach and is very active in the digestion and absorption of food products.

The remainder of the large intestine beyond the cecum includes the **ascending colon,** which runs up the right side of the abdominal cavity; the **transverse colon,** which runs across the upper end of the cavity from right to left, just below the liver and stomach; the **descending colon,** which runs down the left side; and the **rectum,** which executes an S-shaped curve and leads to the outside through an opening, the **anus.**

The large intestine has no villi, though it does have deep glands and an epithelial layer of tall cells until just before the anus is reached. Here the epithelium becomes composed of many layers of cuboidal and flattened cells like the epidermis of the skin. The connective tissue and muscular layers are like those of the small intestine.

The diameter of the digestive tract is greater in the region of the large intestine than in the small intestine, narrowing down at the rectum. The colon withdraws water from the material passing through it, so that the feces evacuated at the anus are much more solid than the material entering the large intestine. The substance of the feces is principally undigested portions of the food such as cellulose. Bacteria are also present in very great numbers.

TYPES OF FOOD

It will be convenient to discuss the types of food taken into the digestive tract not as meats, salads, and desserts, but as condiments, water, minerals, vitamins, carbohydrates, fats, and proteins.

Condiments

Condiments (Latin: seasonings) are substances added to food to affect the taste and odor. They are not digested, but are passed out with the feces. They include spices such as pepper, cinnamon, ginger, and mustard. As a result of the pleasure these offer to those who have developed a taste for them, the stomach is stimulated to pour forth its digestive secretions. Meals which begin with an appetizer delectable to the diner are more quickly and fully digested than those which seem to him humdrum and ordinary. Even the odor and anticipation of tasty food will start the release of gastric secretions. Therefore condiments serve a useful purpose, even though they are not digested and absorbed into the body.

Water

Water constitutes the greatest bulk of the body, and its unceasing loss from the body must be replaced for the continuation of life. Some of this may be obtained from the chemical breakdown of foods, as in the final disintegration of glycogen into water and carbon dioxide. For another example, the fat stored in a camel's hump may be broken down with the release of water. But much of the water requirement of the body is provided by drinking water or some liquid which is mostly water. About three quarts of water per day are lost by the average individual, and perhaps a little more than half of this may be supplied by the normal diet. The remainder should come from drinking of liquids.

Minerals

The **minerals** needed by the body usually are supplied in the form of salts. These salts are formed by combination of an acid with an alkaline substance containing a metallic element. Ordinary table salt, sodium chloride, for example, contains the metallic element sodium combined with the acidic element chlorine. Sodium by itself is very destructive of living matter, and chlorine is a poisonous gas. But the compound of the two has characteristics quite different from either of its constituents alone.

Sodium and chlorine are each present in the body as ions (electrically charged particles) or in combined form in the amount of about 100 grams (there are about 453.6 grams in one pound avoirdupois weight). They are lost through perspiration and in the urine, so that they must be replaced in the diet. Under normal circumstances sodium chloride is the only mineral added to the diet in pure form. Other inorganic substances are present in such small quantities in the body that ordinary foods contain enough of them to replace the minute amounts lost by the body. Ten grams of salt (about one third of an ounce) in the average daily food intake is sufficient to replace the lost sodium and chlorine.

Practically all of the sodium chloride in the body is in the body fluids such as blood and lymph. Its activity is concerned with maintaining two balances: acid-alkali, and osmotic pressure. The body fluids are approximately neutral as to proportions of acid and alkali. If an excess of one or the other occurs, such as the production of large amounts of lactic acid by muscle, it is neutralized through a buffering process involving the sodium. If a great deal of some alkaline substance such as sodium bicarbonate is introduced into the body, the chlorine is used in neutralizing the alkali. The nature of this buffering mechanism will be discussed in the next chapter.

Most of the other minerals used are incorporated into the cytoplasm of the cells. If the body fluids had no salts in them, an unbalance would occur between the relatively concentrated salt solutions inside the cells and the dilute solutions of the body fluids. There would then develop a pressure at cell membranes directed toward passing water into the cell, diluting the cytoplasm to a concentration equal to that of the body fluid. This pressure is known as **osmotic** (Greek for pushing) **pressure.** The presence of sodium chloride in body fluids in amounts sufficient to balance the concentrations of other inorganic substances inside the cells prevents this flooding of the cytoplasm.

In addition to contributing to these uses of sodium chloride, the chlorine appears in the stomach secretions as hydrochloric acid (hydrogen + chlorine, abbreviated to HCl), which provides a necessary condition for efficient gastric digestion.

Potassium is another metallic element important in the economy of the body. Unlike sodium, potassium is almost entirely contained within the cytoplasm of cells. Among other things, potassium is essential for normal muscular contractions, including heartbeat, and for impulse conduction in the nervous system. About 250 grams of potassium are present in the body at any one time, but loss is relatively small, so that replacement is no particular problem, especially in view of the considerable quantities of potassium present in both plants and animals used by humans as food.

The cytoplasm of cells contains calcium. The calcium appears to decrease the permeability of cell membranes, acting toward a stability of contents, in opposition to the effect of sodium and potassium, which tend to increase membrane permeability. The effect is dramatically illustrated by the effect of the parathyroid secretion described in Chapter 1. An increase in parathyrin increases the amount of calcium in the blood, and following this, in nervous tissue. The nerve cell membranes become less permeable and therefore less able to conduct impulses, or less sensitive. Exaggerated cases lead to coma. On the other hand, removal of parathyrin from the body causes a decrease of the amount of calcium in the nerve cells, resulting in an increase in membrane permeability and nerve sensitivity, leading in extreme cases to convulsions and death. Calcium is also used in the building of bones and teeth. The effect of vitamin D seems to be both increased intestinal absorption of calcium from the food, and increased rate of use of calcium in the hard structures of the body.

Phosphorus is associated with calcium in the building of bones and teeth. As phosphate it is also important, you remember, in the chemistry of muscular contraction. It is an essential constituent of nervous tissue. It is involved in the absorption of sugar through the intestinal wall, and the retention of sugar during urine formation. It is important in the buffering process by which the acid-alkali neutrality of the body is maintained.

Magnesium occurs in the cytoplasm of all living cells. Like calcium, it is present and important in the making and maintaining of bones and teeth. It lowers the permeability of cell membranes, and decreases nervous sensitivity even more than does calcium.

Iron is particularly important as a constituent of the hemoglobin in red blood corpuscles. A modified form, myoglobin, gives color to red muscles. Both hemoglobin and myoglobin have a strong affinity for oxygen. Iron is also essential as an ingredient in some of the enzymes used by the body, particularly those called cytochromes, which are involved in oxidation reactions by which energy is released.

Copper is a necessary substance for the building of hemoglobin from the iron obtained in the food. Copper is not a constituent of hemoglobin, but it facilitates the reaction. This type of influence is known as **catalysis,** and copper is here used as a catalyst. In the absence of copper the construction of hemoglobin goes on very slowly, or not at all. When copper is present the reaction proceeds readily. Only very minute quantities of copper are necessary. One investigator has stated that if you hold a copper penny in your mouth for a minute, you will obtain enough copper to last you all day. An ordinary diet furnishes enough copper without this expedient, however. Copper is also used in oxidative enzymes, in addition to its action as a hemoglobin catalyst.

Iodine is an ingredient of the secretion of the thyroid gland, a structure located in the throat. The thyroid secretion regulates the body's use of oxygen, and so is essential to life. Iodine is present in considerable quantities in the oceans and in soils deposited by salt water. Fresh-water deposits do not usually contain much iodine, however, and vegetables grown in such soil and animals feeding on such ground will not have much iodine in them unless they are near enough to the ocean to get the benefit of wind-wafted dust from evaporated salt spray. The region of the Great Lakes in the United States is one of the iodine-deficient areas of the world. The thyroid gland responds to a shortage of iodine supply by enlarging, producing what is known as a **goiter** (Latin: throat). People living in this "goiter belt" would do well to include sea foods in their diets, or to use "iodized salt," a table salt containing a small quantity of sodium iodide in addition to the sodium chloride. Iodine taken as iodine is poisonous, just as uncombined chlorine would be, but in the form of an iodide it is highly useful to the body.

Sulfur is an important constituent of many protein substances in the body, especially in the nervous system, in hair and nails, and in connective tissues.

Manganese appears to be essential in some enzymes of the body.

Fluorine has come into prominence recently as a substance useful in preserving the health of teeth by contributing to the resistance of the enamel. In even relatively small concentrations, uncombined fluorine is an active poison. The most satisfactory concentration of the combined fluoride in drinking water seems to be about one part per million of water.

Cobalt, zinc, aluminum, and a few other elements are found in minute quantities in living cells, and may have important actions, especially in enzymes, but not all of these are well understood as yet.

Vitamins

The **vitamins** are organic compounds having the characteristics of catalysts. They are essential in regulating certain important chemical processes in the body, or are incorporated into essential compounds, but are required in only very small amounts. Their absence from the diet is a serious lack, and is evidenced by impairment of bodily health. Their existence was postulated at about the turn of the century, based especially on the work of the Dutch colonial physician Christiaan Eijkman (1858–1930) in Java. He had long tried to isolate a germ as the cause of the wasting disease **beriberi** which affected so many of his patients. As a result of his observations on the occurrence of disease in fowl fed husked rice in contrast to the healthy birds fed rice with the husks on, he came to the conclusion that something in the rice husk was essential to the prevention of the disease. A later worker believed that this and similar substances belonged to a group of chemical substances known as amines, and called the ones necessary for life vitamines. However, it was later shown that not all such substances are amines, so the name was changed to vitamins.

When more than one of the vitamins appeared in the scientific literature, it became important to give each a distinctive name. At first they were given letter names — vitamins A, B, C, D, and so forth. This practice is still common, although many of the vitamins seem to be a group of substances rather than just one.

Vitamin A appears in the human diet dissolved in animal fats such as butter, cream, egg yolk, and fish liver oils. A group of substances known as **carotenes** found in plant foods may be converted by the human body into vitamin A. These carotenes are yellow in color, and are found in yellow and green vegetables such as lettuce, carrots, sweet potatoes, corn, pumpkin, and muskmelon. The vitamin may be stored chiefly in the liver, but also in lungs, kidneys, reproductive organs, and the retinas of the eyes. The vitamin seems to be essential for the preservation of the health of epithelial cells. In its absence epithelium becomes horny and degenerate, appearing as dry skin, inflamed eyes, damaged respiratory tract, inability of glands such as the salivary glands to secrete, and a greatly increased susceptibility to many infections. One of the clinical tests for vitamin A deficiency is the detection of night blindness, a loss of visual acuity in dim light. The transformation of a light impulse into a nerve impulse which may be sensed by the body involves the breakdown of a substance known as **visual purple,** which occurs in the retina of the eye. One of the components of visual purple is vitamin A, so that rebuilding of this visual purple for continued sensitivity to light is dependent upon a supply of this vitamin. Hence, a person without an adequate supply of vitamin A will not be able to reconstitute visual purple in sufficient quantity to provide for good vision.

Vitamin B was supposed to facilitate the body's use of sugar, helping in the oxidation reaction which releases energy. Further study has shown that what was originally thought to be one substance — the one that Eijkman found in rice hulls — is a considerable number of related products. These began to be numbered — vitamins B_1, B_2, and so forth — but now they are more commonly designated by specific names. Some members of this vitamin B family will be described below; others are also under study and more will be known about this group as time goes on. In fact, the whole field of vitamin research is still in the pioneering stage, and much more remains to be discovered about the number, nature, and actions of these substances.

Thiamin, or **vitamin B$_1$,** is the substance postulated by Eijkman. It is named from the Greek word for sulfur, for it was the only vitamin then known to contain that element. It occurs in lean meats, seeds, and leaves; unlike vitamin A, which is soluble in fat, thiamin is soluble in water. It is not readily destroyed by cooking or canning. It is not stored in the body to any great extent. Thiamin is concerned in the breakdown of lactic and pyruvic acids. In the absence of thiamin, these acids accumulate in muscle and nerve tissues, producing pain, weakness, and paralysis. There is a loss of appetite together with weakness of the digestive tract; growth stops. Recovery from these conditions upon the administration of thiamin is spectacularly rapid. Thiamin may be manufactured by some of the bacteria in the human digestive tract, and a portion of the normal requirement may be met from this source. The sulfa drugs or antibiotics, such as penicillin, which destroy bacteria or inhibit bacterial growth, may greatly decrease this thiamin supply. Unless the supply is made up by additional thiamin in the diet, symptoms of thiamin deficiency may appear in humans who have had such medication.

Riboflavin, or **vitamin B$_2$,** is named from ingredients of its molecule — the sugar ribose and the nitrogen-containing flavin. It occurs in about the same dietary sources as thiamin, and is not stored in much greater amounts. Riboflavin is involved in several enzyme reactions in the metabolism of carbohydrates, and its absence from the body is evidenced by a cracking and scaling of the skin, especially about the mouth and eyes, and a reaction against light which produces profuse flowing of tears and forceful closure of the eyes.

Niacin, a shortened form of nicotinic acid vitamin, is the name for another member of the vitamin B family. It occurs in about the same foods as thiamin, and is not stored to any great degree. A deficiency in niacin in the body results in a disease known as **pellagra** (Latin: rough skin), characterized by skin lesions and degeneration of the nervous system. Pellagra seems to be especially prevalent among people subsisting largely on a diet of corn. As in the previous members of the vitamin B family, niacin acts in enzyme reactions involving oxidation of carbohydrates.

Pyridoxin, or **vitamin B$_6$,** is found in the same foods as thiamin, and there is some evidence that it may be stored in the liver. It is important in the metabolism of some of the derivatives of proteins and fats. Its absence results in skin disorders and nervous difficulties such as insomnia and extreme irritability. It also seems to be concerned in the manufacture of hemoglobin in red blood cells.

Pantothenic acid occurs even more widely than thiamin, and seems to be present normally in all parts of the body. It probably acts in some carbohydrate metabolic reaction, but the details are not well understood. It is manufactured by bacteria in the human intestine, so that an adequate supply is normally readily available. The exact proportion and arrangement of atoms in the pantothenic acid molecule seem to be essential to its activity; deviations from this set pattern produce compounds without the characteristic vitamin performance, and in some organisms seem to compete with pantothenic acid in the formation of necessary enzymes, causing symptoms of vitamin deficiency by crowding it out and substituting for it even when the vitamin is present. Pantothenic acid is not alone in this attribute, as most vitamins and enzymes in the body are similarly specific. Pantothenic acid prevents or retards the graying of hair in some animals such as rats, and at one time it was widely hailed as the "anti-gray-hair vitamin" for humans, but apparently it has no such effect on human hair.

Folic acid occurs in liver, yeast, and green leaves. Its absence results in a lowering of the numbers of red corpuscles, white corpuscles, and platelets in the blood.

Biotin occurs in liver, kidney, egg yolk, milk, and most vegetables. It may be stored in the human liver and kidneys. It is apparently involved in oxidations in the body, and is particularly prominent in embryonic and cancerous tissue, both of which use energy at a high rate. Biotin is produced by intestinal bacteria, so that antibiotics which affect these bacteria may produce a biotin deficiency.

Para-aminobenzoic acid (often shortened to **PABA**) occurs in liver, yeast, and plant seeds. Its action in humans is not well understood. It seems to be essential for the metabolism of many bacteria, and enters into direct competition with some of the sulfa drugs.

Choline, inositol, B$_{12}$, and other substances associated with the B family are still under active investigation; their actions seem to be interrelated with those of other B vitamins as enzymes regulating the metabolism of food products in the body.

Vitamin C is also known as **ascorbic acid.** It is found in raw milk and in fresh fruits and vegetables, but is destroyed upon heating, as in pasteurization or cooking, and upon standing. Vitamin C, like the B vitamins, is soluble in water. Humans, monkeys, and guinea pigs are the only animals so far found incapable of manufacturing their own vitamin C, and they seem to be unable to store it for very long, either. This circumstance made **scurvy,** the condition resulting from lack of vitamin C, a common disease among sailors in earlier times, since they depended upon stored foods for their diet while at sea. It was James Lind (1716–1794) who insisted that limes be provided at every port for British sailors, and although this practice was ridiculed by those who didn't know of its efficacy, it reduced the incidence of scurvy on British ships to a negligible factor. From this provision have come the names "limey" for a British sailor and "Limehouse" for the shipping district of London. The vitamin seems to be necessary for the proper consistency of the ground substance of connective tissue. This material, described in Chapter 1, binds together the connective tissue cells and fibers of the body, including bone. In the absence of vitamin C this ground substance becomes liquefied, resulting in the breakdown of many tissues, especially the walls of the smaller blood vessels. Ensuing hemorrhages produce painful swellings, anemia, weakness, and even gangrene.

Vitamin P has been postulated as similar to vitamin C in its sources and action, although not identical. Vitamin P is a mixture of closely related compounds. Its absence produces abnormal permeability of blood capillaries so that bleeding occurs more readily than usual. Some of the evidence on vitamin P is conflicting, and more definite knowledge must await further investigation.

Vitamin D is soluble in fats, and is found in fish liver oils, egg yolk, butter, and cream. It is very stable, surviving cooking and storage. Humans are able to store this vitamin, and even to manufacture it if they are exposed to ultraviolet radiation as from the sun. This circumstance accounts for the apparent discrepancy in the occurrence of the symptoms of vitamin D deficiency: in this country the disease is more common among the poorer children of cities, where diets are inadequate and exposure to the ultraviolet rays of the sun is infrequent; in India it is more common for rich children to show the symptoms, since the diet is deficient in vitamin D in both groups, but the well-to-do children are kept indoors, and not exposed to the sun's rays as much as the poorer children. The disease, known as **rickets,**

results from the inability of the body in the absence of
vitamin D to combine phosphorus and calcium to harden
bones.

Vitamin E is soluble in fats and is found in green vegetables and in seeds. There may be some storage, especially
in muscular and fatty tissues. Its action in man is an
unsolved problem. In some animals such as rats it affects
the health of skeletal muscle and of reproductive organs.
Rats fed on a diet devoid of vitamin E show degeneration
of skeletal muscle. The males exhibit degeneration of the
sperm-forming cells of the testis. Females form eggs
normally, and embryos may start to develop, but part way
through the period of pregnancy the embryos die and are
aborted. However, attempts to find similar results in
humans by treating the conditions with vitamin E have
generally resulted in failure.

Vitamin K is a fat-soluble substance found chiefly in
green leaves. It may be stored in the liver to some extent.
Its presence is important in normal blood-clotting. Without
vitamin K, blood would clot much more slowly than it
does, with the possibility of serious or fatal hemorrhages.
It may be manufactured by bacteria in the human intestine.

Carbohydrates

Carbohydrates are named from the fact that they contain
atoms of carbon, and of hydrogen and oxygen in the same
proportion as in water. Not all substances fulfilling these
criteria are carbohydrates, and a few carbohydrates do not
quite meet this standard. But it is generally satisfactory.

The carbohydrates involved in human digestion include
the sugars and starches. Sugars may be classed as single
and double sugars. A single sugar has the chemical formula
$C_6H_{12}O_6$, indicating that in the make-up of one molecule
there are six atoms of carbon, twelve of hydrogen, and six
of oxygen. Double sugars have the formula $C_{12}H_{22}O_{11}$; a
little mental arithmetic will show that a double sugar is
made up of two single sugars fastened together by the
withdrawal of one molecule of water (H_2O). Starches have
the formula $(C_6H_{10}O_5)_n$, in which n represents some integer,
usually 5 or greater. Starches appear to be constructed of
single sugars which become attached to each other to make
a larger molecule, each single sugar losing a molecule of
water in the process.

It will be shown later that sugars and starches are manufactured by plants, and directly or indirectly, plants alone
are the source of carbohydrates (and, indeed, all organic
foods) both for themselves and for all animals.

Of the single sugars, there are three commonly absorbed by the body: **glucose, fructose,** and **galactose.** All three have the same numbers of the same atoms, but their assembly into molecules follows slightly different patterns. Glucose and fructose are found in many fruits, but galactose is not found free normally. It is a product of the breakdown of the double sugar lactose.

The double sugars common in human diets are **sucrose, lactose,** and **maltose.** Sucrose is cane sugar, beet sugar, and maple sugar. It is formed by the union of glucose and fructose, and breaks down into these two during digestion. Lactose is milk sugar, composed of glucose and galactose. Maltose is formed from the breakdown of starches, and is composed of two molecules of glucose united with the withdrawal of one molecule of water.

These double sugars are normally broken into their single sugar constituents during digestion. Starch is broken down into maltose and then this into glucose, which is readily absorbed. Details of this process will be discussed later.

Fats

Fats are combinations of glycerol and fatty acids, or of some complex alcohol other than glycerol and fatty acids, or by extension, of certain complex alcohols alone, such as sterols. The chemical formulas of fats are more complicated than those of carbohydrates, but they are still made up of the three elements: carbon, hydrogen, and oxygen. In fats the number of hydrogen atoms is much more than twice as great as the number of oxygen atoms. Tri-stearin, for example, has the formula $C_{57}H_{110}O_6$. Digestion of these involves separating the fat into the fatty acids and the alcohol (usually glycerol) which may be absorbed.

Proteins

Proteins are still more complex organic substances, always containing carbon, hydrogen, oxygen, and nitrogen, and sometimes other elements such as sulfur or phosphorus. The building blocks of which protein molecules are manufactured are known as **amino acids.** Twenty-three of these amino acids have been isolated from various proteins, and the structure of each acid is such that it may combine with any of the others by a mechanism known as the **peptide linkage.** The amino part ($-NH_2$) of one molecule may unite with the acid part ($-COOH$) of another in such a way that a molecule of water (H_2O) is released, and the two amino acids are connected through the link $-CONH-$.

Such a compound formed by combining two amino acids is called a **dipeptide.** Several amino acids may unite to form a **polypeptide.** More complex molecules are known as **peptones, proteoses,** and finally the most complicated are called proteins. Proteins may have fantastically large numbers of atoms in their make-up — numbers ranging in the thousands, hundreds of thousands, or even millions. At the upper end of the scale, protein molecules pass into a group of bodies known as viruses, about which there is discussion as to whether or not they are living organisms.

DIGESTION

Of these substances found in food — condiments, water, minerals, vitamins, carbohydrates, fats, and proteins — not all are digested. The condiments may pass through the digestive tract without being absorbed by the body. The water, minerals, and vitamins are absorbed directly without being broken down. The complex carbohydrates will be changed to single sugars, the fats to fatty acids and alcohols, and the proteins to amino acids, however. These changes are the process of digestion, and it is these processes that will be considered next.

Enzymes

Digestive reactions take place under the influence of enzymes. Enzymes are organic catalysts. The idea of catalysis was described earlier in this chapter in connection with the role of copper in hemoglobin formation. Enzymes act similarly, speeding up a reaction very greatly without becoming an ingredient of the final products of the reaction. Enzymes are proteins. They are usually classified by the reaction they catalyze, and further by the structure which produces them. Most enzymes are given names ending in –*ase*, but a few of the enzymes which were known and named before this convention was adopted retain names by which they were first described.

The mode of operation of enzymes is not definitely established. One theory holds that the enzyme combines with one of the reacting substances, and the other substance reacts with this combination more readily; after the products are formed, the enzyme splits away and can be used again. A second theory states that the enzyme, being a large protein molecule, attracts to its surface the two reacting substances, a process known as **adsorption,** permitting the reaction to take place faster by bringing the substances into close contact. In any case, the efficiency of the enzymes depends a great deal on conditions such as temperature, degree of acidity, and the amounts of reactants and products present.

Digestion in the Mouth

The first enzyme to which food in the digestive tract is exposed is **ptyalin.** This enzyme facilitates the breakdown of starches to maltose. Ptyalin is inactivated by the concentration of hydrochloric acid found in the stomach, but starch digestion may go on while the food is in the mouth, during swallowing, and even for some time after the food is in the stomach before the acid penetrates throughout the food. However, there may remain some undigested starch in the food as it enters the small intestine. Starch is known to exert some inhibiting influence on the enzymic digestion in the stomach, so that partial breakdown of this starch by ptyalin is beneficial to gastric activity. The action of ptyalin may be facilitated by thorough chewing of the food, which keeps the food in the mouth longer and breaks it up so that ptyalin has more ready access to starches.

Digestion in the Stomach

Digestion in the stomach was studied by Lazzaro Spallanzani (1729–1799), who tied strings to pieces of food, persuaded animals to swallow the food, and then after a period of time withdrew the string to see what had happened to the food. He found that meat was broken down in the stomach. Later, William Beaumont (1785–1853) performed some famous observations on gastric digestion by taking advantage of a wound received by Alexis St. Martin (Fig. 3.13). St. Martin had been shot in the abdomen, and the wound healed in such a way that an opening remained through the abdominal wall into the stomach. Beaumont discovered the activity of the enzyme pepsin; he observed its performance in the acid conditions of the stomach and compared the rate and degree of digestion under different conditions such as varying emotional states of the subject.

The stomach secretes slight amounts of gastric juice all of the time. The pleasant sensations aroused by smell, taste, or even thought of food increase the release of these secretions into the cavity of the stomach. The presence of food in the stomach stimulates the secreting cells even more. A substance called **gastrin** has been found in the lining of the stomach. This gastrin seems to enter the blood stream and be transported to the acid-producing cells of the stomach wall, stimulating them to increased production. This qualifies gastrin as a **hormone** (Greek: stimulator), which may be defined as a substance secreted in one place in the body and carried by the blood to another place where it stimulates a reaction. After the food has passed into the intestine, the presence of undigested fat there stimulates the intestinal wall to produce another hormone, **enterogastrone,** which slows down gastric secretion and movements.

The stomach secretions contain a considerable amount of hydrochloric acid (HCl) and some enzymes, as well as water and mucus. The hydrochloric acid is produced by the parietal cells of the gastric glands. The formation of the acid is an incompletely understood process, but one of the best theories to account for it is this: carbon dioxide (CO_2) produced in the body in an energy-releasing reaction combines with water (H_2O) to form carbonic acid (H_2CO_3). Molecules of this compound spontaneously separate into two electrified portions called **ions,** a hydrogen ion charged positively (H^+) and a bicarbonate ion charged negatively (HCO_3^-). The bicarbonate ion enters the blood in exchange for a chloride ion (Cl^-) from the sodium chloride in the

Fig. 3.13 Beaumont's history-making observations of St. Martin's stomach resulted in great advances in our knowledge of digestive processes.

blood. The hydrogen ion and the chloride ion pass into the duct of the gland and enter the cavity of the stomach still as separate ions or as their combined product, hydrochloric acid (HCl). Thus this strong acid is not formed within a living cell.

Pepsin is the most important of the stomach enzymes. It is secreted by the chief cells in an inactive form known as **pepsinogen,** which is activated to pepsin by the hydrochloric acid. Pepsin acts on proteins, causing peptide linkages to break open and combine with the components of a water molecule, reducing the complexity of proteins to proteoses and peptones.

Since pepsin causes the breakdown of proteins, the question arises, how does the stomach prevent digestion of itself? If pepsin were formed within a chief cell, the acidity would not be high enough for it to be very active; furthermore, there are in the stomach and intestinal walls inhibitors of enzyme action known as **antienzymes,** which neutralize the enzymes and thus prevent the digestion of the living tissues.

In young humans there may be found another enzyme known as **rennin.** This changes the milk protein **casein** to another protein, **paracasein,** and a proteose. The paracasein combines with calcium and settles out as a curd. The paracasein curd is retained in the stomach until it is further digested by pepsin. In adults, rennin is absent, or present in very small amounts, and its action on casein is taken over by pepsin.

A third stomach enzyme is known as **gastric lipase.** It attacks fat, breaking it into fatty acids and alcohols, but the action of gastric lipase is very slight. Apparently the great acidity of the stomach contents during digestion inhibits lipase activity. If foods are coated with fat, as is often the case with fried foods, this fat may not be digested off until the food is well along the small intestine; this may prevent the complete digestion of the food underneath the fatty coat.

Digestion in the Intestine

As the food goes into the duodenum from the stomach it is soft and semiliquid in consistency. Taking some liquids with the food helps bring about this consistency. Some of the starch has been changed to maltose and some of the proteins to proteoses and peptones. However, in the intestine will be found other enzymes which attack starch, fats, and proteins, so that as far as the digestive process is concerned the stomach is a helpful but not necessary organ. In addition to storing and softening the food, the stomach serves as a disinfector, for very few bacteria can survive the high degree of acidity in the stomach.

If the stomach is removed, and the esophagus connected to the small intestine, there is little interference with normal digestion. Precautions must be taken about the amount of food eaten at one time, for the stomach serves as a temporary storehouse capable of receiving a whole meal and then dispensing it to the intestine in small portions. A little more pains should be taken to destroy possibly harmful bacteria in the food of a stomachless person, but such an individual could lead a nearly normal life. His sense of hunger would not function, and his appetite might be diminished. But his capacity to digest and absorb food would be nearly as great as ever.

One disadvantage of the absence of a stomach is the necessity of keeping the small intestine in almost constant use. When a person eats three meals a day, the intestine has work periods and rest periods. During the rest periods the enzyme-secreting cells may accumulate a supply of enzymes, and these may be released in considerable quantities when food arrives. Digestion is efficient under such conditions. If one eats between meals, he places demands upon his intestine before it has completely recovered from its last work period, and interrupts the accumulation of enzymes which could have been saved for the next regular meal.

The small intestine is the site of most of the digestion and absorption in the human body. In addition to its own secretions, the duodenum receives secretions from the liver and the pancreas. The contribution from the liver is known as bile. This is produced continuously and passes into the bile duct. When there is no food in the duodenum, the entrance of the bile duct into it is usually closed. The bile in the bile duct then enters the gall bladder and is concentrated and stored. When food, especially fat, reaches the duodenum, it stimulates the release of a hormone called **cholecystokinin** from the Greek for gall bladder mover. The hormone is secreted by the cells in the intestinal wall. This hormone travels through the blood stream to the gall bladder, and causes this organ to contract, forcing its contents back into the bile duct. The opening of the bile duct into the duodenum relaxes, and bile is passed into the intestine.

The principal constituents of bile are water, bile salts, bile pigments, fats, mucus, cholesterol, and inorganic salts.

The bile salts are compounds of sodium with complex organic acids. They are very important in the **emulsification** and absorption of fats. The process of emulsification is one of breaking fat masses into smaller and smaller droplets. The more finely divided the fats become the more readily digested they are, because the more surface is exposed to enzyme action. In addition to this activity, bile salts are able to combine with the fatty acids produced in fat digestion, making these substances more soluble and more readily absorbed. After the combination is absorbed and taken to its destination, the bile salts split off and through the blood stream return to the liver where they are reused in making more bile. Bile salts are also important in facilitating the absorption of most of the fat-soluble vitamins, especially vitamins D, E, and K. Vitamin A may be absorbed readily in the absence of bile salts, but carotene is only slowly absorbed unless bile salts are present. The bile pigments are breakdown products of hemoglobin, and are on their way toward being disposed of by the body. In this sense bile is an excretion as well as a secretion. A substance is **secreted** when it is manufactured and employed in some subsequent reaction in the body. A substance is **excreted** when it is the product of some chemical reaction and is passed out of the body as a waste material. Excretion is distinguished from **elimination,** which is the disposal of a substance which has not taken part in any reaction within the body; undigested substances passed through the digestive tract and out the anus are eliminated. The bile constituents other than the bile salts and pigments are either reabsorbed into the body through the intestinal wall, or disposed of in the feces.

The contribution of the pancreas includes several enzymes in a solution made alkaline by the presence of sodium bicarbonate. The flow of pancreatic juice into the duodenum is influenced by nervous reaction to the presence of food in the intestine and by the action of two hormones, secretin and pancreozymin. **Secretin** is released from the lining of the intestine upon the appearance of hydrochloric acid, fatty acids, and protein products from the stomach. It travels through the blood to the pancreas, and stimulates the outpouring of the alkaline fluid. **Pancreozymin,** similarly released from the intestinal wall, results in the release of the enzymes from the pancreas cells into this flow of alkaline secretion. The alkaline secretions of the pancreas and liver neutralize the acid coming from the stomach so that the contents of the intestine become slightly alkaline soon after they have left the stomach.

The pancreas produces enzymes attacking carbohydrates, fats, and proteins. The principal carbohydrate-splitting enzyme is **amylase.** It is more powerful than ptyalin, and completes the breakdown of starches to maltose. There is also present in pancreatic juice a small amount of **maltase,** the enzyme which facilitates the breakdown of maltose into glucose.

The fat-splitting enzyme is called **pancreatic lipase.** It acts only in an alkaline medium and changes fats to fatty acids and alcohols. Its work is greatly facilitated by the emulsification of fats by bile salts.

There are at least three protein-digesting enzymes derived from the pancreas. **Trypsin** and **chymotrypsin** act on proteins, proteoses, and peptones, breaking them down into polypeptides, dipeptides, or amino acids. Trypsin and chymotrypsin differ in the specific peptide linkages they attack. **Carboxypeptidase** attacks polypeptides, producing simpler compounds, even to amino acids.

Trypsin and chymotrypsin are secreted by the pancreas in inactive forms, called **trypsinogen** and **chymotrypsinogen.** The intestinal wall produces a substance, **enterokinase,** which changes trypsinogen to trypsin when it reaches the duodenal cavity. Whether enterokinase or trypsin or both are responsible for the activation of chymotrypsin has not been firmly established. The antienzymes in the intestinal wall protect the proteins of that wall from digestion by trypsin and chymotrypsin.

The small intestine produces its secretions continuously, but in varying amounts dependent upon conditions such as mechanical stimulation by the presence of food and hormonal stimulation by secretin, and possibly by another hormone, **enterocrinin,** secreted by the intestinal lining and increasing the rate of secretion from intestinal glands.

The intestinal juice contains enzymes acting on carbohydrates, fats, and protein products. The carbohydrate-splitting enzymes include **maltase,** which breaks maltose into glucose; **sucrase,** which separates sucrose into glucose and fructose; and **lactase,** which divides lactose into glucose and galactose. In the case of each of these, each molecule of the double sugar is combined with a molecule of water to produce the two single sugar molecules.

An **intestinal lipase** is active in the changing of fats to fatty acids and alcohols. While a large part of this work is done under the influence of pancreatic lipase, the intestinal lipase contributes to the digestion, and in the absence of the pancreatic product is able to digest a large amount of fat.

The enzymes of the intestine acting on protein products are **peptidases,** which attack the polypeptides and dipeptides left from the assault of the pancreatic enzymes. These products are changed to amino acids, which are then ready to be absorbed into the body. See Table 3.3.

TABLE 3.3

DIGESTIVE ENZYMES OF THE HUMAN

ENZYME	SECRETED IN	ACTS IN	ACTS ON	PRODUCTS
Ptyalin	Salivary glands	Mouth Pharynx Esophagus Stomach	Starches	Maltose
Pepsin	Stomach	Stomach	Proteins	Proteoses Peptones
Rennin	Stomach	Stomach	Casein	Paracasein
Gastric lipase	Stomach	Stomach	Fats	Fatty acids Alcohols
Amylase	Pancreas	Intestine	Starches	Maltose
Pancreatic lipase	Pancreas	Intestine	Fats	Fatty acids Alcohols
Trypsin	Pancreas	Intestine	Proteins Proteoses Peptones	Polypeptides Dipeptides Amino acids
Chymotrypsin	Pancreas	Intestine	Proteins Proteoses Peptones	Polypeptides Dipeptides Amino acids
Carboxypeptidase	Pancreas	Intestine	Polypeptides	Dipeptides Amino acids
Maltase	Intestine	Intestine	Maltose	Glucose
Sucrase	Intestine	Intestine	Sucrose	Glucose Fructose
Lactase	Intestine	Intestine	Lactose	Glucose Galactose
Intestinal lipase	Intestine	Intestine	Fats	Fatty acids Alcohols
Peptidases	Intestine	Intestine	Polypeptides Dipeptides	Amino acids

ABSORPTION

Absorption of the products of digestion takes place in the small intestine. Alcohol may penetrate the stomach lining, but other substances do not enter the body here. The large intestine absorbs water and some inorganic salts. But all other substances taken into the body through the digestive tract pass through the wall of the small intestine. To some extent this absorption may be accounted for by the diffusion of dissolved substances through the walls of the digestive tract. But the blood, which has some glucose in it at all times, is able to accept glucose from the intestine even when the concentration of glucose in the intestine is less than that in the blood. There must be a specific selective activity of the living cells of the intestinal lining in transferring these products from the intestinal cavity to the body. The mechanical explanation of this activity is not yet forthcoming. It is known that white corpuscles migrate in and out of the intestinal wall, and it may be that they carry substances across the barrier. It is also true that the rate of absorption of different sugars, for example, is quite different through the living intestinal wall from the absorption rates through a dead intestinal wall; for instance, the three single sugars produced by intestinal digestion are all absorbed at the same rate in the absence of the living epithelium, but when this epithelium is present and active, glucose is absorbed more readily than galactose, and galactose more readily than fructose. The protoplasm of the lining cells may form compounds with the digested food products, as glucose phosphate, and thus incorporate them into the cell for a time, and then pass them on to the rest of the body.

The sugars find their way into the blood. Each villus contains a loop of blood capillaries which pick up the sugar. The veins leaving the intestine all converge into one vessel which enters the liver and there branches repeatedly into a meshwork of capillaries. From the capillaries sugar diffuses into liver cells and is converted to **glycogen.** Glycogen is a form of starch, and is produced by coupling together the molecules of single sugar, usually as sugar phosphates, by the withdrawal of water and the separation of the phosphate. Glycogen is insoluble, and remains in the liver until it is reconverted to sugar. Some glycogen is also made in muscle cells; its activity in muscle tissue was described in Chapter 2.

Amino acids are absorbed into the blood, distributed to all parts of the body, and almost immediately incorporated into the active metabolism of living cells. They are resynthesized into proteins specific to the particular cell in which they are used. In a few cases in which incompletely digested proteins are absorbed, the body may be subject to a strong reaction known as **anaphylaxis.** This reaction is expressed as a rash, as asthma, or as some similar symptom to which people refer in saying that such a food doesn't agree with them.

Fatty acids and glycerol pass through the intestinal epithelium into lymph vessels, and are reunited into fats in the lymph. Bile salts facilitate this process. The reconstituted fat in the lymph vessels is in the form of tiny emulsified droplets. This gives the lymph a milky appearance. From this circumstance is derived the name **lacteals** (Latin for milky) given to the lymph vessel branches projecting into the villi. The lymph vessels from the intestine unite into a large vessel, the **thoracic duct,** which passes up through the chest to empty into a vein just above the heart. This means that the fat is detoured around the liver and enters the blood stream beyond it. The fat is then distributed to many parts of the body where it may be deposited in fatty tissue or used for energy by the cells, or even incorporated into the cytoplasm of cells. Carbohydrates and fats are used principally as sources of energy, whereas amino acids are used to build and repair protoplasm. Proteins may also be used for energy, but usually not when carbohydrates and fats are available.

HYGIENE OF THE DIGESTIVE SYSTEM

The prime consideration here is the selection of a suitable diet. The details of such a diet will vary widely with the characteristics of the person — his age, condition of health, personal idiosyncrasies, and so forth — and with the availability to him of various foods. The diet should contain an adequate supply of the essential water, minerals, and vitamins; it should have enough carbohydrates and fats to supply the energy he needs without providing a great excess for storage as superfluous fat; and enough proteins yielding the particular amino acids his body needs for its construction of protoplasm. Nutrition, the specific study of these needs and the foods which provide them, is a science of considerable magnitude, far beyond the scope of this book.

Since the digestive system is in use continually day in and day out, a few hints as to its best use are in order. Some have already been included earlier in this chapter. A healthy person with a suitable diet rarely experiences any difficulty with his process of digestion. A relaxed person in a pleasant frame of mind finds his digestion proceeding smoothly without causing disturbances. Tension, worry, or rushing a meal create overloading problems; emotional states such as anger or worry react through the nervous system to slow down secretion of enzymes and peristalsis of the digestive tract, interfering with normal digestion. Extreme fatigue slows down digestion, and decreases appetite so that inadequate food is supplied. Lack of exercise also interferes with appetite, and lowers the tone of the digestive tract muscles and the rate of blood flow, both of which slow down the process of digestion. The use of drugs — sodium bicarbonate, laxatives, cathartics, and so forth — prevents the proper adjustment of the body to normal working conditions. These medicines may act as a crutch, relieving a temporary difficulty, but like a crutch preventing the body from developing the strength it needs to get along without artificial aid. If such medication is deemed by a physician to be necessary at all, it is usually on a temporary and decreasing basis to wean the system away from reliance on such unnatural props.

SUMMARY

To summarize the work of the digestive system: Condiments affect the taste and odor of food, stimulating the release of salivary and gastric secretions. Water, minerals, and vitamins may be absorbed without being digested; they are necessary for the efficient action of many phases of the body's metabolism. Absorption of most carbohydrates, fats, and proteins takes place only after they are broken into smaller molecules by chemically combining with water.

Food in the mouth is chewed by the teeth and mixed with the secretions of the parotid, submaxillary, and sublingual glands. This secretion contains mucus, which softens the food, and ptyalin, which is an enzyme facilitating the breakdown of starches to maltose. The tongue then pushes the food back through the pharynx, and into the esophagus. Here it is taken up by peristaltic contractions and forced through the cardiac sphincter into the stomach. In the stomach it is kneaded by peristaltic contractions of the lower part of the stomach. In the stomach the food is attacked by rennin (in infants and children). This starts the breakdown of the milk protein, casein. Pepsin, in the presence of hydrochloric acid, breaks some proteins into proteoses and peptones. Some gastric lipase is secreted, which changes fats into fatty acids and glycerol or other alcohols.

Food passes into the intestine slowly after it has been further liquefied in the stomach. Here it encounters the bile secreted by the liver. Bile salts emulsify fats. Pancreatic juice contains several enzymes affecting the food. Amylase completes the change of starches to maltose. Pancreatic lipase breaks fats into fatty acids and glycerol. Trypsin, chymotrypsin, and carboxypeptidase change proteins, proteoses, and peptones into polypeptides, dipeptides, and amino acids. The wall of the intestine secretes sucrase, lactase, and maltase, which change double sugars into single sugars. Intestinal lipase aids pancreatic lipase in splitting fats. Peptidases complete the breakdown of polypeptides and dipeptides to amino acids.

Blood in the capillaries of the intestinal villi picks up the single sugars and amino acids. The blood is carried to the liver, where most of the sugars are dehydrated and condensed into glycogen. Amino acids are absorbed from the blood by any living cells in the body. Fatty acids and glycerol are reconstituted into fats in the lacteals, pass through lymph channels by the liver into the blood stream, and are stored in fatty tissue. Water and some salts are absorbed by the large intestine. Fats and carbohydrates are used for energy, amino acids and some fats for building and repairing the body's own protein and other cytoplasmic substances.

Our next step will be to study the provision and use of oxygen, which is necessary for the release of energy from the foods absorbed, and the excretion of the carbon dioxide waste resulting from that reaction.

REVIEW QUESTIONS

1. What is the contribution of the digestive tract to the body's welfare?
2. Describe the structure and varieties of teeth in a human.
3. Describe the activities of the tongue.
4. Locate and describe the structure and secretions of the salivary glands.
5. How does food get from the mouth to the stomach?
6. Describe the gross and microscopic structure of the stomach.
7. How does food pass through the stomach and intestines?
8. Distinguish among the parts of the intestines according to location and activity within the parts.
9. Describe the relations of pancreas and liver to the duodenum.
10. State the contributions to the body of the types of food, including particular minerals and vitamins.
11. Into what absorbable substances are carbohydrates, fats, and proteins digested?
12. How do enzymes facilitate digestion?
13. State the action and site of action of each digestive enzyme.
14. How is self-digestion prevented in the digestive tract?
15. How is the release of the various enzymes controlled?
16. What is the fate of the digested foods after they are absorbed?
17. What considerations are important in planning a diet for yourself?
18. What is the effect of emotional state on digestion?

GENERAL QUESTIONS

1. In what ways are the lips especially adapted to serve as guardians of the entrance to the digestive tract?
2. What changes in a baby's life might result if he were born with his first set of teeth fully developed?

3. Does the cramped space for third molars indicate that the human body is inefficiently constructed?

4. Describe the benefits dentists may bestow on human teeth.

5. Describe in some detail the activity of the mouth and its associated structures on a bite of beef sandwich.

6. How do you suppose muscles operate to enlarge the cavity of the pharynx?

7. How would the activities of the digestive tube be changed if the musculature were skeletal instead of visceral?

8. Why is it more advantageous to have a single layer of tall cells lining the stomach and intestine and several layers of flat cells lining the mouth, pharynx, esophagus, and anus rather than the reverse?

9. What happens to the body fluids of people on a salt-free diet?

10. Suggest a possible mechanism whereby vitamin D increases both the intestinal absorption of calcium and the use of calcium in bones.

11. Plan a diet containing the minimum foods which will have all the food substances essential for human well-being.

12. Why do you suppose vitamins were not known a hundred years ago?

13. Would it be practical to treat cancer by depriving the patient of biotin?

14. Suggest a research program to determine the nature and action of vitamin P.

15. Trace from their entrance into the mouth until their use by the body: carbohydrates; fats; proteins.

16. Suggest a hypothesis to account for the fact that the intestine absorbs glucose more readily than it does fructose.

CHAPTER 4

The Respiratory System

RESPIRATION

In Chapter 2 you read that glycogen is broken down to lactic acid in the process of providing the energy used in muscle contraction. You learned also that some of the lactic acid was further broken down to carbon dioxide and water, providing enough energy to rebuild the rest of the lactic acid into glycogen. This reaction illustrates the essential features of respiration. Respiration may be defined as an oxidation reaction which provides energy for an organism.

Briefly summarized, the lactic acid ($C_3H_6O_3$) combines with oxygen ($3O_2$), releasing energy. The products of the reaction are carbon dioxide ($3CO_2$) and water ($3H_2O$). You will see by counting the atoms going into and coming out of this reaction that there are no gains of atoms or losses of atoms, but merely a regrouping.

That reaction seems simple enough; but in the body it is a very complicated procedure which takes place in many steps. Each step is activated by one or more enzymes. Since respiration is such a fundamental process, without which no organism can carry on, scientists have tried to analyze the process completely. So many other phases of the organism's life are directly related to respiration that understanding of that process is very important. The entire story is not yet known, but much has been worked out, and more is being investigated. Some idea of the complexity together with an insight into the method of oxidation in the body may be gained from a study of one step in the process.

Lactic acid ($C_3H_6O_3$) is first oxidized to **pyruvic acid,** having the formula $C_3H_4O_3$. Chemically the process of oxidation may take place by addition of oxygen, by subtraction of hydrogen, or by loss of electrons. In this case the second method is employed, lactic acid losing two atoms of hydrogen to become pyruvic acid. The loss of the hydrogen atoms involves the following events:

A substance called **coenzyme I** is built from niacin, adenosine diphosphate, and the sugar d-ribose. Coenzyme I accepts the two hydrogen atoms given off by lactic acid under the influence of an enzyme called **dehydrogenase.** The lactic acid has thus become pyruvic acid.

A series of protein substances containing iron atoms and called **cytochromes** is present in every living cell. This series

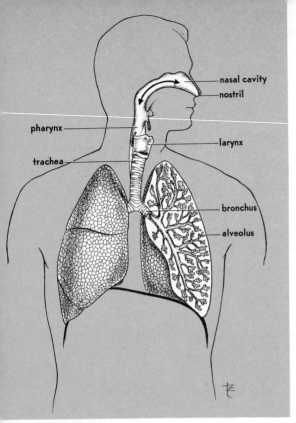

Fig. 4.1   Human respiratory tract. Follow the pathway of air into and out of the lungs. Where does this pathway cross the pathway of food?

includes some or all of these: cytochrome a, cytochrome b, cytochrome c, and cytochrome oxidase. Coenzyme I will give up its two hydrogen atoms to cytochrome b, thereby becoming available again to oxidize lactic acid to pyruvic acid. Cytochrome b will in turn give the hydrogen atoms to cytochrome a, which will pass them on to cytochrome c. Cytochrome oxidase acts as an enzyme, combining oxygen with these two hydrogen atoms, forming water. The oxygen is provided by the respiratory system to the blood and by the blood to the cell oxidizing the lactic acid.

The process of oxidation of lactic acid to pyruvic acid is typical of the mechanisms by which oxidations go on. Coenzyme I may, however, unload its two added hydrogen atoms to another enzyme, **xanthine oxidase,** derived from riboflavin, which passes them on to cytochrome c, from which they may be removed by cytochrome oxidase.

Pyruvic acid is further oxidized in several steps, eventually giving off carbon dioxide and more water. These further steps involve various enzymes and hydrogen acceptors such as coenzyme I and the cytochromes. By using this type of procedure the body carries on oxidations at temperatures which do not damage or destroy living cells.

ANATOMY OF THE RESPIRATORY TRACT

Oxygen

Free oxygen is found in the earth's atmosphere in a concentration of about 21 percent. Oxygen is brought to the blood through the respiratory tract (Fig. 4.1) and then carried by the blood to the tissues of the body. The respiratory tract is in constant use. It is also one of the most vulnerable parts of the body to infection and injury. Therefore, a knowledge of it is not only necessary in understanding human biology, but also helpful in maintaining good health.

Nose

Air normally enters the tract through the **nose.** The nasal cavity is divided into two parts, right and left, by a **septum.** Each part has an entrance, the nostril, and an exit into the top of the pharynx. The cavities are very much contorted due to the projection into them of plates of the turbinal bones. The lining of the cavity is a mucous membrane (Fig. 4.2). At the nostrils the many-layered epithelium of the skin curves into the nasal cavities, but the

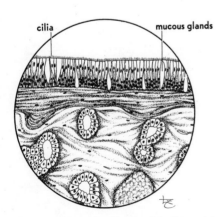

Fig. 4.2   Microscopic structure of the lining of the nose cavity. How does the nose filter the air?

main area of the nasal cavity lining is made of a single layer of tall prismatic or pyramidal cells bearing on their exposed surfaces tiny hairlike projections of protoplasm known as **cilia.** These cilia carry on a whiplike beating in waves of lashing and recoiling that gives to them the appearance of wheat stalks rippling in a wind. Each cilium bends toward the nostrils with some force, and then returns somewhat more limply to its original position.

Interspersed among these prismatic cells bearing cilia are occasional rounded or goblet-shaped **mucous cells,** which by their secretions keep a continuous supply of mucus on the surface of the epithelium. It is in this mucous medium that the cilia beat. The mucus traps some solid particles in the air entering the nose, filtering out dust and dirt to a considerable degree. If the entering air is dry, it is moistened by evaporation of water from the mucous lining. The connective tissues beneath the epithelium are abundantly supplied with blood vessels, and this helps maintain the normal temperature of the nose tissues, so that cold air inhaled will be partially warmed before it reaches the pharynx.

Pharynx

After the inhaled air has passed through the nasal cavities it enters the pharynx. The upper part of the pharynx is lined with the same type of mucous lining found in the nose, but the part of the pharynx common to both digestive and respiratory tracts has the many-layered epithelium characteristic of the lining of the mouth cavity.

Larynx

If no swallowing is going on at the moment, the passage into the **larynx** is open, and air may pass through it. The larynx is lined with the many-layered epithelium through part of its length, but near the bottom we find a single layer of tall pyramidal cells with cilia and mucous cells such as occurs in the nose. This continues down the trachea into the lungs.

The larynx is supported by a group of hyaline and elastic cartilages. These and the action of the larynx in producing the voice will be described later.

Trachea

The **trachea** is also supported by a series of hyaline cartilages. These are horseshoe-shaped bars or incomplete rings stacked up on each other and imbedded in the connective tissue and muscle surrounding the epithelial lining. The open portions of the horseshoes are toward the back, the gap being closed by elastic connective tissue. The esophagus is just behind the trachea, and if the rings of the trachea were complete any solid food swallowed would rub along down against the trachea as if against a corrugated board. The corrugated surface in the front gave the windpipe its name; trachea is from the Greek for rough.

The ciliated lining of the trachea is quite effective in keeping solid particles from getting into the lungs. If a particle of food, for example, gets into the trachea, it is usually caught in the mucous coat and pushed back up into the pharynx by the ciliary beating.

Lungs

Part way down the chest the trachea divides into right and left **bronchi.** Each bronchus is a somewhat smaller duplicate of the trachea in structure, except that in these tubes the incomplete rings of cartilage gradually give way to isolated plates. Each bronchus further subdivides repeatedly into smaller and smaller **bronchioles,** and these into very numerous smaller branches until the very finest branches end in tiny cavities called **alveoli** (Fig. 4.3).

The subdivisions of a bronchus, including the branchlets and alveoli, constitute a lung, and each lung is encased in a membranous sac, the **pleura.** In passing from the bronchus to an alveolus the epithelial lining changes from tall pyramidal to very thin flat cells, always one-layered. The cartilage supports become thinner and finally disappear; the smaller branches and alveoli are supported by fibrous connective tissue and have a few fibers of visceral muscle. Close to the walls of the alveoli runs a rich network of blood capillaries. Here the gases of the air are separated from the fluid of the blood only by a thin film of water lining the alveolus, the thin wall of the alveolus, and the thin wall of the capillary. Oxygen from the inhaled air dissolves in the moisture that lines the alveolus and then is absorbed into the blood.

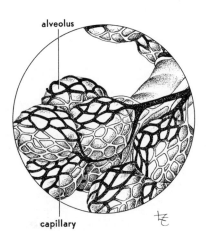

alveolus

capillary

Fig. 4.3   Microscopic structure of the lung. Note the saclike alveoli budding off from the finer branchlets and the very rich supply of blood capillaries. Does the air come in direct contact with the blood?

PHYSIOLOGY

Oxygen Transportation

The liquid portion of the blood is able to dissolve only a small amount of oxygen. Thus, 100 milliliters of blood leaving the lungs carries in solution only about $\frac{1}{4}$ milliliter of oxygen (1000 milliliters is a little more than 1 quart). But a combination of sodium and hemoglobin in red corpuscles has the ability to unite with oxygen, forming sodium oxyhemoglobin. This ability is so great that 100 milliliters of blood leaving the lungs may have as much as 19 milliliters of oxygen in its plasma and corpuscles together.

Hemoglobin is a complex protein, capable of acting as a very weak acid; that is, it may form small amounts of hydrogen ions (H^+) and hemoglobin ions (Hb^-).

$$HHb \rightarrow H^+ + Hb^-$$

Hb is a sort of shorthand for the remainder of the hemoglobin molecule after the hydrogen ion has separated off. It is shorter than writing the formula: $C_{3036}H_{4831}N_{840}S_8Fe_4O_{816}^-$!

The blood is slightly alkaline, containing among other salts a considerable amount of sodium bicarbonate which ionizes into sodium ions (Na^+) and bicarbonate ions (HCO_3^-).

$$NaHCO_3 \rightarrow Na^+ + HCO_3^-$$

Many of the hydrogen ions from the hemoglobin unite with the bicarbonate ions, forming carbonic acid.

$$H^+ + HCO_3^- \rightarrow H_2CO_3$$

Carbonic acid breaks up, forming water and carbon dioxide.

$$H_2CO_3 \rightarrow H_2O + CO_2$$

The carbon dioxide diffuses from the blood into the alveolus and is exhaled.

The sodium ion (Na^+) formerly associated with the bicarbonate ion now becomes associated with the hemoglobin ion (Hb^-), and the combination takes up oxygen absorbed into the blood from the alveolus. This forms sodium oxyhemoglobin.

$$Na^+ + Hb^- + O_2 \rightarrow NaHbO_2$$

Sodium oxyhemoglobin is carried in the red corpuscles from the lung to other capillaries in the body. It may, for example, be carried to a capillary in a muscle which has used oxygen in the process of lactic acid oxidation. The concentration of oxygen is therefore low in the muscle. Oxygen is released from the sodium oxyhemoglobin.

$$NaHbO_2 \rightarrow NaHb + O_2$$

This oxygen diffuses through the capillary wall into the muscle, where it is taken up by myoglobin.

Carbon Dioxide Transportation

At the same time some of the excess of carbon dioxide in the muscle formed from the same process of oxidizing the lactic acid enters the blood, having united with water, forming carbonic acid.

$$CO_2 + H_2O \rightarrow H_2CO_3$$

This carbonic acid ionizes.

$$H_2CO_3 \rightarrow H^+ + HCO_3^-$$

The sodium hemoglobin remaining when oxygen separates from sodium oxyhemoglobin also ionizes somewhat.

$$NaHb \rightarrow Na^+ + Hb^-$$

There is an interchange of these ions, producing the only slightly dissociated hemoglobin, and the more readily ionized sodium bicarbonate.

$$H^+ + HCO_3^- + Na^+ + Hb^- \rightarrow HHb + NaHCO_3$$

These substances are carried back to the lungs by the blood, where the hemoglobin and sodium bicarbonate ionize. Then sodium oxyhemoglobin and carbonic acid are formed as was described earlier. The carbonic acid breaks into carbon dioxide and water, some of which is exhaled.

These various chemical reactions are controlled by relative concentrations of the reactants and by enzymes specific for the reactions concerned. A summary is shown in Table 4.1.

TABLE 4.1

CHEMICAL CHANGES IN BLOOD

Blood in capillaries in lungs:

$HHb \rightarrow H^+ + Hb^-$
$NaHCO_3 \rightarrow Na^+ + HCO_3^-$
$H^+ + HCO_3^- \rightarrow H_2CO_3 \rightarrow H_2O + CO_2$ (escapes through trachea)
$Na^+ + Hb^- + O_2 \rightarrow NaHbO_2$

Blood in capillaries in tissues:

$NaHbO_2 \rightarrow NaHb + O_2$ (escapes into tissue cells)
$CO_2 + H_2O \rightarrow H_2CO_3 \rightarrow H^+ + HCO_3^-$
$NaHb \rightarrow Na^+ + Hb^-$
$H^+ + HCO_3^- + Na^+ + Hb^- \rightarrow HHb + NaHCO_3$

Buffering

The degree of acidity of the blood (slightly alkaline) is very important in maintaining normal metabolism. Slight deviation either way from the rather narrow range of efficiency may produce serious disturbances. It has been found that the best conditions prevail when the amount of sodium bicarbonate in the blood is about twenty times the amount of carbonic acid in the blood. If the acidity tends to become too great, more carbonic acid is broken up in the lungs with the release into the air of carbon dioxide and water. If the blood tends to become too alkaline, the sodium bicarbonate brought to the lungs produces more than usual carbonic acid and sodium hemoglobin. Further than this, there are various other devices which normally take part in preserving the acid-alkaline balance. Hemoglobin may accept excess carbon dioxide into its molecule, making a compound known as hemoglobin carbamate. Other proteins may do the same, or may take on an excess of sodium ions. Some phosphate salts are capable of absorbing more hydrogen or sodium ions, taking up whichever is in excess and giving off whichever is in low supply. This balancing process, known as **buffering,** is able to maintain the constant slight alkalinity of the blood in spite of very considerable changes in tissue acidities.

Control of Breathing

A further expression of this self-regulating mechanism is shown in the involuntary control of breathing movements. A group of nerve cells in the lower part of the brain, known as the respiratory center, is especially sensitive to the concentration of carbonic acid in the blood. Any increase in this concentration causes the respiratory center to increase the breathing movements with the result that more carbon dioxide is disposed of through the lungs. A secondary result of this increased rate of breathing is an increased supply of oxygen brought to the blood. In vigorous activity, when a great deal of carbon dioxide is produced in the body, the breathing rate is greatly increased and the excess of carbon dioxide is pumped out of the body. Of course, the increased rate of breathing also provides more oxygen, needed to rebuild the muscle fuels.

If you are in a room in which the air is stale — having more than the usual amount of carbon dioxide — or if you have been breathing only very shallowly for a time, your respiratory center will sometimes stimulate a yawn, which is an inhalation followed by an exceptionally long and deep exhalation, expelling some of the accumulated carbon dioxide from your lungs.

You can control your breathing rate voluntarily if you wish, but if you do not pay attention to it the respiratory center of the brain regulates it. You cannot commit suicide by holding your breath, for if the brain is deprived of oxygen, the part of the brain governing voluntary actions suffers first, and when voluntary control is gone, the respiratory center takes over control, starting breathing again.

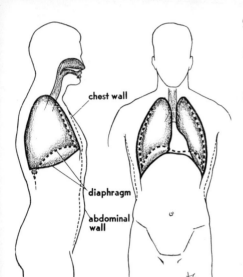

Fig. 4.4 Diagram of breathing movements. The solid lines show the outlines of the body when air has been inhaled; the broken lines show the outlines of the body when air has been exhaled.

Breathing Movements

Movements of the chest walls during breathing are diagramed in Figure 4.4.

The active effort in breathing movements is exerted only by the trunk muscles, as will be described a little later. The lung walls have elastic connective tissue and visceral muscle in their make-up, but these are capable of no active expansion and of only a relatively weak contraction. The pleura, the membrane surrounding the lung, at the level of the bronchus leading into the lung, is reflected back along the inner wall of the chest cavity. The space between the lung cover and the chest lining is practically nonexistent, containing only a thin film of liquid between the membranes. Inhalation occurs when the chest cavity is enlarged because the lung wall adheres to the chest wall, and the air pressure within the lung is greater than the pressure between lung wall and chest wall; this enlarges the lung and decreases the air pressure within the lung cavity. When the pressure is lowered inside the lungs, the pressure of the atmosphere surrounding the body is greater than that in the lungs, and air is forced in. Therefore, it is not exactly true that the lungs draw air in. They expand as the chest expands, and atmospheric pressure forces air in, equalizing the air pressure inside and outside the lungs.

Exhalation occurs when contraction of the chest wall, added to the pressure of the lung walls themselves, raises the pressure of the air within the lungs above atmospheric pressure. Air is thus forced out.

When the chest wall is pierced deeply enough to allow air to enter the space between the chest lining and lung wall, the lung collapses, because its elasticity is no longer counteracted by a difference between the atmospheric pressure of the air inside and that of the air outside the lung wall. One lung of some tuberculosis patients is collapsed intentionally in order to rest it. The air let into the chest cavity may be withdrawn later, reinflating the lung.

Enlargement of the chest wall is brought about by the contraction of the external oblique muscles of the ribs and the muscles of the diaphragm. When these rib muscles contract, they pull the ribs closer to each other. The uppermost ribs are pretty well anchored, so that the result of this pulling together of the ribs is the lifting of the lower ones. But these lower ribs are hinged to the spinal column in such a way that as they pull upward they swing out laterally and push out in front. The lower ribs slant down when the muscles are relaxed, but when these ribs are pulled up, becoming more nearly horizontal, they push the front chest wall out. If you place your hands on the front and back of your chest during heavy breathing, you can demonstrate this point. If you then place your hands on the sides of your chest and repeat the deep breathing, you will find that the chest expands from side to side, too, as the ribs roll out in swinging up. When you see a human skeleton, examine the joints of the lower ribs to see how this takes place.

The **diaphragm** (Greek for partition) is an arched dome of muscle that separates the thoracic and abdominal cavities. It is composed of a muscle attached at one end to the wall of the trunk and at the other end to a central tendon which makes up the middle portion of the diaphragm; the muscle is shaped like one of Saturn's rings, or like a metal washer. The central tendon is pierced at a few places where structures such as the esophagus pass through. In its relaxed state, the diaphragm makes a rounded roof over the liver and stomach. When the diaphragm muscle contracts, the dome flattens down somewhat, pushing the liver and stomach down and lowering the floor of the chest. This enlarges the chest cavity in the vertical dimension, as the raising of the ribs did in the two horizontal dimensions, front to back and side to side.

When the diaphragm contracts, the liver and stomach are forced deeper into the abdominal cavity, and these organs in turn push out the abdominal walls. When the diaphragm relaxes, the elasticity of the abdominal walls added to contraction of their muscles restores the previous position of the organs, pushing the stomach and liver back up into the dome under the diaphragm. At the same time the rib muscles relax, allowing the ribs to drop back to their original position. This diminishes the volume of the chest cavity by reducing three of its dimensions, and air is pushed out through the throat and nose. Forcible exhalation, as in blowing, is brought about by contraction of the internal oblique muscles of the ribs, which pull the ribs down.

In an adult at rest, inhalation and exhalation occur at a rate of about 16 to 18 cycles per minute. The amount of air forced in and subsequently forced out in one cycle is about 500 milliliters (slightly more than one pint). This amount is very greatly increased at times of maximum physical effort, when air exchange at one breathing cycle may be as much as 4000 milliliters.

In summary, then, contraction of the diaphragm and external rib muscles enlarges the chest cavity, causing the lungs to expand and lowering the air pressure within them. Atmospheric pressure on the outside forces air in. Some of the oxygen in the air dissolves in the fluid film lining the alveoli, diffuses through the alveolus, capillary, and red corpuscle walls and unites with the sodium hemoglobin there, forming sodium oxyhemoglobin. This is carried by the blood stream to all the tissues, where the oxygen is released. The oxygen is used in energy-releasing reactions, which also produce carbon dioxide and water. These unite, forming carbonic acid, which is neutralized to sodium bicarbonate and returned to the lungs. Here carbon dioxide is released and forced out during exhalation. Some water goes with it.

The contraction and relaxation of the breathing muscles is under the influence of the respiratory nerve center, a series of nerve cell groups in the brain, which are affected by the amount of carbon dioxide in the blood. It is thought that this effect is due to the ready penetration of the carbon dioxide into the nerve cell, forming carbonic acid, and that this acid concentration serves to stimulate the nerve impulses.

VOICE

Voice Production

Only a small proportion of the kinds of animals have the ability to produce a voice. Although most mammals have a voice, only humans have made an effective use of the voice for the communication of a great variety of ideas and information. This development may account in considerable measure for the ascendancy of humans among animals. The capacity for increasing knowledge by sharing, and the capacity for intelligent cooperation are dependent upon efficient use of the voice.

The use of the larynx in producing sounds depends upon the muscular manipulation of the cartilages supporting the vocal membranes. Four cartilages are important in this mechanism (Fig. 4.5): The **cricoid cartilage** is the lowest of these, and gets its name from the Greek for ringlike, because of its resemblance to a man's finger ring. In front it is a narrow band, but on the back side of the larynx it widens greatly to make most of the back wall. The **thyroid cartilage** makes most of the front wall of the larynx, perched above the narrow portion of the cricoid. Its name comes from the Greek for shieldlike; the thyroid cartilage is a large, curved shield bending around the front of the larynx, but not extending behind the lateral margins. Two **arytenoid cartilages** are joined to the top of the expanded part of the cricoid cartilage at the back of the larynx. They are smaller than the other two cartilages, and shaped somewhat like triangular pyramids.

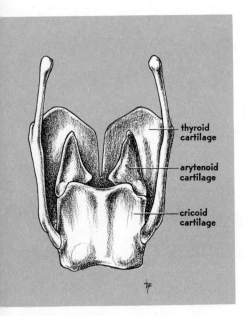

thyroid cartilage

arytenoid cartilage

cricoid cartilage

Fig. 4.5   Cartilages of the larynx. View from the back.

The triangular base of each arytenoid pivots on its farthest back corner, resting on the cricoid cartilage. The front corner of the base of each arytenoid is connected by an elastic ligament to the middle of the inner surface of the thyroid cartilage. This ligament, covered by a mucous membrane stretching to the thyroid and cricoid cartilages, is known as the **vocal cord,** and the membrane is the **vocal membrane.** Hence the corner of the arytenoid cartilage to which it is attached is called the **vocal process.**

The third lateral corner of the base of the arytenoid is the **muscular process.** To it are attached two muscles (Fig. 4.6). One, the **posterior cricoarytenoid,** runs from the muscular process to the posterior border of the cricoid cartilage; when it contracts, it pulls the muscular process laterally and back, pivoting the arytenoids in such a way that the vocal processes of the two cartilages are widely separated from each other. Then the space between the two vocal cords is open, allowing air to pass through the larynx without interference. This is the position maintained during breathing when the voice is not used.

The other muscle, the **lateral cricoarytenoid,** attached to the muscular process runs forward to the inner surface of the lateral part of the cricoid cartilage. When it contracts, it pulls the muscular process forward, pivoting the vocal process toward its mate until they almost touch, narrowing the opening between the vocal cords. When air is exhaled between the cords while they are close together, they are set into vibration, and the voice is produced.

The sound may be varied in pitch by changes in tension or length of the vocal cords. The pitch depends upon the number of blasts per second of the air passing between the cords, which alternately come together and separate. The number of blasts per second is greater the greater the tension or the shorter the length of the vocal cords. The tension may be increased or decreased by contraction of still other muscles. See Figure 4.7.

Efficient control of these muscles to make a satisfactory singing instrument or well-modulated speaking voice comes with practice. This is emphasized by the difficulties encountered by boys at the time the voice is "changing." The deeper voice of a man in contrast to that of a woman or a young boy is a result of the greater size of the man's larynx, hence the greater length of his vocal cords. The enlargement proceeds slowly throughout childhood, and then at the onset of maturity there is a great acceleration of this growth. This provides the boy with a larynx having quite different range from the one he has learned to operate.

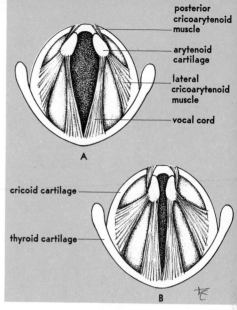

Fig. 4.6 Diagram of top view of larynx. **A,** Posterior cricoarytenoid muscles contracted, pulling the muscular processes of the arytenoid cartilages laterally, separating the vocal cords. **B,** Lateral cricoarytenoid muscles contracted, pulling the muscular processes of the arytenoid cartilages forward, bringing the vocal cords together.

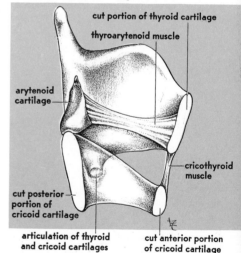

Fig. 4.7 Hemisection of larynx from median view. When the cricothyroid muscle contracts, the front of the thyroid cartilage is pulled down toward the cricoid cartilage. The thyroid cartilage pivots on its articulations with the cricoid cartilage; hence, the entire thyroid cartilage rocks forward, stretching the thyroarytenoid muscle and the vocal membrane. This raises the pitch of the voice. When the thyroarytenoid muscle contracts, it pulls the thyroid cartilage back and up, slackening the vocal cords. This lowers the pitch of the voice.

When he tries his previously effective methods of producing a certain pitch, he finds them producing a very different result from what he expected. In an attempt to return to the pitch he is accustomed to hearing in his own voice, he tenses the vocal cords greatly, and his voice "breaks" sharply upward. After a few embarrassing episodes and some practice, he learns to master the changed instrument, and controls the pitch much better. A skilled singer knows just how much to contract his muscles to pass from one note to another without groping for it.

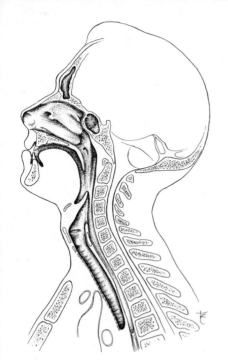

Fig. 4.8   Resonating cavities in the head, throat, and chest. The sound of the voice reverberates in the cavities shown, and the quality of the voice is largely due to the shape of the spaces in which it resounds.

The loudness of the sound coming from the larynx depends upon the amount of air passing through at a given time, regulating the violence of vibration of the vocal membranes. The quality of the voice depends upon the shape and size of the cavities in which the sound resonates — the lung, trachea, larynx, pharynx, mouth, and nose cavities. See Figure 4.8. These resonating cavities, especially the mouth, determine the consonants pronounced. The vowels, though sounded by the larynx, are differentiated in the pharynx and mouth. The effect of the resonating cavities may be determined by whispering, which does not employ the vibrations of the vocal cords, but merely allows the outgoing air to resonate in cavities of different shapes.

The falsetto voice, by which men can produce a higher pitch than is otherwise possible, is achieved by tensing the vocal membranes in such a way that only the edges vibrate, not the entire membranes.

Laryngitis

An infection of the larynx (laryngitis) which produces inflammation and swelling of the vocal cords results in a bulky, misshapen vocal membrane instead of the slender edge normally present, so that vibration may be difficult or impossible to accomplish. This produces the hoarse voice, uttered only with great effort, or the temporary loss of voice. Attempts to use the voice in this condition may aggravate the damage and postpone healing, and may even result in permanent thickening of the vocal membrane, so that the voice never returns to its original quality, but remains somewhat rough and harsh. Hence, any hoarseness is a warning that rest and special care of the larynx are in order lest such permanent damage be inflicted. Prolonged yelling, as at football games, is especially dangerous, particularly in the cold air.

HYGIENE OF THE RESPIRATORY SYSTEM

The pathway of air to the lungs has been traced through

the nose, which is the normal route. Air may also reach the pharynx and lungs through the mouth. This does not provide for the efficient filtering, moistening, and warming accomplished by the nasal cavities, however, and is not an advisable route for breathing unless the nasal route is blocked.

In spite of the services of the nasal cavities, infectious organisms do get into the respiratory tract. The constant outward movement of the stream of mucus in the trachea and nose helps to prevent such germs from accumulating, but the system is not perfect. Other bodily defenses are adequate to prevent serious injury from this source in a healthy person, but if the body is weakened by fatigue, undernourishment, excessive exposure to cold, or other de-bilitating conditions, it is more easily subject to infections. Many of these are grouped together in popular terminology as "colds." In addition to being a source of discomfort to the patient and a potential source of infection for those in his immediate neighborhood, a cold may be an entering wedge for other even more serious infections. Irritation of the nasal membranes by infection may cause the blood vessels to swell, partially closing the nasal passageways, and may also provoke a discharge of mucus from the cells producing it. This causes difficulty in breathing, as is familiar to anyone with a "cold in the nose."

Since a cold indicates both the presence of the germ in considerable quantities and a lowered resistance of the sufferer, he is doubly susceptible to attack by other germs, such as those of pneumonia, influenza, and tuberculosis. If his resistance was low to begin with, and what capacity he had for fighting infection is being used in fighting the cold, it would be wise for the patient to get as much rest as possible to help his bodily forces in their struggle. Any unnecessary activity or exposure not only retards his recovery from the cold, but increases his chances of suc-cumbing to additional infections.

The condition of anaphylaxis described in the previous chapter as occurring to some individuals upon absorbing incompletely digested proteins may also affect the respira-tory tract. Hay fever is an example of this type of affliction. In hay fever sufferers the proteins of the pollen of some plants cause swelling of the nasal membranes together with an excessive secretion of mucus. The mechanism of such a seizure is thought to be as follows:

The sensitive individuals responded to their first exposure to the offending protein by manufacturing a substance known as an **antibody** in the cells exposed to the offending substance, or **antigen.** When a large enough quantity of antibody is formed, another exposure to antigen results in a reaction between antigen and antibody which releases large quantities of the substance **histamine,** which brings about the nasal congestion and stimulates vigorous contraction of visceral muscle, as in the lower parts of the respiratory tract, producing asthma. Histamine also causes the release of gastric secretions, much as does gastrin. The actions of histamine may be counteracted to some extent by such antihistaminic drugs as benadryl and pyribenzamine, taken under a physician's prescription.

SUMMARY

The respiratory system exposes a large enough surface of the blood vessels to air to provide for absorption of oxygen and release of carbon dioxide, while protecting this surface from mechanical or bacterial injury. The blood then carries the oxygen to the tissues of the body, and the carbon dioxide from those tissues back to the lungs, where exhalation occurs.

The larynx is a specialized portion of the respiratory tract using the outgoing air for sound production under voluntary control.

We have traced the processing and making available to the body of food and oxygen. We have seen that both the digestive and respiratory systems depend upon the blood stream to complete the work they started by delivering useful substances to the points of need. Next we shall investigate the circulatory system in greater detail.

REVIEW QUESTIONS

1. Define respiration.
2. Trace the fate of the hydrogen atoms removed from lactic acid when pyruvic acid is formed.
3. Describe the structure of the nose cavity and its lining.
4. Describe the structure of the larynx, the trachea, and the lungs.
5. Explain the chemical changes involved in transportation of oxygen and carbon dioxide in the blood.
6. Explain buffering.
7. How is the breathing rate controlled automatically?
8. Explain the muscular movements during breathing. How do these bring air in and force air out?
9. Describe the production of voice, and changes in its pitch.
10. What are the advantages of breathing through the nose rather than through the mouth?
11. What is a "cold"?
12. Describe hay fever physiologically.

GENERAL QUESTIONS

1. Why is oxidation considered of such great importance in the human body?
2. How is vitamin B involved in respiration?
3. What are the advantages of the single layer of tall cells over the many-layered flatter cells in the lining of the nose cavity? Why would it be disadvantageous to have this single layer continued through the pharynx?
4. Do you suppose the lining of the nose, larynx, and trachea absorbs any oxygen from the air passing by?
5. What is the relation of the ribs to the rest of the body which produces chest expansion in two dimensions when they are raised?
6. Each skeletal muscle of the body seems to have its opponent, which reverses its action. What muscles oppose the action of the diaphragm? of the external oblique muscles of the ribs?
7. In normal breathing, how many barrels of air are forced into and out of the lungs during one day, assuming one pint per cycle at an average of $17\frac{1}{2}$ cycles per minute? (1 barrel equals $31\frac{1}{2}$ gal.)
8. Trace one atom of oxygen from the air to a muscle, where it becomes part of a carbon dioxide molecule, and trace this back to the outside air again.
9. Why is whispering more difficult to understand than talking of the same loudness?
10. Analyze the bodily events during laughing, coughing, sneezing, hiccoughing.
11. Explain the movements of a singer's larynx as his voice moves up and down one octave.
12. What happens in your respiratory tract when you "get a cold"?
13. How is breathing controlled during long speaking or singing?
14. Since the respiratory system furnishes a large surface, why wouldn't the skin make a better respiratory organ than the lungs?
15. Would any structural changes be necessary if the human body were to use nitrogen for energy instead of oxygen?

CHAPTER 5

The Circulatory System

CIRCULATION

The circulatory system is the railroad industry of the body. It carries large quantities of freight and many passengers from one part of the body to another. The rolling stock consists of water. The freight consists of digested foods, oxygen, numerous secretions, and waste products. The passengers include various types of blood corpuscles.

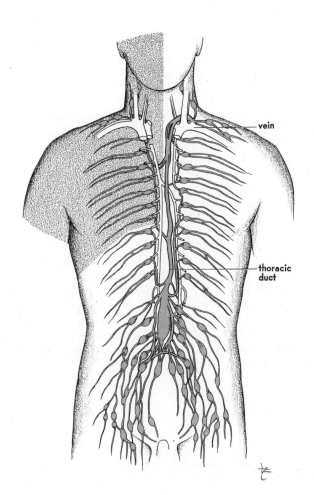

vein

thoracic duct

Fig. 5.1 Main lymph channels in the body. The right and left channels coming up from the trunk unite and empty into a vein on the left side; the corresponding vein on the right side receives lymph from the right arm and the right side of the head, neck, and shoulder region. Where does the lymph come from?

The blood is contained within the blood vessels, which penetrate most tissues of the body. Exchange of substances between the blood and the tissues takes place through the walls of the thinnest vessels, the **capillaries.** *Capillary* comes from the Latin for hairlike. Only water and substances in solution in water diffuse into the cells from the capillaries, or into the capillaries from the cells.

LYMPH SYSTEM

The cells of most tissues are almost surrounded by a watery liquid containing substances diffused both from the blood and from the cells. This substance is called **lymph** (Latin for water).

Partly because of blood pressure due to heart action, more water leaves the capillaries than returns to them. The excess accumulates in the lymph. The lymph is drained away from tissues in special lymph vessels which eventually lead to the blood system at the junction of the veins from the head and from the arm on the right or left side.

The left entrance receives the lymph from the entire left side of the body, and from the right side below the diaphragm. You have already read about the drainage into the thoracic duct of all of the lymph vessels bearing fats from the intestine. The right main lymphatic duct drains the right side of the body above the diaphragm. Thus the excess water is brought to a large blood vessel, from where it may be distributed to water-excreting organs such as the lungs, skin, and kidneys. See Figure 5.1.

BLOOD

The **blood** contains many substances in solution, and some colloidal materials in suspension. It also contains three kinds of cells: red corpuscles, white corpuscles, and platelets. These cells make up about half the substance of the blood. The fluid, noncellular part of the blood is called **plasma** (Latin: potion).

PLASMA

The plasma is about 90% to 92% water, the remainder being dissolved and suspended materials, chiefly proteins. It contains digested food products such as glucose, fats, and amino acids; sodium, potassium, calcium, and magnesium chlorides, carbonates, and phosphates; and waste products such as carbon dioxide, urea, and creatinine. See Table 5.1.

TABLE 5.1

AVERAGE CHEMICAL COMPOSITION OF NORMAL HUMAN
BLOOD IN GRAMS PER 100 MILLILITERS

	WHOLE BLOOD	PLASMA	RED CORPUSCLES
Water	78.0	90.7	66.0
Inorganic salts	0.8	0.93	0.7
Glucose	0.07	0.08	0.065
Fatty acids	0.36	0.37	0.34
Lecithin	0.3	0.2	0.4
Cholesterol	0.2	0.2	0.2
Amino acids	0.007	0.0065	0.008
Proteins:			
Albumin	2.5	5.0	
Globulins	1.38	2.6	
Fibrinogen	0.25	0.37	
Hemoglobin	15.0		34.0
Urea	0.03		
Uric acid	0.003	0.004	0.002
Creatinine	0.003	0.0025	0.0035
Creatine	0.003	0.000	0.006

In the interests of knowing more about the proteins in blood plasma and of making concentrations of these for use in medical treatment of patients with certain illnesses, Edwin J. Cohn and other investigators have succeeded in separating the plasma into "fractions." The first of these is **fibrinogen** (Latin: fiber producer). This protein, under the influence of the enzyme **thrombin** (Greek: clot), is able to initiate blood clotting by forming a mat of fibers. This process will be described in greater detail later.

The second fraction includes the **gamma globulins,** among which are the substances giving the body immunity to certain infectious diseases such as measles and poliomyelitis.

The third fraction includes substances known as **isoagglutinins,** concerned in clumping red corpuscles under certain conditions; and **beta globulins,** bearing enzymes.

The fourth fraction contains the **alpha globulins** and the hormones.

And lastly, the fifth fraction includes **albumins,** which contribute to the maintenance of the osmotic pressure of the blood, and hence its volume and consistency.

The value of this separation is apparent when you consider the advantage of using the concentrated second fraction in the treatment of infectious disease, or the fifth fraction in restoring blood volume after severe hemorrhage, without putting in whole blood with its attendant dangers.

The isoagglutinins in fraction three are the source of some concern to a physician contemplating blood transfusions from one person to another. Use of blood fractions will eliminate much of the difficulty, but transfusions of the whole blood may produce death unless care is taken to determine that the blood types of donor and recipient are similar, or at least not antagonistic.

Blood Types

The first blood types that were distinguished among humans are called the O, A, B, and AB types. People belonging to group O have red corpuscles which do not clump upon exposure to isoagglutinins of other types. Since their cells do not clump ordinarily no matter what blood they may enter, these people have been called "universal donors," for it was thought they could give blood to any other human without producing clogging of blood vessels with accompanying serious distress and perhaps death. However, this is a dangerous generalization, and, if possible, small quantities of prospective donor and recipient blood should be tested with each other outside their bodies before any extensive transfusion is performed.

People belonging to group A have in their red corpuscles a protein A which will bring about their agglutination in the blood of recipients whose corpuscles do not contain this protein, namely those recipients belonging to groups O and B.

People belonging to group B have a protein B in their corpuscles, and these corpuscles will be clumped if injected into the blood of those having no protein B in their own corpuscles, namely members of groups O and A.

Those belonging to group AB have both proteins in their red corpuscles, and such corpuscles will be agglutinated in the blood of any person not having both proteins, which would be any person in group O, A, or B. See Table 5.2.

TABLE 5.2

REACTIONS OF DIFFERENT TYPES OF BLOOD WHEN MIXED

The corpuscles from a person belonging to group	If injected into the blood of a person in group			
	O	A	B	AB
O	will not clump	will not clump	will not clump	will not clump
A	will clump	will not clump	will clump	will not clump
B	will clump	will clump	will not clump	will not clump
AB	will clump	will clump	will clump	will not clump

Other human blood groups (M, N, MN) have been described more recently, but there seems to be less danger of fatal difficulties arising from transfusion of bloods dissimilar with respect to these groups, for the concentration of these proteins is much less than those of A and B.

Rh Factor

The Rh factor (named because it was found first in the Rhesus monkey) is an additional problem in blood typing. This factor seems to act according to the principles of allergy. Those who do not have the Rh factor in their blood, known as Rh-negatives, may develop a sensitivity to the factor after one transfusion of blood containing such a factor (Rh-positive blood). Any subsequent contact with Rh-positive blood may result in the destruction of the red corpuscles containing the Rh factor. This is particularly significant in the case of children born to an Rh-negative mother if the father is Rh-positive. In this case, the children may be Rh-positive or Rh-negative. If one child is Rh-positive, the mother's blood will build isoagglutinins against the factor, but these will not affect this child seriously. However, the next Rh-positive child conceived by this mother will bear the full force of the attack of her isoagglutinins on his red corpuscles, and the damage may be fatal to the child.

These various groups may be subdivided, since at least two kinds of A protein and eleven of Rh protein are known.

The occurrence of these various blood types among humans has been studied statistically. Attempts have been made to correlate the results with other characteristics such as skin color, geographical origin, and so forth, in order to substantiate a division of humans into discrete races. However, the incidence of blood groups does not correspond well with that of many other features, so that distinctions are not well established. Percentage variations may occur, but not absolute distinctions.

CORPUSCLES

Red Corpuscles

Red corpuscles are extremely numerous, making up the vast majority of the cells of the blood. The average adult man in good health has in his body between 35,000,000,000,000 and 40,000,000,000,000 red corpuscles. The average woman usually has a few trillion less than a man of the same weight.

Red corpuscles are built in the marrow of bones. Before they enter the blood stream from the site of formation, they lose their nuclei. Each resulting cell is shaped like a

balloon squeezed between two fists (Fig. 5.2). In face view
it appears circular, but the front and back surfaces are
hollowed out. This biconcave disc shape has several advantages. It presents a very large surface compared to the
amount of substance involved. No part of the corpuscle
is very far removed from the surface. The corpuscle swells
slightly in going from oxygen-rich blood to carbon dioxide-
rich blood, and shrinks correspondingly in going into
oxygen-rich blood again. This change in volume may be
accomplished in a biconcave object with a minimum of
stress on the membrane. As it swells, the concavity becomes
less, actually relaxing the membrane. When it shrinks, the
cell collapses slightly, restoring the biconcavity to its
former degree.

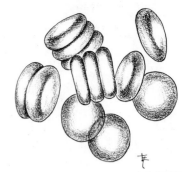

Fig. 5.2   Red blood corpuscles. When removed
from the body, these corpuscles may stack themselves like a pile of coins.

The work of the red corpuscle in transporting oxygen in
its hemoglobin was described in Chapter 4. The absence
of a nucleus means that little or no metabolism goes on in
the red cell except for the activity of the hemoglobin, so
that little or no oxygen and food are used by the red cell.
It also means that the cell cannot maintain itself as nucle-
ated cells usually do, and the cell is worn out readily. The
mechanical stress and the chemical changes in its environment weaken and eventually break up the corpuscle after
a time. Special cells known as **macrophages** (Greek: large
eaters) destroy the fragments, and restore some of the
hemoglobin components to the blood stream. Bone marrow
tissue may reuse these substances in making new red
corpuscles. The other hemoglobin components appear in
the bile as bile pigments.

The macrophages responsible for this filtering off and
stripping down of the broken red cells are located principally in an organ called the **spleen.** This is a rather large
structure located in the abdominal cavity to the left of the
stomach. See Figure 5.3. Blood passes through it slowly
and in considerable quantities, so that the macrophages
have time to pick out the broken red cells before the blood
leaves the spleen and continues its circulation about the
body. The spleen also serves as a storehouse for blood.
During times of bodily stress when blood is needed in
greater quantities than usual, the spleen may contract
forcibly, sending additional blood into the general circulation. At times of rest it will relax and expand, taking up more
blood. If the spleen is surgically removed, as in treatment
of some disease, its activity in destroying red corpuscles
is mostly taken over by the liver.

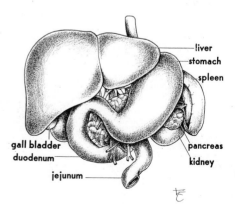

Fig. 5.3   Position of the spleen in the abdomen.

It has been estimated that red blood cells are broken
down and destroyed in the average adult human at a rate

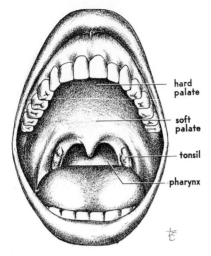

Fig. 5.4   Location of the tonsils. Why are these so often removed from humans?

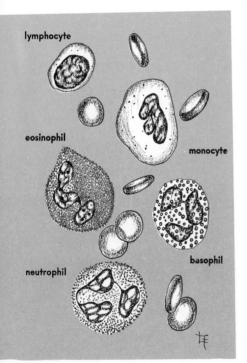

Fig. 5.5   White corpuscles. A few red corpuscles are shown for comparison of sizes. The red corpuscles are nearly 1,000 times as numerous in the blood as the white corpuscles.

of about ten million per second. A corresponding rate of manufacture of new red corpuscles occurs in the bone marrow. Any one red cell may be active for about one to four months, usually not much more than one month.

White Corpuscles

The **white corpuscles** also are manufactured in bone marrow, as well as in many specialized structures known as **lymph nodes.** These are clusters of developing white corpuscles in a connective tissue framework occurring along the pathway of lymph vessels. Some lymph nodes become quite large, as, for example, the **thymus** at the top of the chest, a spreading, glandular mass particularly prominent in young children. The **tonsils** (Fig. 5.4) are lymph nodes located at the entrance to the pharynx. In this exposed position they may be subject to infection, resulting in the disease known as tonsillitis. They may be removed without doing serious permanent injury to the body, for after they are gone there will still remain several hundred lymph nodes scattered throughout the body, especially along the head, neck, armpit, groin, and intestinal wall.

The white corpuscles normally number about fifty billion in an adult, but during infections this number may be greatly increased.

White corpuscles are of several kinds, differing from each other in details of structure and staining properties (see Figure 5.5), but they all seem to be concerned in one way or another with the defense of the body against foreign invasions. In Chapter 1 were mentioned some of these cells which crawl out of the capillaries and wander about in the connective tissue, eating foreign bodies such as bacteria. Within the lymph and blood streams they perform the same function, destroying disease-causing bodies by various means. Methods used by these cells in addition to taking the bacteria into themselves and disintegrating them include the following:

Substances known as **opsonins** (Greek: seasonings) are secreted; these react with the surface of bacteria, making them much more readily attacked by the white corpuscles, as if a delectable sauce had been added to a previously unpalatable morsel.

Other secretions, **agglutinins** (Latin: glues), alter the bacterial surfaces in such a way that the bacteria tend to stick together in large clumps, enabling a white corpuscle to pick them up in wholesale lots rather than individually.

Lysins (Greek: looseners) are secreted which dissolve the bacterial wall, thus destroying it.

The bacteria themselves may secrete **toxins** (Latin: arrow poisons). These are poisonous to the human tissues, tending to inhibit the activities of white corpuscles.

Antitoxins are developed in the body which neutralize the effect of the toxins by combining with them to make an innocuous compound.

Precipitins cause the toxins to precipitate, or come out of solution, thus making them accessible to the phagocytes. In the case of an infection in the blood, the bacteria with their high rate of multiplication and their toxinformation are counteracted by the white corpuscles with their ability to destroy some bacteria physically and to neutralize the toxins chemically. Under ideal conditions some bacteria may double their numbers in an hour; if you imagine an extremely light infection of the blood with, for example, one hundred bacteria, and if you imagine no obstacle in the path of their continued growth at the rate of doubling in numbers every hour, then one day later there would be over a billion and a half bacteria present. After another day there would be over two and a half quintillion, expressed: 2,500,000,000,000,000,000. But with sufficient healthy and vigilant white corpuscles on hand, this rate of bacterial increase would be greatly reduced, and the invaders eventually wiped out.

If a bacterial invasion occurs in some tissue other than blood or lymph, as in the skin, for example, white corpuscles crawl out of the nearest blood capillaries and enter the affected area in large numbers. Some actively destroy the bacteria, while others form a barrier or wall around the infection site, preventing the spread of the bacteria. The enclosed section, containing dead and dying bacteria, white corpuscles, lymph, and other secretions, is called an **abscess,** the contents of which are called **pus.** If the white corpuscles are successful in limiting the infection to the abscess, the bacteria are eventually destroyed. Unless the pus pocket is artificially drained it may break through to the surface and heal, with or without leaving a scar.

Many times disease-carrying organisms are destroyed by white corpuscles or their toxins are neutralized by chemicals already in the blood or other tissues before disease symptoms are produced. Unless a considerable quantity of antitoxins is on hand, however, there may be a lag of several days in producing the secretions in sufficient amounts to counteract toxins. The body may also not be able to manufacture white blood cells fast enough to prevent great increase in numbers of disease-causing organisms. Thus the organisms may increase in number, causing disease symptoms.

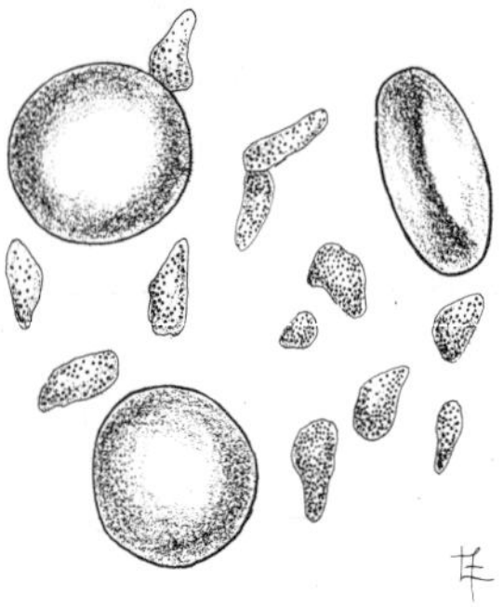

red
corpuscle

blood
platelet

Fig. 5.6 Blood platelets. A few red corpuscles are shown for comparison of sizes.

Often a physician can prescribe prepared antitoxins, opsonins, or other substances developed in other animals for use in infected humans. Immunization procedures applied to healthy persons may prevent the onset of certain diseases should infection occur. Immunization procedures usually involve injection of the proteins which act as antigens in stimulating the body to produce the appropriate antibody secretions. These proteins may be in the form of dead bacteria, weakened toxins, or other substances sufficiently like the antigens to produce the desired reaction. If the body produces these antibodies in large numbers, they are available instantly to deal with an invasion of bacteria, and the protected person is said to become **immune.**

Platelets

The **platelets** are formed in bone marrow, and number about two trillion in a healthy, human adult. They are much smaller than the other kinds of corpuscles, and do not have a discrete nucleus. See Figure 5.6. They are involved in maintaining and repairing the blood vessels; they adhere to any foreign body, especially to broken blood vessels, helping to narrow the opening and decrease the loss of blood. They are especially noteworthy for their role in blood clotting.

The importance in blood clotting of the plasma constituent fibrinogen was described earlier: Under the influence of the enzyme thrombin, fibrinogen precipitates out of the plasma as small, needlelike crystals of fibrin. These crystals mat together forming a meshwork. Blood corpuscles are caught in this meshwork and fill in the spaces, making a solid plug, the blood clot.

But thrombin is not normally present in blood in significant amounts. The substance **prothrombin,** formed in the liver (and perhaps in bone marrow) under the influence of vitamin K, is present in the third fraction of blood plasma. It is transformed into thrombin by the action of **thromboplastin** (Greek: clot; and Latin: maker). Thromboplastin occurs in most tissues and in the blood platelets.

Platelets escaping from the normal blood channels break down rapidly, releasing thromboplastin. This, together with the thromboplastin of tissues into which blood flows from a broken blood vessel, brings about the formation of thrombin. A small amount of **antithrombin** in the blood inactivates the first bit of thrombin formed, so that it takes a few minutes for enough thrombin to be produced to precipitate fibrin from fibrinogen to make the blood clot. Not all of the platelets are broken in this clot formation, and some cling to the fibers of the clot. Under their influence the fibers shrink, squeezing out a yellowish serum, and the clot retracts and hardens. This may take some hours.

During this time the platelets are closing up the rupture in the blood vessel, and after the healing has occurred, the clot may either fall off if it is on the surface of the body, or be resorbed if it is in the interior. A bruise, such as a "black eye," is simply a clot forming at a break in a blood vessel under the skin. As the clot is resorbed the discoloration disappears.

The disease known as **hemophilia,** a hereditary condition found, for example, in some of the royal families of Europe, consists of an abnormal stability of platelets, which do not break and release thromboplastin at the time of hemorrhage. The interesting way in which this condition is inherited will be described in Chapter 12.

If there were no antithrombin in the blood, any slight injury, or even normal body movements which would break a few platelets, might initiate a serious blood clot. But there is enough antithrombin to stop these little outbursts.

ANATOMY OF THE CIRCULATORY SYSTEM

The propelling force which pumps the blood throughout the body is furnished by the **heart.** The cardiac muscle of the heart contracts rhythmically, pushing blood out of the heart into thick-walled vessels known as **arteries.** These branch into smaller and smaller vessels until the numerous thin-walled **capillaries** are reached. These collect into **veins,** which lead the blood back to the heart.

Heart

The heart itself (Fig. 5.7) consists of four chambers, the **right auricle** and **ventricle** and the **left auricle** and **ventricle.** In any one complete circulatory cycle, blood passes through the right side of the heart once and the left side once.

Pulmonary Circulation

Blood coming from the body through the veins enters the right auricle and passes through the right ventricle and into the **pulmonary** (Latin: lung) **artery.** This divides into right and left branches and carries blood to the lungs. In the lung capillaries the blood exchanges its carbon dioxide for oxygen, and flows into **pulmonary veins.** Two of these from each lung enter the left auricle.

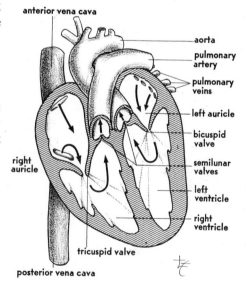

Fig. 5.7   The chambers of the heart. Trace the two pathways of blood through the heart.

Systemic Circulation

From the left auricle blood flows into the left ventricle, which forces it into the **aorta.** The aorta is the main artery of the body. It extends upward from the left ventricle in a great arch, thence downward through the diaphragm into the abdominal cavity. Numerous branches from this vessel lead arterial blood to all parts of the body. The first branches are given off almost immediately after the aorta leaves the heart. These are the **right** and **left coronary arteries** which supply the walls of the heart. **Coronary veins** drain this blood back into the right auricle. See Figure 5.8.

At the top of the arch are given off three large arteries: the **innominate,** the **left common carotid** (Greek: stupor-producing, so named because pressure on this vessel stops the flow of blood to the brain, inducing unconsciousness), and the **left subclavian** (Latin: under the clavicle). The innominate passes toward the right shoulder, and soon divides into the **right common carotid** and the **right subclavian arteries.**

The common carotid arteries pass through the neck toward the head. At the level of the larynx each divides into an **internal carotid** and an **external carotid artery.** The internal carotid arteries pass into the interior of the skull and supply the brain and the eyeballs. Blood from capillaries here flows into branches of the **internal jugular** (Latin: collarbone) **veins,** which run into the single large **anterior vena cava** (Latin: hollow vein) emptying into the right auricle.

The external carotid arteries break into numerous branches supplying the more superficial parts of the head and upper part of the neck. Blood from this region returns through the two **external jugular veins,** each of which passes into a **subclavian vein** which leads to the anterior vena cava.

The branches of the right and left subclavian arteries are comparable, so the following description of one will do for both. A subclavian artery gives off four branches, and then continues as the **axillary** (Latin: armpit) **artery** out into the shoulder and arm. Blood from here returns through the **axillary vein** to the subclavian vein.

The four branches from the subclavian artery are: the **vertebral artery,** supplying blood to the vertebral column, from which it is drained by the **vertebral vein** into the anterior vena cava; the **thyroid artery** to the neck and shoulder, drained by the **thyroid vein** into the anterior vena cava; the **internal mammary** (Latin: breast) **artery** to the front wall of the chest, drained by the **internal mammary**

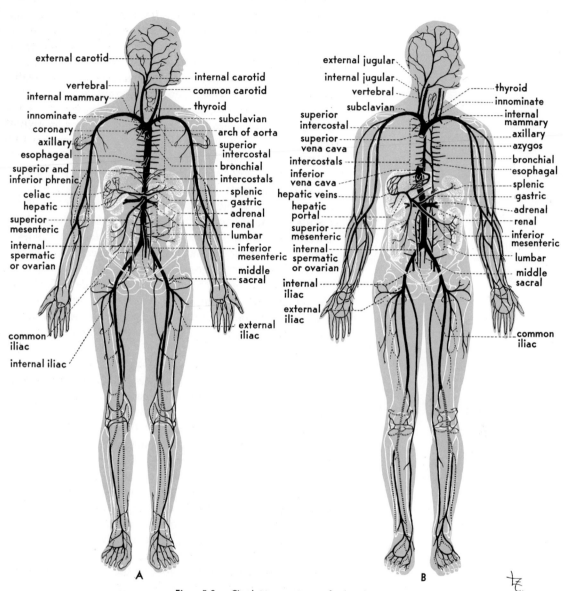

Fig. 5.8 Circulatory system of the human. A, Arteries. B, Veins.

vein into the anterior vena cava; and the **superior intercostal artery** to the back wall of the top of the chest and the neck, drained by the **superior intercostal vein** into the anterior vena cava.

As the arch of the aorta curves to the left, dorsally, and posteriorly, and passes down through the chest, it gives off **bronchial, esophageal,** and **intercostal arteries** to the bronchi, esophagus, and wall of the chest. These regions drain respectively into **bronchial, esophageal,** and **intercostal veins,** which empty into an **azygos vein,** a tributary of the anterior vena cava. The right azygos vein is fairly long, starting in the abdominal cavity and running up along the backbone to empty into the anterior vena cava above the heart. The left azygos is divided: the lower half runs from the abdomen up to about the level of the seventh or eighth thoracic vertebra, and then crosses over to join the right azygos; the upper part starts above the crossover point, and joins the right azygos near the top.

As the aorta passes through the diaphragm it gives off **phrenic** (Greek: diaphragm) **arteries** to this structure. **Phrenic veins** drain blood into the **posterior vena cava,** the largest vein of the body, entering the right auricle from below.

In the abdominal cavity the aorta gives off three unpaired branches to the digestive tract. The first of these is the **celiac** (Greek: abdominal) **artery.** This sends out three branches: The **hepatic artery** goes to the liver; the blood it carries is drained by the **hepatic vein** into the posterior vena cava. The **gastric artery** supplies the stomach. The **gastric vein** is a tributary of the **hepatic portal vein,** a large vessel leading from the abdominal digestive tract into the liver. Within the liver the hepatic portal vein breaks into smaller and smaller vessels and finally into capillaries, allowing the liver to withdraw any excess of single sugars obtained by the blood from the intestine. These capillaries reunite into tributaries of the hepatic vein. The **splenic artery,** the third branch of the celiac artery, goes to the spleen. The **splenic vein** empties into the hepatic portal vein.

The **superior mesenteric artery** branches from the aorta a little lower than the celiac artery, and supplies the small intestine and much of the large intestine. Blood from these organs is collected into the **superior mesenteric vein,** which leads to the hepatic portal vein.

Near the bottom of the abdomen the aorta gives off the **inferior mesenteric artery** to the descending colon and the rectum. The **inferior mesenteric vein** returns to the hepatic portal vein.

The remaining branches of the abdominal aorta with one exception are paired — right and left. Several **lumbar arteries** supply the abdominal wall; this region is drained by **lumbar veins,** which enter the posterior vena cava.

Adrenal arteries go to the adrenal glands near the kidneys; **renal arteries** supply the kidneys; and **internal spermatic** or **internal ovarian arteries** supply the reproductive organs, testes or ovaries. The corresponding **adrenal, renal,** and **internal spermatic** or **internal ovarian veins** lead to the posterior vena cava.

Near the bottom of the abdominal cavity the aorta divides into three parts: the large, lateral **common iliac arteries,** and the small **median sacral artery.** The latter goes along the front surface of the sacral and caudal vertebrae. Drainage is through the **median sacral vein** into the posterior vena cava.

Each common iliac artery divides into an **internal iliac artery** to the pelvic region and its organs, and an **external iliac artery** to the leg. The corresponding **internal** and **external iliac veins** unite into a **common iliac vein** which empties into the posterior vena cava. See Table 5.3.

This pattern of distribution of blood vessels has been given not only to describe the major arteries and veins in humans, but to serve as reference for a later discussion of the significance of the remarkable similarity in pattern found in a seemingly widely diverse group of animals — fishes, reptiles, birds, mice, giraffes — many strikingly different animals. This similarity in pattern is characteristic not only of blood vessels but of the structure and physiology of the other systems of the body as well. In fact, it is easier to understand some details of the structure of humans from a study of similar details in other animals. For instance, the fact that a separate branch of the aorta follows along the much reduced caudal vertebrae in humans seems to take on added meaning when you find that its equivalent in other animals is the main blood supply of the tail.

PHYSIOLOGY OF CIRCULATION
Heart Cycle

To understand the process of circulation of the blood, let us consider the action of the heart. The pathway of blood through the heart has been described. Blood from the tissues of the body returns through the anterior and posterior venae cavae and the coronary veins to the right auricle. Blood pours into the auricle most of the time. At the same time blood from the lung capillaries is pouring into the left auricle through the pulmonary veins.

TABLE 5.3

BLOOD VESSEL DISTRIBUTION IN THE HUMAN

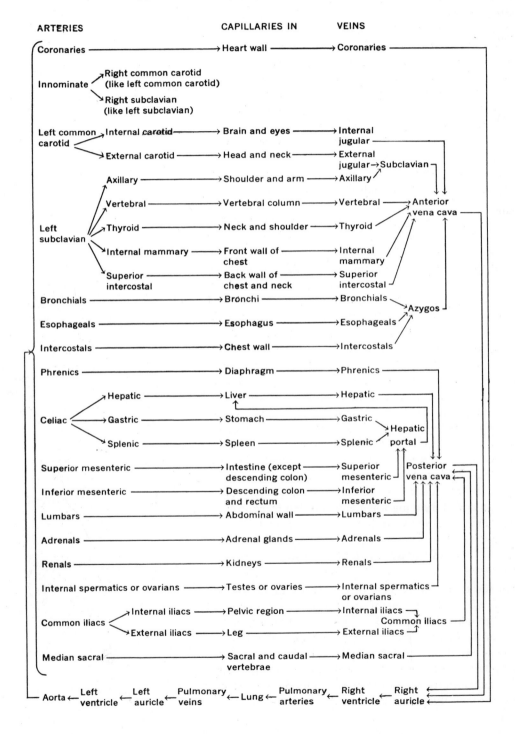

The passages from auricles to ventricles are open much of the time. They are controlled by flaps of tissue known as valves, which allow the blood to flow through these passages in only one direction. The valves are operated principally if not entirely by the pressure of the blood itself. Between the right auricle and right ventricle occurs the **tricuspid valve,** composed of three curved sheets of tissue which fold back against the inner walls of the ventricle while blood is going from auricle to ventricle, but are raised, meeting at the edges and closing the entrance, when blood is forced from the ventricle.

Similarly the opening between left auricle and left ventricle is opened and closed by the **bicuspid** or **mitral** (Greek: turban) **valve.** This is similar to the tricuspid valve, but has only two flaps. See Figure 5.9.

Near the entrance of the anterior vena cava into the right auricle is a patch of specialized cardiac muscle known as the **sinuauricular node.** This initiates the rhythmic contraction of the heart muscle. All heart muscle seems to have the ability to beat rhythmically, but since this node seems to have the fastest rhythm, it acts as a pacemaker for the heart. If it were removed, the heart would continue to beat, but at a slower rate.

About every $\frac{8}{10}$ of a second the pacemaker starts a beat, which spreads rapidly through both auricles. The contraction of the auricles, known as **auricular systole** (Greek: shortening), takes about $\frac{1}{10}$ of a second. This empties the blood in the auricle into the ventricle, on both sides. At the end of this systole the auricles relax and start filling with blood again. Simultaneously the wave of contraction is funneled through a special strand of cardiac muscle, the **auriculoventricular bundle,** into the wall between the two ventricles. From here it sweeps across both ventricles, which contract in their systole, forcing the blood into the pulmonary artery (from the right ventricle) and aorta (from the left ventricle). See Figure 5.10.

As the ventricles start to contract, the pressure they exert on the blood contained in them forces the tricuspid and mitral valves to close. The edges of the valves are fastened to the side walls of the ventricles by stout muscular and connective tissue cords; hence the ventricular pressure will not force them past the closure into the auricles. See Figure 5.9.

This same pressure which closes the tricuspid and mitral valves opens similar valves at the exit from the ventricles into the arteries. These valves, one set of three flaps for each ventricle, are called the **semilunar** (half moon) **valves.**

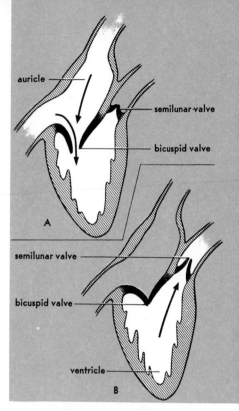

Fig. 5.9   Operation of the heart valves. **A** shows the heart at the time blood passes from the auricle to the ventricle, and **B** shows the heart at the time blood passes from the ventricle to the aorta. Explain the mechanics of valve opening and closing.

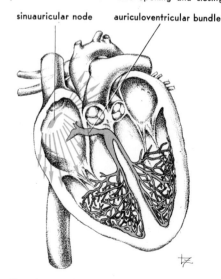

Fig. 5.10   Neuromuscular system of the heart. These fibers are imbedded in the heart wall, and carry the beat impulse.

The ventricular systole lasts about $\frac{3}{10}$ of a second. At the end of that time the ventricle walls relax, and the pressure of the blood in the arteries closes the semilunar valves.

During **ventricular systole** the auricles have been filling with blood again, and as the ventricle walls relax, the pressure of the blood in the auricles opens the tricuspid and mitral valves, and blood flows from the veins through the auricles into the ventricles. The entire heart remains relaxed for $\frac{4}{10}$ of a second before the sinuauricular node sets off another auricular systole. The relaxation periods of the heart are called **diastoles** (Greek: lengthenings).

In normal heartbeat, to summarize: The auricle is in systole for $\frac{1}{10}$ of a second, and in diastole for $\frac{7}{10}$ of a second. The ventricle starts its systole as the auricle starts its diastole. Ventricular systole lasts for $\frac{3}{10}$ of a second, and its diastole for $\frac{5}{10}$ of a second. The entire cycle then runs for $\frac{8}{10}$ of a second, giving about 75 beats per minute. See Table 5.4.

TABLE 5.4

HUMAN HEART CYCLE

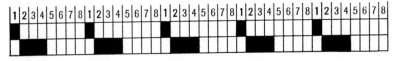

Auricle
Ventricle

Each square represents $\frac{1}{10}$ of a second.
Systoles are blacked.
Diastoles are left blank.

Arterial Flow

Blood leaving the left ventricle in spurts at ventricular systole enters the aorta. This vessel has walls largely composed of elastic connective tissue. When the surge of blood enters, the walls of the aorta are pushed out; after the start of ventricular diastole the aorta walls begin to return to their normal position because of their elasticity. This mechanism smooths out the intermittent jets of blood into a more nearly steady flow. The great variations in pressure, however, are carried along the larger arteries and may be felt along these as the pulse. Blood flows through the aorta at a rate of about 400 millimeters ($15\frac{3}{4}$ inches) per second.

As the aorta gives off arteries and these subdivide into smaller and smaller vessels, the elastic connective tissue in the walls is partly replaced by visceral muscle, and the diameter of these vessels is partly under nervous control.

The total cross-sectional area of the arteries at a given distance from the heart is somewhat greater than that of the aorta, but since the vessels are more numerous and smaller, they collectively present more surface to the blood stream, increasing frictional resistance to flow. The friction is not so much between vessel wall and blood stream as between parts or shells of the blood stream itself. As in a river where the water next to the banks is stationary or in very slow motion, whereas the water in the middle of the river is flowing the fastest, so in blood vessels, the flow is most rapid in the center. In the aorta, for example, the flow five millimeters in from the wall is much faster than that one millimeter in; in the center it is much faster than five millimeters in. In an artery only two millimeters in diameter the blood flow in the center will be about as fast as that one millimeter in from the wall of the aorta.

Capillary Flow

The network of capillaries taken together presents a cross-sectional area several hundred times as great as that of the aorta. Hence, as when a river widens out into a large lake, flow will be very slow here. The capillaries themselves are very tiny, sometimes barely large enough to let a single red corpuscle at a time squeeze through. Therefore the surface area is tremendously increased, and frictional resistance likewise increased. This great surface area, together with the extreme thinness of the capillary walls, provides the place for exchanges between blood and tissues with the greatest facility.

Blood flow rate in the capillaries of the human retina has been measured, and found to be between 0.6 and 0.9 millimeter per second, or about $\frac{1}{500}$ as fast as in the aorta. It takes much of the pressure built up in the arterial system by the contractions of the heart to force the blood through the capillaries into the veins.

Venous Flow

The veins have much weaker muscles than the arteries, their walls being largely fibrous connective tissue. Like the arteries their cross-sectional area is much less than that of the capillaries taken collectively, and blood flow through them is faster than in the capillaries. The sum of the cross-sectional areas of the veins entering the right auricle is about twice that of the aorta as it leaves the left ventricle. There are valves at frequent intervals along the veins which prevent reversing of the flow. The pressure in the veins would not alone prevent occasional stagnation or retrogression of venous circulation. Circulation through the veins is aided by muscular movements of the body which, by squeezing the veins, help to push the blood along. The enlargement of the chest in inhalation aids circulation by lowering the pressure here, so that the relatively greater pressure in the veins in the neck and in the abdomen will force blood into the heart. Holding your breath, by maintaining atmospheric pressure within the chest, interferes with the return of blood to the heart, and if this is persisted in for many seconds, blood will accumulate in veins leading to the chest, making you "blue in the face."

Flow Rate

By injecting special dyes or drugs into the blood and watching for signs of their appearance at another point, the time of circulation may be determined. For example, one complete round may be traced by putting a dye into a vein of one arm, and watching for it to appear in the corresponding vein of the other arm. To get there it must go through the right side of the heart, the lung capillaries, the left side of the heart, the axillary artery, the capillaries of the arm, and into the vein. This takes about 21 seconds on the average. If the appearance of the dye in the arm artery rather than the vein is timed, the result is 18 seconds. From the arm to the heart takes about 6 seconds, and the circulation through the lungs about 11 seconds. Therefore the 21 seconds may be divided up as follows: arm to right side of the heart — 6 seconds; right side of the heart through the lungs to the left side of the heart — 11 seconds; heart to axillary artery — 1 second; axillary artery through capillaries to axillary vein — 3 seconds.

BLOOD PRESSURE

One of the simpler ways of determining the efficiency of the circulatory system is the measurement of blood pressure. A physician may do this by wrapping around your upper arm an inflatable cuff. When he pumps air into the cuff with a hand bulb, the expanding cuff exerts pressure on the arm. The pressure in the cuff may be measured with a mercury **manometer,** a column of mercury with a calibrated gauge; or some other device. With his **stethoscope** the physician listens to the blood flow through the artery at the inner side of the elbow. See Figure 5.11. When the pressure in the cuff is great enough to stop circulation through this artery he releases the pressure just enough to find the threshold between allowing a little trickle of blood through the artery and none at all. He reasons that the pressure registered on the gauge is equivalent to that exerted in forcing blood through the artery a ventricular systole, so he speaks of this as the systolic pressure. Then he lowers the pressure in the cuff until he hears the blood coming through the artery in spurts — during ventricular systole, but not during diastole. He gradually allows more air to escape from the cuff until the spurting effect is replaced by a more steady flow, indicating that the pressure in the cuff is not great enough to stop flow during diastole, and this reading gives him the diastolic pressure of the artery. If he wishes, the physician may also take measurements on the blood pressure in the veins by a similar method.

The average systolic arterial pressure of healthy twenty-year-old men is 120 millimeters of mercury; the average diastolic arterial pressure is 80 millimeters. The average pressures for women of the same age are five to ten millimeters less. The average systolic pressure of people of both sexes at the age of sixty is around 135 or 140 millimeters; the average diastolic pressure is from 87 to 89 millimeters.

An increase in the amount of fat carried by the body will increase the blood pressure noticeably. Emotional conditions will bring about temporary rises in blood pressure, as will exercise. Prolonged or repeated high blood pressure puts a strain on both the heart and the arteries. The heart

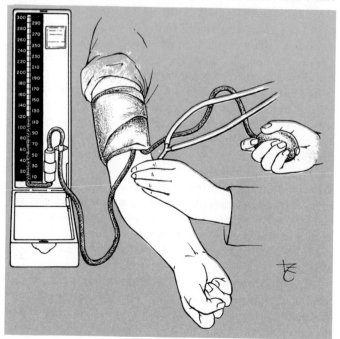

Fig. 5.11 A physician taking the blood pressure of a patient. Why does the physician use a stethoscope? Why does he put one end of the stethoscope on the inner side of the elbow? Why does he ask you to double your fist when he measures your blood pressure?

may be more subject to heart failure as a result of this increased stress. The arteries may deposit inorganic salts in their walls, a condition known as hardening of the arteries. High blood pressure is often found to result from emotional instability.

Capillaries are capable of independent control over their own volume in response to changes in their surroundings or to nervous stimulation. During rest of a muscle, for example, capillaries will be smaller, and some may collapse entirely. When the muscle becomes active, the capillary walls expand, allowing more blood to pass through.

SUMMARY

The circulatory systems are pathways through which food, oxygen, waste products, secretions, and blood corpuscles are transported. Some substances diffuse out of the blood through capillary walls; other substances diffuse from the tissues into the blood through capillary walls. Some substances are collected in the lymph and return to the blood through lymph vessels. Water is the vehicle facilitating diffusion and transportation.

The blood plasma, in addition to carrying dissolved and suspended food and wastes, has proteins of significance. Fibrinogen is involved in the process of blood clot formation, in which thromboplastin from the blood platelets is also important. Gamma globulins provide immunity from some diseases. Isoagglutinins may bring about the clumping of red corpuscles injected into the blood from some other individual. Beta globulins are associated with enzymic activity. Alpha globulins are associated with hormones. Albumins take part in maintaining blood volume.

Red corpuscles contain hemoglobin, which carries oxygen from the capillaries in the lungs to capillaries in other tissues. These corpuscles are manufactured in bone marrow, lose their nuclei before they enter the blood, and normally survive only a short time before they are broken down in the spleen or liver.

White corpuscles destroy objects not native to the blood, such as invading bacteria. They may engulf and digest the bacteria, and secrete substances which bring about the destruction of bacteria and bacterial secretions.

Blood platelets carry thromboplastin, involved in blood clotting.

The blood vessels include the heart, arteries, capillaries, and veins. Blood from most of the vessels in the body pours through veins into the right auricle. From here it passes the tricuspid valve into the right ventricle. Contraction of the right ventricle forces blood through semilunar valves into the pulmonary artery to the lung capillaries. Pulmonary veins carry the blood to the left auricle. The blood passes the mitral valve into the left ventricle. Contraction of the left ventricle forces blood past semilunar valves into the aorta. Numerous branches carry this blood to capillaries in most parts of the body. Blood is collected from capillaries into veins, which converge to the right auricle.

The heart chambers contract and relax in a rhythmic cycle. The two auricles contract during one tenth of a second. As they relax, the two ventricles contract during three tenths of a second. Then the ventricles relax, and no further heart chamber contractions occur for four tenths of a second, after which the auricles contract again. The blood is forced into the pulmonary artery and aorta in spurts at each ventricular contraction. The elasticity of the blood vessel walls tends to smooth out the series of spurts into a somewhat more steady flow, although the pulse can be detected in such places as the wrist and the temple. As the vessels through which the blood passes become smaller and more numerous, the total cross-sectional area is greater, blood flow becomes slower and steadier, and blood pressure decreases.

Because of its own responsiveness to conditions in its environment, including nerve impulses, the circulatory system readily becomes adjusted to such changes as those of temperature, muscular activity, and chemical composition of the tissues through which the blood vessels pass.

REVIEW QUESTIONS

1. What is lymph?
2. Describe the lymph system.
3. List and state the significance of the plasma fractions.
4. Explain blood types and their practical importance.
5. Explain how the Rh factor may endanger an unborn child.
6. Describe a red blood corpuscle, and its origin and destruction.
7. Describe the kinds of white blood corpuscles. Where are they formed?
8. Discuss the secretions formed by white blood corpuscles.
9. What is immunity, and how may it be developed?
10. Describe the process of blood clotting.
11. Describe the structure of the heart.
12. List the principal arteries and veins and their connections.
13. Describe the flow of blood through the heart, and the control exerted over it.
14. Describe the flow of blood through arteries, capillaries, and veins.
15. How is blood pressure measured?

GENERAL QUESTIONS

1. Under what conditions might administration of each of the five plasma fractions be advisable?
2. Can you account for the failure of blood type distribution to agree with such characteristics as skin color and geographical origin?
3. How can the body manufacture and destroy red corpuscles at the rate of 10,000,000 per second?
4. Suggest a way for determining the number of white corpuscles in a human body without doing serious damage to that body.
5. Suggest a way for determining the volume of blood within you without draining it all out to measure it.
6. If a hundred bacteria grew unhindered for two days, as described on page 111, and each bacterium has a volume of one cubic micron, how large a mass of bacteria would the two-day total be?
7. If you have once had a disease, can you have it again?
8. How could you stop hemorrhage in a person afflicted with hemophilia?
9. Why does the heart need special arteries and veins, when it always has blood in it?
10. Trace a drop of blood, naming the vessels and parts of the heart through which it passes in going from the:

    (a) brain to the appendix;
    (b) appendix to the right arm;
    (c) right arm to the right leg;
    (d) right leg to the diaphragm;
    (e) diaphragm to the brain.

11. What causes the semilunar valves to close after ventricular systole?
12. What prevents blood from flowing from auricles into veins?
13. How can the pulse beat travel along an artery faster than the flow of blood in that artery?
14. In what ways are capillaries better suited than arteries or veins for exchange of substances between blood and tissues?
15. How accurately do you suppose the inflated cuff method determines blood pressure?

CHAPTER 6

The Excretory System

EXCRETION

Excretion is the disposal of the waste products from metabolic activity of the body. Excretion has been differentiated from elimination, which is the disposal of substances passing through the digestive tract and not used by the body.

Two methods of excretion have already been discussed in this book. The disposal of bile pigments, wastes from the breakdown of red corpuscles, was described in Chapter 3, and the exhalation of carbon dioxide and some water was discussed in Chapter 4. There remain two other pathways of excretion — the sweat glands of the skin, and the kidneys and their associated organs.

SKIN

The skin (Fig. 6.1) consists of an outer **epidermis** (Greek: upon the skin), made of many layers of epithelial cells, and the inner **dermis** (Greek: skin), composed of connective tissue. The innermost cells of the epidermis, next to the dermis, are tall cells active in metabolism. As we proceed toward the surface we find the cells becoming flatter and less active, until the outermost ones are dead and flattened to minute scales, which slough off individually or in groups. The outer layers of dead cells act as a bumper, protecting the more delicate cells below from friction and other sources of possible injury. As these dead cells are rubbed off, they are replaced from below by divisions of the living cells and, according to recent evidence, by the passage of white corpuscles into the epidermis and their transformation into epithelial cells.

In addition to serving as a protection for the body, the skin contains sense organs, helps in the radiation of heat from the body, and is a site for excretion from sweat glands. The sweat glands (Fig. 6.2) are shaped like long, narrow tubes, the inner end of which is twisted and coiled in the dermis. (Oliver Wendell Holmes, physician as well as poet, spoke of them as "fairies' intestines.") About the contorted portion is a network of blood capillaries.

Sweat

Substances are actively secreted from the blood into the cavity of the sweat gland and forced to the surface

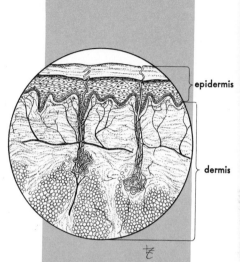

Fig. 6.1   Microscopic structure of the human skin. How does the skin protect the rest of the body?

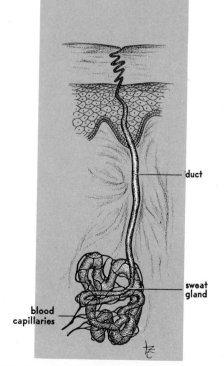

Fig. 6.2   Diagram of a sweat gland in the skin. How does the gland obtain the materials from which to secrete sweat?

under some pressure. These substances include water, sodium chloride, a waste product from protein breakdown known as **urea,** and small amounts of potassium chloride and lactic acid. During bodily rest, sweat is secreted continuously, but the amounts are small and not usually noticeable because usually evaporation keeps pace with secretion. During vigorous exercise, or when the environment is hot and humid, the amount of secretion is greatly increased and may not evaporate as rapidly as it reaches the surface of the skin. A film of perspiration, or even drops, may then collect.

In prolonged copious sweating, considerable amounts of water and salt may be lost, as much as a quart of sweat per hour being given off in some cases. If this loss is replaced by drinking water without providing salt, a shortage of sodium and chlorine may occur in the body, resulting in severe muscle cramps. Therefore, it is wise for those indulging in sweat-producing activities to replenish their salt supplies as well as to increase their water intake, using good judgment in the amounts taken.

Body Temperature

In addition to the disposal of some wastes accumulated during metabolism, sweat helps in the maintenance of constant body temperature. The temperature of the human mouth averages about 37 degrees Centigrade, or 98.6 degrees Fahrenheit. There are individual differences in normal temperature, and in one person the temperature is normally slightly higher toward the end of the waking period than toward the end of the sleeping period. The temperature of the internal organs is approximately 100 degrees Fahrenheit. The constancy of temperature in health is maintained by the control of several factors by the nervous system.

Heat is gained by the body in the oxidation of foods. Some of the energy released in oxidation is used in muscle contraction and other chemical processes, but much of it is released as heat. The amount of heat gained depends not only on the amount of food eaten, but to a large extent on the type of food used. The unit of energy used in quantitative measurements is the **Calorie,** written with a capital letter to distinguish it from the calorie, which is one thousandth as great. A Calorie is the amount of heat energy used in raising one kilogram of water from 14.5 to 15.5 degrees Centigrade. Cellular oxidation of carbohydrates yields about four Calories per gram; of proteins slightly more; and of fats more than nine Calories per gram.

Furthermore each of these types of food has an influence on the use of stored foods, known as the specific dynamic action. Except for proteins this is small, but certain amino acids derived from food proteins seem to stimulate some liver cells to oxidize stored food substances, producing heat over and beyond what could be accounted for by the currently incoming foodstuffs. (The formation of urea in the liver is one result of extra heat production by the specific dynamic action of proteins.)

The amount of heat produced varies with the amount of work done by the body. The amount of energy required to maintain the body in a state of physical, mental, and emotional relaxation without voluntary movement or even absorption of food from the intestine is about 1400 to 1800 Calories a day. An active day involving light work may double these figures, whereas heavy muscular work may run the amount up to 5000 Calories a day.

Heat is lost by the body chiefly by radiation, convection, and conduction from the skin, and by evaporation of water through the lungs and sweat glands. Small amounts may be lost in the urine and feces, and in warming the inhaled air.

Heat loss may be controlled in several ways. The nervous system exerts an influence over the size of the blood vessels in the skin. When the environment is warm and heat loss by radiation is therefore low, the skin vessels are expanded, bringing more blood to the surface; this makes for maximum exposure of the blood and maximum heat loss. In colder environments, the skin vessels are contracted, resulting in a minimum of heat loss by radiation.

The greater quantities of sweat secretion in warm weather provide for more evaporation of water. Heat energy is necessary for the transformation of liquid water to water vapor, and body heat is dissipated by this means. If the air surrounding the body is humid, the change to water vapor is retarded, and sweat will be secreted faster than it can be evaporated. Or if nonporous clothing is worn so that water vapor cannot escape from the body, sweat will accumulate on the skin.

If the heat loss becomes greater than the heat produced by the oxidations within the body, the temperature falls slightly. Voluntary exercise may produce enough heat to restore the temperature to normal. If voluntary exercise is not used, or if it is inadequate, involuntary muscular contractions ensue. One example of involuntary muscular contractions is shivering; another is contraction of the skin muscles, producing "gooseflesh."

The body temperature has a narrow range in health. A few degrees change indicates that some condition has damaged the temperature control mechanisms. A fever may mean a toxic infection, or some other injury to the body. A few degrees drop in body temperature interferes with the efficiency of many essential enzymes. A temperature ten degrees Fahrenheit above normal completely disrupts the action of the nervous system.

KIDNEYS

Urea

When amino acids are disintegrated in the body, the waste products include water, carbon dioxide, and ammonia (NH_3). Ammonia is chemically very active, and would be a poison to the body but that it combines readily with water and carbon dioxide to form ammonium carbonate; $(NH_4)_2CO_3$. This is found wherever in the body the ammonia may be released. Ammonium carbonate is carried by the blood to the liver, where, combining with the amino acid **ornithine,** it produces another amino acid: **arginine,** releasing water and some carbon dioxide. Then the arginine, in the presence of the enzyme arginase, combines with water to produce urea ($CO(NH_2)_2$) and ornithine. Ornithine is re-used to manufacture more urea. Urea is carried by the blood throughout the body, and in the kidneys is separated from the blood by a double-filtration process.

Kidney Structure

In order to understand the double-filtration process, we shall examine first the structure of the kidneys. Just as the lung may be thought of as a tree of which the bronchus is the trunk and the most active parts are the hollow fruits at the tips of the branches, so the kidney resembles a tree with the **ureter** (Greek: urine duct) as the trunk, with a great number of branches, and with hollow fruits at the tips of the smallest twigs.

The hollow fruits at their tips are known as **Bowman's capsules,** named for William Bowman (1816–1892), an English physiologist and histologist. A small branch of the renal artery pushes in the wall of this capsule much as you might push your fist into one side of an inflated toy balloon, doubling one wall back against the opposite wall to form a double-walled boxing glove. This arterial branch ravels out into a number of loops

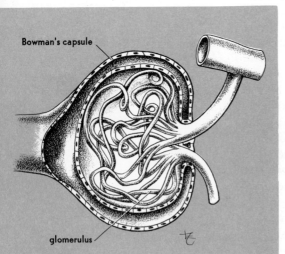

Bowman's capsule

glomerulus

Fig. 6.3 Diagram of a Malpighian corpuscle. Blood comes in from the artery at the top right, passes through the capillaries under pressure, and leaves through the vessel at the lower right, after having lost some of its liquid and soluble contents to the capsule.

distributed about the space mostly enclosed by the double-walled capsule. See Figure 6.3. This composite structure including the capsule and the tuft of loops, or **glomerulus** (Latin: little thicket), is known as a **Malpighian corpuscle,** after the Italian microscopist Marcello Malpighi (1628–1694).

The part of the twig to which the Bowman's capsule is attached is greatly twisted about the capsule; this section is known as the **proximal** (Latin: nearest) **convoluted** (Latin: rolled together) **tubule.** It is only about a quarter of the diameter of the capsule (50 microns, contrasted to 200 microns), but it may be about 15 millimeters long. In contrast to the extremely thin cells of the capsule, the proximal convoluted tubule has large, cuboidal or pyramidal cells. See Figure 6.4.

The Malpighian bodies and proximal convoluted tubules are located around the periphery of the kidney in the part known as the **cortex** (Latin: bark), distinguished from the middle of the kidney, the **medulla** (Latin: pith). The proximal tubule straightens out and passes down into the medulla as the **loop of Henle.** This section of the twig executes a horseshoe bend in the medulla and retraces its path into the cortex. This is the thinnest part of the tubule, in some places narrowing down to a diameter of 15 microns. The whole loop may be about 16 millimeters long.

Once back in the cortex, the twig goes through a second contortion, and is known as the **distal** (Latin: far) **convoluted tubule.** This is relatively a shorter section, about 5 millimeters long, which empties into a **collecting tubule** with some of its fellows. The collecting tubules run together like the boughs of a tree, until they finally converge into the ureter. One human kidney may have half a million Malpighian corpuscles and associated tubules.

Returning to the blood vessel we left breaking into loops to form the glomerulus, we find that these loops reunite into the continuation of the artery. This leaves the Malpighian corpuscle and goes to the region of the proximal and distal convoluted tubules, where it breaks up into capillaries. These capillaries deploy along the tubule walls, and then reunite into tributaries of the renal vein.

Careful observation has shown that the diameter of the artery at the entrance to the glomerulus is about twice the diameter at the outlet of the glomerulus; hence the area of the opening is about four times the area at the exit. This

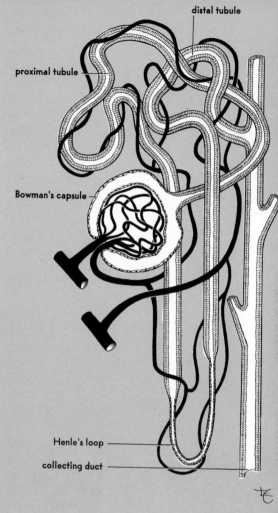

distal tubule

proximal tubule

Bowman's capsule

Henle's loop

collecting duct

Fig. 6.4 Diagram of a single kidney tubule. The solution squeezed out of the glomerulus into the capsule passes through the tubule, and some products are withdrawn and restored to the blood.

TABLE 6.1 **132** CHAPTER 6

COMPOSITION OF HUMAN URINE

Average daily excretion in grams

Water	1200.0
Urea	30.0
Uric acid	0.7
Hippuric acid	0.7
Ammonia	0.7
Amino acids	0.2
Creatinine	1.2
Sodium	4.0
Potassium	2.0
Calcium	0.2
Magnesium	0.15
Chlorine	7.2
Phosphate	3.2
Sulfate	2.2
Other solids	7.55

means that the blood passing through the glomerulus is under considerable pressure, since more blood enters than can leave. The Malpighian corpuscle then acts as a filter, the water and some of the dissolved substances diffusing out of the blood plasma through the thin walls of the blood vessels and capsule into the kidney tubule.

Kidney Physiology

Since the walls of the glomerulus and capsule are so thin, their cells act as membranes rather than as secretory cells. The protein fractions in the plasma have such large molecules that they do not filter into the tubule, but the particles of inorganic salts, sugar, urea, and creatinine are small enough to diffuse into the cavity of Bowman's capsule and from there are passed into the proximal convoluted tubule. ✓ The proximal convoluted tubule cells are very much larger than those of the capsule, and actively secrete selected substances from the tubule back into the blood, and from the blood into the tubule. Those returned to the blood by the tubule include all of the glucose, nearly all of the water and inorganic salts, and some of the urea.

Most of this is accomplished by the proximal tubule, although the distal tubule helps in reabsorbing water, and sodium chloride and bicarbonate. Contributed to the contents of the tubule by the cells in its wall are ammonia and **hippuric acid,** both products of the breakdown of amino acids. The highly concentrated urine resulting from this tubular secretory exchange contains most of the urea filtered out at the glomerulus, all of the creatinine, and small amounts of water and inorganic salts. See Table 6.1.

Urinary Bladder

This urine passes through the collecting tubules into the ureter, and is carried down into a temporary storage depot, the **urinary bladder.** See Figure 6.5.

The two ureters enter the urinary bladder near its base and pass through the bladder wall on a long slant. See Figure 6.6. The urine traveling down the ureter from kidney to bladder is propelled by peristaltic contractions of the ureter wall. The part of the ureter passing through the bladder wall opens when the wave gets to it.

After the urinary bladder has accumulated about 250 to 300 cc. of fluid, a feeling of fullness occurs, inducing an urge to relieve the pressure. In adults, emptying the bladder is under voluntary control, and the urine is passed from the bladder through a duct, the **urethra,** to the outside of

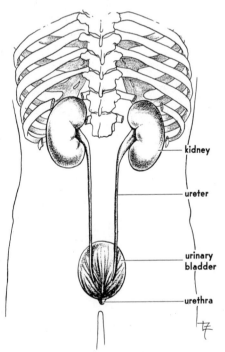

kidney

ureter

urinary bladder

urethra

Fig. 6.5 Human excretory system viewed from the back.

the body. As the bladder walls begin to contract and increase the pressure on the urine, the ureter walls within the bladder wall are pressed together, and the sphincter at the entrance into the urethra is relaxed. This allows the bladder to empty through the urethra rather than into the ureters. After urination, the bladder wall relaxes, the sphincter closes, and the ureter passageways into the bladder may reopen. In this way excretion by the kidneys is continuous, but release of the urine from the body may be postponed until a convenient time.

Urethra

The urethra in a woman is short and opens at the surface by a small orifice between folds of skin known as the **labia.** In a man the urethra is much longer, and traverses the **penis.** More about these structures will be described in Chapter 9.

Fig. 6.6   Diagram of the entrance of a ureter into the urinary bladder. How does this act as a valve preventing backflow?

SUMMARY

Excretion is the disposal of the waste products from metabolic activity of the body. Bile pigments resulting from the breakdown of red corpuscles pass into the intestine, and are carried out of the body in the feces. Carbon dioxide and water leave the body through the respiratory tract. Water, urea, lactic acid, sodium chloride, and potassium chloride are withdrawn from blood by sweat glands and excreted onto the surface of the skin. The kidneys remove water, urea, salts, and other substances from the blood and excrete it through the ureters, urinary bladder, and urethra.

The skin has an epidermis of epithelial cells and a dermis of connective tissue. The outer cells of the epidermis protect the underlying tissues from several kinds of damage. They are replaced as they are rubbed off and lost.

The temperature of the human body is relatively constant in health, with slight normal variations. This constancy is a balance between the heat gained by oxidation of foods and by the specific dynamic action of foods and the heat lost by radiation and by evaporation of water from the surfaces of the body. The balance is maintained by nervous control of the size of blood vessels in the skin, of sweat secretion, and of muscular contraction.

Ammonia is a waste product of amino acid disintegration. It is combined with water and carbon dioxide, forming ammonium carbonate. The ammonium carbonate is carried to the liver by the blood and is there transformed into urea. Urea is carried by the blood to the kidneys, where it is filtered out of the blood, together with water, salts, sugar, and creatinine. The kidney tubules secrete the sugar, most of the water and salts, and some urea back into the blood. The tubules also secrete ammonia and hippuric acid into the urine. The urine from the kidney tubules passes into the ureter and is carried to the urinary bladder, where it is temporarily stored. Emptying of the bladder forces the urine out through the urethra.

In the last few chapters we have seen how the body obtains the fuel and supplies for its metabolic processes, how these are distributed to the parts of the body needing them, and how waste materials are excreted. In the first two chapters we studied the skeletal and muscular systems upon which the movements of the body depend.

In the next two chapters will be described ways in which these metabolic and voluntary processes are controlled both consciously and unconsciously.

REVIEW QUESTIONS

1. What processes are included in the term "excretion"?
2. Describe the structure of the skin.
3. How do sweat glands produce sweat? How do they dispose of it?
4. How is the temperature of a healthy human maintained constant?
5. Describe the formation of urea.
6. Describe the structure of a kidney tubule.
7. How do substances get from the blood to the cavity of a kidney tubule?
8. What prevents the loss of sugar through the kidneys in normal humans?
9. Describe the structure and action of the urinary bladder.

GENERAL QUESTIONS

1. What creates the pressure which forces sweat to the skin surface?
2. What dangers might be involved in using preparations advertised to prevent perspiration? How would such preparations work?
3. What advantage does a human gain from constant body temperature?
4. Account for the redness of sunburn.
5. If you drew a kidney tubule to scale, magnifying it one hundred times, how large a paper and how fine a pencil point would you need?
6. What can a physician tell about conditions in a human body by a chemical analysis of the urine?
7. What would be the requirements of an artificial kidney to replace the real ones during a surgical operation? Can you devise one to meet these specifications?
8. Do all methods of excretion in the body involve water?

The Nervous System

NERVOUS SYSTEM

The muscular movements of the body and the processes of digestion, respiration, circulation, and excretion are all affected by nerve impulses which pass through the nervous system. Branches of the nervous system reach almost every part of the body, from which they receive impulses and to which they carry impulses. The result of this activity is the coordination of processes in the body in adaptation to its environment. The nervous system is associated with such phenomena as consciousness, learning, memory, judgment, and volition.

For convenience in description, the nervous system may be divided into four parts: the central nervous system, the peripheral nervous system, the autonomic nervous system, and the sense organs. The central nervous system includes the **spinal cord,** running through the neural canals of the vertebrae; its enlargement, the **brain,** within the skull; and a series of paired masses near the spinal cord, the **spinal ganglia.** The peripheral nervous system consists of **nerves** running between the central nervous system and various other parts of the body. The autonomic nervous system is made up of another series of paired masses, the **autonomic ganglia,** occurring in the head, neck, and trunk, and the nerves associated with these ganglia. The sense organs are specialized structures such as the taste buds previously described which translate physical or chemical stimuli into nerve impulses.

Neuroglia

The cells making up the nervous system vary tremendously in shape and size, but are constructed along one of two fundamental plans. The **neuroglia** (Greek: nerve glue) **cells** (Fig. 7.1) support the system as a specialized connective tissue, and act as an insulation for the nerve cells, preventing the leakage of an impulse from its proper pathway.

Nerve Cells

The **nerve cells** (Fig. 7.2) have a central portion, the **cell body,** containing the nucleus and some cytoplasm, and two

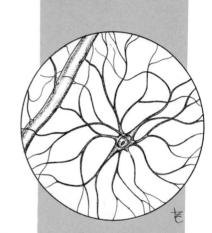

Fig. 7.1 Neuroglia cell. Some of its processes spread out on a small blood vessel. The neuroglia cell is found in the central nervous system, where it serves as a support.

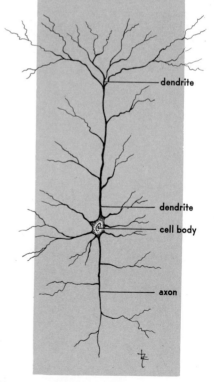

dendrite

dendrite

cell body

axon

Fig. 7.2 Shape of a nerve cell. Impulses pass through from dendrites to axon.

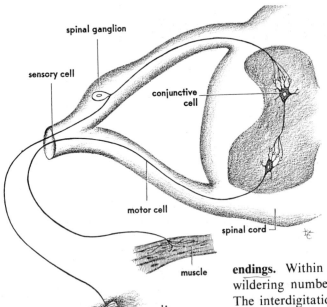

spinal ganglion

sensory cell

conjunctive cell

motor cell

spinal cord

muscle

skin

Fig. 7.3 Reflex arc, showing the connections among the three types of nerve cells. An impulse may start in the skin, pass through a sensory cell, a conjunctive cell, and a motor cell to a muscle.

kinds of cytoplasmic processes, the **dendrites** (Greek: treelike) and the **axon** (Greek: axis). One or more dendrites may be present, but usually only one axon.

The cell bodies are confined to the central nervous system and the autonomic ganglia, but the dendrites and axons extend through the peripheral nerves as well as through the central nervous system. Dendrites convey impulses toward the cell body, and the axon carries impulses away from the cell body. At the ends of the dendrites and axons farthest from the cell body the protoplasmic branches are highly divided into a multitude of tiny branchlets, the **nerve endings.** Within the central nervous system are a bewildering number of associations of these nerve endings. The interdigitation of axon ending fibers of one cell with dendrite ending fibers of another is called a **synapse.** Nerve cells are distinguished by the relation of their synapses:

A **sensory nerve cell** has its dendrite ending in a sense organ, and its axon ending in synapse with another nerve cell. A **conjunctive nerve cell** has its dendrite ending in synapse with an axon and its axon ending in synapse with a dendrite. A **motor nerve cell** has its dendrite ending in synapse with an axon, and its axon ending in a muscle, or a gland, or some other nonnervous structure. See Figure 7.3.

Nerve Impulse

The transmission of nerve impulses is one of the most fascinating unsolved problems in present-day animal physiology. A considerable amount of evidence has been accumulated to support each of two explanations, one electrical and one chemical. According to the electrical theory, a resting nerve cell has within its membrane a surplus of negative electric charges, and just outside the membrane a surplus of positive electric charges. The intact membrane prevents neutralization of these. This state of affairs was produced at the expense of a small amount of energy, provided by oxidizing some food such as glycogen. If the ending of a dendrite is subjected to some physical or chemical change in its environment, called a **stimulus,** it responds by an increase in the permeability of its membrane at the stimulated point. If the stimulation is so strong as to increase the permeability enough for the positive and negative charges to reach each other and establish a small area of neutrality, the impulse is on its way.

This area of neutrality is itself a stimulus sufficient to increase the permeability of the membrane adjacent to it, and the area of neutrality moves along the dendrite.

The originally stimulated area meanwhile restores its previous condition, consolidating its membrane, and re-establishing the opposing layers of positive and negative charges.

But the area of neutrality moves along the nerve cell as a spark moves along a fuse, except that in the case of a nerve the area over which it has passed is reconstituted into a prepared pathway. The speed of the passage of these impulses varies considerably, but in some human nerves it may be as fast as 100 meters per second. The reconstitution of the membrane and its inner and outer coats of electric charges may take only one thousandth of a second. See Figure 7.4.

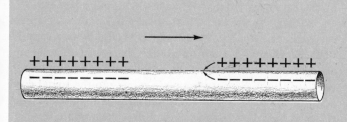

Fig. 7.4   Passage of a nerve impulse along a nerve cell — electrical theory. Normally, the nerve cell has negative charges inside and positive charges outside. As the impulse travels along, the increased permeability of the separating membrane allows the charges to neutralize each other; and this in turn makes the adjacent strip of membrane more permeable for the instant, allowing more neutralization. As the impulse passes along, the membrane behind it is reduced in permeability, and the separation of charges is re-established.

Those who believe in the electrical theory of nerve conduction alone account for the passage of a nerve impulse over a synapse by supposing that when the wave of neutrality reaches the axon ending, that point will be electrically negative to the outer coating of the adjacent dendrite ending, and this circumstance will cause an increase in permeability in that dendrite, initiating the passage of the impulse along the second nerve cell.

Studies made on the synapses in autonomic ganglia show that when a nerve impulse reaches such a synapse, a chemical substance called **acetylcholine** is released. Advocates of the chemical theory of nerve transmission believe that this conveys the impulse across the synapse and to the dendrite of the next nerve cell. Further work shows some evidence that acetylcholine also mediates the transmission of the impulse from an axon ending to a muscle. Indeed, there are enthusiasts who would like to extend this chemical explana-

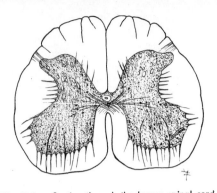

Fig. 7.5 Section through the human spinal cord. The gray matter in the middle has cell bodies; the white matter around the outside has axons. The axons of sensory nerve cells enter the cord on the upper (dorsal) margins.

tion to all phases of impulse transmission in the nervous system. Surely both electrical and chemical phenomena are involved, and a better understanding of their exact roles will come from further investigation.

THE CENTRAL NERVOUS SYSTEM

Spinal Cord

More is known about the specific pathways of particular impulses through the human nervous system than about the fundamental nature of the impulse. If a transverse section is cut through the spinal cord, the cut surface will look something like Figure 7.5. The butterfly-shaped central area, called the **gray matter,** contains cell bodies, dendrites, and axons. The peripheral area, or **white matter,** is made of columns of axons. The whiteness is the color of the fatty sheaths insulating the individual axons.

At the dorsolateral corners of the spinal cord are the paired spinal ganglia. Like the spinal cord, these are located inside the neural canal of the vertebrae. The autonomic ganglia are outside the vertebrae, but near them.

Connected with the spinal cord are 31 pairs of **spinal nerves.** Each spinal nerve fastens to the cord by two strands, a **dorsal root** and a **ventral root.** The spinal ganglia are expansions part way along the dorsal roots, one ganglion to each such root. Sensory impulses coming to the spinal cord pass through the dorsal root, and motor impulses leaving the spinal cord go out the ventral root. See Figure 7.6.

Fig. 7.6 Diagram of spinal nerve roots. How many separate nerve cells are involved in tracing the impulse shown?

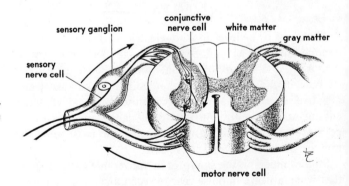

sensory ganglion

conjunctive nerve cell

white matter

gray matter

sensory nerve cell

motor nerve cell

Brain

At its upper end, the spinal cord enlarges into the brain (Fig. 7.7). The part of the brain connected to the spinal cord is the **medulla oblongata.** Its cells are associated with many of the involuntary controls of the body, such as respiration, digestion, circulation, and excretion.

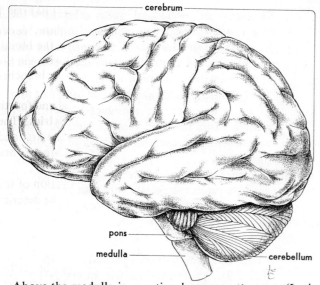

cerebrum

pons
medulla
cerebellum

Fig. 7.7 Lateral view of the human brain, left side.

Above the medulla is a section known as the **pons** (Latin: bridge) **Varolii,** named for the Italian anatomist Costanzo Varolio (1543–1575). This functions in a way similar to the medulla.

Dorsal to the pons Varolii is the large **cerebellum.** This has to do with coordination of muscular effort and with maintenance of tonus.

Above the pons and cerebellum is the **midbrain,** a relay station somewhat like a telephone switchboard center. It is concerned with many impulses coming from the eyes and ears.

Still farther forward is the **diencephalon,** concerned with emotions and with instinctive action patterns, and relaying impulses to and from the cerebrum.

Overtopping all is the **cerebrum** (Latin: brain), by far the largest part of the brain. This is the seat of conscious sensation and voluntary action.

The gray matter in the center of the spinal cord passes up through the brain, spreading out on the surface of the cerebrum and cerebellum, forming the **cortex** of these two parts of the brain.

The slender canal running through the center of the spinal cord expands into larger cavities in the medulla (**fourth ventricle**), the diencephalon (**third ventricle**), and the left and right portions of the cerebrum (**first** and **second ventricles**). These ventricles and the spinal canal contain a lymphlike liquid known as **cerebrospinal fluid.** This helps in nourishing the central nervous system.

The dorsal roof of the fourth ventricle is very thin, and well supplied by branches of the vertebral arteries.

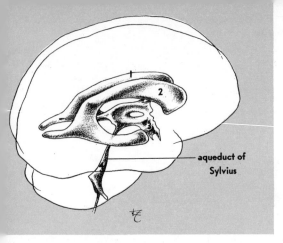

Fig. 7.8 Ventricles of the human brain. The foramina of Monro are the connections between the third ventricle and the first and second ventricles.

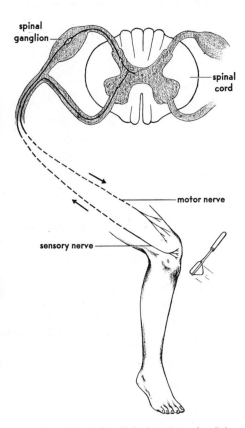

Fig. 7.9 Knee reflex. If the knee is struck a light blow, a nerve impulse passes through a dendrite to a cell body in a spinal ganglion and through an axon from there to the spinal cord. Here, after passing through one or more other nerve cells, the impulse travels out an axon to the leg muscles which respond to the impulse by contracting. What can a doctor learn by observing a knee reflex?

Exchanges of useful and waste substances occur here between the cerebrospinal fluid and the blood. A similar but smaller area of exchange occurs in the roof of the third ventricle, which receives branches from the internal carotid arteries.

The slender passageway between third and fourth ventricles is called the **aqueduct of Sylvius.** The openings from the third ventricle into the first and second ventricles are the **foramina of Monro.** See Figure 7.8.

Further details of the structure and action of the central nervous system will come out in the description of pathways of nervous conduction.

Reflex

The simplest sort of pathway is the reflex (Fig. 7.9). A stretched muscle responds by contracting. This is the mechanism of the knee reflex often tested by physicians. A seated person crosses his legs, and the physician strikes the exposed knee with a hammer. The knee extensor muscles contract. We may trace this reaction through the nervous system:

A dendrite ending in the tendon of the extensor muscle is stimulated by the stretching of the tendon caused by the blow of the hammer. A nerve impulse is initiated, and travels up the dendrite toward the spinal cord. The dendrite is part of a spinal nerve to the leg. At the spinal column the impulse passes into the dorsal root, and to a cell body in the spinal ganglion on that root. The impulse leaves the cell body through an axon, continues along the dorsal root, and into the gray matter of the spinal cord. Here it passes through a synapse between the axon and the dendrite of a conjunctive nerve cell. Then it goes through the conjunctive nerve cell to a synapse with the dendrite of a motor nerve cell. The cell body of this cell is in the ventral part of the gray matter of the spinal cord; the impulse leaves the cord through the axon along the ventral root, passes down the spinal nerve to the extensor muscle, and stimulates it to contract.

This pathway introduces characteristics of nerve conduction found in all the pathways described in this chapter. In passing through any nerve cell, an impulse enters the dendrite, goes through the cell body, and leaves by way of the axon. The nerve impulse is initiated in a sensory cell.

It is terminated in a motor cell. But conjunctive cells may be interposed between these two. An impulse coming from the body to the spinal cord passes through a cell body in a spinal ganglion. Impulses going from the spinal cord to the body pass through the ventral root of a spinal nerve, with the appropriate cell body located in the spinal cord.

Spinal Tracts

If the pathway of the nerve impulse involves two different levels of the spinal cord, the impulse travels in the white matter. The impulse may come in through a dendrite, pass through a cell body in the spinal ganglion, and enter the gray matter of the spinal cord by way of an axon. This axon has a synapse with the dendrite of a conjunctive cell. The impulse passes through this dendrite, through the cell body and the axon, which carries it into the white matter close to the edge of the gray matter, and either up or down. After reaching the appropriate level of the spinal cord, the conjunctive cell axon carries the impulse into the gray matter to a synapse with the dendrite of a motor nerve cell. The axon of this cell carries the impulse along the ventral root of a spinal nerve to its destination. The band of white matter immediately adjacent to the gray matter contains axons from one level of the spinal cord to another. It may be called the **intersegmental tract**. See Figure 7.10.

The remainder of the white matter of the spinal cord is made up of axons connecting various levels of the spinal cord with the brain. In general, the more dorsal tracts carry sensory impulses to the brain, and the more ventral tracts carry motor impulses from the brain, although there is some overlapping of these areas. In the following discussion, refer to Figure 7.10 for clarification of descriptions.

Of the ascending tracts carrying sensory impulses to the brain, the most dorsal is the **spinomedullary tract** between the gray matter at the entrance of the dorsal root of the spinal nerve and the midline. Axons in the spinomedullary tract carry impulses from muscles and tendons of the body to the medulla. In the medulla, the impulses are relayed to the cerebellum, or carried across to the opposite side of the brain and distributed to the diencephalon and cerebrum, so that the left sides of the diencephalon and cerebrum receive impulses from muscles and tendons on the right side of the body, and *vice versa*. In the cerebellum these impulses are concerned in the maintenance of muscle tone and in muscular coordination. In the cerebrum they provide information on the position and degree of contraction of muscles.

Fig. 7.10   Tracts in the spinal cord. The cord is shown cut across with the bundles of fibers outlined.

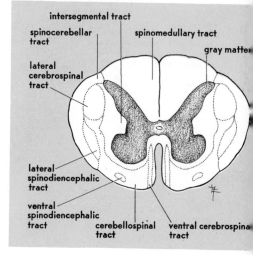

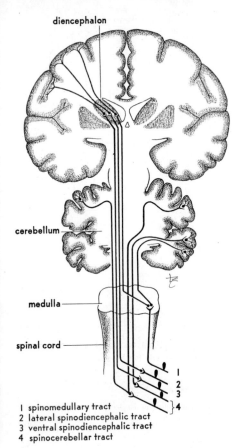

diencephalon

cerebellum

medulla

spinal cord

1 spinomedullary tract
2 lateral spinodiencephalic tract
3 ventral spinodiencephalic tract
4 spinocerebellar tract

Fig. 7.11   Sensory pathways to the brain.

On the lateral side of the spinal cord, the outermost strip is the **spinocerebellar tract.** This carries sensory impulses from muscles and tendons directly to the cerebellum without stopping off and crossing to the opposite side in the medulla.

Just internal to the spinocerebellar tract is the **lateral spinodiencephalic tract.** This carries impulses of temperature and pain sensations from the opposite side of the body, having crossed over in the gray matter of the spinal cord at the level at which they started. The impulses go to the diencephalon, from which they are relayed to the cerebrum.

In the ventral part of the spinal cord white matter is an isolated ascending bundle, the **ventral spinodiencephalic tract.** This carries impulses arising from the sense of touch on the other side of the body. These cross over in the gray matter, enter the ventral spinodiencephalic tract, and pass to the diencephalon, from which they, too, are relayed to the cerebrum. See Figure 7.11.

With some exceptions, the tracts bringing motor impulses from the brain through the spinal cord may be put into two groups in each half of the cord. The **cerebrospinal tract** occupies a large part of the lateral white matter, located between the spinocerebellar and intersegmental tracts, and dorsal to the spinodiencephalic tract. It carries voluntary motor impulses from the cerebrum to skeletal muscles. These cross from one side to the other in the lower part of the medulla, so that an impulse from the left side of the cerebrum will go to a muscle on the right side of the body. A few axons which do not cross over in the medulla pass down the ventral white matter of the spinal cord.

The **cerebellospinal tract** occupies most of the ventral part of the spinal cord white matter, medial to the ventral root of the spinal nerve. It carries impulses from the cerebellum through the midbrain, pons, and medulla to skeletal muscles of the body. Some of these fibers also run in the lateral part of the white matter, ventral to the cerebrospinal tract. Some of these cerebellospinal fibers cross over to the opposite side in the brain, and some do not. See Figure 7.12.

Cerebral Cortex

Any attempt to deal completely with current knowledge of the brain would require in itself a much larger book than this. But some of the more interesting features are worth discussing here. By means of experimental study and observations, various areas of the cerebral cortex have been found to be involved in specific pathways. The main areas are indicated in Figure 7.13.

The back half of the cerebral cortex is concerned with sensory impressions. At the extreme back, in the occipital region, is the visual area, not only providing consciousness of things seen, but also passing critical judgment on them — that is, comparing them with memories of things seen previously, weighing degrees and relationships, and making mental associations. For example, an object may be seen not only as round, white, and of a certain size, but it may be identified as a baseball.

The lower part of the lateral wing of the sensory cortex, the temporal region, is concerned with the senses of hearing, smell, and taste. These may be further narrowed down, and for each there is the same power of elaboration into association and appraisal as was found in the visual area.

The upper part of the lateral wing, the parietal region, receives impulses from the senses of touch, pain, temperature, muscle tension, and so forth. Here the area may be subdivided geographically:

The topmost portion of this area is concerned with sensations from the foot, followed as one proceeds down the

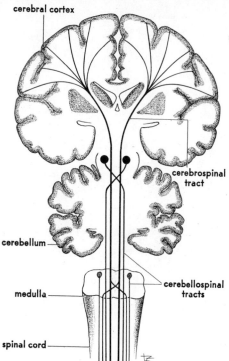

Fig. 7.12   Motor pathways from the brain.

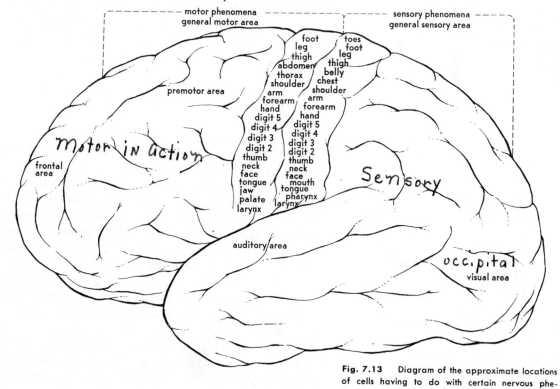

Fig. 7.13   Diagram of the approximate locations of cells having to do with certain nervous phenomena. How were these locations determined?

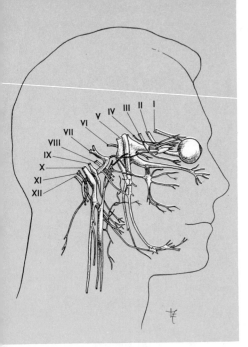

Fig. 7.14 Diagram of the distribution of cranial nerves: **I**, Olfactory nerve; **II**, Optic; **III**, Oculomotor; **IV**, Trochlear; **V**, Trigeminal; **VI**, Abducens; **VII**, Facial; **VIII**, Auditory; **IX**, Glossopharyngeal; **X**, Vagus; **XI**, Spinal accessory; **XII**, Hypoglossal. From what parts of the brain does each pair come?

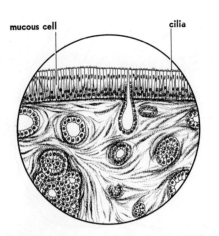

Fig. 7.15 Olfactory epithelium in the nose. How does this compare with the ordinary nasal epithelium (see Fig. 4.2)?

hill by the portions associated with sensations from the leg, thigh, abdominal region, chest, shoulder, arm, hand, neck, face, mouth, and vocal apparatus. Imagine superposed on this area of the brain a human figure hanging by its toes. This gives a rough idea of the distribution of specific sensory areas. Here again the brain cortex is able to appraise and evaluate the sensations and construct analytical judgments.

The front half of the brain is primarily involved in voluntary motor action. Immediately in front of the upper lateral sensory area is the **motor area.** This sends impulses to skeletal muscles of the body. Here again the subdivisions may be represented by the human figure hanging by its toes, and the areas are parallel and comparable to the sensory ones, ranging from the foot at the top to the vocal apparatus at the bottom.

In front of the motor area is the **premotor area,** concerned with more complicated movements which involve combinations of muscles concerned in a reaction such as turning the body toward one side or swallowing food.

The **frontal association area** includes the remainder of the cerebral cortex, in front of the premotor area. This is concerned with the most complex associations made by the brain — understanding of abstract ideas and concepts, formation of judgments as to action patterns, social behavior, moral sense, and so forth. Localization here is so difficult that very little general agreement has been reached on these details.

THE PERIPHERAL NERVOUS SYSTEM

Cranial Nerves

The brain has connected to it twelve pairs of nerves (Fig. 7.14). These are more highly differentiated than the spinal nerves, correlated with the higher degree of specialization of the brain contrasted with the spinal cord. Some of these brain, or cranial, nerves carry only sensory impulses, some carry only motor impulses, and some carry both.

The first pair of cranial nerves are the **olfactory nerves.** These nerves start in the olfactory epithelium of the nose, a specialized area of the nasal cavity. See Figure 7.15. Scattered among the tall, supporting epithelial cells of the olfactory area are nerve cells. The dendrites of these cells are exposed at the surface, terminating in a half dozen or so long, hairlike, protoplasmic processes.

Glands in the epithelium coat the lining with a watery, lymphlike secretion in which dissolve many substances which enter the nose. If an exposed dendrite is sensitive to one of these substances, a nerve impulse is initiated. This impulse travels through the dendrite and the cell body in the epithelium, and along the axon, which is part of the olfactory nerve. The olfactory nerve leads to a special projection of the cerebrum, the **olfactory bulb.** From the olfactory bulb another set of nerve cells carries olfactory impulses to the temporal area of the cerebrum.

The olfactory nerves are the only ones directly exposed to the outside world; they make an entryway by which the poliomyelitis virus may reach the central nervous system.

What are usually listed as the second pair of cranial nerves, the **optic nerves,** are in reality part of the white matter of the brain. They carry impulses from the **retinas** (Latin for nets) of the eyes. The retinas themselves are parts of the brain. During the early development of each human the two prospective retinas pull out from the brain, retaining connection by stalks, and approach the surface of the face, later being incorporated into the eyeballs. Within each retina are three layers of nerve cells. The layer at the back of the retina has dendrites, called rods and cones, which are especially sensitive to light. Their activity will be discussed later in this chapter. The nerve impulses they produce upon stimulation by light pass through their cell bodies and out along axons to the secondary nerve cells, which in turn transmit them to tertiary nerve cells still in the retina. See Figure 7.16.

It is axons of the tertiary nerve cells which form the tract usually called the optic nerve. The two optic nerves reach the brain at the bottom of the diencephalon. Here there is a partial crossover of fibers, so that impulses coming from the medial halves of the two retinas cross over to the opposite side, whereas the impulses from the lateral halves stay on the same side. This crossover site is called the **optic chiasma** (Greek: X-mark).

A few of the impulses passing through the chiasma go to the upper part of the midbrain, from which emanate the impulses which adjust the eye in response to light stimuli. For example, the size of the pupil is regulated in relation to the intensity of light. But most of the impulses go to the diencephalon, cross a synapse into a quaternary set of nerve cells, which, in turn, send the impulses to the visual area of the cerebral cortex.

The impulses coming from different parts of the retina are still distinct, so that, for example, a certain locus on the left upper part of the visual area of the cerebrum receives impulses which come from the lateral upper part of the left retina and the medial upper part of the right retina (crossed

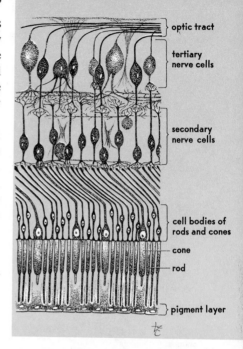

optic tract

tertiary
nerve cells

secondary
nerve cells

cell bodies of
rods and cones

cone

rod

pigment layer

Fig. 7.16   Section through the human retina. The top of drawing is toward the front of the eye. Light passes through the retina to the rods and cones at the back, and nerve impulses pass forward through the retina to the optic tract.

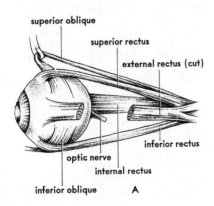

superior oblique

superior rectus

external rectus (cut)

inferior rectus

optic nerve

internal rectus

inferior oblique   **A**

in the chiasma), both of which were stimulated by light from the same object below and to the right of the eyes.

The third pair of cranial nerves is the **oculomotor** pair. Each oculomotor nerve consists of axons carrying impulses from the lower part of the midbrain to muscles which move the eyeball on the same side. Very few oculomotor fibers cross over in the brain.

There are six muscles which may move each eyeball: the four recti muscles and the two oblique muscles (Fig. 7.17).

Fig. 7.17   Muscles of the eyeball: **A,** Side view; **B,** From the back.

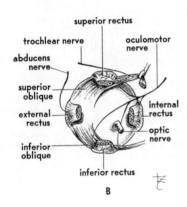

superior rectus

trochlear nerve   oculomotor nerve

abducens nerve

superior oblique

external rectus

inferior oblique

internal rectus

optic nerve

inferior rectus

B

The four recti muscles originate in the back of the orbit on the sphenoid bone immediately surrounding the passage of the optic nerve. The **superior rectus muscle** inserts on the top of the eyeball; when it contracts, it tilts the front of the eyeball up. It is opposed by the **inferior rectus muscle,** attached to the bottom of the eyeball, and acting to tilt the eyeball down. The **internal rectus muscle** inserts on the medial border of the eyeball; when it contracts, it pulls the front of the eye toward the nose; if both internal recti contract at once, the two eyes focus on something close to the head. The **external rectus muscle** inserts on the lateral border of the eyeball, and acts to pull the eye away from the nose. In looking toward the left, you contract the left external rectus and the right internal rectus muscles.

The two oblique muscles are the superior and inferior oblique muscles. The **superior oblique muscle** originates at the same general place as the superior rectus muscle at the back of the eye socket, but ends in a tendon near the inner margin of the socket. This tendon passes through a little cartilaginous ring, or pulley, and turns laterally to fasten to the eyeball at about the same place as does the superior rectus. Contraction of the superior oblique muscle tends to rotate the top of the eye toward the nose. The **inferior oblique muscle** originates in the maxilla in the inner wall of the orbit, near the lacrimal bone, and curves under the eyeball to fasten on the outer edge above the attachment of the external rectus muscle. Contraction of the inferior oblique muscle rotates the bottom of the eye inward.

The oculomotor nerve supplies four of these muscles; these are the superior, internal, and inferior recti, and the inferior oblique.

The fourth pair of cranial nerves is the pair of **trochlear nerves.** *Trochlea* is the Greek word for pulley. Impulses carried by these nerves start in the midbrain just behind the centers for the oculomotor nerve, pass up the lateral and back walls of the midbrain, cross to the opposite side, and run forward to the superior oblique muscles.

The fifth pair of cranial nerves is the **trigeminal** pair. Each trigeminal nerve carries both sensory and motor impulses. The sensory impulses from the skin of the face and front part of the scalp and from the linings of the front parts of the mouth and nasal cavities pass through the trigeminal nerve to the pons Varolii, from which they deploy to cell bodies in the pons, the medulla, and even the upper end of the spinal cord. Then other cells carry the impulses from there to the diencephalon, from where they are transmitted by yet other nerve cells to the sensory part of the cerebral cortex.

The trigeminal nerve also carries motor impulses from the pons to the lacrimal gland and to the levator muscles of the lower jaw, as well as the lower belly of the digastric muscle. Sensory impulses from these muscles return through the trigeminal nerve and pons to the midbrain.

The sixth pair of cranial nerves is the **abducens** pair. *Abducens* is Latin for drawing away from. Each abducens nerve connects a center in the pons Varolii through the lower end of the pons to the external rectus muscle of the eye. It carries only motor impulses.

The seventh pair of cranial nerves is the **facial** pair. These nerves carry both sensory and motor impulses. Sensory impulses from the front two thirds of the tongue, from the back part of the mouth and nose cavities, and from the deeper muscles of the face and head pass through the facial nerves to the lower end of the pons. Motor impulses go from the pons through the facial nerve to most of the muscles of the head and face except those of the eye and the jaw levators. The facial nerve supplies the upper belly of the digastric muscle. It also sends impulses to the submaxillary and sublingual glands.

The eighth pair of cranial nerves is the **auditory** pair. This carries sensory impulses from the ear to the anterior part of the medulla, from which they are distributed to the spinal cord, cerebellum, midbrain, diencephalon, and hearing area of the cerebral cortex. The fibers associated with hearing cross over in the medulla.

The ninth pair of cranial nerves is the **glossopharyngeal** pair. The glossopharyngeal nerves carry both sensory and motor impulses. The sensory impulses come from the back third of the tongue and from the pharynx, and go to the medulla. From here the impulses go through a synapse, cross to the opposite side, and pass to the diencephalon, from which they are relayed to the taste and other areas of the cerebral cortex. Motor impulses leave the medulla and go through the glossopharyngeal nerves to the parotid gland and one pair of pharyngeal muscles.

The tenth pair of cranial nerves is the **vagus** pair. *Vagus* is Latin for wandering. The vagus nerves, connected with the medulla, carry both sensory and motor impulses. The vagus nerve connects to the pharynx, larynx, lungs, heart, esophagus, stomach, small intestine, and gall bladder. It carries impulses concerned with many of the involuntary vital metabolic actions of these organs.

The eleventh pair of cranial nerves is the **spinal accessory** pair. It carries motor impulses from the medulla and the spinal cord to some of the muscles of the neck and shoulder.

The twelfth pair of cranial nerves is the **hypoglossal** pair. It carries motor impulses from the medulla to the tongue muscles. See Table 7.1.

TABLE 7.1

HUMAN CRANIAL NERVES

SERIAL NUMBER	NAME	BRAIN CONNECTION	DISTRIBUTION	NATURE OF FIBERS
1	Olfactory	Olfactory bulb	Olfactory epithelium	Sensory
2	Optic	Diencephalon	Retina	Sensory
3	Oculomotor	Midbrain	Four eye muscles	Motor
4	Trochlear	Midbrain	Superior oblique muscle	Motor
5	Trigeminal	Pons Varolii	Face, scalp, mouth, nose Lacrimal gland, jaw muscles	Sensory Motor
6	Abducens	Pons Varolii	External rectus muscle	Motor
7	Facial	Pons Varolii	Tongue, mouth, nose Head muscles, two pairs of salivary glands	Sensory Motor
8	Auditory	Medulla	Ear	Sensory
9	Glossopharyngeal	Medulla	Tongue, pharynx Parotid gland, pharyngeal muscles	Sensory Motor
10	Vagus	Medulla	Digestive, respiratory, circulatory organs	Sensory and motor
11	Spinal accessory	Medulla	Neck and shoulder muscles	Motor
12	Hypoglossal	Medulla	Tongue muscles	Motor

Spinal Nerves

The spinal nerves are much alike. Each carries both sensory and motor impulses, the sensory traveling over the dorsal root to the spinal cord, and the motor leaving the cord by way of the ventral root. The nerves deploy through the neck and trunk. Those to the limbs run together to form interwoven **plexuses** which give off branches to the muscles of the arms and legs. They also supply the skin of the limbs.

THE AUTONOMIC NERVOUS SYSTEM

The word *autonomic* comes from the Greek for self-governing. In spite of this name, the autonomic nervous system is not independent of the central nervous system, but serves as an instrument through which the central nervous system acts upon visceral and cardiac muscles and glands, all of which are involuntary. The chief autonomic ganglia are connected to each other by a cable of fibers on each side of the vertebral column. A motor impulse to involuntary muscle or gland leaves the spinal cord through the ventral root of the spinal nerve, and passes to an autonomic ganglion, where there is a synapse with a nerve cell whose dendrite and cell body are in the ganglion, and whose axon goes to the destination of the impulse. This ganglion may be one of the chain, or one in or near the organ which is the destination of the impulse. See Figure 7.18.

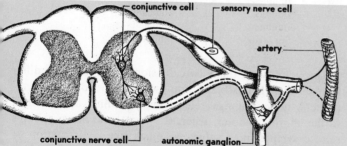

Fig. 7.18 Autonomic nerve pathway. The impulse may start in a sensory nerve cell whose dendrite is distributed in some structure such as an artery. The sensory cell leads into the spinal cord through the spinal ganglion. The impulse passes through one (or more) conjunctive cell, and into a cell whose axon leaves the spinal cord and passes to the autonomic ganglion. Here there is a synapse with the motor nerve cell, which carries the impulse to some structure such as the artery musculature. How many cells are involved in this circuit?

The autonomic system is divisible physiologically into the **sympathetic system** and the **parasympathetic system.** The ganglia of the sympathetic system are located in the thorax and upper abdomen, while the parasympathetic ganglia are in the head, neck, and sacral region. Any auto-nomically-controlled structure in the body usually receives nerves from both divisions of the autonomic system, the stimuli from the sympathetic system bringing about one response, and those from the parasympathetic system the opposite response. For example, the sympathetic stimuli speed up the heartbeat, dilate the pupil of the eye and the bronchi, and inhibit gastric secretion. The parasympathetic stimuli slow down heartbeat, constrict the pupil of the eye and the bronchi, and increase gastric secretion. Sympathetic stimuli cause dilation of blood vessels in muscles, but constriction of blood vessels in the skin; parasympathetic stimuli do the reverse. Sympathetic stimuli slow down movements of the small and large intestines and urinary bladder, whereas the parasympathetic ganglia convey impulses which accelerate these movements. See Table 7.2.

TABLE 7.2

Activities of the Human Autonomic System

	ACTION OF THE SYMPATHETIC SYSTEM	ACTION OF THE PARA-SYMPATHETIC SYSTEM
Eye:		
Pupil	Dilates	Constricts
Ciliary muscles	Relaxes	Contracts
Eyelids	Retracts	
Blood vessels in:		
Cerebrum	Constricts	Dilates
Skin	Constricts	Dilates
Salivary glands	Constricts	Dilates
Muscles	Dilates	Constricts
Coronary vessels	Dilates	Constricts
Heart	Accelerates	Slows down
Sweat glands	Stimulates	
Trachea and bronchi	Dilates	Constricts
Intestinal motility	Inhibits	Stimulates
Stomach secretion of enzymes	Inhibits	Stimulates
Evacuation of rectum	Inhibits	Stimulates
Evacuation of bladder	Inhibits	Stimulates
Adrenal secretion (medulla)	Stimulates	Inhibits

The activity of these two divisions is thought to differ also in the chemistry of impulse transmission. Parasympathetic nerve endings release acetylcholine, as described earlier in this chapter, whereas sympathetic nerve endings release **sympathin,** a substance much like the secretion of the adrenal medulla in its biological characteristics. More will be found on this subject in the next chapter.

In the brain the lower part of the diencephalon, the **hypothalamus,** is the directing center of the autonomic system. The front of the hypothalamus is associated with the parasympathetic system, the back part with the sympathetic system. Complex integrations of autonomic behavior occur in the hypothalamus, especially those associated with water, carbohydrate, and fat metabolisms, with heat regulation, with the reproductive system, and with emotional reactions. Control of the sleep cycle has been assigned to the hypothalamus by some workers. It may be that the back part of the hypothalamus predisposes to waking and the front part to sleep.

THE SENSES AND SENSE ORGANS

The Senses

Traditionally, humans have been said to be equipped with five senses. Analysis has increased this number by reinterpretation, but there are still many unsettled problems with respect to the origin and pathways of sensory impulses. For our discussion we shall include twelve senses.

Touch

The **sense of touch** results from the stimulation of specialized nerve endings, or touch organs, just beneath the epidermis or at the base of hairs. Stimulation results from changes in mechanical pressure on these touch organs because of bending of the skin or hair by the object touched. These organs are not uniformly distributed, being more common and more sensitive on the lips, tongue, and fingertips than on the thigh, abdomen, or middle of the back.

Pain

The **sense of pain** is the most widespread of the twelve senses. Nerve endings in most parts of the body are capable of initiating the pain impulse. Pain endings occur in the skin, in muscles and tendons, and in visceral organs. These endings may be stimulated by a wide variety of physical and chemical forces, and do not distinguish among them. Pain endings are of great service to the body in indicating imminent or actual injury. Pain is powerful enough to override other sensations in registering on consciousness. Tickling and some itching sensations are brought about by stimuli which affect both touch and pain nerve endings simultaneously.

Warmth and Cold

The two temperature senses — **warmth** and **cold** — have distinct nerve endings and distinct organs. Both occur in the skin, but their distribution is not by any means identical. In fact, areas containing many warmth-sensitive endings often contain few cold-sensitive endings and vice versa. If a thermal stimulus is strong enough to affect both types of temperature sense organs, the resulting sensation is interpreted as hot. This may be produced by something very warm, like boiling water, or something very cold, like dry ice. The burning sensation is the same in both cases.

Kinesthesia

The muscle sense which brings to the brain information on the degree of contraction of a muscle is often referred to as the **kinesthetic** (Greek: sense of movement) **sense.** This is aroused by the effect of pressure on or deformation of specialized nerve endings in muscles, tendons, and joints brought about by muscular movement. Impulses coming into the central nervous system over these pathways are used in involuntary adjustments which relieve pressures, coordinate muscle fibers, and smooth out movements. Impulses may also reach the cerebral cortex, where they affect voluntary adjustments of muscle contraction. For examples, the knee reflex described early in this chapter involves a kinesthetic impulse starting in a tendon; adjustment of the larynx in preparation for sounding a selected pitch requires information of a kinesthetic nature from the larynx; and the judgment of the distance to an object seen with the eyes involves information about the degree of contraction of the muscles used in focusing the eyes.

Hunger

The **sense of hunger** arises when the stomach undergoes strong peristaltic contractions, although it is nearly or quite empty of food. There are reports of people having a sense of hunger even after the stomach was removed; this hunger probably arose from contractions of the empty duodenum. The feeling of appetite is different from that of hunger, and is a learned sensation, not an inborn one. It may start, at least in part, from the stomach, but contains factors dependent upon previous associations.

Thirst

The **sense of thirst** arises by stimulation of cells in the pharynx. It is due to loss of water from the cells with which the nerve endings are in contact. This water loss is due to drying of the pharyngeal lining because of decreased salivary secretion, or to decreased concentration of the water in the blood bathing those cells.

Taste

The **sense of taste** was described in Chapter 3. Its specialized nerve endings occur in the taste buds on the tongue, and are sensitive to dissolved substances which stimulate sensations of sweet, sour, bitter, and salty.

Smell

The **sense of smell** is a result of stimulation of nerves in the olfactory areas of the nose, as described earlier in this chapter. Both olfactory regions together have about the area of a one-cent stamp. The sense of smell is more varied than that of taste, with a wide variety of odors being distinguishable. Smell is also much more acute than taste, for humans can distinguish some substances in concentrations of less than one part per billion of air. At the same time, the sense of smell is very easily fatigued. People living near the stockyards or those who cook for a living are apt to be surprised at the relative keenness of the sense of smell in visitors.

Olfactory stimuli are produced by gaseous molecules dissolved in the watery solution coating the olfactory area. This area is not in the direct pathway of air going into and out of the respiratory tract during breathing, so that substances smelled must reach the olfactory area by diffusion or by eddying.

Eyes

The **sense of sight** is due to stimulation of the eyes (Fig. 7.19). The retina is the light-sensitive part of the eye, and its structure was described on page 145. It was pointed out there that the retinas and optic nerves are parts of the brain. With the retina are associated other structures which aid in focusing the light on the retina, and in controlling the path of light rays. The muscles which move the eyeball were also described previously.

The eyeball itself is almost spherical, with a diameter of about an inch. It is guarded in front by the **eyelids** and the **conjunctiva.** The conjunctiva is that part of the epidermis of the skin which covers the eyeball in front, and is continuous with the inner surface of the eyelids.

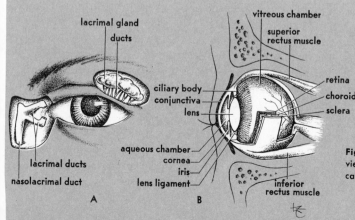

Fig. 7.19 Accessories of the human eye. A, Front view. B, Side view. In what ways is the eye like a camera? In what ways is it different?

One large and several small **lacrimal glands,** or tear glands, are associated with the lateral and upper borders of the eye, pouring a dilute, lymphlike fluid over the conjunctiva, keeping that layer moist, soft, and clean. The secretion is swept across the eye by blinking, and accumulates at the corner of the eye next to the nose, from which it is drained by a tiny **lacrimal duct** on the edge of each eyelid. These two ducts run together to form the **nasolacrimal duct,** which carries the secretion from the eye into the nose cavity. From here tears flow into the pharynx and esophagus.

Irritation of the conjunctiva and some tense emotional states stimulate the lacrimal gland to greater amounts of secretion than the lacrimal ducts can carry off. The excess wells up on the surface of the eye and spills over the lower lid onto the face as tears.

The eyeball has three layers of tissue in its wall, the outermost **sclera,** an intermediate **choroid,** and the innermost retina. The sclera is made of fibrous connective tissue; part of it is visible under the conjunctiva as the "white of the eye." The front part of the sclera bulges out somewhat and is transparent; this part is called the **cornea.**

The choroid is a much thinner connective tissue layer, carrying a wealth of blood capillaries and a heavy deposit of pigment. The front part of the choroid is visible from the outside as the **iris,** named for the Greek goddess of the rainbow.

The iris is perforated by a round hole, the **pupil.** It gets its name from the Latin for a little child because of the tiny reflection of the person looking into another's pupil. The diameter of the pupil is controlled by the contraction or relaxation of the iris. In the iris, between the outer and inner epithelial layers, is found a relatively thick connective tissue layer, supplied with blood vessels and containing a sphincter whose contraction diminishes the pupil; and behind this is a thin layer of muscle fibers arranged radially; these fibers enlarge the pupil when they contract. The inner epithelial layer, forming the back wall of the iris, is pigmented. If no pigment occurs in the connective tissue layer, the eye appears blue because of light dispersal by tiny particles. The blue color of the sky is produced similarly — light scattering by dust particles. In some people the connective tissue layer develops additional pigment, giving the eyes another color. In some babies this latter pigment may not develop until several weeks after birth. A small amount of yellowish pigment in the connective tissue layer produces green eye color. A scattering of darker pigment gives the iris a gray color. Larger amounts of dark pigment produce the brown or black iris. In albinos there is no pigmentation, and the iris appears pink because of the blood vessels in the connective tissue layer.

Control of the muscles of the iris occurs through the autonomic system. Fibers of the optic nerve carry to the midbrain impulses related to the amount of light striking the retina. These impulses, if stimulated by strong light, are routed through cells of the oculomotor nerve, which carries them through the autonomic ganglion just behind the eye, the **ciliary ganglion,** to the muscles of the iris which constrict the pupil. If only weak light enters the eye, the midbrain sends impulses through the upper thoracic part of the spinal cord to sympathetic ganglia and back to the radial muscles of the iris, which dilate the pupil.

Just behind the iris is the **crystalline lens.** The lens in the early embryo was a part of the epidermis. During early development, as the retinal process from the developing brain nears the surface of the body, an area of the epidermis pits in. This pit finally closes over, leaving the epidermis continuous, and a little hollow ball inside. The hollow ball becomes the lens by the great elongation of the cells at its back. These stretch through the cavity until they reach the front cells. See Figure 7.20.

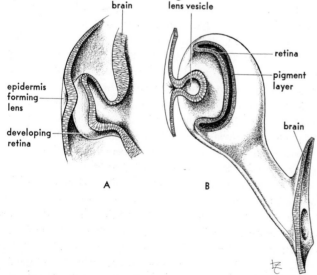

Fig. 7.20   Development of the lens: **A,** Early stage; **B,** Later stage. The lens is a specialized piece of epidermis influenced by the close approach of the part of the brain destined to form the retina. Would the lens form if the brain did not approach the epidermis?

As time goes on, the lens grows by multiplication and elongation of the cells at the sides, top, and bottom. The first elongated cells, in the center, tend to harden and fuse as they grow older, and the older the eye becomes the larger this hardened area is. Accommodation of the lens for focusing on objects at various distances depends upon its

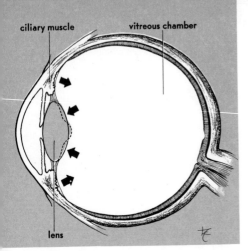

ciliary muscle   vitreous chamber

lens

Fig. 7.21 How the eye is focused. When the ciliary muscle is relaxed, the eye is focused on objects at a distance. When the ciliary muscle contracts, it exerts pressure on the vitreous humor, and this transmits the pressure to the lens. The oldest part of the lens, in the middle, is harder than the younger parts around the edge; hence, the lens is pressed in at the edges, and the center assumes a rounder form, focusing the eye on nearer objects.

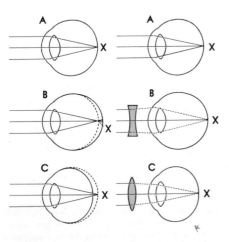

A   X   A   X

B   X   B   X

C   X   C   X

Fig. 7.22 Diagrams to show how glass lenses are used to compensate for improper focusing. A represents the normal eye in which light rays focus properly on the retina. B shows a long eyeball in which the light rays focus before they get to the retina; such a person is near-sighted; a biconcave lens spreads the light rays so that they focus on the retina. C shows a short eyeball, in which the light rays are not focused by the time they reach the retina; such a person is far-sighted; a biconvex lens causes the light rays to converge so that they focus on the retina. X marks the focal point.

capacity to change its contour. This capacity decreases with the increased hardening brought on with time. Usually the hardening occurs at the focus for distant objects. Hence, an older person often has difficulty focusing on near objects, and may require convex glasses for reading or other close work.

The lens is carried in a ligamentous capsule which is fastened to the choroid just behind the iris. The site of junction between lens capsule and choroid is thickened into what is called the **ciliary body.**

The lens and its capsule separate the cavity of the eyeball into two compartments. Between the lens and the cornea is the **aqueous** (Latin: watery) **chamber,** filled with a clear, lymphlike fluid, the **aqueous humor.** Behind the lens is the much larger **vitreous** (Latin: glassy) **chamber,** filled with a gelatinous secretion, the **vitreous humor.**

Within the ciliary body are visceral muscle fibers fastening the choroid to the sclera. When these muscles are relaxed, the vitreous humor fills the vitreous chamber, and the lens capsule is pulled taut, flattening the lens so that it brings to a focus on the retina light rays which are nearly parallel (i.e., coming from distant objects). If the ciliary muscles contract, they pull the choroid forward, relaxing the lens capsule, and increasing pressure on the vitreous humor, which transmits this pressure to the back of the lens. The center of the lens is hard, and resists this pressure, but the circumference is newer and softer, and gives. This produces a lens rounded and thick in the center, thinner at the edges, which focuses on the retina diverging light rays (i.e., rays coming from nearby objects). See Figure 7.21.

Nervous control of this accommodation mechanism is effected in much the same way as change in pupil size: sympathetic pathways through the spinal cord bring about distant vision, parasympathetic pathways via the oculomotor nerve bring about near vision.

The transparency, curvature, and consistency of the conjunctiva, cornea, aqueous humor, lens, and vitreous humor all facilitate the passage of light rays to a focus on the light-sensitive dendrites at the back of the retina. In humans, deficiency in the ability of the eye properly to focus this light may be compensated for by eyeglasses. See Figure 7.22.

Sight

The light-sensitive dendrites in the retina are of two kinds: cones and rods. Cones are short and stubby, and are concentrated in the middle of the back of the retina, getting sparser as the sides of the retina are approached. They are sensitive to light of different colors. Rods are, by contrast, long and slender. They are absent in the center of the retina at the back, but occur in increasing numbers as the sides of the retina are approached. Rods are not sensitive to variation in color, but are sensitive to varying amounts of light. Nerve impulses may be initiated here by stimuli other than light, as you know from the sensation of "seeing stars" if you have experienced a blow on the eye, or the flashes of light sensed if you exert pressure on the eyeball.

This illustrates the rule common to all sensory nerve cells that an impulse reaching the conscious part of the brain is interpreted according to the type of nerve cell over which the impulse comes, not according to the nature of the stimulus. We have already seen that an extremely cold object, stimulating both cold- and warmth-sensitive nerve endings, gives a burning sensation. Not only is the type of sensation determined by the specific pathway, but so is its localization. Bumping the elbow may cause pressure on a nerve carrying sensory impulses from the hand; the sensation aroused includes a tingling of the fingers, which received no stimulation. Stimulus of a nerve stump leading to a lost tooth or limb may be interpreted in the brain as pain in the lost member.

Light is thought to possess many characteristics of wave motion, and the distance between two consecutive wave crests is known as a **wave length.** This, in the case of light waves, is very short; light visible to the human eye has a wave length ranging from 0.32 to 0.75 microns. Longer waves are not sensed by the rods and cones, but are felt by the warmth receptors of the body as heat waves.

The retina is sensitive to shorter waves than those of 0.32 micron wave length, but such waves do not penetrate the focusing structures in front of the retina. A person who has lost the lens of one eye may see some of these shorter (ultraviolet) rays which reach the retina.

The retina is extremely sensitive to small amounts of light, being about 3000 times as sensitive as a rapid photographic film.

In the rods may be found a light-sensitive pigment called **visual purple.** Upon stimulation of light waves having a wave length between 0.385 and 0.65 microns (violet through orange), visual purple breaks down into a yellowish pigment known as **retinene,** and a protein. It is this chemical reaction which releases the energy that starts a nerve impulse in the rod. Further exposure to light may break the retinene down to vitamin A plus a protein. When the light is withdrawn, resynthesis of visual purple occurs. It will be noticed that red light does not affect the rods.

The longer the rod is kept in the dark, the more sensitive it is to light.

The method of stimulation of cones by light is not as well understood. Pigments whose breakdown initiates nerve impulses have not been identified in the cones. But experimental evidence lends support to the idea that three substances may be present in different cones, one most sensitive to red light, one to green light, and one to blue-violet light. See Figure 7.23.

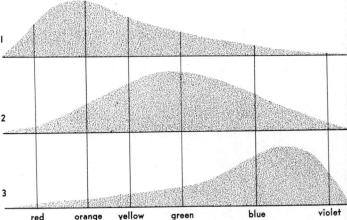

Fig. 7.23   Sensitivity to color of three hypothetical types of cones. **Number 1** is the "red-sensitive," **Number 2** is the "green-sensitive," and **Number 3** the "violet-sensitive" cone. The height of the curve at each wave length (color) indicates the degree of sensitivity to that wave length. Color sensation is, according to the theory, the synthesis of responses to impulses from all three types of cones.

A red object reflects into the eye light waves which stimulate the breakdown of the pigment in red-sensitive cones, starting nerve impulses which give a red sensation in the cerebral cortex. Orange objects affect both red-sensitive and green-sensitive cones in a certain proportion; the resulting nerve impulses bring about an interpretation of orange. The amount of light, the proportion of various wave lengths, and the sensitivity of the rods and cones of the eye determine the particular nerve cells stimulated, and the brain bases its interpretation on the impulses it receives.

It will be recalled that the nerve impulses pass through two synapses before they reach the optic nerve. A certain amount of correlation and combination of impulses occurs here before the impulses reach the visual area of the cerebrum.

At the area through which the axons of the tertiary cells pass to form the optic nerve, there are no rods or cones. This area constitutes the "blind spot" of the eye — light falling here initiates no visual response. With both eyes open, the two blind spots do not overlap in the field of vision, so that the blind spot is not often recognized. With one eye closed, however, the blind spot may be found by

Fig. 7.24 The blind spot. Close your left eye, and look intently at the cross on the left side of the diagram. Now, move the diagram toward and away from you; at about eight to ten inches you should be able to find the place where the white circle disappears and the entire strip, except for the cross on which you focus, looks black. Why is this?

focusing on one point, and moving a small object such as a pinhead in the area to the side of the point focused on. In a certain place, the object will seem to vanish. See Figure 7.24.

Ears

The remaining two senses, **hearing** and **equilibrium,** are associated with the ears.

For convenience in description a human ear may be divided into the outer ear, the middle ear, and the inner ear (Fig. 7.25). The **outer ear** includes the visible appendage on the side of the head called the **concha** (Latin: clamshell), and the **auditory canal** leading to the **eardrum,** or **tympanic** (Latin: drum) **membrane.** The walls of the auditory canal are lined with skin. In the skin are hairs, oil glands, and wax glands. The hairs help keep out larger foreign bodies, and the secretions of the oil and wax glands coat any foreign objects that get in. This helps prevent damage from such things as dirt particles rubbing against the delicate eardrum.

Sound travels through all kinds of matter in the form of waves, alternating compressions and expansions of the material through which they pass. The wave length of audible waves in air varies from half an inch to seventy feet. Since the speed of sound in air at room temperature is about 1130 feet per second, in contrast to the speed of about 186,000 miles

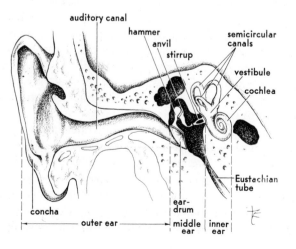

Fig. 7.25 Diagram of the human right ear. The outer ear runs in as far as the eardrum, and the middle ear includes the hammer, anvil, and stirrup and the Eustachian tube.

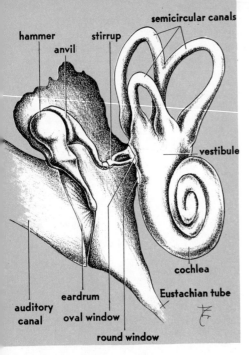

semicircular canals

hammer
anvil
stirrup

vestibule

cochlea

eardrum
Eustachian tube
auditory
canal
oval window
round window

Fig. 7.26 Position of the human ear bones. How is a vibration affecting the eardrum transmitted to the oval window?

per second for light in air, and since the wave lengths of sound are so much greater than those of visible light, the **frequency,** or number of waves passing a given point per unit time, is much less for sound than for light. The frequency of middle C on a piano is given as 256 per second; the frequency of green light is given as 576,000,000,000,000 per second.

The concha of the ear catches sound waves and funnels them into the auditory canal so that they impinge on the eardrum. The eardrum is not stretched taut over a round frame, as in the membrane of a snare drum, for example. It is pulled inward at the center by attachment to a bone in the middle ear, and the stress on its different parts is unequal. When it vibrates in response to the stroke of a sound wave, it does not simply reproduce the wave which sets it in motion, but vibrates also in frequencies which are multiples of the one it received. Thus, if middle C is struck on a piano, waves arrive at the ear with a frequency of 256 per second. The eardrum vibrates not only at this frequency, but also at 512 per second (high C); 768 per second (G above high C); 1024 per second (two octaves above middle C); and so forth.

Also, if two tones are struck at once, for example, middle C (256/second) and the G above it (384/second), the membrane will vibrate not only at these pitches but at frequencies represented by the difference, 128 per second, which is low C, and by the sum, 640 per second, which is high E. This ability of the eardrum to respond with frequencies other than those of the stimulus is used to advantage in mechanical reproduction of sound by the telephone, radio, and so forth. The higher frequencies are transmitted, and the eardrum reconstructs the lower pitches from the sound waves it gets from the receiving instrument.

The eardrum is the wall between the outer and middle ear. The **middle ear** is a cavity in the temporal bone, connected to the pharynx by a passage called the **Eustachian tube,** named for Bartolommeo Eustachio (1524?–1574), an Italian anatomist. The opening of the tube into the pharynx is normally closed, but when the muscles expand the pharynx during swallowing, the tube is opened, and the pressure of air in the middle ear and that in the pharynx are equalized. This prevents distortion of the eardrum by a pressure differential on the two sides. If one climbs a high mountain, reducing the atmospheric pressure on the outside of the eardrum, or goes down into a mine, increasing the pressure, occasional swallowing will permit the air inside the middle ear to become equal in pressure to that outside, in the auditory canal. The presence of the Eustachian tube is not an unmixed blessing, for it is also a means of carrying infective organisms into the middle ear, particularly if one blows his nose strongly enough to force open the Eustachian tubes and drive infectious matter toward the ear.

Swung across the middle ear cavity is the chain of three tiny bones mentioned in Chapter 1 (Fig. 7.26). The **hammer** is fastened by its handle to the eardrum, and articulates by its head with the **anvil.** Whenever the eardrum vibrates, then, the hammer vibrates, too, and transmits its vibrations to the anvil. The long arm of the anvil is jointed to the head of the **stirrup,** and the foot piece of the stirrup is fastened to an opening into the inner ear by an elastic ligament.

The foot piece of the stirrup has an area about one twentieth that of the eardrum, so that if there were no loss along the way, sound would be concentrated twenty times in crossing the middle ear. But there is some loss in overcoming air resistance and inertia, so that the concentration of force amounts to about ten times that on the eardrum.

The **inner ear** (see Fig. 7.26) is a fluid-filled cavity hollowed out of the temporal bone. The fluid is called **perilymph,** and is in direct communication by means of a duct with the cerebrospinal fluid coating the brain.

Within the cavity is a membranous sac, in form like the bony cavity but slightly smaller, separated from the periosteum of the bone by the perilymph. This membranous sac contains **endolymph,** which is very much like the perilymph in constitution. The membranous sac may be divided into three portions for description: the **cochlea** (Latin for snail shell), the **vestibule** (Latin for entryway), and the **semicircular canals.**

The cochlea (Fig. 7.27) is a spirally coiled portion of the membranous sac. The cavity of the membranous sac here is divided into three parts by membranous partitions. One of the partitions is partly supported by bone.

The vestibule is between the cochlea and the semicircular canals. In the vestibule wall are two openings, the **oval window** and the **round window.** The oval window is filled with the foot piece of the stirrup, and the frame of the window is connected to the stirrup by the elastic ligament mentioned before. As a sound wave strikes the eardrum, the compression of air forces the eardrum to bend into the middle ear cavity. This moves the chain of bones so that the stirrup pushes through the oval window into the inner ear. This pushing in is not a straight thrust, but

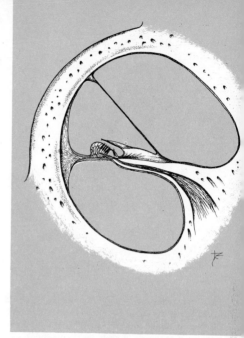

Fig. 7.27   Cross section through the cochlea. Note the division into three channels, and the special organ of hearing in the smallest of the three.

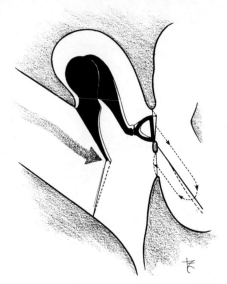

Fig. 7.28   Rocking of the stirrup. As the tympanic membrane is pushed in by a sound wave, the chain of bones is pushed in as shown. When the tympanic membrane rebounds, it pulls the bones back out. The stirrup pivots on its lower border, rocking in and out, and thus transmits the vibrations to the inner ear. As the stirrup pushes in, it exerts pressure on the liquid in the inner ear. This pressure forces the membrane in the round window to bulge out. As the stirrup is withdrawn, the air pressure in the middle ear pushes the membrane in the round window back in. What would happen if the round window were closed with unyielding bone?

a rocking motion pivoted about the lower border of the foot piece. See Figure 7.28.

If the remainder of the inner ear were entirely encased in bone, this pressure of the stirrup would either burst the inner ear walls or not allow the stirrup to move, for the perilymph is nearly incompressible. But the round window in the vestibule wall is covered with an elastic membrane, and when pressure on the perilymph is increased by rocking in of the stirrup the increased pressure is relieved by bulging out of the membrane across the round window. Similarly, when the wave of rarefaction of air reaches the tympanic membrane, and the chain of bones is pulled outward, the foot piece withdraws from the oval window, and pressure is reduced on the perilymph; then the air pressure in the middle ear pushes the membrane of the round window in, so that the reduced pressure at the oval window is compensated.

The alternating pressure-surges in the perilymph are readily transmitted through the membranous sac to the endolymph. Of the three chambers partitioned off in the cochlea, the smallest is of importance in changing these endolymph-transmitted vibrations into nerve impulses.

On one wall of this chamber (Fig. 7.27) stand some tall, columnar cells with sensitive, hairlike protoplasmic processes projecting from their distal ends. Above these hair cells lies a fibrous curtain floating in the endolymph. Vibrations cause this curtain to brush the processes of the hair cells. The base of each hair cell is in contact with a dendrite which leads impulses to the auditory nerve.

Hearing

Each dendrite seems to respond to vibrations of a certain definite frequency, perhaps because the hairs of the part of the wall on which the hair cells stand vibrate most at the specific frequencies. The widest part of the cochlea seems to be sensitive to the highest pitches, and the apex to the lowest. Of course the wall fibers are bound together, and the hair cells are closely packed, so that a vibration of a limited area in resonance with a specific pitch will carry with it the immediately adjacent wall and cells. But the center of the vibrating area will send more forceful nerve impulses, and the hearing area of the cerebrum will interpret the impulses as coming from this area of greatest intensity. The loudness of sound determines the extent of area vibrating by regulating the force of vibration, and this determines the number of nerve impulses per second reaching the brain, and the number of separate nerve fibers bringing impulses to the brain as a result of sound reception.

The **timbre,** or quality of sound by which different voices or different musical instruments may be distinguished, is a property of the proportion of overtones, or vibrations with frequencies which are multiples of the fundamental frequency, occurring in the sound. A flute, for example, has weak overtones, in contrast to a clarinet or a violin, in which overtones are prominent in varying ratios.

Semicircular Canals

The semicircular canals are placed above the vestibule. The three canals of one ear are each perpendicular to the other two. One is nearly horizontal when the head is erect, and the other two are vertical. The anterior vertical canal runs diagonally from lateral front to medial back, and the posterior canal runs at right angles to this, from lateral back to medial front. See Figure 7.29.

All three canals connect at both ends with the vestibule, and at one connection for each canal there is a swelling known as the **ampulla** (Latin: flask). Within each ampulla is a patch of sensitive cells carrying hairlike protoplasmic processes. See Figure 7.30.

Equilibrium

The endolymph in the canals is a rather viscous fluid. If the head is rotated in a horizontal plane, as in turning from side to side, the inertia of the endolymph makes it drag behind the walls of the canal. If you pick up a bowl of soup and start turning the bowl around rapidly, the soup lags a while before it catches up with the bowl. If the bowl be stopped, the soup continues its circular motion for a while before it slows to a stop. Similarly, the semicircular canal wall may stop, and the endolymph continue to circulate for a time.

When the head starts to rotate, the movement of the canal wall carries the roots of the sensitive hairs with it, but the rest of the hair is dragged behind by the endolymph. This initiates a nerve impulse traveling through the auditory nerve. When the head stops, the root of the hair stops, but the hair itself is carried forward by the still swirling endolymph. This causes other nerve impulses to pass over the auditory nerve.

These nerve impulses stimulate contraction of muscles of the eyes and of the limbs and trunk of the body, helping in maintaining balance and coordination of movement. If you

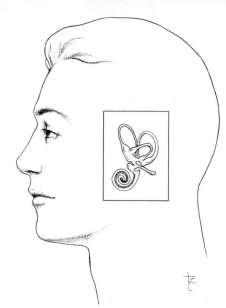

Fig. 7.29   Position of the inner ear (here enlarged out of proportion) in the head. Note the angles at which the semicircular canals are placed. The two vertical ones are perpendicular to each other, diagonal to the median plane of the head.

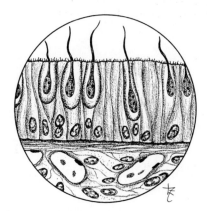

Fig. 7.30   Sensory cells in the ampulla. Each is connected at the base to a dendrite of a sensory nerve cell of the auditory nerve.

pirouette for several turns, and then stop suddenly, your eyes continue to make movements as if you were still whirling around, and the sense of sight registers a spinning of your environment, giving you a dizzy feeling.

Another demonstration of the action of nerve impulses from semicircular canals comes from an experiment with the vertical canals. If you place a yardstick upright on the floor, and bend over until your forehead touches the top of the yardstick, and then you circle around the stick four or five times, and straighten up and walk toward a goal, such as a doorway, you will find yourself pulling over to the side opposite the direction in which you went around the stick.

Within the vestibule are two pouches, one known as the **utriculus,** and the other as the **sacculus.** In the wall of each is another patch of sensitive hair cells. Above this patch is a gelatinous mat containing some lime concretions called **otoliths** (Greek: ear stones). In an upright position this mat with its otoliths rests on the hairs, sending stimuli to the brain through the auditory nerve. In another position, such as standing on your head, you will feel a different sensation, because the otolith mat has dropped away from the hair cells. If you lay your head horizontally, the mat will slide over to one side of the hair cell patches. See Figure 7.31.

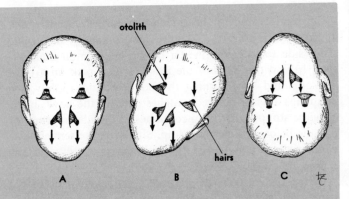

Fig. 7.31 Diagram showing effect of the position of otoliths on the sensitive hairs of the ampullae. In **A,** the head is upright; in **B,** the head is tilted; in **C,** the head is upside down. What stimuli reach the brain? How does the brain interpret these?

These otoliths, then, give you a sense of the position of your head with respect to gravitational forces even when your head is not moving. This is the sense of static equilibrium, in contrast to the sense of dynamic equilibrium provided by the ampullae of the semicircular canals.

HYGIENE OF THE NERVOUS SYSTEM

Biologically, the chief distinguishing feature of man among animals is the relatively great size and complexity of his cerebral cortex — a quantitative difference, to be sure, but a significant one as far as his behavior is concerned.

Like the muscular system, the nervous system may be trained for highly efficient use, or it may be neglected to the detriment of the individuals concerned. In fact, the training of the muscular system for athletic sports or skilled work involves the nervous system as much as or more than the muscles themselves.

In preparing for effective mental activity, such as studying a lesson, both external, environmental conditions, and internal, physiological conditions are important. The nervous system is an integrated part of the body, and the body in good health is much better prepared for mental work than the body diseased or in pain. Proper nourishment; absence of nerve poisons such as drugs, tobacco, alcohol; and a good circulation are important.

As for external conditions, the body should be reasonably comfortable, but not so relaxed that it goes to sleep. Lighting should be such that the eyes work well — adequate light so that straining is not necessary, but absence of glare so that the eyes are not dazzled. Temperature, ventilation, and noise should be conducive to stimulating thought without impinging on the consciousness. That is, the temperature should be 65 to 70 degrees Fahrenheit. The air should be reasonably fresh, and in slight but inconspicuous motion. And the amount of noise should be below the level of interference with study.

Internal conditions include a rested condition, or absence of muscular or nervous fatigue; emotional calm; and a positive motivation for learning. You learn more quickly and more thoroughly if you are mature enough to develop a liking and an enthusiasm for information and for a self-constructed arrangement of that information in your own mind. You are then like a successful hardware merchant who acquires an abundance of wares and has them so organized that he can produce what is wanted immediately from his stock. Occasionally there will be a hardware merchant who is imaginative enough to put two or three pieces of equipment together in a way no one has ever done before, and he has an invention. Artists, research scientists, and outstanding students in all fields do that with mental wares, producing new ideas, which are recombinations of familiar thoughts into new patterns. The capacity for producing new ideas may be developed by following a program of well-chosen mental exercise.

For many centuries, philosophers have argued about the existence of free will among humans. Whether or not all of our decisions are predetermined by the experiences of our past, people act as though they had free will and made decisions of their own. Even when the victim of armed robbery hands over his wallet to the gunman, he acts as if he has a choice between surrendering his money or his life.

Assuming for the moment that you may choose your own course of action, it would seem wise to plan a set of rules which seem to you to promise the most satisfying life under the conceivable circumstances. These rules may be subject to future change as you learn more about your life, but the existence of such plans may save you from aimless frustration and unhappiness. The type of motivation you have determines to a considerable degree your personality and your emotional state. A person with a humanity-centered, religious, enthusiastic outlook is prepared to meet any circumstance, good or bad, and make the most of it. Happiness, peace of mind, is most certain when it comes as a by-product of directed and conscientious activity.

You live with society and with yourself. Neither self-seeking nor social adjustment should be forgotten in your plans for a healthy mental life. Self-improvement, self-development are essential even and especially to the most altruistic individuals. The more versatile and skilled you are, the better service you can render to your fellows. But also, the more smoothly you can function in your social contacts, the more effective collaborator you are with your society in accomplishing its objects, the more contributions you can make to its advance, and the better prepared you are for possible leadership. Every good leader has been a good follower. Maturity in dealing with yourself and good adjustment to society are the keys to lasting satisfaction and happiness.

SUMMARY

The nervous system transmits impulses which stimulate and coordinate such bodily activities as sensation, movement, and secretion. The nervous system includes the brain, spinal cord, spinal ganglia, autonomic ganglia, nerves, and sense organs.

A nerve cell has a cell body with cytoplasmic branches, the dendrites and axons. A nerve impulse is a traveling change in the electrical conditions at the membrane of the nerve cell. Transmission from one cell to another may be chemical, electrical, or both.

Tracts of nerve fibers in the spinal cord and brain are made of axons, carrying impulses of a similar import. The brain is composed of parts concerned with specific types of activity. The medulla and pons deal with involuntary controls of bodily activity. The cerebellum takes part in coordination and tonus control. The midbrain is a relay station. The diencephalon is involved in emotions and instinctive action patterns. The cerebrum is concerned with conscious sensation and voluntary action.

Cranial and spinal nerves transmit impulses to and from the central nervous system. Twelve pairs of cranial nerves are usually recognized in the human. These are more highly differentiated than are the spinal nerves.

The autonomic nervous system carries impulses to involuntary muscles and to glands. The system may be divided into sympathetic and parasympathetic parts, whose impulses result in opposing reactions.

The senses, each with its distinctive organs and nerve connections, are touch, pain, warmth, cold, kinesthesia, hunger, thirst, taste, smell, sight, hearing, and equilibrium. The last three have the most complicated sense organs, the eyes and the ears.

There are hygienic conditions under which mental activity is most efficient. These include bodily health, proper nourishment, absence of nerve poisons, bodily comfort, fresh air, absence of distracting sensory stimuli, absence of bodily fatigue, emotional calm, and positive motivation for mental activity. Skill in mental activity may be developed by practice. A high degree of ability to deal with ideas contributes greatly to satisfaction and happiness.

REVIEW QUESTIONS

1. List the general subdivisions of the nervous system.
2. Describe a neuroglia cell; a nerve cell.
3. How does a nerve impulse travel along à nerve cell? across a synapse?
4. What is acetylcholine?
5. Describe the architecture of the spinal cord.
6. List the parts of the brain and their actions.
7. Describe the location and action of the cerebrospinal fluid.
8. Describe the pathway of a nerve impulse in the knee reflex.
9. Describe the kinds of impulses traveling in the various spinal cord tracts.
10. List the cranial nerves, their connections, and the types of impulses they carry.
11. Describe the muscular movements of the eyeball.
12. What is a plexus?
13. Describe the structure and action of the autonomic nervous system.
14. List and locate the twelve senses.

15. Distinguish between hunger and appetite.
16. Describe the eye and its accessory structures.
17. Explain the process of focusing the eye.
18. Why do your fingers tingle when you bump your elbow?
19. Explain the physiology of vision.
20. Describe the structure of the ear.
21. How are sound waves changed into nerve impulses?
22. Describe the sense of equilibrium.
23. Describe the importance of the Eustachian tube.
24. What is timbre? How is it sensed?
25. What is the best way to prepare for studying?

GENERAL QUESTIONS

1. How is reverse conduction of nerve impulses prevented in nerve cells?
2. How could you test to see which of the two theories of nerve impulse conduction is more nearly accurate?
3. In some cases, the cerebrospinal fluid becomes invaded by disease organisms. A doctor may remove this fluid and put sterile air in its place. What changes does this "air conditioning" bring about in the patient?
4. Using the general rules of nerve impulse pathways, and your knowledge of the tracts, nerves, and centers of the nervous system, trace the routes of the impulses in these events:

    (a) Accumulation of carbon dioxide in a muscle in the calf of your right leg stimulates the relaxation of the muscular wall of the artery supplying that muscle.
    (b) Fatigue in a muscle fiber in the left forearm results in another fiber of the same muscle being contracted, maintaining muscle tone.
    (c) A rise in temperature of the right hand results in increase in rate of secretion by its sweat glands.
    (d) You see and feel a snowball hit the front of your chest. Your arm extends to pick up some snow to make a ball to throw at your assailant.
    (e) The sound of a classroom bell stimulates you to rise from your chair.

5. What would be the result of a successful surgical interchange of the distal connections of your olfactory and auditory nerves?
6. How would your life be changed if you suddenly lost your kinesthetic sense?
7. The retina has been described as a glorified warm-sensitive spot. Criticize this view.
8. Two loud tones, one at 480 and one at 320 vibrations per second, impinge on your eardrum. Name six other frequencies at which the eardrum will vibrate as a result of these tones.
9. How may happiness be achieved?

CHAPTER 8

The Endocrine System

HORMONES

An **endocrine gland** is an organ that secretes a hormone. *Endocrine* comes from the Greek for internal ordering. Some hormones were discussed in Chapter 3, where they were defined as substances secreted in one place, transported by the blood, and used in another place where they regulate some metabolic activity. Hormones produced by the stomach and intestine regulate the activity of the digestive tract as was described in Chapter 3.

In Chapter 1, mention was made of two hormones which affect skeletal metabolism. Several other endocrine glands have been studied, together with the hormones they produce. Much has been found out, but much remains to be understood. Not only do the hormones have profound effects on metabolism, and not only do some endocrine organs produce several hormones, but also these organs and hormones have interrelationships with each other which complicate their study.

Like the nervous system, endocrine organs regulate and control processes in the body. Unlike the nervous system, endocrine control is slow and reasonably steady. The blood acts as a reservoir, carrying a relatively unchanging amount of hormone to the cells affected by it. The hormones are organic chemical compounds acting as catalysts in metabolic processes.

Secretion is Latin for separation; it involves the absorption from the blood of certain raw materials, chemical synthesis of these materials into a different substance by cellular cytoplasm under the direction of the nucleus, and release of the new substance. In a gland such as the salivary glands or sweat glands, this release is into a duct or onto an outer surface. In endocrine glands the secretion is released into a blood capillary.

Interestingly enough, many hormones from one animal seem to be effective in another quite different animal, and exchanges between animals as distinct as frogs, chickens, and humans may be quite successful. There is something fundamental and basic about chemical coordination in living organisms.

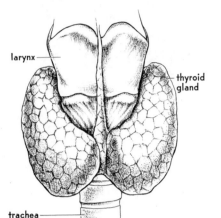

larynx

thyroid gland

trachea

Fig. 8.1 Human thyroid gland. The two lobes of the gland are usually connected across the midline by an isthmus of tissue.

THE THYROID GLAND

This gland is located in the throat, just below and lateral to the thyroid cartilage, from which it gets its name. The gland has two lobes, one on either side of the trachea. These lobes are usually connected by a small isthmus of thyroid gland tissue below the larynx. See Figure 8.1.

Microscopic examination of the thyroid tissue shows little hollow balls and cylinders with walls composed of a single layer of cuboidal cells (Fig. 8.2). The height of these cells seems correlated with the degree of activity: quiescent cells are low and flattened, whereas very actively secreting cells are tall and columnar. Each ball or cylinder, known as a **follicle,** contains a colloidal substance which serves as a temporary storage place for the secretion of the thyroid cells. The follicles are encased in a connective tissue meshwork, very amply supplied with blood and lymph vessels. Much more blood circulates through the thyroid gland in relation to its size than through most other tissues, almost four times as much as through the kidney, liver, or brain, and eight times as much as through the intestinal walls.

The secretion of the thyroid gland is called **iodothyroglobulin.** This is made by combining the amino acid **tyrosine** (Greek: cheese) with iodine to make **di-iodo-tyrosine,** then combining two molecules of tyrosine to make two other amino acids, d-alanine and **thyroxin** (so named because it was erroneously thought to be an oxy-indole compound). Then di-iodo-tyrosine and thyroxin combine with other amino acids to make the iodothyroglobulin. Thyroxin by itself has considerable hormonal activity, but in the combined form its activity is quicker and greater.

The action of the thyroid hormone is an increase in the rate of oxidation reactions in the body. The more hormone present in the blood, the more rapidly is food absorbed from the intestine and released from storage depots such as the liver and fat deposits, and the more oxygen is used and carbon dioxide and water released.

The human with a high production and release of thyroid hormone exhibits a high basal metabolic rate, abundant energy, a healthy appetite, and little deposition of fat. On the contrary, the deficient production of thyroid hormone may lead to low metabolic rates, sluggishness, a constant feeling of fatigue, and obesity.

At one time this action was used in so-called "reducing pills," concoctions containing thyroid secretions, given to people wishing to lose weight. Not only did these pills cause

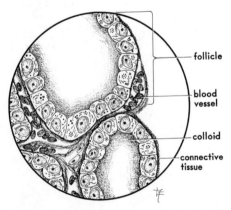

follicle

blood vessel

colloid

connective tissue

Fig. 8.2 Microscopic structure of the thyroid gland. A single layer of cells surrounds each follicle, with blood vessels between follicles.

their unfortunate consumers to lose weight, but they also brought about exaggerated nervousness, mental breakdown, serious metabolic disturbances, and incapacity for normal activity. This costly lesson illustrates the folly of disregarding interrelationships in physiology. Any substance as biologically potent as a hormone has not one effect but a very great many, and disturbance of an adjusted organism by changing the balance of its hormones has far-reaching and largely unpredictable effects. Hormone therapy should be administered only under the guidance of a physician, and then with great caution, for no two people will respond exactly alike, and the physician must feel his way along a course of treatment by observing the results on the patient.

✓Thyroid hormone increases the sensitivity of both nerve and muscle cells. It is especially important in growing infants and children, in which metabolism is normally high. A lack of thyroid hormone in early life results in a dwarf, or **cretin,** stunted and deformed physically and mentally.

The anterior lobe of the pituitary gland in the head was mentioned in Chapter 1 as the source of growth hormone. It is also the source of another hormone, **thyrotrophin** (Greek: thyroid nourisher), which increases the secretory activity of the thyroid gland. In turn, the thyroid secretion slows down the pituitary production of thyrotrophin, so that a balance is maintained. If the thyroid secretion is too little, thyrotrophin stimulates further secretion of thyroid hormone. As thyroid secretion increases, thyrotrophin secretion is diminished, and an equilibrium is reached.

In the absence of an iodine supply, the thyroid gland cannot manufacture its hormone, and, as we read in Chapter 3, it responds by enlarging into a goiter. Inclusion of iodides in the diet relieves this condition. The enlargement is under the influence of increased thyrotrophin in the absence of the thyroid hormone.

THE PARATHYROID GLANDS

There are normally four parathyroid glands in a human, two in the back wall of each lobe of the thyroid gland. See Figure 8.3. The glands contain densely packed epithelial cells with interwoven connective tissue and an abundant blood supply, distinct from that of the thyroid gland. The hormone secreted by these glands has not yet been chemically analyzed completely so that its exact chemical structure is unknown. It seems to be a protein.

Its action on bones, blood, and nervous activity was briefly noted in Chapter 1. Extracts from the parathyroid gland may be injected into an animal with normal parathyroid

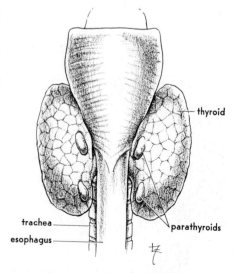

Fig. 8.3 Position of the parathyroid glands. The larynx, trachea, and thyroid glands are shown from the back.

glands. This increase in the amount of hormone in the blood results in an increase of osteoclasts in bone, breaking down the bone with release of calcium and phosphate into the blood. There is also a diminution of the ability of kidney tubules to withdraw phosphates from the urine, so that more phosphate is excreted than usual. Therefore the phosphate level in the blood decreases, but the calcium concentration remains above normal. In the case of a deficiency of parathyroid hormone the blood calcium level falls below normal, and the amount of phosphate in the blood is increased.

Whether or not there is a parathyrotrophic hormone secreted by the pituitary gland similar to thyrotrophin is the subject of much debate and conflicting evidence. Injection of pituitary extracts seems to affect parathyroid hormone action, but complete removal of the pituitary gland seems to have no effect on parathyroid activity.

More will be known about the physiology of parathyroid secretions when these secretions are purified so that one or more specific compounds may be identified as hormones, and their particular endocrine action studied.

DIGESTIVE TRACT HORMONES

The hormones gastrin, enterogastrone, secretin, cholecystokinin, and enterocrinin have been described in Chapter 3. Other possible hormones have been postulated, such as **villikinin** (Latin: hair, and Greek: mover), a hormone secreted by the duodenum, which stimulates more active muscular action in intestinal villi. These suggestions need further investigation.

Insulin

One further hormone related especially to the digestive system has been well established. The pancreatic **islands of Langerhans,** described by Paul Langerhans (1847–1888) in 1869, secrete a hormone known as **insulin** (Latin: island). These islands are little patches of cells scattered about the regular pancreatic cells. The patches may be recognized by their staining qualities, by their less regular arrangement, and by their much richer blood supply, in contrast to the enzyme-secreting cells. There are over a million islands of Langerhans in an adult human pancreas. See Figure 8.4.

Insulin is a protein substance which regulates several phases of the body's use of sugar, fat, and protein. In the absence of insulin, the glycogen stores of the liver and of the muscles are depleted, and cannot be restored.

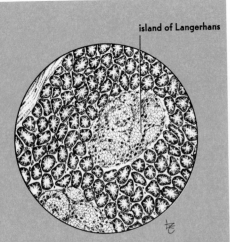

island of Langerhans

Fig. 8.4 Microscopic structure of the islands of Langerhans in the pancreas. Note the difference in arrangement and in staining qualities between island and other pancreas cells.

Larger than normal quantities of glucose appear in the blood, and since these are not used, they spill over into the urine. Fats are only partly broken down, and incompletely oxidized fatty products appear in the blood and urine. Reacting to the inability to metabolize carbohydrates and fats properly, the body breaks down proteins.

There is loss of weight, greatly increased appetite, muscular weakness, high production of acids in the body, and eventually coma and death unless insulin is made available. An overproduction of insulin or addition of excess insulin to the normal supply lowers the amount of glucose in the blood, oversensitizes nerve and muscle tissues, and inhibits and eventually destroys normal islands of Langerhans.

The control of insulin secretion is based on the amount of glucose in the blood reaching the pancreas. If the sugar concentration increases, more insulin is released. When the sugar levels drops, the insulin secretion is diminished.

As an interesting example of the way in which biological knowledge is acquired, we might consider a few of the steps in the unfolding of the insulin story. We shall see that scientific progress depends upon sharp observation, logical thought, alertness in taking advantage of "lucky accidents," and contributions from many workers all over the world.

The disease caused by insulin deficiency, **diabetes mellitus,** was known to medical writers of ancient Rome. Association with sweet taste of the urine was mentioned by a writer in India in the sixth century. But more exact knowledge has had to wait upon the last sixty-five years. Claude Bernard, the renowned French physiologist, sought for the cause of diabetes in the actions of the liver during the latter part of the last century.

In 1889, Minkowski and Mehring reported the results of experimental removal of the pancreas from dogs. They had performed the operation in studying the effect of pancreatic enzymes. A laboratory attendant called the attention of the investigators to the fact that the urine of these dogs attracted an unusual number of flies. Examination of the urine revealed the presence of sugar. This started a train of thought along the lines of the possible relationship between the pancreas and diabetes. Previously, extracts of the thyroid gland had been shown to relieve the symptoms of a disease caused by deficient thyroid secretion, so Minkowski attempted to make an extract of the pancreas which would alleviate diabetes. But he was unsuccessful, reporting his failure in 1892. Failures as well as successes should be reported in the scientific literature, for they are of great value to other workers in the field.

Also in 1892, Caparelli reported some success with an extract of pancreas made in salt water. But the success was not great enough to warrant optimism.

In 1897, Hougounenq and Doyon reported their efforts to treat diabetes with pancreatic extracts given by way of the mouth, but these efforts had produced no change in the course of the disease.

In 1898, Blumenthal described his work with alcoholic extracts of pancreas. These extracts increased the use of sugar by diabetics 40%, but the extracts produced ulcers in humans, and killed experimental animals, so he abandoned the project.

The effectiveness of the alcohol extracts was tantalizingly encouraging to other investigators, though, and in 1908 Zuelzer reported that alcoholic extracts of very fresh pancreas taken at the height of digestive activity produced successful clinical results.

In 1911, Scott worked on the idea that those specialized islands of tissue that Langerhans had distinguished in 1869 were the source of the secretion which prevented diabetes, and that the enzymes of the rest of the pancreas destroyed the island secretion during ordinary methods of extraction. He tied off the pancreatic ducts in order to allow the enzyme-secreting cells to degenerate, and after some time reopened his experimental animals and made his extracts under the assumption that the island cells were the only ones actively secreting. However, not all of the enzyme-secreting cells were destroyed; furthermore, the alcoholic extract that Scott prepared lowered the blood pressure of the recipients too much.

In the same year, Starling and Knowlton reported on an acid extract with which they obtained two positive results and one negative. The latter made enough impression on them to cause them to doubt the efficacy of their methods.

The intervention of the First World War in 1914 interrupted the work of many investigators just when success seemed imminent.

In 1922, Banting and Best reported successful treatment of human diabetic patients with an extract made by Scott's method. Together with Collip, these investigators developed a process of extracting insulin in large quantities by treating fresh beef pancreases at slaughterhouses with alcohol to inactivate the enzymes, then putting the glands through a series of chemical operations which concentrated and purified the hormone. In 1926, Abel crystallized the hormone and determined its chemical formula.

This brief account omits the names of many who contributed to our knowledge of insulin and its use in human therapy, but the sample is enough to give you an idea of the slow but relentless progress made in understanding biological phenomena.

Nowadays, a person with diabetes may live a normal life if he reduces the amount of carbohydrates in his diet and takes injections of insulin. Regular insulin has its strongest effect about 6 hours after injecting; the effect is gone in another 6 hours. Globin-zinc-insulin is slower and longer lasting in its effects, and protamine-zinc-insulin even more so, so that injections of these may be less frequent for adequate effect.

THE PINEAL BODY

The **pineal** organ is an outgrowth from the roof of the third ventricle of the brain. See Figure 8.5. Attempts have been made to find endocrine activity associated with the pineal body, but results are conflicting. In some cases of extreme sexual precocity in humans — cases of sexual maturity in the first few years of life — tumors have been found in the pineal gland. Other cases of apparently similar pineal tumors have no such effect however.

Surgical removal of the pineal body from animals has proved to have no effect in some cases, and to inhibit growth and speed up maturity in others. Experiments with pineal extracts yield equally contradictory results. The problem of the activity of the pineal organ in humans is still very baffling, and merits further research.

Fig. 8.5   Position of the pineal body and the pituitary gland.

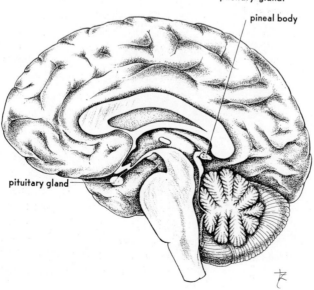

pineal body

pituitary gland

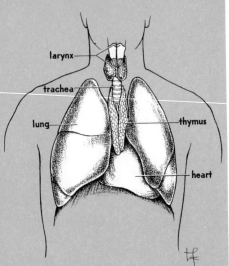

Fig. 8.6 Location of the thymus gland in the chest and neck.

176 CHAPTER 8

THE THYMUS

The **thymus** (Greek: sweet-smelling sacrifice) is located in the chest in front of the aorta, lungs, and trachea. See Figure 8.6. It is a spongy, irregular mass of considerable size in children, diminishing in adults. Microscopic examination of the thymus (Fig. 8.7) shows it to be a lobulated structure, each lobule having a cortex and medulla. The cortex is made of the same type of tissue as that found in lymph nodes. The medulla contains some lymph cells, but also some other clusters of cells, which has led to the supposition that the thymus may be an endocrine gland. However, evidence is as confusing as in the case of the pineal organ.

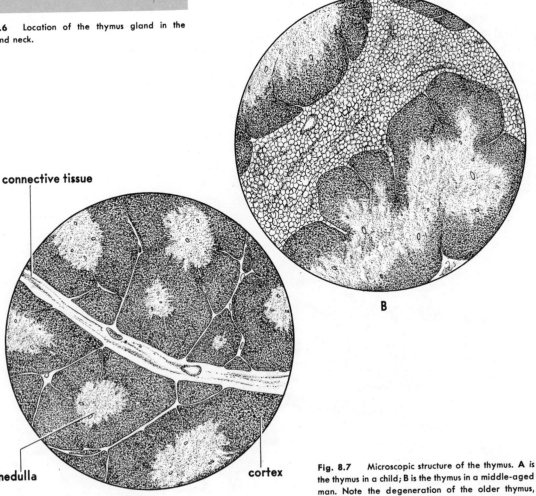

Fig. 8.7 Microscopic structure of the thymus. **A** is the thymus in a child; B is the thymus in a middle-aged man. Note the degeneration of the older thymus, with the increase in the amount of connective tissue.

Removal of the thymus of experimental animals has been reported by some workers to result in disturbances of growth and of sexual development, but other investigators have found no such effects. Treatment with thymus extracts produces varying results. One group of workers found that these extracts injected into rats for several generations produced increasing precocity of growth and sexual maturity. These results have not been duplicated successfully in other laboratories. Still other workers found a thymus extract which produced the symptoms of diabetes, but this, too, has failed of confirmation. With the pineal body, the thymus must be considered for the present as an organ about whose possible endocrine action there is much doubt. Both present a challenge to students of endocrinology.

THE ADRENAL GLANDS

The **adrenal** (Latin: next to the kidney) **glands** are two small masses of tissue, perhaps two inches in greatest length, one perched above each kidney. See Figure 8.8. Each gland is made up of a cortex and medulla which are, actually, two entirely separate organs, though one encloses the other.

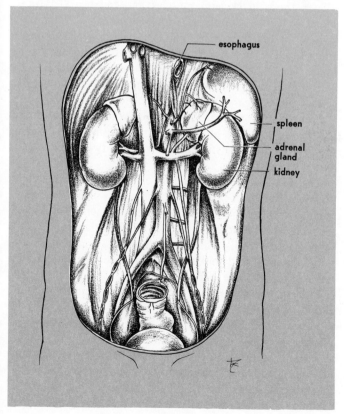

Fig. 8.8   Location of the adrenal glands in the abdomen.

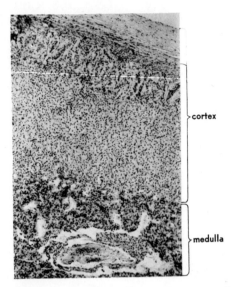

cortex

medulla

Fig. 8.9 Microscopic structure of the adrenal gland. Note the distinctive appearance of the cortex and the medulla.

Their tissues are distinct, their hormones quite different, and their blood supply and nerve supply individual. The adrenal glands receive a tremendous amount of blood for the amount of tissue in them, being comparable to the thyroid gland in this respect. See Figure 8.9.

Adrenal Medulla

The hormone of the adrenal medulla is variously called **adrenin,** adrenaline, epinephrine, and other names. Adrenin itself is not an amino acid, but is related to the amino acid tyrosine, the same one involved in thyroid hormone formation. Adrenin, however, is a simpler compound than the thyroid hormone.

The actions of adrenin in the body are almost exactly the same as the actions of the stimulated sympathetic division of the autonomic nervous system. That the hormone is not simply a stimulant of the sympathetic nerves is shown by the undiminished effect of adrenin after sympathetic nerves have been cut and have degenerated. Adrenin constricts blood vessels in the skin and most viscera, but dilates those in skeletal muscles and the heart. It raises blood pressure, supplying more blood to the brain. It speeds up the heartbeat, inhibits visceral muscle contractions (except in the pregnant uterus, the skin, and some blood vessels), dilates the pupil of the eye, increases the working capacity of skeletal muscle, causes the liver to release more sugar, the lungs to provide more oxygen, and the rate of sugar oxidation to go up markedly. After adrenin is released into the blood, the spleen contracts, releasing more blood into the stream, and the ability of the blood to clot is increased.

The similarity of the action of the adrenal medullary hormone to that of the sympathetic nerves seems reasonable when we realize that in the early development of a human, the cells of the adrenal medulla differentiate out of the same patch of cells which gives rise to sympathetic autonomic ganglia, and that there is evidence that sympathetic nerve endings give off a substance, sympathin, which induces the characteristic effects of sympathetic stimulation, acting much like adrenin. The adrenal medulla may be removed from both glands without endangering life or normal metabolism except in times of great stress.

Review of the actions of adrenin and the sympathetic nervous system lends plausibility to the "emergency theory" of those actions. According to this idea, the release of adrenin from the adrenal medulla and the greater than usual stimulation of sympathetic nerves occur at times of bodily stress or danger. The release of adrenin has been found to occur as a result of fright, anger, severe pain, asphyxia, low temperatures, and vigorous muscular exercise, all acting through the sympathetic nervous system on the gland. The bodily condition brought about by the action of adrenin is one of extra capacity — higher energy output, greater muscular efficiency, greater protection against hemorrhage by withdrawal of blood from the skin and increase in clotting ability, and better conditions for the nervous system by enlarged pupils, more blood to the brain, and so forth. Some of these effects are used to advantage in medical treatment of conditions such as restoration of heartbeat in heart failure, relief of asthma by relaxing bronchi, and helping blood clot in severe hemorrhage. An oversupply of adrenin may produce dangerously high blood pressure, violent heartbeat, throbbing head, blurred vision, nausea, pallor, panting, and increased amount of sugar in the blood. The use of adrenin to improve the performance of participants in sports is very ill-advised, for the damage it may do to the body's metabolism is great. Stimulation of natural release by pep talks and appealing to emotions is accepted practice, however.

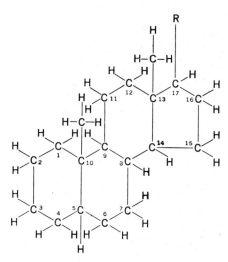

Fig. 8.10 Basic steroid formula. The upper diagram represents the structural formula, with **C** standing for a carbon atom, and **H** for a hydrogen atom. **R** stands for some other groups, perhaps with carbon and hydrogen, perhaps also some oxygen (**O**). The carbon atoms are numbered for convenience in denoting added atoms. The lower diagram shows the skeleton of the diagram with letters omitted for convenience. Compare this with some of the later figures in this chapter, which show variations on the basic formula.

Adrenal Cortex

The adrenal cortex is composed of cells which arose in close association with those forming the reproductive organs — ovaries or testes. Chemically the hormones produced by the adrenal cortex and those by the reproductive organs are closely related. They are built on the plan of a **steroid,** as illustrated in Figure 8.10. So far, three groups of active hormones have been described as associated with the action of adrenal cortex secretion:

The **corticosterone group,** consisting of corticosterone, 11-dehydrocorticosterone, 17-hydroxycorticosterone, and 11-dehydro-17-hydroxycorticosterone, increases the breakdown of proteins in the body with the release of glucose. This increases the amount of glycogen in the liver and muscles, and the amount of sugar in the blood, contributing to the endurance and efficiency of muscular activity, postponing fatigue.

The **desoxycorticosterone group,** including desoxycorticosterone and 17-hydroxydesoxycorticosterone, affects the permeability of cell and capillary membranes and the distribution of sodium and potassium. In the absence of adrenal cortex hormones, the sodium so prominent in body fluids is lost through the kidneys, together with a

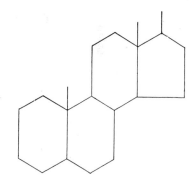

great deal more water than usual, and potassium is withdrawn from cells into the blood. See Figure 8.11.

After these are removed from the adrenal secretion there remain substances which have not yet been identified. This residue is known as the **amorphous fraction.** This seems to be essential to the proper action of the kidneys, particularly in permitting reabsorption of sodium into the blood from the urine in the kidney tubule.

The various components of the cortex secretion seem to be more successful as a group than as separate parts, for attempts to remedy deficiencies by purified compounds are not as effective as therapy by the undivided total secretion. Perhaps there are still other compounds of biological significance awaiting discovery.

Unlike the adrenal medulla, the adrenal cortex is necessary for life. Total removal of adrenal glands without replacement by secretions results in great muscular weakness, low metabolic rate, lowered blood volume and blood pressure, breakdown of digestive activity, and rapid death.

THE PITUITARY GLAND

The **pituitary** (Latin: phlegm-producing — it was originally thought to secrete mucus for the nose) **gland** is located in the head just below the diencephalon. It is attached to the hypothalamus by a stalk, and has prominent nervous connections with the hypothalamus. See Figure 8.5.

The gland, like the adrenal, is really two glands by origin and by action. The **anterior lobe** of the gland arises from cells in the roof of the mouth, whereas the **posterior lobe** arises as an outgrowth of the diencephalon. The cells of the anterior lobe are epithelial, while those of the posterior lobe resemble nervous tissue.

The anterior lobe seems to be the executive center of the endocrine system. It secretes hormones with a considerable number of effects. Its **growth hormone** has already been discussed, in Chapter 1, in connection with its action on the skeletal system. In addition to its effect on the skeleton, other metabolic processes are influenced by the growth hormone or by some substance not yet separated from it. These are the use of sugar, fat, and protein in the body. The presence of this pituitary factor increases the amount of sugar in the blood, antagonizing the effect of insulin; it partially breaks down the fat in adipose tissue, flooding the blood and liver with incompletely oxidized fat products; and it seems to be essential to the specific dynamic action of proteins mentioned in Chapter 4. The continued secretion of growth hormone is dependent upon the presence

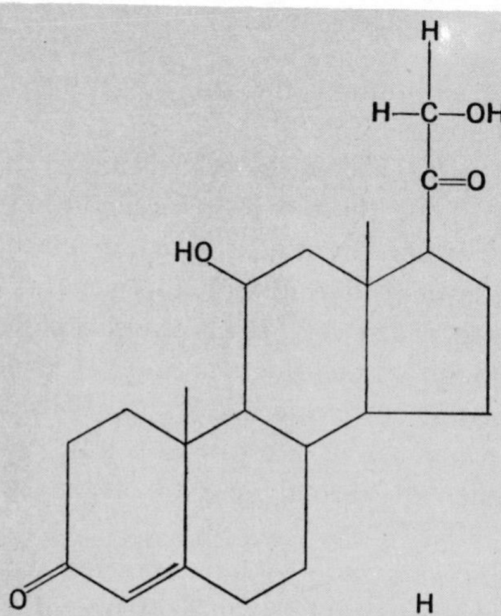

Corticosterone

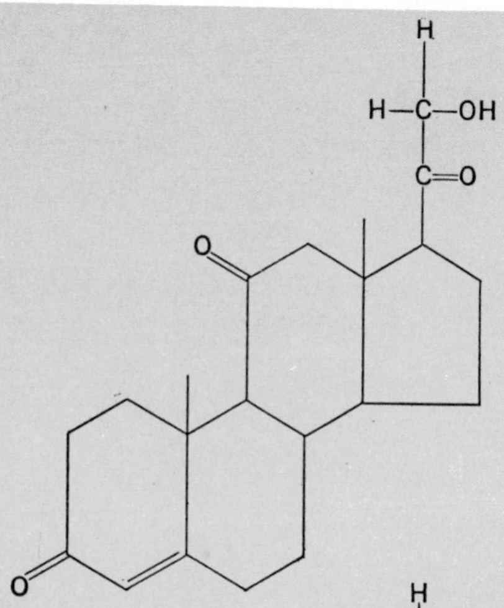

11-Dehydrocorticosterone

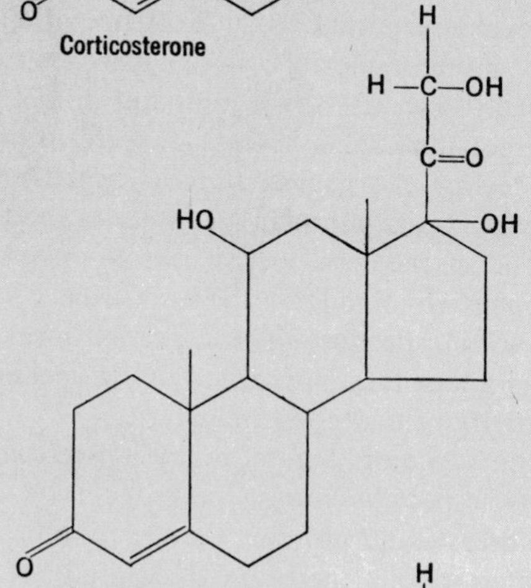

17-hydroxycorticosterone

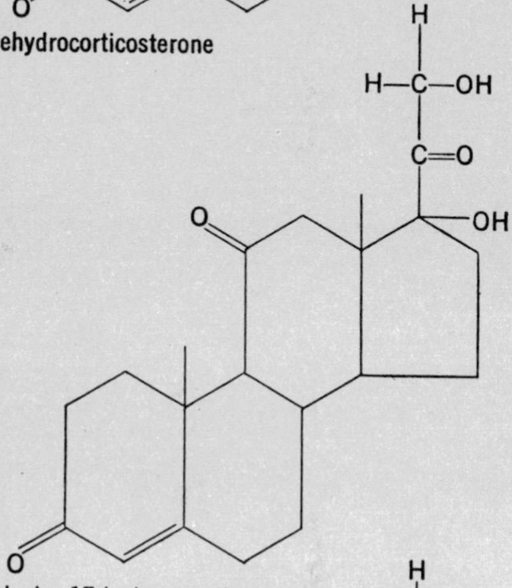

11-dehydro-17-hydroxycorticosterone

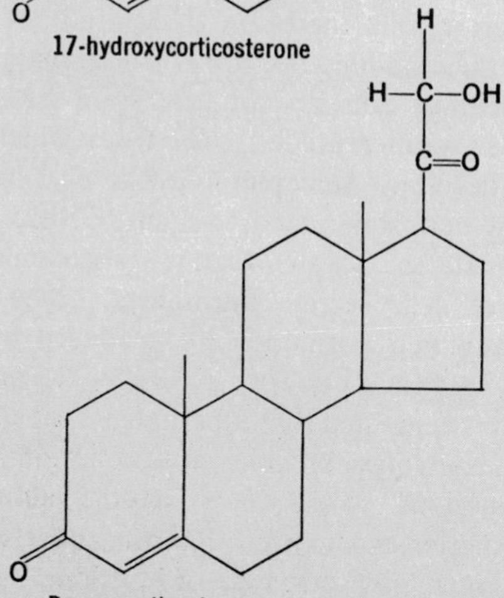

Desoxycorticosterone

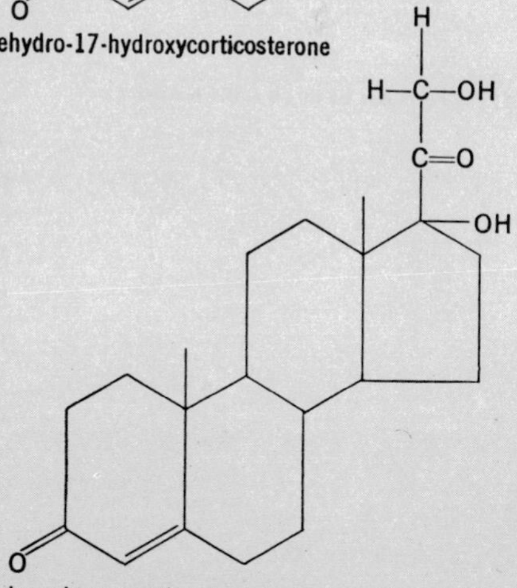

17-hydroxydesoxycorticosterone

Fig. 8.11 Formulas of the six adrenal cortex hormones.

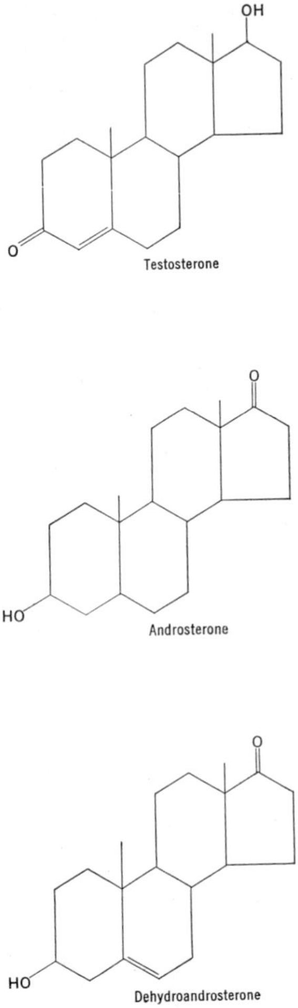

Testosterone

Androsterone

Dehydroandrosterone

Fig. 8.12 Formulas of three testis hormones.

of thyroid hormone, continuing the story of interrelation and mutual control already noted.

Thyrotrophin was mentioned earlier in this chapter. It promotes the secretion of the thyroid hormone, and is inhibited by the presence of the thyroid hormone in the blood. Thus the controlled level of thyroid secretion is maintained.

Corticotrophin (also called ACTH, adrenocorticotrophic hormone) is a hormone stimulating the adrenal cortex to greater production of the corticosterone group of hormones. Corticotrophin is produced in the anterior lobe, and its absence may prevent the normal activity of the adrenal cortex entirely.

The presence of a parathyrotrophin is in some doubt, although much evidence points to the existence of such a hormone. Even more doubtful is the pancreatrophic hormone supposed to increase the secretion of insulin.

There are two gonadotrophic hormones, secreted by the anterior lobe, affecting the **gonads** (Greek: begetters), or reproductive organs. **Gonadotrophin I** stimulates the testes and ovaries to produce the reproductive cells — sperms and eggs. **Gonadotrophin II** stimulates the endocrine cells of the testes and ovaries to produce their respective hormones. More will be said about these hormones in the account of the endocrine activity of the testes and ovaries.

Prolactin (Latin: coming before milk) is secreted by the anterior lobe, especially during pregnancy. Its effect is to enlarge the breasts and promote the secretion of milk.

Within the anterior lobe there are three kinds of cells distinguishable by their staining reactions. The **chromophobe** (Greek: color repelling) **cells** do not take stain well, and are thought to be undifferentiated cells from which the other two types develop. **Acidophil** (Greek: acid-loving) **cells** are stained by acid stains, and **basophil** (Greek: baseloving) **cells** by basic, or alkaline stains. Since only the latter two types of cells secrete hormones, it has been postulated that only two hormones are produced by the anterior lobe, and that each performs several of the actions described above. It is suggested that experimental separation of specific hormones involves breaking down one composite hormone into fractions which have specific activities. Whether this is a better explanation than that one type of cell may produce more than one type of hormone, or that the acidophil and basophil cells may be divided into distinct subtypes must depend for the present on personal opinion. Further study may bring out more evidence on this problem. At any rate, the acidophil cells seem to be responsible for the hormones having growth, corticotrophic, and prolactin effects, and the basophilic cells produce the hormones with thyrotrophic and gonadotrophic effects.

The **posterior lobe** secretes two hormones: **pitocin** and **pitressin**. Pitocin stimulates the contraction of the walls of the uterus. Pitressin raises blood pressure, stimulates intestinal peristalsis, and promotes the retention of water in the body by kidney tubules. Whether pitressin is a compound hormone or a single hormone with many actions is not yet clear.

THE TESTIS

In the **testes** are found scattered cells, the **interstitial** (Latin: standing between) **cells,** which are endocrine in action. They are stimulated to activity by the appearance of gonadotrophin II in the blood supplying the testis. The most potent secretion of the interstitial cells is called **testosterone,** but **androsterone** and **dehydroandrosterone** have been isolated, and they have lesser strength. Their formulas are shown in Figure 8.12; their similarity to adrenal cortex hormones is evident. The testis hormones act to produce the secondary sex characteristics which distinguish the male from the female — distribution of hair on the face and in the pubic region, enlarged larynx, deep fat deposition, enlargement of the male reproductive ducts and glands, and sexual activity directed toward the female.

THE OVARY

The ovary secretes two hormones, **estradiol** and **progesterone.** A slight change in the estradiol produces **estrone,** which is about one tenth as potent. The formulas for these substances are shown in Figure 8.13. They are very like the formulas of the male hormones and the adrenal cortex hormones. They are also not greatly different from the formulas of cholesterol and the bile salts, shown in Figure 8.14.

Estradiol brings about development of the secondary sex characteristics of the female — growth pattern of pubic hair; fat deposition just under the skin, producing the rounded, "curvaceous" form of a woman in contrast to the more angular body of a man; enlargement of the breasts and the female reproductive ducts and glands; and sexual activity directed toward the male.

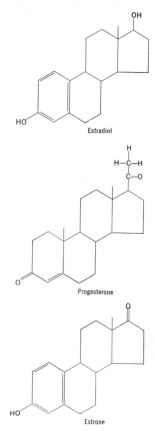

Fig. 8.13   Formulas of three ovary hormones.

Fig. 8.14   Formulas of cholesterol and bile salts. S stands for sulfur, Na for sodium.

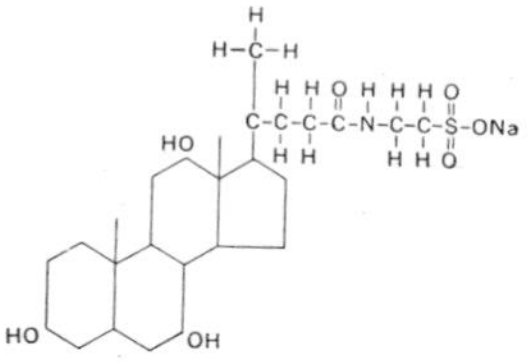

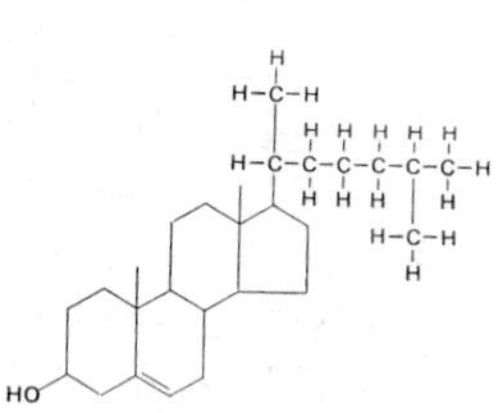

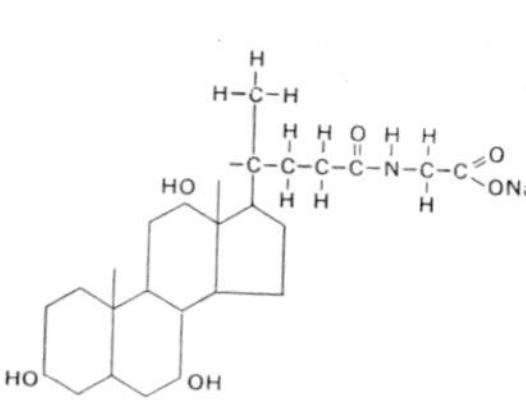

Menstrual Cycle

Estradiol and progesterone are involved in a rhythmic series of changes in women known as the **menstrual** (Latin: monthly) **cycle.** Since the cycle is continuous, after it has once started at **puberty,** until it stops at **menopause,** we may begin our description at any point of the cycle.

The most conspicuous event externally is the flow of blood through the reproductive tract to the outside, a process known as **menstruation.** This is followed by an increase in the amount of gonadotrophin I in the blood. The gonadotrophin I stimulates an ovary to speed up the maturing of one egg. In its maturing, the egg is surrounded by a cluster of nurse cells, the egg and nurse cells together constituting a <u>follicle.</u>

The nurse cells of the follicle secrete estradiol. This inhibits further production by the pituitary of gonadotrophin I, and stimulates rapid restoration of the lining of the uterus. The superficial part of this uterus lining is lost during menstruation, and is rebuilt by the remaining deeper parts. As it is being rebuilt, a number of helically coiled arteries penetrate the new portion, providing a profuse network of capillaries.

About two weeks after menstruation begins, the uterus wall is very thick and well supplied with blood vessels. The follicle has greatly enlarged. Gonadotrophin I is no longer present in as great quantity as it was earlier in the cycle. Then the follicle bursts, exploding its egg right through the ovary wall and out into the body cavity. Normally the current produced by the ciliated lining of the reproductive duct carries the egg into the duct on its way to the uterus.

The sudden release of estradiol by the rupture of the follicle increases the amount of that hormone in the blood. The pituitary gland, in response, releases greater quantities of gonadotrophin II. This stimulates the healing and modification of the broken follicle into a structure called the **corpus luteum** (Latin: yellow body). This corpus luteum secretes progesterone, which inhibits the release of gonadotrophin II by the pituitary gland, and stimulates the maintenance of the thick uterus wall with its high vascularity.

If the egg passing into the uterus is not fertilized, and does not burrow into the uterus wall, the corpus luteum ceases to produce progesterone, usually about ten days after release of the egg from the ovary. After the supply of progesterone in the blood is gone, the coiled arteries supplying the surface layers of the uterus lining constrict, reducing the blood supply to the surface; this gradually weakens the tissues there, including the blood vessel walls. Then, as blood pressure forces blood through these coiled arteries, and they relax, permitting a surge of blood to pass, the weakened tissues give way and a breakdown of the uterus lining occurs, with the loss of some blood — usually about 30 cc. — at menstruation. This breakdown and blood loss may last about three or four days, and by that time gonadotrophin I will have stimulated the ovary to start maturing another egg, and the follicle will be releasing estradiol, which helps rebuild the uterus lining.

If the egg passing into the uterus has been fertilized, the resulting embryo will burrow into the wall and establish contact with the deeper tissues of the uterus, building a tissue known as the **placenta** (Greek: flat cake), composed of contributions from both the embryo and the uterus wall. The placenta produces a hormone which stimulates the corpus luteum to continue secretion of progesterone, so that the disappearance of the pituitary gonadotrophin II will not cause the cessation of the progesterone secretion, and thus the sloughing off of the uterine lining. As long as

TABLE 8.1

THE MENSTRUAL CYCLE

Average number of days after start of menstruation	Events in the anterior lobe of the pituitary gland	Events in the ovary	Events in the uterus
0–5	Gonadotrophin I released	Maturation of a follicle speeded up	Uterine wall sloughs off; menstrual flow occurs
5–15	Gonadotrophin I production inhibited	Follicle secretes estradiol	Uterine wall restored
15		Follicle explodes egg into body cavity, releasing estradiol in large amounts	
15–25	Gonadotrophin II released	Corpus luteum formed and it secretes progesterone	Uterine wall is maintained
25–28, if egg is not fertilized	Gonadotrophin II production inhibited	Progesterone secretion stops	Uterine wall weakens and finally sloughs off
25–birth, if egg is fertilized	Gonadotrophin II production inhibited; prolactin secreted near end of pregnancy	Placental hormone stimulates corpus luteum to continued secretion of progesterone	Placenta formed and secretes a hormone; uterine wall remains intact until after embryo is born
Sometime after birth	Gonadotrophin I released	Progesterone no longer secreted	Placental hormone no longer secreted; menstruation occurs

the placental hormone is in the blood going to the ovary, the progesterone will continue, and the uterus will remain intact.

It is supposed that prolactin appears toward the end of pregnancy when the ovarian and placental hormones diminish in quantity. Sometime after the birth of the child, the menstrual cycle, held in abeyance during pregnancy, will recommence, and the hormonal control will be re-established. See Table 8.1.

SUMMARY

The endocrine organs secrete hormones which regulate many phases of metabolic activity. The thyroid hormone controls the rate of oxidation reactions. The parathyroid glands control the distribution of calcium between bones and blood. The digestive tract hormones regulate the release of digestive enzymes. Insulin maintains the use of sugar by the body at a beneficial level. The pineal and thymus glands are enigmas at present, possibly affecting the time of physical and sexual maturity. The adrenal medulla produces a hormone which provides exceptional muscular and nervous capacity during times of stress. The adrenal cortex hormones control the sodium distribution and affect the carbohydrate metabolism and kidney action. The pituitary gland regulates some of the other endocrine organs, facilitates growth, and interacts with the reproductive organs through its anterior lobe secretions; it raises blood pressure, conserves water, and stimulates visceral muscle by its posterior lobe hormones. The testis and ovary secrete hormones which develop differentiating sex characteristics. The menstrual cycle is a series of actions facilitating reproduction, controlled by the hormones of the ovary, pituitary body, and placenta.

The interrelations of these secretions on the same phases of metabolism and on each other are very complicated. Endocrinology is one of the most recent developments in biology, and much remains to be explained. But the importance of the system is fundamental in the life of a human. Together with the nervous system it integrates the diverse activities of the body into a smooth-working, adaptable unit.

REVIEW QUESTIONS

1. Define endocrine; hormone.
2. What are the differences between endocrine and nervous control of bodily events?
3. Describe secretion.

4. Locate and describe the thyroid gland. What is the action of its secretion?

5. Describe the interactions of thyroid and pituitary secretions on each other.

6. Locate and describe the parathyroid glands. What is the action of their secretion?

7. Describe the sources and actions of the hormones especially affecting the digestive tract.

8. Describe the development of our knowledge of insulin.

9. Discuss the status of knowledge about the actions of the pineal and thymus glands.

10. Describe the location and structure, and the actions of the secretion of the adrenal medulla; the adrenal cortex; the anterior lobe of the pituitary gland; the posterior lobe of the pituitary gland.

11. Describe the actions of the hormones of the testis and ovary.

12. Describe the events associated with the menstrual cycle, assuming that fertilization occurs.

GENERAL QUESTIONS

1. What is the significance of the interchangeability of hormones among different kinds of animals? How can hormones be successfully interchanged, whereas blood cannot?

2. The thyroid gland is sometimes said to determine one's personality. Criticize this view.

3. An individual becomes very obese. Malfunction of what endocrine glands might have produced this? How could it be determined which gland is concerned in any particular case?

4. Using the insulin story as a model, invent an account of the discovery of the hormone regulation of the menstrual cycle.

5. Galen (131–201 A.D.), the greatest medical scholar of his time, maintained that the thyroid gland sweetened the voice. Today, we believe its secretion regulates oxidation. Account for this disagreement.

6. Were Starling and Knowlton justified in their doubts?

7. How could you determine whether a sprinter had been injected with adrenin just before his race, if you had no laboratory equipment available?

8. A woman fifty years old has her pituitary gland surgically removed. What hormones should be supplied to her artificially?

9. Is it possible for a person's sex to change from one to the other? If so, how? If not, why not?

10. One of the best commercial sources for female sex hormones is the urine of male horses. Account for this.

CHAPTER 9

The Reproductive System

Sexual Reproduction

In the Introduction were listed certain characteristics of life. Among these was the capacity for reproduction — development of new organisms of the same kind as the existing ones. In the most familiar organisms, reproduction is a sexual process. Fundamentally this amounts to the production of two cells which fuse to initiate the development of a new individual. In animals such as humans these two cells are quite different. One, the egg, produced by the female, contains an abundance of cytoplasm around its nucleus, the cytoplasm carrying a large store of food which is used in the early growth of the new organism. The other cell, the sperm, produced by the male, is stripped down to little more than the nucleus and a wisp of cytoplasm drawn out into a long, slender propelling device.

Whereas the reproductive organs which produce these cells originate similarly in the embryos of the two sexes, they later differentiate considerably. You saw in the last chapter that the hormones they secrete are distinct, although nearly alike; likewise, the secondary sex characteristics whose development they stimulate are distinctive. The fundamental reproductive organs and their accessories are also unlike. Therefore we shall consider the reproductive systems of the two sexes separately.

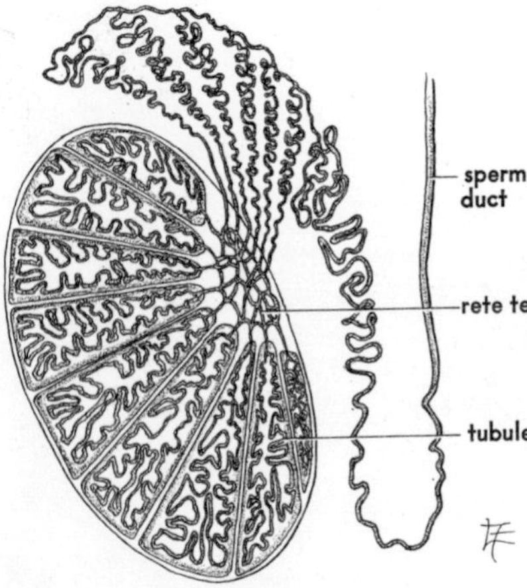

Fig. 9.1 Diagram of the human testis. Note the tubules confined to individual chambers.

sperm duct

rete testis

tubule

THE MALE REPRODUCTIVE SYSTEM

In the male, the organs that produce reproductive cells are the testes. These appear in the developing embryo in the abdominal wall adjacent to the kidneys and adrenal cortex; but before the infant is born they migrate forward and down in front of the urinary bladder and between the ureters to the bottom of the abdominal cavity. The bottom wall of the abdomen recedes before them, forming a pouch, the **scrotum** (Latin: skin), which carries the testes. Experiments have shown that the temperature within the scrotum is a few degrees below that in the kidney region of the abdomen, and that the abdominal temperature exerts an adverse effect on the production of sperms. In a few cases the testes fail to complete this descent into the scrotum, and are retained within the abdominal cavity. Such testes are usually sterile, producing no active sperms because of the higher temperature in the abdomen.

Ordinarily, after the testes have entered the scrotum, the opening between the scrotal and abdominal cavities is closed off by connective tissue except for the passage of sperm ducts, blood vessels, and nerves. If this closure does not occur, a loop of the intestine may slip into the scrotum, a condition known as hernia. This may be remedied by withdrawing the intestinal loop, and grafting a bit of muscle across the opening into the scrotum.

Each testis consists of a large number of tubules and some interstitial cells packed into partitioned chambers. See Figure 9.1. The tubules are long, slender, contorted cylinders, solid until puberty, but then developing a central cavity and thick walls. The walls are made of two kinds of cells. The most numerous are the sperm-forming cells which line the periphery, and gradually work in toward the middle as they mature. A few larger supportive cells nourish the sperm cells before they leave the tubule.

Tucked into the chinks of the twisted tubule are the interstitial cells which secrete the male sex hormones. A few connective tissue fibers also occur around the tubules. See Figure 9.2.

No sperm cells are formed until the time of puberty, usually about the age of fourteen or fifteen years. After that time sperm cells are formed in large numbers throughout mature life, diminishing in rate as the man gets older, although possibly not ceasing altogether as long as he lives.

As sperm cells accumulate in the cavity of a testis tubule, the tubule wall cells secrete a lymphlike fluid which bathes them. In time the pressure of this secretion forces some of the fluid and its contents, the sperms, along the tubule toward a larger duct.

The several tubules in each testis, about 800 in all, each about 27 inches long, run into a network of passageways known as the **rete** (Latin: net) **testis.** This is connected by several small ducts to one large **sperm duct.** The rete testis and its small ducts act as a temporary storehouse of the sperm cells.

The sperm duct coils about the surface of the testis, and then straightens out, passing up into the abdominal cavity. Here it hooks over the entrance of the ureter into the urinary bladder, and curves downward again, joining the urethra soon after it leaves the bladder. See Figure 9.3.

Just before the sperm duct enters the urethra it has a conspicuous swelling, the **ampulla,** which is another temporary storehouse of sperms. At the end of the ampulla is a blind outpouching called the **seminal** (Latin: sperm) **vesicle** (Latin: little bladder). This secretes a fluid which is

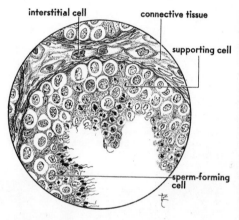

Fig. 9.2   Microscopic structure of the testis. Each tubule has a wall composed of several layers of cells; the tubules are packed in connective tissue containing interstitial cells.

alkaline enough to stimulate vigorous swimming movements of the sperm cells. These sperm cells have the ability to swim when they are in the rete testis, but the slight acidity there, due to release of carbon dioxide, inhibits their activity. When the acidity is counteracted by the seminal vesicle secretion, the sperms may become very active. The seminal vesicle secretion also contains some sugar (fructose) which provides a source of energy for the sperm cells, which break the sugar molecules into lactic acid.

At the junction of the two sperm ducts with the urethra there is another large gland, the **prostate** (Greek: standing before) **gland.** The secretion of this gland is also alkaline, helping to neutralize the lactic acid formed by the sperm cells.

A little farther down the urethra, below the entrance of the sperm ducts, is the **bulbo-urethral gland.** This secretes a lubricating fluid which facilitates the passage of the sperms and their accompanying secretions through the urethra.

The remainder of the urethra passes through the **penis.** Surrounding the urethra in the penis is a spongy labyrinth of blood sinuses, the **corpus spongiosum** (Latin: spongy

Fig. 9.3   Human male reproductive tract. Trace the pathway traveled by sperm cells from the testis to the outside of the body.

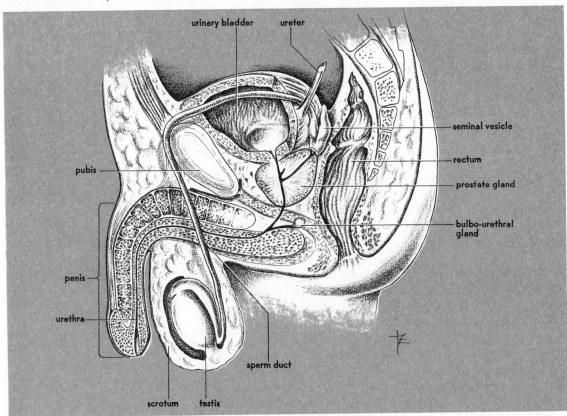

body). Nearby, in the front part of the penis, are two similar structures, the **corpora cavernosa** (Latin: hollow bodies). These three structures receive blood from a branch of each internal iliac artery, and drain blood into the tributaries of the internal iliac veins. See Figure 9.4.

Normally the arteries supplying the corpus spongiosum and corpora cavernosa are nearly occluded, so that only a small amount of blood passes through them. But stimulation leading to a discharge of sperm from the sperm ducts causes the arteries to expand, so that a sudden torrent of blood enters the spongy chambers. This causes a swelling of the penis, pinching the veins which drain the chambers, so that the blood in them is under great pressure. This makes the penis stiffen and project out from the body as a rigid tube, much as a flaccid fire hose attains rigidity when it is full of water under high pressure. After the discharge of sperms has occurred, the arteries of the penis contract, the veins gradually drain off the extra blood, and the penis relaxes once more.

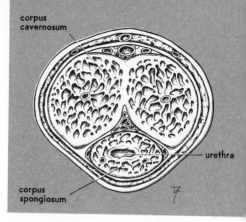

Fig. 9.4   Cross section of a human penis. Note the large blood sinuses, and the urethra passing through the smallest one.

Ejaculation

The process of discharge of sperms, known as **ejaculation** (Latin: throwing out), occurs according to the following sequence:

Distention of the rete testis and ampulla of the sperm duct, or stimulation of the end of the penis initiates a parasympathetic reflex which brings about the erection of the penis by filling the corpora spongiosum and cavernosa. The bulbo-urethral gland releases its lubricating secretion. Then the prostate gland secretion is sent into the urethra through several small ducts by the contraction of visceral muscles in the gland. Then contraction of the musculature in the ampullae sends about half a billion sperm cells into the urethra. Finally, the seminal vesicles release their very bulky secretion. Then muscular contractions of the penis force this combined mass of sperm and secretions through the urethra to the outside.

During sexual intercourse, the sperm and their accompanying secretions are deposited in the vagina of the female. But in the absence of sexual intercourse, the discharges take place periodically, as the sperm pathways become congested. Normally this ejaculation takes place at night, when the person sleeps, since the parasympathetic system is in the ascendancy then. Or, the preliminaries of erection may waken the individual. This ejaculation is a normal act in sexually mature males, being in one sense comparable to

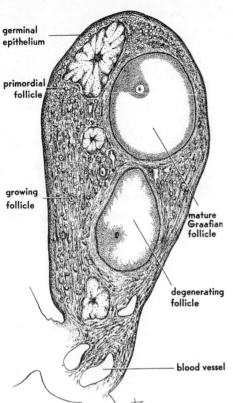

germinal epithelium

primordial follicle

growing follicle

mature Graafian follicle

degenerating follicle

blood vessel

Fig. 9.5 Microscopic structure of the human ovary. Notice the different sizes of follicles, the smallest at the outer part of the ovary, the larger ones working inward.

the menstrual cycle in the female, for it disposes of reproductive cells prepared but not used for reproduction.

A general lack of knowledge of the details of human reproduction has given unscrupulous people an opportunity to prey on uninformed boys. Stories of the loss of manhood because of night ejaculations have frightened some boys into purchasing quack remedies to prevent a normal action. If such remedies had been efficacious in preventing these ejaculations, then, indeed, something serious would be wrong.

Other advertising warns unsuspecting dupes about one testis being larger than the other, or a feeling of "worms" in the scrotum. Normally, the left testis is larger than the right, and normally the sperm ducts and blood vessels may be felt through the wall of the scrotum. But such is the susceptibility of many of us to accept at face value anything printed in black and white, or told us by a supposed authority, that a great deal of unnecessary fear and unhappiness results.

Much variation in the frequency of ejaculations occurs among men. It may occur almost every day, or it may occur only a few times a month, or less. The vigor of secretion of the glands along the sperm duct, the rate of sperm formation, and the general state of health and nervous sensitivity of the body influence this frequency.

THE FEMALE REPRODUCTIVE SYSTEM

The organs producing eggs are called **ovaries** (Fig. 9.5). These are located in the abdomen, about at the place where the testes arose in the male. Each ovary is about three centimeters in height, two in width, and one in thickness. Along its periphery is a layer of epithelial cells. Just beneath this is a dense coat of connective tissue fibers. Within this the tissues of the ovary may be divided into cortex and medulla.

The cortex contains the prospective egg cells and the follicles in various stages of maturity. The medulla is made up of connective tissue, blood vessels, lymph vessels, and nerves, collectively called the <u>stroma</u>. This stroma permeates the cortex, too, surrounding the follicles.

The cycle of development of ovarian follicles was described in Chapter 8. In a sexually mature woman, one egg is normally matured approximately every four weeks. The ovaries usually alternate in this, first one ovary and then the other being involved. If two or more eggs from the same or both ovaries mature at the same time, and are fertilized, fraternal twins, or triplets, etc., are produced.

If one fertilized egg divides into two cells which separate and each develops a new individual, these individuals are called identical twins.

The four weeks between two consecutive releases of eggs is an average figure. Extremes have been recorded of a menstrual cycle recurring every two days, and another every eight months or more. But normal variation does not extend beyond the range of three to five weeks. The time varies with each individual and at different times in the same person.

After an egg bursts out of the ovary into the abdominal cavity it is usually picked up immediately by the **oviduct.** This structure is a hollow tube lined with ciliated cells. The expanded open end of the oviduct moves about, sweeping around the ovary like a vacuum cleaner, drawing into itself any loose objects such as the egg, which is only about one tenth of a millimeter in diameter, and easily carried by the ciliary currents. By this ciliary movement the egg is carried down into the **uterus,** a thick-walled organ to which both oviducts lead. See Figure 9.6.

The cyclic changes in the uterus lining have been described in Chapter 8. At the time of arrival of the egg in the uterus, the uterine wall is thick, soft, and well supplied with blood vessels. If there were sperms placed in the vagina within the previous few days, some of these sperms may have

Fig. 9.6 Human female reproductive tract. Trace the pathway an egg travels.

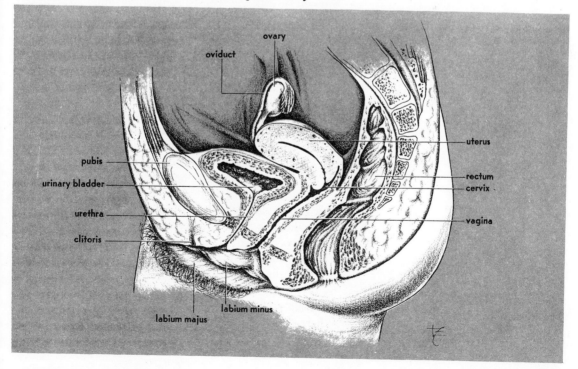

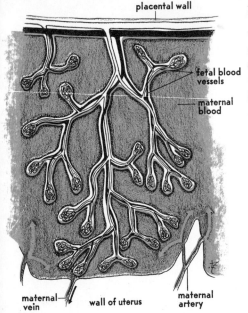

placental wall

fetal blood vessels

maternal blood

maternal vein

wall of uterus

maternal artery

Fig. 9.7 Diagram of the two circulations in the placenta. The blood of the mother is brought to the placenta by blood vessels in her uterus. It is released from her vessels and seeps through the tissue of the placenta. The blood vessels of the embryo penetrate the placenta and are intact. The bloods, therefore, do not mix; but substances may diffuse from one blood to the other through the walls of fetal vessels.

wriggled up the uterus into the oviducts, where one of them would have found and fused with the egg. This fertilized egg, called a **zygote,** will then burrow into the wall of the uterus when it reaches there. Together with the uterus wall it will form a **placenta,** which is a connective tissue mat containing blood vessels developing in the new individual and blood vessels contributed by the uterus. These two sets of blood vessels come into close contact with each other, so that food substances and oxygen diffuse from the mother's blood vessels into those of the developing individual, or **embryo** (Greek: internal swelling or growth), and wastes from the embryo diffuse into the blood stream of the mother. There is no actual contact of bloods, so that interchanges between embryo and mother must be by diffusion through the membranes of both. See Figure 9.7.

If the egg reaching the uterus has not been fertilized, it remains in the cavity of the uterus for a time, but eventually, if it still encounters no sperm cell, it begins to disintegrate and is lost at the next menstruation.

The most likely time for fertilization to occur is soon after the egg enters the oviduct. The length of time the sperm cells can live depends in part upon the degree of acidity of their environment. The fluid in the vagina is usually somewhat acid, but this may be counteracted by the alkalinity of the prostate and seminal vesicle secretions brought in with the sperms. Actively swimming sperm cells may migrate through the narrow **cervix** (Latin: neck) at the bottom of the uterus and into the uterus and oviducts.

In some cases the sperms may die in a few hours; in others they may survive a week or more. This, together with the lingering of the egg in the uterus, means that there may be fertilization no matter in what part of the menstrual cycle sperms are deposited in the female reproductive tract. However, during menstruation, the sperm cells have an almost insuperable obstacle in the flow of blood. And in many individual cases, the duration of sperm or egg may be very short. Moreover, the time of release of the egg in the cycle is variable, so that the fertile and infertile periods of a menstrual cycle are not the same for all women, and no predictions are safe unless a careful physiological study is made of the particular case.

The **vagina** (Latin: sheath, or scabbard) leads from the uterus to the outside. Its opening to the outside is bordered by two fleshy flaps on each side. The outer, larger ones are the **labia majora,** and the inner ones are the **labia minora.** Where the labia minora join each other in front there is a tiny structure, the **clitoris,** which is comparable in origin to the penis of the male. It is very much smaller, and has no urethra running through it, but it does have three spongy bodies corresponding to those of the penis; these become turgid during sexual excitement, and contribute impulses to the reflexes involved in sexual intercourse.

The vagina and urethra open separately into the space between the labia minora, the urethra by a tiny opening in front of the much larger vagina.

In the vagina, near the exit, there is a membrane, the **hymen** (Greek: membrane), partially closing the vagina. This may be ruptured during sexual intercourse, but its presence or absence is not a sure test of virginity, for it may be broken accidentally in a fall, or it may not be entirely destroyed at intercourse.

HYGIENE OF THE REPRODUCTIVE SYSTEM

The physiology of the reproductive system is so complex and involved with emotional factors that its use is both a matter of great interest and an urgent problem to every human who has reached the age of puberty. Not only this generation but also the next is vitally affected by its functions. Almost every phase of human society is directly concerned with perpetuation of the species. The fundamental group unit, the family, is based on the reproductive process. Much of the human world's activity is taken up with founding and caring for a family, or preparation for these activities.

The great advantage of belonging to a species which accumulates a knowledge of its past is the opportunity to benefit by the experience of untold millions of individuals who have gone before. Many of the lessons learned by this cumulation of experience are codified in social standards. These are always subject to revision with further knowledge and experience, but in general they are of great value as guides for human conduct.

For example, human experience has shown the wisdom of monogamy. If the sexual interest of a man and woman in each other is synthesized with common cultural, social, economic, and philosophical or religious interests into a love and mutual understanding, such a marriage has the greatest potentialities for happiness and satisfaction of the husband and wife, for their contributions to society, and for the best development of the children of that marriage.

The problem of how to select a marriage partner and how to bring about a suitable marriage is one of the greatest importance to young men and women. How do you know when you are in love? In some places, marriages are arranged by the parents of those to be married; what about love in such cases? Does one fall in love at first sight?

In answer to these questions, love is an association which grows, lives, changes in its characteristics. Certainly sexual attraction is a prominent factor in it, but just as certainly, it is not the only one. It is the most conspicuous one for most American youth, brought up in an environment which does much to accentuate and emphasize sexual attractions. But the average young man or woman acquires enough wisdom and judgment to require more of his marital choice than sexual attractiveness. Community of interests, similarity in ethical and social standards, and an eagerness to contribute to the other's genuine happiness (not to be confused with temporary pleasure) are cardinal points in any good rating scale.

Realizing the importance of emotions aroused by sexual attractiveness in the selection of a bride or bridegroom, how far should one go in investigating sexual experiences during courtship? The fondling, kissing, and caressing summed up in the term "petting" are part and parcel of the preparation for sexual intercourse. In married couples, such preparations insure the most satisfactory experiences from intercourse. Usually a man is more readily brought to a state of sexual excitement than a woman, and the physical signs of affection he shares with her help to bring her to a state of preparedness. In this way, both may experience a high peak of sexual pleasure together. If the man is too impatient, he may obtain his satisfaction and not be able to provide his wife her satisfaction. Repeated frustrations of this sort may injure the possibilities of later satisfactions for both.

If, during courtship, a man and a woman carry on caresses to a point at which sexual release is imminent, one of two results may occur: The power of the excitement aroused may overwhelm any inhibitions they have, and they may indulge in sexual intercourse which they will greatly regret later; or they may repress the urge to carry their reflexes through to consummation, building a block to the completion of sexual intercourse. This block will grow at each succeeding frustration, and when, after marriage, sexual intercourse is desired, this block must be broken down, with consequent dissatisfactions and misunderstandings.

This does not mean that no physical intimacy is to be allowed before marriage. But it does mean that it should be carefully controlled, and kept well within bounds. These bounds will depend upon the feelings and experiences of the individuals concerned, and can best be measured by them. Whenever the tendency toward letting oneself go sexually appears to be approached, unmarried lovers should feel that they have gone far enough. Self-examination, if honestly done, will determine for each one about where his threshold is.

During the early stages of courtship, very little physical contact is wise. After engagement, as marriage approaches, a gradually increasing degree of caressing strengthens the attachment and encourages love to grow. Then, after marriage, consummation of these intimacies by sexual intercourse will be a natural, unrestrained, and supremely satisfying experience. The giving of two people to each other will seem to be the physical expression of a more complete giving of two lives to each other, and the foundation for continued growth of love is firmly laid.

The frequency of sexual intercourse after marriage depends in part upon the choice of the two individuals and in part on their state of health, particularly that of the wife. As stated before, the husband is normally more readily sexually aroused, and it devolves upon him to use some restraint, to consult the wishes of his wife, and to prepare her gradually. On the other hand, it is pleasing to the husband occasionally to have the wife initiate the courting which precedes sexual intercourse.

When the reproductive contact results in the formation of a zygote, and pregnancy ensues, sexual intercourse may still take place until a month or two before the expected birth of the baby without serious danger. The embryo is encased in its own membranes within the uterus, and will not be disturbed by the presence of sperm in the mother's reproductive tract. As was stated in Chapter 8, no eggs are released from the ovary during pregnancy, for the menstrual cycle is held in abeyance.

Pregnancy greatly distends the uterus, and brings about other profound changes in the metabolism of the mother. At the time of birth, the uterus wall begins to undergo peristaltic contractions, the bones of the pelvic girdle pull apart enlarging the opening through which the baby is to go, and the baby begins to pass through the vagina. The contractions of the uterus and the pressure on other organs are very painful, so that usually the mother is partially or completely anesthetized during this process, commonly known as "labor."

After the baby has been expelled from the vagina, the connection between the baby and the placenta, called the **umbilical** (Latin: navel) **cord,** is cut, and the cut end sewed up at the middle of the baby's abdomen. Soon thereafter, the placenta works loose, due to the uterine contractions, and this is expelled as the "afterbirth."

If the pelvic girdle opening is too small for the safe passage of the baby, the attending physician may perform a Caesarean operation, so called because Julius Caesar was supposed to have been delivered that way. The doctor cuts open the abdominal wall and the uterus wall, and removes the baby directly.

In rare cases, an egg breaks out of the ovary and is not picked up by the oviduct. Such an egg may float about in the abdominal cavity for a time, and then disintegrate. If it should be fertilized by a sperm which swam up the oviduct and out into the body cavity, the zygote may settle against almost any organ in the neighborhood — the body wall, the intestine, the kidney, the outside of the uterus — and build a placenta and develop. Such a growth is abnormal, and should be removed surgically.

After a Caesarean operation, a woman must usually wait some time for the uterus and abdominal wall to heal thoroughly before she can safely undertake another pregnancy. Even after a normal birth, it is sometimes wise to wait a year or so before initiating a new embryo.

The reproductive capacity of a woman, unlike that of a man, usually comes to an end at the age of forty-five or thereabouts. A process called the menopause occurs, bringing to a stop the recurrent menstrual cycles. In some women this period is accompanied by profound and distressing metabolic changes, inducing nervous upsets and temporary ill-health; in others the change is gradual and does not bring about such unhappy symptoms. In any case the menstrual cycle and the release of eggs stop. Sexual desire diminishes, but may not entirely disappear.

SUMMARY

The reproductive systems provide sperms and eggs and, in the female, a place for development of the embryo until birth. The release of sperms by the male and their reception by the female are brought about by nerve reflexes with which are associated highly emotional reactions. These are of great importance in human social life, and knowledge of them and a method of dealing with them are necessary to the happiness of every individual. The normal expression is through marriage, but, lacking this, an individual may sublimate his sexual passion into a life of artistic creation or service to mankind without the normal outlet.

REVIEW QUESTIONS

1. Define reproduction.
2. Describe the structure of the male reproductive system.
3. What are the actions of the secretions of the various glands associated with the sperm duct and urethra?
4. Describe the events associated with ejaculation of sperm.
5. Describe the structure of the female reproductive system.
6. How does an egg get from the ovary to the uterus?
7. Describe a placenta.
8. Where may union of a sperm and an egg occur?
9. What is the hymen?
10. Discuss the social aspects of use of the reproductive system.

GENERAL QUESTIONS

1. Is it conceivable that sexual reproduction in some organisms could come about through the union of sex cells which are alike? Why or why not?
2. What do you suppose regulates the time at which a male first starts forming sperm cells?
3. What, in the testis, corresponds to the stroma of the ovary?
4. Explain the origin of the Dionne quintuplets.
5. What influences on the life of a pregnant mother may affect the structure or personality of the embryo in her uterus?
6. How could a physician determine the fertile and sterile periods of a woman's menstrual cycle?
7. What social regulations are a result of the bisexual nature of the human race?
8. Devise a balance sheet for weighing the importance of various factors in predicting a happy marriage.
9. What criteria are helpful in determining the extent of physical contact advisable for unmarried couples? Be as specific as possible.
10. Describe love.

CHAPTER 10

Embryology

Fertilization

In Chapter 9, the reproductive organs of men and women were described, and their products: sperm cells and egg cells. The sperm cells may be released from the male reproductive system and discharged into the female reproductive tract. If a sperm cell encounters an egg cell in the upper reaches of this tract, it will unite with the egg, and the resulting union will develop into a new human being. The story of this process will be the subject of this chapter.

The egg, at fertilization, is about one tenth of a millimeter or a little more in diameter. The sperm contributes very little except its nucleus to the bulk of the egg, so that the fertilized egg is very little larger than the unfertilized egg. It normally takes about three days for the egg to pass down the oviduct into the uterus. If it is fertilized near the upper end of the oviduct, some development occurs before it reaches the uterus.

Cell Division

The zygote divides into two cells, each receiving part of the substance of the egg nucleus and part of the substance of the sperm nucleus. Within each of the two cells these nuclear parts are reassembled into one nucleus, possessing the hereditary potentialities of the new individual, derived in part from each parent. The mechanism of cellular division will be discussed in Chapter 11, and the problems of the hereditary potentialities in Chapter 12.

Normally, the two cells formed by the division of the zygote remain adhering to each other. Should they separate and continue their development, identical twins would result.

Each of the two cells divides again, producing four. These in turn divide, forming eight. Each of the eight divides, forming sixteen, and so forth. These divisions are not all simultaneous. For example, one of the cells in the four-cell stage may divide before the others, so that at one moment there may be five cells. But usually the other three are not far behind.

These early stages of development in human embryos are difficult to get. One doesn't use humans as freely as he uses other experimental animals. The early human embryos examined by embryologists have been those aborted, or those removed with a pregnant uterus which must be taken to save a woman's life. The youngest human embryo found and studied so far was a two-cell stage recovered from the oviduct. It was composed of nine cells, so that it had just started on its fourth round of cell divisions.

These divisions continue, but not with such regularity as in the early ones. After a time the embryo consists of a little ball of cells known as a **morula** (Latin: little mulberry). See Figure 10.1.

Trophoblast

About six days after the zygote was formed, the morula burrows into the cushiony wall of the uterus. At this time there may be distinguished in the morula two regions, the peripheral **trophoblast** (Greek: nourishing sprout) and the central **inner cell mass.**

The cells of the trophoblast develop very rapidly, digesting the uterus wall until they have weakened it enough to move in. The uterus wall heals over the outside of the parasitic embryo, which is now completely embedded. The nuclei of the trophoblast divide so rapidly that the cells cannot keep pace. Thus it comes about that while the inner layer of trophoblast, next to the inner cell mass, is epithelial, the outer portion is simply an undivided coating of cytoplasm with numerous nuclei scattered through it. This **syncytium** (Greek: fused cells) breaks into the walls of uterine blood vessels, so that little lakes of blood wash against it. From this blood the syncytial trophoblast absorbs nourishment which provides for further growth of the embryo. At this stage the entire embryonic mass may be about a millimeter long, and not quite as wide or thick. It is about a week and a half old.

Inner Cell Mass

Within the trophoblast, the inner cell mass has grown much more slowly. In fact, this group of cells is now separated from the trophoblast by considerable spaces. The cells are now arranged in two layers, the upper one (toward the nearest part of the trophoblast) known as **ectoderm** (Greek: outer skin), and the lower one as **endoderm** (Greek: inner skin). The cells are cuboidal or columnar in shape, and separated by a narrow space, or by none at all. Curving over the ectoderm like a dome is the **amnion,** composed of very thin, flattened cells. The space between the amnion and the ectoderm is the **amniotic cavity.** Similarly, below

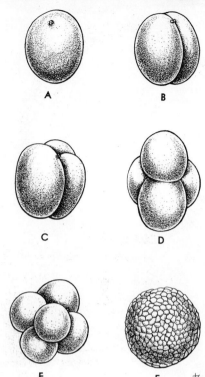

Fig. 10.1   Early cell divisions in the mammal egg, leading to the morula stage. Diagrammatic.

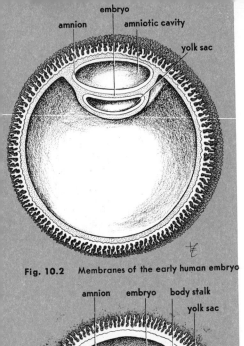

Fig. 10.2 Membranes of the early human embryo

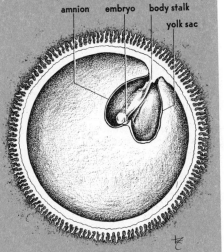

Fig. 10.3 Human embryo in the middle of the fourth week. Note the attachment to the placenta by a body stalk.

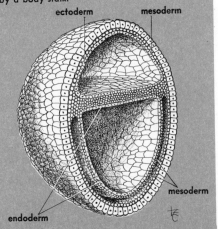

Fig. 10.4 Formation of the mesoderm layer.

the endoderm there is a pouch lined by flattened cells. This pouch is known as the **yolk sac.** At this stage the embryo may be called a **gastrula.** See Figure 10.2.

At what will be the posterior end of the embryo, it is still connected to the trophoblast. This connection is called the **body stalk.** See Figure 10.3. In the ectoderm of the embryo near this stalk appears a longitudinal furrow, the **primitive groove.** Cells work in, divide, and pass anteriorly along this groove, wedging themselves between the ectoderm and endoderm as they move forward. They contribute to the layer known as **mesoderm** (Greek: middle skin).

The mesoderm increases rapidly, and grows out around the edge of the ectoderm and up over the amniotic cavity, forming an outer wall of the amnion; similarly, other mesoderm cells turn the corner of the endoderm, and pass around the yolk sac making an outer coat here. See Figure 10.4.

Notochord

The mesoderm passing up the midline of the embryo between ectoderm and endoderm rounds up into a long, cylindrical rod, the **notochord** (Fig. 10.5). The cells of this structure become turgid with fluid, and make an elastic but stiff skeletal support for the body.

Nervous System

The notochord stimulates the ectoderm immediately overlying it to form a furrow, the **neural groove,** which dips in toward the notochord. As time goes on this groove gets deeper and then closes over at the surface, forming a hollow tube above the notochord. This hollow tube, derived from the inrolled ectoderm, will become the central nervous system. Most of its length will be the spinal cord, but at the anterior end (farthest from the body stalk) it will enlarge and differentiate into the brain. The ectoderm which reunited over the top of the groove becomes the epidermis of the back.

Some cells between the epidermis and the neural tube are left hanging in space, not joining either one. These are called **neural crest cells,** and will give rise to the spinal and autonomic ganglia, the adrenal medulla, and the sheaths of cranial and spinal nerves. The nerves themselves will grow out of the neural tube and ganglia.

Digestive Tract

Meanwhile, the amniotic cavity is expanding, and pushes around the anterior end of the embryo, folding underneath the head end, undercutting the embryo. A little later, a similar process begins at the posterior end of the embryo. See Figure 10.6.

This begins to narrow down the upper end of the yolk sac, so that the lower part will be connected to the embryo by a narrower neck or stalk.

The endodermal layer now roofs a cavity which is the expanded upper end of the yolk sac. The undercutting of the amnion at each end makes floors to the upper cavity of the yolk sac, but leaves the middle open through the yolk stalk. The anterior floored end is known as the **foregut,** the middle open portion as the **midgut,** and the posterior floored part as the **hindgut.** These divisions are not hard and fast, as continued undercutting increases the lengths of the foregut and hindgut at the expense of the midgut. The endoderm will eventually form the lining of the digestive tract and the respiratory tract. See Figure 10.6 again.

Mesoderm

To return to the mesoderm, the notochord became differentiated out of the median strip. To either side the mesoderm occupies part of the space between ectoderm and endoderm. At the lateral margins of the embryo, the mesoderm divides into two sheets, one following the amnion up over the embryo, and the other following the yolk sac down under the embryo. When the amnion begins to undercut the embryo and compress the neck of the yolk sac, the two lateral sheets of mesoderm are brought close together, but

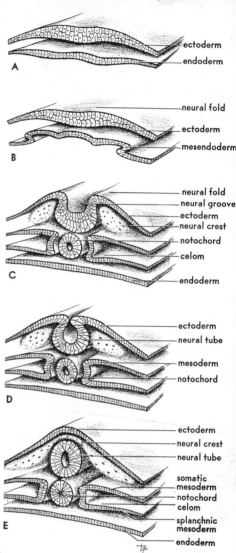

Fig. 10.5   Formation of the neural tube. Note how the epidermis inrolls and cuts off the tube from the surface.

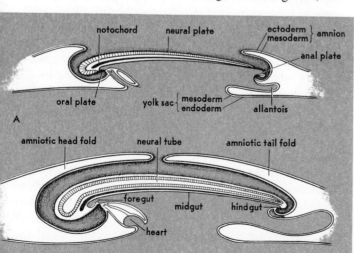

Fig. 10.6   Diagrams of the formation of head and tail folds. Note how the embryo is undercut at each end.

they do not fuse. The space between them, although greatly diminished, remains as the body cavity or **celom** (Greek: hollow). The sheet outside the celom, covering the amniotic cavity, is the **somatic** (Greek: body) **mesoderm,** and the sheet inside the celom, covering the yolk sac, is the **splanch-nic** (Greek: visceral) **mesoderm.** It will be seen that the somatic mesoderm lies against ectoderm, and the splanchnic mesoderm against endoderm.

In the splanchnic mesoderm just under the foregut the heart develops (Fig. 10.7). It appears first as two tubes or hollows in the mesoderm, lined by a coat of very thin cells. Soon a heavier layer of mesoderm cells covers these two tubes, making the primordium (Latin: first beginning) of the muscular wall of the heart. Later the two inner tubes will fuse into one, and then, much later still, divide again into two pathways. Other parts of the circulatory system develop throughout the mesoderm as separate patches, which later link up into one system.

The mesoderm at either side of the notochord is not divided into somatic and splanchnic layers, but is at first one continuous mass. Gradually there begin to appear in it little blocks of condensed mesoderm cells, paired on the two sides of the notochord. These blocks are called **somites** (Greek: little bodies).

From the medial parts of these somites develop the vertebrae which will envelop the notochord and neural tube. None of these somites appears in the anterior end of the embryo, so vertebra formation occurs only behind the head.

Lateral to the formation of vertebrae, the somites differentiate into skeletal muscles. The development of these muscles out of segmentally arranged blocks of tissue produces a pattern of muscles showing segmentation. Later some of these segmental muscles will fuse with each other, producing long muscles stretching up and down the back; others, like the rib muscles, retain their segmental arrangement throughout life. In the region of the limbs, segmental muscles move away from their place of origin and invade the arms and legs, developing in association with the skeletal elements differentiating out of mesoderm.

In the head, mesoderm remains diffuse and not apparently segmented, but skull elements, muscles, and connective tissue develop out of it.

Lateral to the somites but medial to the somatic and splanchnic sheets is the area of mesoderm which will form the kidneys, the reproductive organs, and the adrenal cortex.

To summarize the sources of the principal systems of the body: From the ectoderm come the epidermis of the skin, and the nervous system, together with the glands connected with them: sweat glands, oil glands, pituitary, and adrenal medulla. From the endoderm come the linings of the digestive and respiratory tracts, and the glands associated with them: salivary glands, liver, gall bladder, pancreas, thyroid, parathyroid, and thymus. From the mesoderm come the skeletal, muscular, circulatory, excretory, and reproductive systems, and the adrenal cortex.

With these sources in mind, we may visualize the embryo developing from week to week and see that differentiation occurs very early. The later months of prenatal life are given over largely to growth.

3 Weeks

An embryo three weeks old (Fig. 10.7) is about two millimeters long, and already has ten pairs of somites. The brain has differentiated into three divisions: forebrain, midbrain, and hindbrain. In the skin at either side of the hindbrain develops a specialized ingrowth which will become the inner ear. It will later sink into the head away from the skin and come to lie near the brain. The forebrain also bulges out on each side, beginning to form the retinas of the eyes and the optic nerves. The foregut has two little ventral pouches, one behind the other in the midline. The anterior one will later become separated as the thyroid gland, and the posterior one will remain attached as the larynx. The hindgut also has a midventral outpouching, known as the **allantois** (Greek: sausagelike). This grows out into the body stalk and helps form the placenta. In its walls are the blood vessels (mesodermal) which carry blood between the body of the embryo and the placenta. The mesoderm shows the beginnings of kidneys. The heart is now one tube, and at about the three-week stage it begins to beat, starting an actual circulation of blood through the first few blood vessels formed, especially those in the placenta. Limb buds show up as little swellings in the sites of the future arms and legs. The first signs of vertebrae appear. In fact, except for skeletal muscles and reproductive organs, every system in the adult body has shown at least some differentiation by the end of three weeks after fertilization.

4 Weeks

At four weeks the embryo has grown to a length of five millimeters and has about forty pairs of somites (Fig. 10.8). It weighs about one fiftieth of a gram. The limb

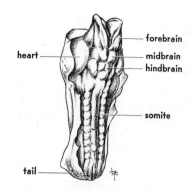

Fig. 10.7 Human embryo three weeks old. The head is forming, and most of the body systems are under way.

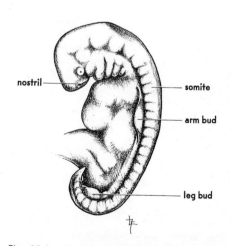

Fig. 10.8 Human embryo four weeks old. The limb buds appear, and the openings through the pharynx wall are prominent. The tail is also conspicuous.

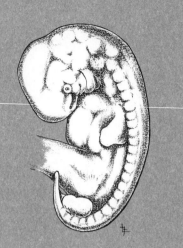

Fig. 10.9 Human embryo five weeks old. Note the further development of the head and limbs.

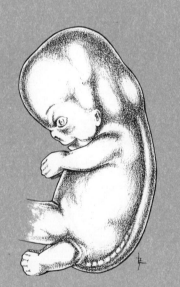

Fig. 10.10 Human embryo six weeks old.

buds are much more conspicuous now, looking like rounded knobs on the sides of the body. The brain has divided further, the forebrain now being divisible into cerebrum and diencephalon, and the hindbrain into cerebellum and pons, and medulla. The retinas have recurved on themselves, and stimulated the epidermis opposite them to form lenses. The inner ears have sunk into the head. The beginnings of the nasal cavity appear. Neural crest cells have formed spinal ganglia, and nerves begin to develop. The tongue begins to appear, and the foregut differentiates the pharynx. This early pharynx establishes connections with the ectoderm of the throat region, and openings form through the sides of the throat into the pharynx much like those gill openings which are permanent features in fishes. The larynx has elongated into a trachea, and bifurcated at the far end to form the beginnings of lungs. The stomach is distinguishable from esophagus and intestine. The liver, gall bladder, and pancreas appear. The midgut is now reduced to a very short portion close to the allantois. The yolk sac is degenerating. The chest and abdomen are separated by the beginnings of a diaphragm. The heart has divided again into right and left channels. More blood vessels have formed and gone into service. Part of the early kidney has already degenerated and more is forming.

5 Weeks

At the end of the fifth week the embryo is about eight millimeters long (Fig. 10.9). The limbs have developed so far that hands and feet are evident. The pituitary body has started. The reproductive organs begin to differentiate. The pulmonary artery separates from the aorta, and develops, growing toward the lungs. The first signs of bone appear — in the collarbones and the lower jaw.

6 Weeks

At the end of six weeks the embryo is about twelve millimeters long (Fig. 10.10). The beginnings of fingers and toes are distinguishable. A prominent tail is present, representing about one sixth of the length of the embryo. The external ears begin to grow. Several layers of cells are forming the retinas. The thymus and parathyroids bud off from the pharynx. The openings from the pharynx through the throat wall close up. The axial skeleton is well formed in cartilage. Somite formation is complete. Muscles have developed, showing segmental arrangement. Tooth germs appear in the jaws. The salivary glands show up, as does the spleen. The urinary bladder, adrenal cortex, oviducts, and external organs of the reproductive system appear. The autonomic ganglia and adrenal medulla begin to develop.

7 Weeks

At the end of the seventh week the embryo is about eighteen millimeters long (Fig. 10.11). The neck differentiates, and the head straightens out somewhat. The face becomes distinguishable. Eyelids form on the eyes. Bone formation occurs in the limbs, upper jaw, and frontal bone. Tooth buds appear where the infant's milk teeth finally develop. In girls bone formation starts earlier and finishes sooner than in boys. The reproductive organs differentiate into either testes or ovaries. The two parts of each adrenal gland meet. The autonomic system is well established. Most of the skeletal muscles of the adult are identifiable.

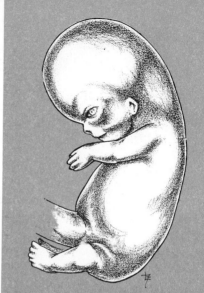

Fig. 10.11   Human embryo seven weeks old.

8 Weeks

At the end of the eighth week the embryo is about 25 millimeters (one inch) long and weighs about one gram (Fig. 10.12). The limbs have all their joints. The tail is much reduced. The cerebrum has greatly enlarged. Most of the distinguishing features of the human anatomy have appeared. The liver is very large. The appendix is formed. Breasts appear (in both sexes). The lymphatic system is developed. But most interesting of all, many of these structures begin active metabolism of the sort characteristic of the adult. The gray and white matter of the spinal cord have differentiated enough so that simple reflex actions occur. Stimulation of the skin produces movements of the limbs, or bending of the head, showing that nerves and muscles are connected. The spleen is forming red blood corpuscles. The liver secretes bile. The embryonic kidney begins to separate waste products from the blood. Adrenin appears as a secretion from the adrenal medulla. The testis interstitial cells secrete testosterone. The adrenal cortex is probably active. The embryo is a going concern.

3 Months

At the end of three months the embryo is 60 millimeters long and weighs about fifteen grams (Fig. 10.13). The face is quite recognizable. Eyelids are fused. Lip movements resembling sucking occur. There are the beginnings of

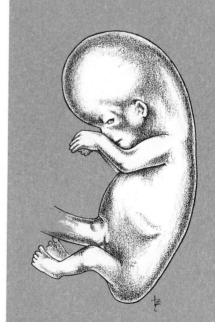

Fig. 10.12   Human embryo eight weeks old.

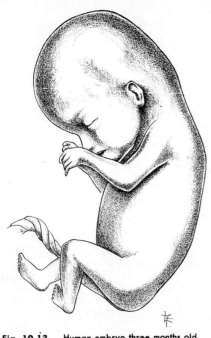

Fig. 10.13 Human embryo three months old.

hair. The fingers have nails, and can curl up into a fist independently of other arm movements. The kidneys are secreting urine into the amniotic cavity. Shallow respiratory movements of the chest occur. The vocal cords and all twenty milk teeth are present, the teeth buried in the jaws. Islands of Langerhans appear in the pancreas. The stomach secretes mucus.

4 Months

At the end of four months the embryo is about 120 millimeters long and weighs about a quarter of a pound (Fig. 10.14). It undergoes spontaneous movements within the uterus. Swallowing movements occur, and the amniotic fluid may be found in the digestive tract. Experiments involving putting saccharine in the amniotic fluid resulted in speeding up the swallowing movements, indicating activity of taste buds. A small amount of fat is deposited by the embryo. Fingerprint patterns have been formed. A thick coating of hair, the **lanugo** (Latin: wool), has formed over the red and wrinkled skin. Ptyalin, pepsin, and insulin are being secreted.

Fig. 10.14 Human embryo four months old.

5 Months

During the fifth month hair becomes apparent on the head (Fig. 10.15). The hair cells in the cochlea develop. The enamel and dentine of the milk teeth are formed. The heart beats at a rate of about 160 per minute.

6 Months

The sixth month sees the reopening of the eyelids and the beginning of the shedding of the lanugo.

7 Months and Later

During the seventh month the lanugo is shed and, together with secretions from the oil glands of the skin, forms a cheesy coating which is washed off at birth. The pituitary gland secretes growth and gonadotrophic hormones. In response to the latter, the testes of a male embryo begin their descent into the scrotum, which is normally complete at the time of birth. The eyes and ears are sensitive to light and sound respectively.

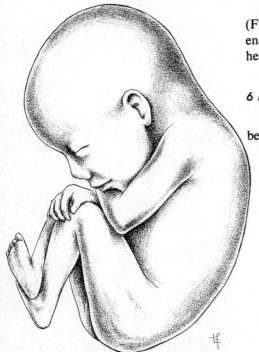

The infant is about 16 inches long and weighs about three pounds at the end of the seventh month. It grows another two inches and two pounds during the eighth month. At the time of normal birth, after nine months, it will be about 20 or 21 inches long and will weigh seven or eight pounds. The process by which birth is brought about, due to a relative decrease in the amount of progesterone in the blood, was described previously.

SUMMARY

The fertilized egg takes a week to form a morula and imbed itself in the uterine wall. From then on, the systems of the body differentiate very rapidly. The circulatory system goes into action by the end of three weeks, and by the end of two months, the embryo is a recognizable human being with all systems well represented, and many of them performing. The remaining seven months is devoted to polishing up the finer details of structure and physiology, and to growing.

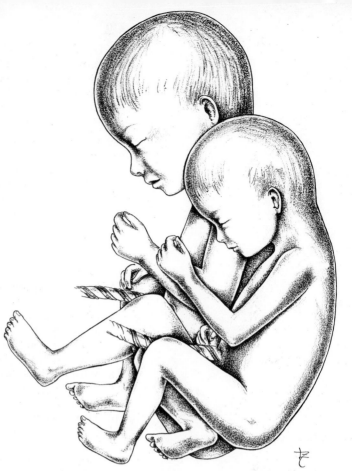

Fig. 10.15   Later human embryos. The smaller one is five months old and the larger one six months old.

Some of the phases of this embryological story will concern us again in later parts of this book. In the next chapter, however, further details of the mechanism whereby cells divide will occupy our attention. Cell division is most rapid in the earliest stages of embryonic development, gradually slowing down as time goes on. In mature adults, however, some cell division still goes on, particularly in the skin, in bone marrow, and in lymph nodes.

REVIEW QUESTIONS

1. Review the process of fertilization in the human.
2. Describe a human sperm and a human egg.
3. How does a zygote become a morula?
4. How does a morula build a placenta?
5. Describe the formation of amnion and yolk sac.
6. Describe the differentiation from the inner cell mass of ectoderm, endoderm, and mesoderm.
7. What parts of the adult body come from ectoderm? endoderm? mesoderm?

8. Describe the notochord.
9. Does an adult have a celom?
10. Describe the human embryo at the end of each month of its prenatal life.

GENERAL QUESTIONS

1. Is it justifiable to judge the events in the early embryology of a human by studying the early embryology of a laboratory animal such as a rat?
2. Is it correct to speak of the human embryo as a parasite?
3. Are there advantages in having a syncytium in the trophoblast?
4. The human embryo has no yolk. Why does it have a yolk sac?
5. Are segmental muscles more or less efficient than nonsegmental muscles?
6. Is there any significance to the appearance and disappearance of the tail and of the lanugo?
7. At the end of the eighth week, many of the organ systems are in operation. Yet, if removed from the uterus before the seventh month, the embryo would almost certainly not be able to live. Why not?
8. What might cause spontaneous abortion of an embryo?
9. Could fraternal twins influence each other's development? Could identical twins?
10. How does it happen that almost all babies are developed normally through a complicated process, with each event occurring at a suitable time, and with few abnormalities occurring?

CHAPTER 11

Cell Division

Living cells are very active units, carrying on a vast array of physical and chemical processes unceasingly. Substances come and go; cells absorb products from their environment, change their chemical constitution, incorporate some of the resulting substances into their own protoplasm and excrete others as wastes. These incorporated substances remain for a time, and are broken down and discharged, later to be replaced by new ones.

Throughout this process there remains a relative constancy of organization. Like a busy railroad station where people mill about and trains come and go, even with this continual change of contents a cell is generally recognizable as a specific structure, no matter how dynamic the activity within.

In cells the most stable structure is the nucleus, and within the nucleus the most enduring structures are the chromatin granules. Yet even these, being mixtures of chemical compounds, are subject to changes of atoms, to increase in quantity, to regrouping of parts, and to other chemical and physical changes as a result of forces which reach them.

These chromatin granules appear to contain the heritable substances which determine the specific traits characteristic of the organism to which they belong. These substances are complex proteins, and differ not only between one species and another, but also between one granule and another, if we may judge by results of genetic experiments. It is not certain whether this difference is primarily a chemical one involving composition and arrangement of the atoms in its molecule, or involving spatial relationships with other such proteins, or perhaps some yet undiscovered principle.

When the zygote divides, forming two cells, and these divide again, and so forth through the many, many divisions which produce a human being from a fertilized egg, it passes through a series of events collectively known as **mitosis** (Greek: thread formation). In the production of sperms and eggs, gonad cells go through a modified form of mitosis known as **meiosis** (Greek: diminishing) in which the number of chromatin granules passed on to the daughter cells is reduced to one half.

MITOSIS

In mitosis, the normal actions of a cell are slowed down or held in abeyance for a time, and the energies of the cell are used in the process of division. After the division has been completed, the daughter cells take up again the metabolic activities which characterize the particular type of cell they represent.

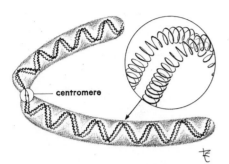

Fig. 11.1   The chromonema is finely coiled and then thrown into major coils in addition. What advantage is there in this form?

Interphase

The period of metabolic activity during which division is not in process has been called the **interphase.** The chromatin granules in the nucleus are not readily distinguishable in the living cell, but may be brought out by treatment with chemicals which kill, fix, and stain them. They appear at first glance to be scattered at random throughout the nucleus, but careful study has produced evidence that they are arranged in a definite pattern. For the most part the granules are merely bulges on a fine thread. The thread and its granules, known as a **chromonema** (Greek: colored thread), is helically coiled in very minute turns. These have been named the **minor coils.** See Figure 11.1. There may be hundreds or even thousands of granules along each chromonema. In a human cell, except for those produced by meiosis, there are forty-eight such chromonemata.

Along each chromonema there is a particular region that contains no chromatin granules. This region is the **centromere** (Greek: point part); it may occur at any point along different chromonemata, but for any one chromonema it is always at a specific place.

The forty-eight chromonemata in a human cell make up twenty-four pairs. One member of each pair was obtained from the egg and one from the sperm which formed the zygote of which the cell concerned is a descendant. The two members of each of twenty-three pairs are much like each other in length, position of centromere, and spatial arrangement of chromatin granules. The remaining pair of chromonemata are like each other in females, but are quite different from each other in males. These are the two **sex chromosomes,** and their likeness or difference is correlated with the sex of the person carrying them. More will be said about these in Chapter 12.

The characteristic structure of each pair of chromonemata is distinguishing, and certain pairs may be identified no matter from what sort of human cell they may be taken. See Figure 11.2.

1   3   5   7   9 11 13 15 17 19 21 23

2   4   6 8 10 12 14 16 18 20 22

Fig. 11.2   Diagram of human chromosomes. By size and shape each pair of chromosomes may be distinguished.

Stages

In cell division, the first visible changes occur in the nucleus, when the chromonemata condense into **chromosomes** (Greek: colored bodies). This stage is called the **prophase** (Greek: earlier figure). Then the nuclear boundary disappears and these chromosomes line up in or near one plane in the cell. This is **metaphase** (Greek: middle figure). Following this each chromosome separates into two parts, and these two parts migrate away from each other to the ends of the cells. This is **anaphase** (Greek: up and down figure). Next the chromosomes at each end of the cell reconstitute a nucleus. This is **telophase** (Greek: final figure). Then the cytoplasm divides between the two nuclei, bringing about the interphase again.

Fig. 11.3   Early prophase stage.

Prophase

The transition from interphase to prophase is marked by a duplication of the chromatin granules of each chromonema. These granules are or contain complex proteins which seem to be autocatalytic — that is, they catalyze the formation of their own substance. At any rate, one chromonema becomes two, except for the fact that the centromere does not appear to divide at this time. Thus, not only have the granules divided, but the strand which connects them divides, too.

Each chromonema now contorts itself into a helix with larger turns than those already present, retaining the minor ones; these larger coils are the **major coils.** See Figure 11.3. This coiling considerably shortens and thickens the structure, so that it becomes more readily visible in stained preparations; the structure is now called a chromosome. It is composed of two chromonemata held together by the undivided centromere, and by the condensation around them of a sheath, or **matrix.**

Meanwhile, events are transpiring in the cytoplasm. The centrosome was mentioned in the introduction as a body near the nucleus. It contains one or two centrioles. If there is but one at interphase it soon divides into two.

The centrioles in prophase move away from each other as if repelling each other by some force. The distance between them increases until they are oriented on opposite sides of the nucleus near opposite ends of the cell. The cytoplasm about each centriole becomes dense and gelatinous, and in fixed and stained preparations gives the appearance of radiating lines. See Figure 11.4. These lines are probably produced during the preparation of the cell for study, since evidence shows that in the living cell, no actual

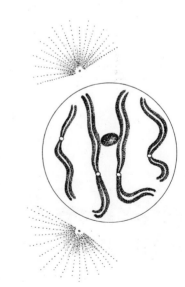

Fig. 11.4   Middle prophase stage.

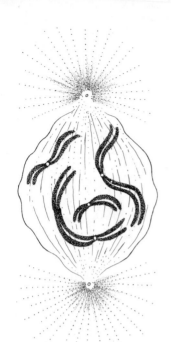

Fig. 11.5   Late prophase stage.

Fig. 11.6   Metaphase stage.

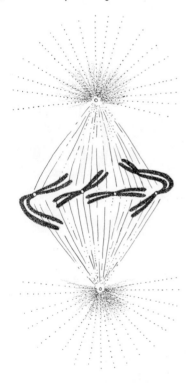

fibers exist. It is likely that the molecules of the gelatinous substance are long, and are oriented in a radial manner.

Some attempt has been made to explain many of the phenomena of mitosis on the basis of attractions and repulsions. According to theory, unlike bodies attract each other, and like bodies repel each other. For example, two magnets will be drawn to each other if their unlike poles are approximated, but will repel each other if their like poles are brought together. Similarly, positive and negative electric charges attract each other, but repel charges of their own kind.

If this principle is applied to the arrangement of molecules in the substance surrounding the centriole, it may be postulated that these molecules are attracted to the centriole, but repel each other. The resultant of these two forces arrays the molecules in a radial pattern. The protein precipitation brought about in the chemical preparation of cells for microscopic study produces an appearance of radiating fibers. The radiations about one centriole are known as an **aster.**

After these centrioles have reached opposite sides of the nucleus, the nuclear membrane gradually dissolves and disappears. The gelatinous area around each centriole enlarges into the nuclear area, producing a barrel-shaped gelatinous condensation between the two centrioles and enclosing the chromosomes. This formation is known as the **spindle.** Like the asters, microscopic preparations of the spindle present the appearance of fibers radiating out from the centrioles. See Figure 11.5.

Metaphase

The chromosomes now act as though they were repelled by the centrioles, and are arranged in a plane equidistant from the two centrioles. Further, they appear to repel each other, so that in that equatorial plane between the two poles, the chromosomes are spread out all through the cell. This is the metaphase stage. See Figure 11.6.

Anaphase

Now the centromere of each chromosome divides. The repelling force between the two resulting centromeres seems to be stronger than any other force in the cell, and the centromeres very quickly push away from each other, one going toward one centriole and one toward the other. The centromere seems to drag with it the chromonema of which it is a part. The chromonemata seem to be drawn apart passively, as if they had a mild attraction for each other and were separated only by the superior force of the centromeres. See Figure 11.7.

This passage of the centromeres and their chromonemata to the poles of the cell disrupts the radiating arrangement of the molecules in the spindle much as an ant scurrying through fine iron filings oriented in a magnetic field would disarrange the filings temporarily. But the filings will be restored to their pattern as soon as the ant passes by. Similarly the orientation of molecules in the spindle seems to return as soon as the chromonema has passed. In fact, this restoration of the radial arrangement may exert enough force to contribute to the migration of the chromonemata by giving them a push from behind. This separation of chromonemata to the poles of the cell is the anaphase. It will be noted that the retention of one centromere until metaphase, and the separation of the two centromeres resulting from the division of the one, result in a representative of each of the forty-eight chromonemata reaching each pole. Therefore each of the new cells will contain a representative of every chromatin granule of the parent cell.

Telophase

The reconstruction of the chromonemata at each pole into a nucleus occurs in telophase. The procedure is about like prophase in reverse. The spindle gradually fades away, becoming liquefied and dispersed into the cytoplasm and nuclei of the two new cells. The centriole at each end becomes incorporated into a centrosome. The matrix around each chromonema disappears. The chromonema itself unwinds the major coils and thus disappears from view, for the size of the chromonema with only its minor coils and no matrix is usually not enough to make it visible with a microscope. The nuclear membrane appears. Finally, the cell membrane, where it is intersected by the equatorial plane, develops an increased surface tension, and contracts as if someone were tightening a belt around it. This cutting in of the membrane eventually divides the cytoplasm into two parts. The distribution of mitochondria, Golgi bodies, stored food, and so forth in the cytoplasm does not seem to follow as rigorous a scheme as the distribution of chromatin. The two resulting cells readjust their shapes with respect to the forces acting on them, and interphase begins. See Figure 11.8.

Time of Mitosis

The entire cell division may take a half hour, an hour, or several hours in particular instances. The result which

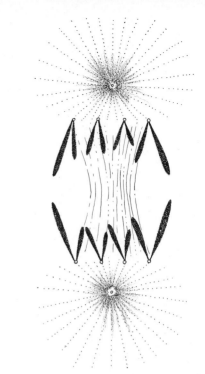

Fig. 11.7   Anaphase stage.

Fig. 11.8   Telophase stage.

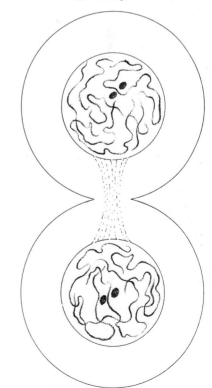

seems most significant beyond the increase in number of cells is the complete representation of all chromatin granules of the parent cell in the two daughter cells.

Place of Mitosis

Mitosis occurs very rapidly in embryonic cells, but tends to slow down as the body gets older. In some places such as bone marrow and lymph nodes, cell division goes on throughout life. In others, as in the nervous system, it stops early. In still others, as in the skin, it continues at a moderate pace, but is capable of a burst of activity under certain conditions. In the case of wound healing, for example, two processes are involved. The uninjured cells adjoining the wound migrate into the damaged area, filling in and covering over the space left by the destruction of tissues; and some of these cells divide, forming new cells which grow and contribute to the restoration of the injured area.

Regeneration

This capacity for producing new cells by mitosis is especially characteristic of connective tissue cells and lymph cells. Broken bones may stimulate the production of new osteoblasts to deposit new bone. A torn blood vessel will restore itself if the flow of blood is controlled. These restorations of damaged or lost tissue are called **regeneration** (Latin: producing again). In comparison with many animals, humans have only limited powers of regeneration. A tissue such as epidermis or bone may be regenerated, but not an entire structure such as a finger, or a stomach. There are animals which possess such remarkable powers of regeneration that they may be cut in two and each piece will heal into a whole animal, or they may be passed through a sieve which breaks them into many pieces, and these pieces may become reassociated into one individual. Such animals are on a very low plane of differentiation contrasted to a human.

MEIOSIS

Egg and Sperm Formation

Meiosis occurs in the preparation of sperms and eggs. Each meiosis consists of two cell divisions. In the testis, these two divisions produce four cells of equal size, each capable of becoming a sperm by losing most of its cytoplasm and rearranging the remainder into the typical sperm form. In the ovary, the first division of meiosis produces one large and one small cell. The large cell divides again, producing

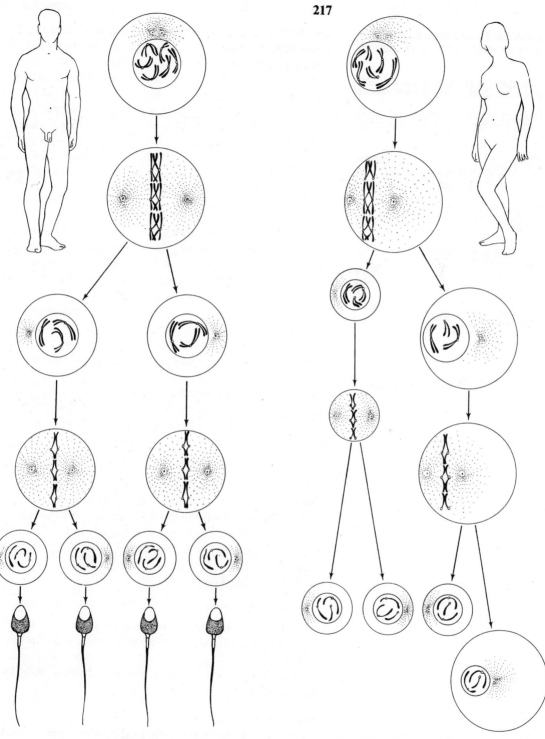

Fig. 11.9 Formation of sperm and egg cells. All potential sperm cells are formed, but three of four possible egg cells are lost along the way.

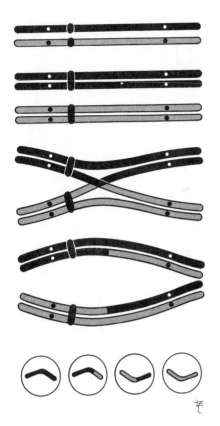

Fig. 11.10 Crossing over. As the chromosomes pair off at prophase of meiosis, there may be a break in one or more chromonemata as they twist about each other. If on reassembling after the breaks, two chromonemata exchange parts, the crossing over may result in a change of gene groups from one to another.

one large and one small cell. The small cell from the first division may or may not divide again. The two or three small cells formed in meiosis degenerate and do not serve as eggs. The one large cell contains nearly all of the food stored by the follicle cells, and is the egg. This inequality of division provides the zygote with a food supply ample to last it until it can build a placenta and begin securing nourishment from the blood of the mother. See Figure 11.9.

What brings about the difference in procedure between meiosis and mitosis is not well understood, but the procedure itself may be described as follows:

Prophase

At the start of prophase, the chromonemata do not duplicate themselves as they do at the beginning of mitosis. Instead, the two members of each pair of chromonemata line up side by side. It was mentioned earlier that there are twenty-four pairs of chromonemata.

Then the pairs condense into major coils, shortening and thickening and acquiring a matrix. During this condensation into major coils, the two chromonemata may break in places. If the two chromonemata of a pair happen to break at comparable levels, as may occur if the twisting is tight, they may heal these breaks by reassembling as they were, or by an exchange of parts. See Figure 11.10. This exchange of parts is called **crossing over.** Its significance in inheritance will be discussed in the next chapter.

Metaphase

After major coil formation, the cell approaches a metaphase stage. Each chromosome divides, except for the centromere. A spindle forms between the centrioles as in mitosis, the nuclear membrane is dissolved, and the chromosomes are arranged on the equatorial plane. Each chromosomal mass now contains four chromonemata with two centromeres. See Figure 11.11.

Anaphase

At anaphase the centromeres remain undivided, but the two centromeres in each chromosomal mass separate from each other, each dragging with it one member of the chromonema pair, each member already divided into two chromonemata.

Second Division

After telophase, the cytoplasm divides, and in each daughter cell the second division begins. The chromonemata have divided, so that prophase is passed through quickly, and the chromosomes are lined up on the metaphase equatorial plane. This time, each centromere does divide, taking with it one chromonema, so that this division resembles normal mitosis except for one feature:

In ordinary mitosis, the forty-eight chromonemata of interphase become ninety-six at prophase and metaphase; these separate into two groups of forty-eight each at anaphase and telophase. In meiosis, the forty-eight chromonemata of the preceding interphase form twenty-four pairs at early prophase, twenty-four tetrads at late prophase and metaphase, and two groups of twenty-four pairs each at anaphase and telophase of the first division. In the second division, the twenty-four pairs at interphase remain twenty-four pairs during prophase and metaphase, and become two groups of twenty-four chromonemata each at anaphase and telophase.

This means that each sperm cell or each egg cell has only twenty-four chromonemata. When they unite at fertilization each contributes its twenty-four, resulting in the original number of forty-eight in the zygote. From then until the new individual forms eggs or sperms of its own, every cell division will be a mitosis.

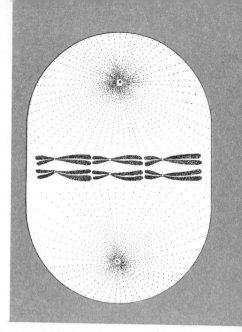

Fig. 11.11   Metaphase of meiosis. The chromosomes line up in pairs, each member of a pair being split into two chromonemata. What is the significance of this arrangement?

SUMMARY

In humans, each body cell nucleus carries forty-eight chromonemata. During division of these cells, these forty-eight are duplicated and the resulting ninety-six chromonemata are distributed so that the two cells resulting from the division of one cell each receive a copy of each of the original forty-eight.

The exception to this method of division occurs in the production of sperm and egg cells. Meiosis occurs here, including two divisions. In the first division the forty-eight chromonemata line up in twenty-four pairs. Each pair forms a major coil and each pair member is duplicated but the duplicated parts remain attached at the centromere. The pair members then separate, each member already divided but still attached at the centromere. There are now two groups of chromonemata consisting of twenty-four members, each member already divided. In the second division the duplicated parts of each pair member separate; thus each daughter cell contains only twenty-four chromonemata, one half the original number. Each sperm and egg, therefore, has but twenty-four chromonemata. The zygote resulting from the union of sperm and egg at fertilization, therefore, has forty-eight chromonemata, the original number.

REVIEW QUESTIONS

1. Review the actions of the parts of cells.
2. Differentiate between mitosis and meiosis.
3. Is there any metabolism in a dividing cell?
4. Describe a chromonema.
5. What part do centrioles play in mitosis?
6. Describe what happens to chromonemata during mitosis.
7. Where do mitoses take place in an adult human?
8. Describe regeneration.
9. Differentiate between sperm formation and egg formation.
10. Differentiate between the first and second divisions of meiosis.

GENERAL QUESTIONS

1. What do you suppose stimulates the onset of mitosis in a cell?
2. If we cannot see chromatin granules in a living cell, can we be sure they are not produced during killing and staining?
3. Propose an explanation for centriole and centromere movements other than the one of attraction and repulsion.
4. Discuss the nature of the nuclear membrane, and its disappearance and reappearance during mitosis.
5. If we speak of the two-cell stage as the first cell generation in an embryo, the next mitotic cycle produces four cells, or the second cell generation, the next mitotic cycle produces eight cells, or the third generation, and so forth. How many cells would there be in the twenty-fifth cell generation if each mitotic cycle involved every cell present at the time?
6. Propose a mechanical explanation for the separation of the cytoplasm into two cells at telophase.
7. How would our lives be changed if our powers of regeneration were as extensive as those of organisms which may be passed through a sieve and recover?
8. What brings about the pairing of chromonemata in meiotic prophase?
9. What changes would be brought about if eggs and sperms were formed by mitosis instead of meiosis?
10. To what extent may the two cells resulting from mitosis of one cell be different from each other?

CHAPTER 12

Genetics

EXPERIMENTAL EMBRYOLOGY

Perhaps the one most tantalizing problem in present-day biology concerns the way in which a zygote is able to produce a complex organism such as a man. At least two of the sciences which have arisen in this century and developed with astonishing speed are concerned chiefly with this problem:

A student of **experimental embryology** undertakes to study the early development of the organism from the zygote by tampering with its parts, altering the environment, and rearranging structures to see what effects result. From these observations conclusions may be drawn as to what force influences this or that phase of development.

For example, in an amphibian embryo at the stage when the brain is beginning to differentiate, and the diencephalon bulges out forming an eye still with undeveloped retina and optic nerves, a piece of one of these bulges may be transplanted to some place in the middle of the back. As a result, the skin of the back overlying the transplant will develop a lens, whereas the skin of the face, which normally would have produced a lens, fails to do so. From this and similar experiments it may be concluded that any epidermal cells at that stage may become a lens if and only if stimulated by something in the undeveloped retina.

There was a time, shortly before, when this undeveloped retina was itself epidermis, and under the influence of the notochord it inrolled and became nervous tissue. The notochord itself grew out of a predetermined spot on the embryo as it started to form a gastrula. This spot was determined as a result of two factors: the distribution of the stored food in the egg and the point at which the sperm first touched the egg in fertilization.

GENETICS

A student of **genetics** undertakes to trace the occurrence of distinguishable traits through consecutive generations of organisms and to determine the mechanisms of such transmission. From time immemorial humans have taken note of the resemblance of children to their parents, and speculated on whether a child "had its father's ears or its mother's eyes." Genetics began with such observations and progressed through statistical analyses of accumulated data to reasoning out explanations for the results of such analyses, devising experiments to check these explanations, and predicting future events from the hypotheses confirmed.

Not only is it fascinating to discover the procedure involved in transmitting eye color or musical ability, but it is also important to know how a human zygote becomes a human being instead of a grasshopper or an oak tree. How does it come about that the head is borne on the neck instead of in the middle of the abdomen? At this point experimental embryology and genetics join forces, and share their hypotheses and methods in a frontal attack on this problem of the mechanics of development. Encouraging success has greeted the work of the last fifty years in these fields, and enthusiasm is at a high peak for further discoveries. Knowledge so acquired will be significant in many far-flung areas of biology and other departments of human achievement.

History of Genetics

Records of genetical observations made 6000 years ago have been preserved. Such famous ancient Greek philosophers as Pythagoras, Empedocles, and Aristotle arrived at hypotheses to account for human inheritance.

In the seventeenth and eighteenth centuries of our era, when, by use of the microscope, human sperm cells had been discovered by Hamm and Leeuwenhoek, speculations as to the structure of the sperm and its importance in heredity were rife. Pierre-Louis Moreau de Maupertuis (1698–1759) postulated that each parent contributed a particle concerned with the development of each structure in the embryo, and that the two particles collaborated in production of this structure. Sometimes one particle dominated the other, as when a characteristic seemed to be inherited from one parent rather than the other. Maupertuis supported his belief by statistical analyses and by animal experimentation.

Jean Baptiste Pierre Antoine de Monet, Chevalier de Lamarck (1744–1829) advocated the idea that the environment of an organism was largely responsible for its characteristics, and that whatever was passed on by way of inheritance was strongly affected by environment. For examples, toothless animals got that way by swallowing their food whole, and not using their teeth. Giraffes achieved the long neck by stretching it generation after generation in an effort to reach higher leaves on trees. And antlers were developed on deer from their habit of fighting with their heads. This caused blood to rush to their heads and secrete the antlers.

Charles Darwin (1809–1882) tried to combine the ideas of de Maupertuis and de Lamarck by suggesting that tiny particles from every organ in the body were collected into each sperm or egg, and these particles brought with them the characteristics of that particular structure as it was at the moment. Hence, both hereditary and environmental influences were included in the material passed on to the next generation.

Mendel

Johann Mendel (1822–1884), though not widely known in his lifetime, gave a powerful impetus to genetics by condensing the results of his observations into a few general rules of wide application. Mendel became an Augustinian monk, taking the name Gregor, and specialized as a teacher of natural sciences. At the monastery in Brünn in what is now Czechoslovakia he cultivated garden plants and made a special study of the characteristics of peas.

He found that it was possible to obtain strains of peas which bred true for certain characteristics — that is, the same character showed up in every individual grown from the same batch of seeds. For example, there were pea plants which produced yellow seeds, and if these were planted, only peas bearing yellow seeds were produced. Similarly, there were green-seeded forms which produced nothing but green-seeded plants.

Mendel crossed these two varieties. He allowed the male reproductive cell of the yellow-seeded variety to fertilize the female reproductive cell of the green-seeded variety; or, he would allow the male cell of the green-seeded variety to unite with the female cell of the yellow-seeded pea. In either case his results were the same. He found that all of the offspring of such a cross produced yellow seeds. This confirmed the notion of de Maupertuis that the characteristic of one parent could dominate that of the other, but it pointed out that the dominance depended on the specific characteristic and not on the particular parent from which it was inherited. From this observation has come the "Law of Dominance," which states that *of two differing characteristics in the inheritance of an organism, one may be expressed in its entirety to the total exclusion of the expressions of the other.*

But Mendel didn't stop here. He carefully saved the yellow seeds of this first generation of his cross, planted them the next year, and allowed the plants which developed from them to fertilize themselves. This time, the results were of great interest. From all of the cases he observed, there turned out to be 6022 plants with yellow seeds, and 2001 plants with green seeds. This is a ratio of approximately 3 : 1.

What particularly struck Mendel's eye was that seeds intermediate in color between yellow and green did not appear. From this he concluded that there must be some discrete unit concerned with determining seed color, and this unit does not fuse or amalgamate with others. This unit he called a **factor.** The factors for green seeds remained unchanged even in a generation showing nothing but yellow seeds. When the second generation of the cross produced some green-seeded plants, the seeds proved to be just as green as those of the green-seeded grandparents, and furthermore, these seeds, when planted, produced nothing but green-seeded plants in the third generation. This resulted in another generality, the "Law of Unit Characters," which states that *each characteristic is trans-mitted as a discrete, unchanging unit.*

If the law of unit characters is accepted as a working hypothesis, it should be possible to think through the fate of these factors in the experiments just described. The first generation of the cross, called the **first filial generation,** must have received at least one factor for yellow seeds from one parent and one factor for green seeds from the other. The yellow factor dominated the green factor, so that these plants produced yellow seeds. In handing these factors on to the second filial generation, the first filial generation kept the factors distinct from each other. The most plausible explanation of the appearance of the second filial generation that Mendel's ingenuity conceived, and the one generally accepted today, is as follows:

Each organism has two factors for seed color. The original parents had two for yellow, let us say G and G, or two for green, let us call them g and g. One of each of these was passed on to the first filial generation, each plant of which then had two factors for seed color, G and g.

In preparing the male cells for the next generation, the plant of the first filial generation could contribute to it one and only one of these factors. Perchance it might be G for one cell, g for the next. Of the thousands of such cells formed, about half would contain the yellow-seed factor, and half the green-seed factor. Likewise, in pre-paring the female cells, some of these would acquire the G and some the g, in approximately equal numbers. The choice of fertilization partners is unaffected by the factors for seed color, so that a male cell carrying the G might unite with a female cell containing a *G* or one containing a *g*. Similarly, the male cell carrying a *g* might find either type of female cell. As a result, in random choices, there should be about equal numbers of the four different possibilities formed: *GG*, *Gg*, *Gg*, and *gg*. See Table 12.1.

TABLE 12.1

INHERITANCE OF SEED COLOR IN PEAS

MALE CELL CARRIES

		G	g
FEMALE CELL CARRIES	G	GG	Gg
	g	Gg	gg

Of these four possibilities, three would produce plants with yellow seeds (*GG*, *Gg*, *Gg*), and one would produce plants with green seeds (*gg*). This accounts for the ratio that Mendel found in his investigations. Had there been more than one factor contributed by each parent for seed color, the expected ratio would have been different from 3:1.

If this theoretical explanation is sound, it should be usable to predict further results. The green-seeded plants in the second filial generation, having the two factors *gg*, should be able, if self-fertilized, to produce nothing but green-seeded plants. This was found to be true. Of the yellow-seeded plants in the second filial generation, about one third should breed true if self-fertilized. This was found to be true. The other two thirds of the yellow seeds should produce, as did their parents, both yellow-seeded and green-seeded plants in a ratio of about 3:1. This was found to be true.

It will be noted that the terms "approximately" and "about" are used, and that Mendel's results were not exactly 3:1 — 6022 divided by 2001 is about 3.01. Even if the male cells containing *G* and those containing *g* were produced in exactly equal numbers, and the same were true of the female cells, the union of every male cell with some female cell is extremely unlikely. Many are lost before fertilization occurs. Furthermore, the random assortment of male cells and female cells at fertilization gives no assurance that male cells carrying the *G* factor will unite with exactly as many *G*-carrying female cells as *g*-carrying female cells. So the results are comparable to those obtained by flipping pairs of pennies a large number of times and counting the number of times one finds two heads, two tails, or one of each. The more samples counted, the more likely the experimental results are to approach the calculated ratio.

The postulate that each organism carries two factors, one obtained from its male parent and one from its female parent, and that each of its reproductive cells will carry one of these two factors, should call to your mind the discussion of meiosis in Chapter 11. It was pointed out there that in meiosis the chromonemata, being chains of chromatin granules, were carefully paired off, and then the pairs separated so that each sperm or egg carried one representative of each pair. It is not a great leap to suspect that the chromonemata carry these hereditary factors that Mendel suggested, and that quite possibly the chromatin granules are, or contain, these factors. Nucleus structure in peas is quite similar to that in humans, and meiosis occurs in peas much as it does in humans. Therefore the behavior of chromatin granules in meiosis, in fertilization, and in subsequent mitoses of the new individual is quite comparable to the distribution of hereditary factors.

When this attractive hypothesis was constructed, after Mendel's death, the hereditary factor carried on the chromonema was called a **gene** (Greek: origin). This correlation of factor behavior with chromatin granule behavior emphasizes Mendel's statement that *when the reproductive cells are prepared, the factors separate and are distributed as units to each male or female cell.* This has been called the "Law of Segregation."

Mendel was not satisfied with working on just one characteristic of peas. He also made observations on the inheritance of seed shape, flower and seed coat color, pod shape and color, height of the plants, and position of the flowers. Results of these studies confirmed those of seed color. See Table 12.2.

TABLE 12.2

SUMMARY OF MENDEL'S RESULTS ON PEAS IN THE SECOND FILIAL GENERATION OF CROSSES		
CHARACTERISTIC	DOMINANT	RECESSIVE
Seed color	6022 Yellow	2001 Green
Seed coat color	705 Violet	224 White
Seed shape	5474 Round	1850 Wrinkled
Pod color	428 Green	152 Yellow
Pod shape	882 Inflated	299 Constricted
Stem length	787 Tall	277 Dwarf
Flower location	651 Axial	207 Terminal

One further type of problem studied by Mendel deserves discussion here. He made observations on inheritance of two characteristics simultaneously. He crossed a strain which bred true for yellow, round seeds with one which bred true for green, wrinkled seeds. The first filial generation of this cross produced seeds all of which were yellow and round. Mendel was interested to know whether the next generation, resulting from the self-fertilization of this first filial generation, was to have round, yellow seeds and wrinkled, green seeds in the ratio of 3:1. What he actually counted was: 315 plants with round, yellow seeds; 108 with round, green seeds; 101 with wrinkled, yellow seeds; and 32 with wrinkled, green seeds.

He explained these results by proposing that the factors for seed color and those for seed shape were quite independent of each other, and that if you compared one characteristic at a time, you would still find the 3:1 ratio. From the data just given, for examples, the round-wrinkled ratio was 423:133, and the yellow-green ratio was 416:140.

If we analyze this as Mendel did by trying to trace the fate of the factors, we shall find that the first filial generation carries factors represented by *WwGg*, in which *W* stands for round, *w* for wrinkled, *G* for yellow, and *g* for green. In forming reproductive cells, such a plant will give approximately half of them *W* and half of them *w*. Of those carrying the *W* factor, approximately half will also have the *G* and the rest the *g*. Similarly there would be *wG* and *wg* reproductive cells. If we put these in chart form, we may compute results as in Table 12.3.

TABLE 12.3

SECOND FILIAL GENERATION OF A CROSS INVOLVING TWO PAIRS OF CHARACTERISTICS				
		MALE CELL CARRIES		
		WG	Wg	wG	wg
	WG	WWGG	WWGg	WwGG	WwGg
FEMALE CELL CARRIES	Wg	WWGg	WWgg	WwGg	Wwgg
	wG	WwGG	WwGg	wwGG	wwGg
	wg	WwGg	Wwgg	wwGg	wwgg

Here it will be seen that nine out of the sixteen possibilities will show both dominant characteristics — round and yellow. Furthermore, as the chart is set up, the nine will appear in the triangle formed by the top row, the left-hand column, and the diagonal connecting the ends of these two lines. Three of the sixteen (*WWgg* and *Wwgg*) will be round and green-seeded, three (*wwGG* and *wwGg*) will be wrinkled and yellow-seeded, and one, shown in the lower right corner (*wwgg*), will be wrinkled and green-seeded.

In his original data, Mendel would have had exactly this ratio if his figures had been 315, 105, 105, and 35. His actual results — 315, 108, 101, and 32 — are remarkably close to this. His explanation has been crystallized in the "Law of Independent Assortment," which says that *the distribution of one pair of factors is independent of the distribution of another pair of factors.*

If the reader wishes, he might follow this reasoning a step further, and analyze the expected results of a cross involving three characters; for example, what would be the results in the second filial generation from crossing a strain having tall (dominant) plants with round, yellow seeds with a strain having dwarf plants with wrinkled, green seeds?

A little terminology may be useful in discussing Mendel's ideas. An organism having both genes alike (e.g., *GG* or *gg*) is said to be **homozygous** (Greek: like yoked); one with the two genes for the same character unlike (e.g., *Gg*) is **heterozygous** (Greek: different yoked). The dominating gene (e.g., for yellow seed) is called **dominant;** and the other (e.g., for green seed), **recessive.** The genes an organism carries are called its **genotype** (Greek: original stamp); and the appearance of the organism with respect to the character, its **phenotype** (Greek: apparent stamp). Thus a pea plant with the phenotype yellow seeds may have either of two genotypes: *GG* or *Gg;* but one with a phenotype green seeds will have only one possible genotype: *gg.*

This work of Mendel's was presented to the local natural history society, and published by them in 1865. But his results ran counter to the prevailing notions of his time, which supposed that hereditary factors were subject to ready modification by the environment, and were not such rigidly fixed and mathematically exact entities as Mendel proposed. Administrative work connected with the monastery and its difficulties with the Austrian government took up most of Mendel's time after 1868, and he did not publish the work on bees he was engaged in.

Later Geneticists

Very little notice was taken of his work until 1900, when three European workers, each independent of the others, had reached conclusions similar to those of Mendel, and in preparing for publishing his own work, each had run across Mendel's published papers in reviewing the literature on the subject. Each was astounded at the work of Mendel, and called the attention of the scientific world to his achievements. Since that time, Mendel has been very highly regarded as a scientific scholar and founder of the modern science of genetics.

The idea of the ready effect of environment on hereditary transmission received another blow in the germ plasm theory of August Weismann (1834–1914). According to this, early in embryonic development certain cells, the **germ plasm,** appear to be set aside as potential reproductive cells, and from then on they specialize into nothing else. Meanwhile, the remaining cells differentiate into the multitudinous structures which make up the rest of the body, the **somatoplasm.**

The somatoplasm matures, grows old, and dies. But, said Weismann, the germ plasm is passed on from generation to generation, and is potentially everlasting, forming the continuity of life from one generation to the next. The germ plasm preserves and carries on the hereditary treasure of the race, whereas the somatoplasm expresses the heredity, and then dies. The somatoplasm is readily affected by environmental forces, but the germ plasm is not.

One of the scientists who rediscovered the work of Mendel was Hugo de Vries (1848–1935). He developed a theory which modified that of Weismann somewhat. According to de Vries sudden changes of considerable degree could occur occasionally in the germ plasm. These are called **mutations** (Latin: changes). These would become evident in the altered phenotype of the organism and the alteration would be relatively permanent, handed down from one generation to another.

The technique developed by Mendel of planning and carrying out crosses to determine the mechanism of heredity, carefully counting the numbers of different phenotypes resulting in ensuing generations and analyzing these results, has been pursued by ever greater numbers of geneticists since 1900.

One of the most famous of these, Thomas Hunt Morgan (1866–1945), began his work on the fruit fly, *Drosophila,* about 1910. The work of Morgan and his collaborators has made this organism the best known animal in the whole field of genetics. These fruit flies are small, easily cultured in the laboratory in large numbers, grow from egg to sexual maturity in less than two weeks, and their body cells possess only four pairs of readily distinguishable chromonemata. From the staggering volume of information on the genetics of the fruit fly we may select a few ideas for discussion. Those who are interested in further knowledge of the subject may consult the many books on genetics, or the original papers.

Sex Determination

As in humans, each body cell of a fruit fly has one pair of sex chromosomes. Also as in humans, these sex chromosomes are alike in the female, different in the male. The two in the female are referred to as **X-chromosomes;** the two in the male are the X-chromosome and the **Y-chromosome.**

The female produces eggs each with an X-chromosome. The male produces sperms, half of them with an X-chromosome, half of them with a Y-chromosome. If the sperm with the X-chromosome fertilizes an egg, the zygote will develop into a female with two X-chromosomes. If the sperm with a Y-chromosome fertilizes an egg, the zygote will develop into a male, having an X-chromosome and a Y-chromosome.

Sex-Linkage

In the pursuit of his investigations on *Drosophila*, Morgan in 1910 found a few white-eyed male flies in his cultures. Normally, fruit flies have red eyes. This appearance of white eyes is an example of the mutations suggested by de Vries. Morgan mated some of these white-eyed males to red-eyed females. Among the offspring were white-eyed females. From these Morgan built up a stock of flies that were pure white-eyed.

It was soon found that red eye is dominant over white eye, but the tabulation of results of some crosses showed startling peculiarities. For example, a white-eyed female fly mated with a red-eyed male fly produced only white-eyed males and red-eyed females. When heterozygous red-eyed females were mated with red-eyed males, all of the female progeny were red-eyed, but about half of the males showed red eyes and the others white eyes.

This sex differential made Morgan suspect that the sex chromosomes were involved, and these anomalous results can be readily explained if it is postulated that the genes concerned are borne on the X-chromosome. A female would then have two genes for eye color, and would be red-eyed unless both of these genes were for white eye. But a male, having only one X-chromosome, would have only one gene for eye color, so that he would be red-eyed or white-eyed depending on which gene was borne on the X-chromosome he got from his mother. For the explanation of the two examples given in the preceding paragraph, see Table 12.4.

TABLE 12.4

INHERITANCE OF EYE COLOR IN *DROSOPHILA*

1. Cross between a white-eyed female (ww) and a red-eyed male (WY):

		MALE CELL CARRIES	
		W	Y
FEMALE CELL CARRIES	w	♀ Ww *red*	♂ wY *white*

2. Cross between a heterozygous red-eyed female (Ww) and a red-eyed male (WY):

		MALE CELL CARRIES	
		W	Y
	W	♀ WW *red*	♂ WY *red*
FEMALE CELL CARRIES	w	♀ Ww *red*	♂ wY *white*

Linkage

This explanation fitted in with an earlier observation made in 1906 by William Bateson and Reginald C. Punnett, two English geneticists working on sweet peas. They were tracing the inheritance of flower color and pollen grain shape. They found upon crossing plants having purple flowers and cylindrical pollen grains with plants having red flowers and spherical pollen grains that the first filial generation had purple flowers and cylindrical pollen grains. These plants, they postulated, should produce equal numbers of four kinds of reproductive cells with respect to these two characters: *RS*, *Rs*, *rS*, and *rs*, where *R* and *r* stand for purple and red, and *S* and *s* stand for cylindrical and spherical. This they crossed with a plant having red flowers and spherical pollen, capable of producing only one kind of reproductive cells with respect to these characters: *rs*. They expected from this cross four phenotypes in equal numbers. The four phenotypes appeared, but not in the expected ratio. Instead, the ratio turned out to be 7 purple, cylindrical : 1 purple, spherical : 1 red, cylindrical : 7 red, spherical.

Bateson and Punnett accounted for the preponderance of two kinds by suggesting that the gene for flower color and the gene for pollen grain shape were borne on the same chromonema. At the first division of meiosis in an organism of the first filial generation, at which the chromonemata separate, whatever two genes (e.g., "purple" and "cylindrical") were already on one chromonema would go to one cell, and the other two (e.g., "red" and "spherical") would go to the other. Hence only two types of reproductive cells would be formed: *RS* and *rs*. But since there must have been a few carrying *Rs* and *rS*, in order to give the purple-spherical and red-cylindrical phenotypes, there must have been some breakage of chromonemata and exchange of parts, called **crossing over,** when in prophase they were twisted about each other. This crossing over must have occurred in about one eighth of the cases. See Figure 12.1.

Common sense would have dictated the necessity for the hypothesis that each chromonema must carry more than one gene. In fact, it did, a few years before Bateson and Punnett found this actual case. The American scientist, W. S. Sutton, had stated in 1903 that since organisms had so few chromonemata and so many heritable characteristics, each chromonema must carry many factors. This association of many genes on one chromosome is called **linkage.**

The students of *Drosophila* found many examples of linkage in their studies, and as time went on they developed the knowledge of four linkage groups associated with the four pairs of chromosomes.

Fig. 12.1 The Bateson-Punnett case of linkage in sweet peas. The genes for purple (R), or red (r), flowers occur on the same chromosome as the genes for cylindrical (S), or spherical (s), pollen. The offspring of a purple, cylindrical parent and a red, spherical parent has purple flowers and cylindrical pollen. If this is back-crossed to a red, spherical plant, $\frac{7}{8}$ of the offspring are like one or the other grandparent on the hybrid side, and the other $\frac{1}{8}$ show crossing over.

Chromosome Mapping

From here, the investigators went one step further. They began to tabulate carefully the percentage of crossing over. For example, the genes for white eyes in contrast to red and for yellow body in contrast to gray were on the same chromonema, and had a crossover value of 1.5%. The gene for "bifid" as opposed to "normal" wings was also on that chromonema, having a crossover percentage with the gene for white eyes of 5.4%, and with the gene

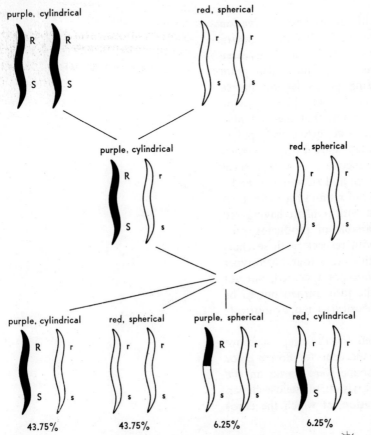

purple, cylindrical   red, spherical

purple, cylindrical   red, spherical

purple, cylindrical   red, spherical   purple, spherical   red, cylindrical

43.75%   43.75%   6.25%   6.25%

for yellow body of 6.9%. From this, it was postulated that genes for bifid wings and yellow body were farthest apart of the three on the chromonema, for the chromonemata broke most often between them; the gene for white eyes was between them, but closer to the gene for yellow body, for the breakage of the chromonema was less frequent between these two than between white eyes and bifid wings. By information such as this, the numerous characters found on various chromosomes were located along the chromonema in positions relative to each other as shown in Table 12.5. The chromosomes were "mapped."

Lysenko

The success of Mendel's explanations as supplemented by later workers is spectacular. The intensive analysis of *Drosophila* genetics is supported by a tremendous mass of data from other organisms, producing overwhelming support for the gene theory of heredity. Yet in Soviet Russia there has grown up another school of thought which discards this accumulation of data and its interpretation, and substitutes for it a concept of environmental control of heredity. This school, led by Trofim Lysenko (1898–   ), holds that heredity is a total action of the organism, not confined to any one part such as chromatin granules, and that while it is relatively stable, it may be shattered completely by exposure to strong environmental forces, and rebuilt according to whatever environment the organism is placed in after the shattering. This view is supported by experimental data of a nature which has not been duplicated in laboratories outside Russia. Lysenko's disdain for controlled experiments and for statistical analysis makes it impossible for geneticists from other countries to accept his views. However, the idea that living organisms may be made over in one generation rather than waiting for slow evolutionary processes seemed attractive to the governmental authorities in Russia, and Lysenko's ideas were declared official Soviet science by high Communist Party authority. All opposition to them was silenced in Soviet-controlled educational institutions and experiment stations. This in itself is exactly contrary to the spirit of scientific investigation throughout most of the history of science. The action savors of the Nazi distinction between Aryan and non-Aryan science. When men are required to make theory conform to current political doctrine rather than to objective observations and

TABLE 12.5

LINKAGE MAP FOR *Drosophila melanogaster*, SHOWING RELATIVE POSITIONS OF
MANY OF THE KNOWN GENES IN THE CHROMOSOMES

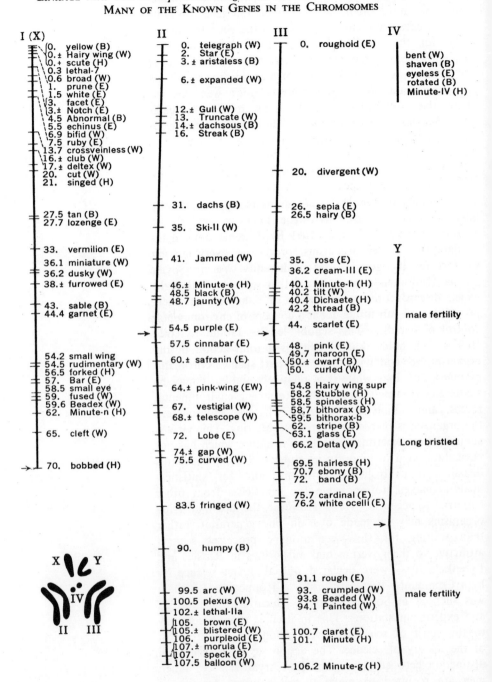

I (X)	II	III	IV
0. yellow (B)	0. telegraph (W)	0. roughoid (E)	bent (W)
0.± Hairy wing (W)	2. Star (E)		shaven (B)
0.+ scute (H)	3.± aristaless (B)		eyeless (E)
0.3 lethal-7			rotated (B)
0.6 broad (W)	6.± expanded (W)		Minute-IV (H)
1. prune (E)			
1.5 white (E)			
3. facet (E)			
3.± Notch (E)	12.± Gull (W)		
4.5 Abnormal (B)	13. Truncate (W)		
5.5 echinus (E)	14.± dachsous (B)		
6.9 bifid (W)	16. Streak (B)		
7.5 ruby (E)			
13.7 crossveinless (W)			
16.± club (W)			
17.± deltex (W)		20. divergent (W)	
20. cut (W)			
21. singed (H)			
27.5 tan (B)	31. dachs (B)	26. sepia (E)	
27.7 lozenge (E)		26.5 hairy (B)	
33. vermilion (E)	35. Ski-II (W)		Y
36.1 miniature (W)	41. Jammed (W)	35. rose (E)	
36.2 dusky (W)		36.2 cream-III (E)	
38.± furrowed (E)	46.± Minute-e (H)	40.1 Minute-h (H)	
	48.5 black (B)	40.2 tilt (W)	
	48.7 jaunty (W)	40.4 Dichaete (H)	
43. sable (B)		42.2 thread (B)	male fertility
44.4 garnet (E)			
	54.5 purple (E)	44. scarlet (E)	
	57.5 cinnabar (E)		
54.2 small wing	60.± safranin (E)	48. pink (E)	
54.5 rudimentary (W)		49.7 maroon (E)	
56.5 forked (H)		50.± dwarf (B)	
57. Bar (E)		50. curled (W)	
58.5 small eye	64.± pink-wing (EW)	54.8 Hairy wing supr	
59. fused (W)		58.2 Stubble (H)	
59.6 Beadex (W)	67. vestigial (W)	58.5 spineless (H)	
62. Minute-n (H)	68.± telescope (W)	58.7 bithorax (B)	
		59.5 bithorax-b	
	72. Lobe (E)	62. stripe (B)	
65. cleft (W)		63.1 glass (E)	Long bristled
	74.± gap (W)	66.2 Delta (W)	
	75.5 curved (W)		
70. bobbed (H)		69.5 hairless (H)	
		70.7 ebony (B)	
		72. band (B)	
	83.5 fringed (W)	75.7 cardinal (E)	
		76.2 white ocelli (E)	
	90. humpy (B)		
		91.1 rough (E)	
	99.5 arc (W)	93. crumpled (W)	male fertility
	100.5 plexus (W)	93.8 Beaded (W)	
	102.± lethal-IIa	94.1 Painted (W)	
	105. brown (E)		
	105.± blistered (W)	100.7 claret (E)	
	106. purploid (E)	101. Minute (H)	
	107.± morula (E)		
	107. speck (B)		
	107.5 balloon (W)	106.2 Minute-g (H)	

Adapted from Morgan, Sturtevant and Bridges, and Stern; from Sharp, *Introduction to Cytology*,
McGraw-Hill Book Co., New York.

experimental data, they are prevented from being scientists. More recently, Lysenko and his views have been attacked and discredited in Soviet publications.

Nature of Genes

The nature and mode of operation of genes has interested geneticists for some time. At present, it is thought that a gene is a complex protein molecule getting its specificity of action from the specific arrangement of atoms in the molecule. It is supposed to act like or produce enzymes or hormones which regulate particular reactions. For example, the eye color in a fruit fly as well as in a human depends upon pigments deposited. The secretion of those pigments depends upon the presence of appropriate enzymes. If a gene has the proper molecular configuration for the action or production of these appropriate enzymes, the pigment is present. If some change in the molecular structure of the gene prevents this enzyme action, pigment is absent.

The sudden change in the molecular structure of a gene is called a mutation. It may be brought about by the action of some external force, such as X-radiation or cosmic radiation, on the protein molecule, either rearranging the atoms on it or interfering with its exact duplication so that a slightly different arrangement results. The new arrangement gives the gene a modified activity which shows up in the enzymes it can or cannot produce — that is, the expression of the gene.

HUMAN GENETICS

Now let us consider a few of the known facts about the inheritance of characteristics in humans. Most of this information has been obtained by studying family histories, for experimentation on humans in the manner of the work on the fruit fly is quite impracticable. Furthermore, there are many modifying factors in inheritance which preclude simple interpretations. For example, the gene for pigment in the iris which produces brown eyes is dominant over the gene for absence of such pigment, which gives the eye a blue appearance. But degrees of pigment deposition, varying pigments, diluting and intensifying factors, and uniform or splotchy distribution of pigments all combine to make a wide variation in the appearance of the iris.

The same is true of hair color, in which the gene for dark is dominant over the gene for blond, and the gene for red is possibly recessive to both. Modifying genes contribute to the variety of hair colors. Some cases of premature graying of hair are inherited as a dominant gene. A single patch of white hair among normally pigmented hairs, a condition known as **blaze,** is due to a dominant gene. The inability to form any pigment in the body, **albinism,** is a recessive factor.

Curly and straight hair seem to be inherited; a person carrying a gene for curly and a gene for straight hair will have wavy hair. The gene for baldness behaves interestingly, being dominant in men and recessive in women.

As for skin color, it seems to be due to more than one gene. Two pairs of genes are involved in the distinction between the skin pigment of Negroes and the absence of such pigment in Caucasians. Thus, a homozygous Negro has four pigment-producing genes, whereas a white person has four genes unable to produce pigment. A cross between the two produces a mulatto with two of each sort of genes, and a lesser deposit of pigment than his Negro parent. The second filial generation, obtained from the marriage of two mulattoes, may have any number of pigment-producing genes from zero to four, with accompanying varieties of skin color. A gene for the tendency for the skin to produce patches of pigmentation — freckles — is dominant over a gene for the absence of freckles.

With regard to facial features, the gene for prominent bridge of the nose is dominant over the gene for straight or concave noses, but the gene for upturned tip of the nose is recessive to the gene for a straight tip. The gene for full lips is dominant over the gene for thin lips. The gene for receding chin is recessive to the gene for full chin. The protruding chin and lower lip made famous by the Hapsburg family in Europe are due to dominant genes. Dimples in the cheeks and on the chin are due to dominant genes, but are carried by separate pairs of genes. The gene for high cheekbones is dominant.

The shape of the eyeball affects its ability to focus properly. A long eyeball may cause light rays from distant objects to come to a focus in front of the retina, giving a fuzzy and unclear image, whereas light rays from a close object focus on the retina without requiring much contraction of ciliary muscles. Such an eye is called nearsighted. This eyeball shape is inherited as a recessive gene.

The opposite condition — a short eyeball, which causes light rays to focus behind the retina unless the ciliary muscle is contracted — is inherited as a dominant gene.

The tendency toward using one hand more than the other — right-handedness or left-handedness — is determined by the development of the left or right motor area of the cerebral cortex respectively. A tendency to develop the left motor area more — right-handedness — is thought to be due to a dominant gene.

There is some evidence that tendencies toward certain diseases and defects are inherited. Among such conditions are astigmatism, glaucoma, and cataract of the eye; arthritis; diabetes mellitus; and high blood pressure. In the case of many others, such as cancer, evidence is conflicting. Some generalized sensitivity such as allergy seems to be heritable.

Blood types are inherited. A person has two genes for his blood type with respect to the O, A, B, and AB groups. There is one gene for type A antigen, one for type B antigen, and one for neither. A person in group A may have the genotype *AO* or *AA*. Likewise those in group B may have genotype *BO* or *BB*. A person in group O is homozygous for the gene for neither: *OO*. Group AB members have genotype *AB*. This data may be used in computing the possible blood groups to which may belong children of parents whose blood types are known. See Table 12.6.

TABLE 12.6

THE INHERITANCE OF THE BLOOD GROUPS, BASED ON THE STUDY OF THOUSANDS OF FAMILIES		
BLOOD GROUPS OF PARENTS	BLOOD GROUPS WHICH MAY OCCUR IN CHILDREN	BLOOD GROUPS WHICH DO NOT OCCUR IN CHILDREN
O x O	O	A, B, AB
O x A	O, A	B, AB
A x A	O, A	B, AB
O x B	O, B	A, AB
B x B	O, B	A, AB
A x B	O, A, B, AB	—
O x AB	A, B	O, AB
A x AB	A, B, AB	O
B x AB	A, B, AB	O
AB x AB	A, B, AB	O

From Snyder, *The Principles of Heredity, Fourth Edition,* D. C. Heath and Company.

In the case of the Rhesus factor, either one or two genes for the presence of the Rh-antigen makes a person Rh-positive.

Linkage groups have been found in humans, although relatively little is known about them. Near-sightedness and eye color genes have been found on the same chromonemata. Tendency for cataract and curly hair genes have been found linked. Blond hair and blue eyes may show linkage. Blood groups and the pattern of fingerprints seem to be linked.

Sex-linkage is apparent in a few characters, too. The gene for hemophilia, characterized by a great stability of blood platelets, hampering clotting, is carried on the X-chromosome, and behaves in the manner described for white eye in *Drosophila*.

A man will be hemophilic if he has but one gene for the condition — which he inherited from his mother. It takes two genes for hemophilia to produce the condition in a woman. The gene has occurred as a mutation in several separate instances; one such seems to be Queen Victoria.

TABLE 12.7

OCCURRENCE OF THE GENES FOR HEMOPHILIA IN THE DESCENDANTS OF QUEEN VICTORIA

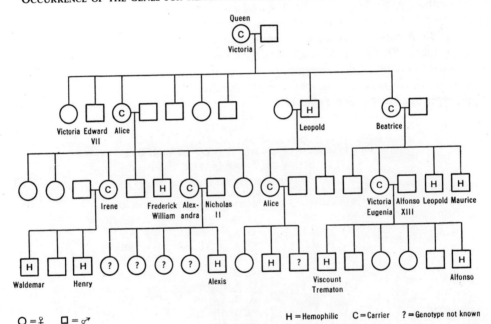

O = ♀   □ = ♂   H = Hemophilic   C = Carrier   ? = Genotype not known

Another character borne on the X-chromosome is red-green color blindness. It affects certain cones of the eye so that the color-blind person cannot distinguish red from green, both appearing gray. If you wish to test yourself, study Figure 12.2.

The Y-chromosome is known to carry genes for webbed feet (fusion of toes) and for excessive hair in the ears, together with genes for the absence of these characters. These, of course, can be inherited only by males.

EUGENICS

Characteristics such as intelligence, musical and artistic ability, and mechanical aptitude show evidence of being inherited, but methods of measuring these characters are so inadequate and the effects upon them of environmental opportunities for development and encouragement of their expression are so important, that definite information on the details is lacking. This consideration, among others, is discouraging to those who advocate a vigorous campaign for eugenics — the improvement of the human race by applying genetic principles. While the aim is laudable — the elimination of hereditary deficiencies and increase in hereditary strengths of the species — the state of knowledge of human heredity at the present time makes any detailed plan hazardous.

Some political units have enacted eugenic laws — for sterilization of the hereditarily feeble-minded, for example — but incomplete understanding of the factors involved in inheritance and expression of human characteristics plus the lack of universal agreement as to what characteristics are desirable and what ones undesirable have made it wise to make haste slowly. Who is to say whether the race would be better or worse off with more people having musical talent, mathematical talent, artistic ability, or mechanical aptitude? On the other hand, some conditions, like St. Vitus' dance and amaurotic idiocy, are clearly heritable and are clearly undesirable. Voluntary efforts to prevent the passing on of these conditions are praiseworthy.

It is believed by many that the quickest way to improve human beings, both physically and mentally, is through the environment. There is abundant evidence that perhaps none of us attain the maximum of our genetic capabilities and that improving the environment can improve our development. Better schools, better nutrition, better housing, and freer communication of ideas are some of the environmental factors involved.

SUMMARY

A student of experimental embryology attempts to describe the forces which influence the organization of an adult organism from a fertilized egg. A student of genetics is concerned with the transmission and action of those influencing forces which are passed on from one generation to another.

Genetics is a comparatively ancient field of speculation, but its scientific development has come chiefly in the last fifty years. The basis for our present genetics theories was laid by Mendel, who expressed his observations in mathematical hypotheses. Later workers correlated his findings with studies of cell division, germ cell formation, and fertilization. Weismann postulated a theory that the hereditary germ plasm was passed on from one generation to the next, whereas the somatoplasm died in each generation. De Vries proposed the idea of sudden changes, called mutations, in hereditary material. Morgan and his associates developed much further knowledge of genetics in extensive work with fruit flies. Among ideas they confirmed or developed were the method of inheritance of sex, linkage, and chromosome mapping.

The structure of genetics built up by these investigators was challenged by a group of Soviet workers headed by Lysenko, who maintained that not genes but the entire organism and its environment were the determining factors in heredity. This view has not been generally accepted outside the Soviet orbit, and even in Russia it has recently undergone attack.

The genes are thought to be complex protein molecules which are enzymes themselves, or produce enzymes. The enzymes control phases of metabolism which determine characteristics of the organism. A change in the molecular structure of a gene constitutes a mutation.

Genetics of the human is not as thoroughly known as genetics of the fruit fly because the human is more complex and is not as readily experimented with as the fruit fly. The inheritance of some physical characteristics is known, and there is evidence bearing on inheritance of such things as intelligence and special abilities. Attempts have been made to use these concepts in controlling the heredity of humans, similar to the controlled breeding of domesticated plants and animals. Many considerations other than genetic ones are involved in eugenics, and further knowledge and thought are necessary before a thoroughgoing eugenics program will be acceptable to most people.

REVIEW QUESTIONS

1. Describe the goal and approach of experimental embryologists.
2. Describe the goal and approach of geneticists.
3. Briefly describe the historical development of our knowledge in genetics.
4. Explain the laws of genetics stated by Mendel.
5. What is a gene?
6. Define: heterozygous, recessive, genotype, phenotype, mutation.
7. Explain Weismann's germ plasm theory.
8. Explain sex-linkage.
9. How are chromosome maps constructed?
10. What was Lysenko's explanation of heredity?

11. How do mutations occur?
12. How is human heredity studied?
13. What is known about human inheritance?
14. What is eugenics?
15. What practical eugenic measures have been taken? What others are advisable?

GENERAL QUESTIONS

1. If the genes for seed color and seed shape in peas had been linked, do you suppose Mendel would have arrived at the Law of Independent Assortment?
2. Construct a diagram to show the inheritance in the second filial generation of a cross involving three characteristics; four.
3. Determine the predicted ratio of phenotypes among the offspring of two mulattoes, each heterozygous for full lips.
4. What is the phenotype ratio expected in a cross between a wavy-haired man homozygous for straight nose, but heterozygous for dark hair, and a wavy-haired woman with up-turned nose, heterozygous for dark hair?
5. Bubbles married a brown-eyed man named Cuthbert, and they had two children with dark hair and blue eyes, two with light hair and brown eyes, and one each with dark hair and brown eyes, and with light hair and blue eyes. Bubbles' identical twin, Doubles, and her husband, Elmsford, had four dark-haired, blue-eyed children, two dark-haired and brown-eyed, and one each light-haired, brown-eyed, and light-haired, blue-eyed. Find the probable genotypes of the four parents.
6. What would be the expected phenotype ratio among the children of a woman heterozygous for hemophilia and color blindness, and a hemophilic man with normal vision?
7. How would you propose proceeding to find out to what extent intelligence is inherited in humans?
8. Map a chromosome showing these crossover percentages:

Between A and B   6%
B and C   3%
C and D   11%
D and E   4%
E and A   10%

9. A mule is the offspring of a cross between a horse and a donkey. Why do you suppose mules are usually sterile?
10. How would a greater knowledge of the chemistry of genes be of help to a geneticist?

Summary to Part I

Part I discusses the biology of one species of living organisms, the human. Parts II and III will extend the scope to the hundreds of thousands of species of plants and animals. While the human is a rather highly specialized example of living organisms, it is the most familiar to us, and it serves to illustrate many of the fundamental characteristics and processes found in life. Thus, you saw how the human body maintained an active metabolism, constantly changing the atoms and molecules which make it up, without destroying its organization. You read about the framework of bone and cartilage and connective tissue which gives the body support; about the muscles which move it; about the digestive tract and respiratory tract which provide it with sources of energy and building materials; about the circulatory system which distributes these and other materials; about the excretory system which does away with wastes; about the nervous and endocrine systems which regulate it. You read also about the method of producing new individuals of the species, and the method of development of these new individuals, and of the method of transmission of the genes which determine the vital characteristics of the new individuals.

You might consider these as problems which are met by a living organism in maintaining itself and continuing its species. These same problems — support, movement, supply of materials, distribution, waste removal, regulation, and reproduction — must be met by every living organism.

In the next two parts, only selected examples will be described, and none of them as fully as the example chosen for Part I. But your attention is especially called to the similarities among organisms. The differences will be more readily apparent, and perhaps more extensively described. One explanation of both differences and likenesses will be discussed in Part IV.

PART II

THE PLANT KINGDOM

LINNAEUS

Carolus Linnaeus is the Latin form of the name of the Swedish botanist who popularized the system of classification of plants and animals we use today. His father, Nils Ingemarsson, had no surname until he went to school to prepare for the ministry. He took the name Linnaeus in honor of a large linden tree near his home. Carolus, or Carl, was born in 1707, the first child in the family. He grew to share his father's enthusiasm for unusual plants, and the family garden was a source of great interest to him because it had plants not to be found in other gardens in the neighborhood.

When Carl was sent to school to study for his father's profession, he proved to be an unsatisfactory pupil. His interest lay in natural history rather than in theology. His father was prepared to withdraw him from school and apprentice him to a shoemaker, but Carl's science teacher urged that he be trained in medicine instead. So Carl was sent to the University of Lund, but later transferred to the University of Upsala.

His meager funds soon gave out, but he had impressed his teachers with his familiarity with plants, and was appointed assistant to the botany professor. He became so interested in his plant studies that he did not complete the work for his medical degree at Upsala.

Fig. II.1   Linnaeus in his Lapland costume.

On behalf of the Swedish government, Linnaeus went on an extended exploring trip in northern Sweden and what is now Finland, collecting great quantities of specimens of plants and minerals to be worked over when he returned. The results of this expedition increased his knowledge and his scientific reputation but did not improve his financial position.

He met the daughter of a well-to-do physician, and fell deeply in love with her. But the physician wasn't willing to see his daughter married to one with such uncertain prospects. He insisted that Carl obtain his medical degree and set up in practice before he would consent to the marriage. The young lady had been able to save some money of her own, and she entrusted this to her suitor to aid his further education.

Linnaeus went to Holland, and enrolled in the medical school at Harderwijk. With his previous training, Linnaeus was able to meet the rather low standards of the school authorities within a month, and received his degree.

Instead of returning to Sweden immediately, Linnaeus continued to travel, visiting in Holland, France, England, and Germany, meeting other botanists and getting acquainted with collections in natural history museums and botanical gardens. During these years he also wrote and published some books, among them the first edition of *Systema Naturae* in 1735. This was an effort to classify all plants, animals, and minerals known to him in a systematic fashion. Later works, *Classes Plantarum* (1738) and *Species Plantarum* (1753), expanded the classification of plants, his particular specialty.

A story is told illustrating the fame which preceded him in his travels. When he arrived in Paris, he hastened to the botanical gardens and found the famous botanist, Bernard de Jussieu (1699–1776), taking a class through the recent additions to the collection and lecturing in Latin. Linnaeus joined the class informally, and followed around, observing as he went. Finally the professor came to a plant which had just arrived, and with which he was not familiar. Linnaeus broke in with the remark: "That looks like a plant from America." De Jussieu turned in astonishment, and said, "You must be Linnaeus!"

Full of honors in Europe, and equipped with his medical degree, Linnaeus returned to Sweden, married his fiancee, and began a practice in Stockholm. He was never happy as a physician, however, and soon became professor of botany at Upsala. Here he continued his studies and his writing while teaching an increasing number of students and enlarging the university collections and gardens.

In his later years, Linnaeus suffered from ill-health, and became involved in an unfortunate wrangle resulting from his placing his son in his own place as professor. The son had little of the ability of his distinguished father, and the dissatisfactions with his services threatened to become a public scandal. Repeated paralytic strokes weakened Linnaeus senior, and he died in 1778. His son died not long after, and Linnaeus' papers, books, and herbarium were sold to England, where they are now preserved by the Linnaean Society.

The great value of Linnaeus' work is the result of the tremendous powers of organization characteristic of his mind. He took principles developed by his predecessors and applied them wisely and consistently, as well as indefatigably, to the ever increasing accumulation of kinds of organisms.

Three features of Linnaeus' method deserve especial consideration. In the first place, he described each organism succinctly. He felt that every animal or plant could be differentiated from all others in no more than a dozen words at the most. This meant keen observation, a vast knowledge of diverse forms, and a capacity for apt expression.

Secondly, he gave to each organism two Latin names: a genus name, a noun; and a species name, an adjective. The genus name was written with a capital letter, the species name with a small letter. These names were supposed to be descriptive of the organism named. He sought for simplicity and ready familiarity in choosing names. For examples: red clover he called *Trifolium* (Latin: three-leaf) *pratense* (Latin: of the meadow); the bloodroot he named *Sanguinaria* (Latin: bloody) *canadensis* (Latin: from Canada); and the white oak *Quercus* (Latin: oak tree) *alba* (Latin: white).

Thirdly, he arranged the plants in order depending upon anatomical features such as the number and arrangement of the flower parts. He recognized that this was quite artificial, and that while it was a very handy device for quickly determining the identity of a plant, it did not necessarily indicate genuine biological relationships. He tried to perfect a more natural classification, based on all of the observable characteristics of the organisms, but this was too great a task for one man or even one generation, and it is a goal toward which present-day biologists still are striving.

OTHER PLANT TAXONOMISTS

Since Linnaeus' time, many botanists have constructed and revised plant classifications. The French botanist, Antoine de Jussieu (1748–1836), published in 1789 a grouping of plants into three main subdivisions: The Acotyledons, without seed leaves; the Monocotyledons, with one seed leaf in each seed; and the Dicotyledons, with two seed leaves in each seed.

August Wilhelm Eichler (1839–1887), a German botanist, published in 1883 his classification, dividing plants into Cryptogams, in which reproductive parts were hidden, and Phanerogams, in which reproductive parts were open to view. Among the Cryptogams he recognized three divisions: the Thallophyta, subdivided into algae and fungi; the Bryophyta, subdivided into liverworts and mosses; and the Pteridophyta, subdivided into horsetail rushes, club mosses, and ferns. The Phanerogams were divided into two groups: the Gymnospermae and the Angiospermae. The angiosperms were subdivided into monocotyledons and dicotyledons.

The Eichler classification was further elaborated by the German botanists, Adolf Engler (1844–1930) and Karl Prantl (1849–1893), who published a great treatise in the years 1887–1909.

Charles Bessey (1845–1915), an American botanist, published in 1894 a somewhat different system subdividing the seed plants. Both the Engler and Prantl and the Bessey system have many followers. These both follow Eichler's fundamental classification, however, and it is this scheme which will be adopted in this book.

PLANT PHYLA

We shall divide the entire plant kingdom into four great divisions, or **phyla.** Several characteristics differentiate one phylum from another, but we shall start with elementary ones, to be elaborated later.

Plants in the Phylum **Thallophyta** have a body which is not divided into distinct vegetative tissues and organs. Plants in the Phylum **Bryophyta** have differentiated vegetative tissues and organs, but no vascular tissues. Plants in the Phylum **Pteridophyta** have differentiated vegetative tissues and organs, including vascular tissues, but most do not form seeds. Plants in the Phylum **Spermatophyta** do form seeds.

This classification has seemed to many botanists unsatisfactory. The Phylum Thallophyta includes such diverse plants that it is often divided into several phyla: **Cyanophyta, Euglenophyta, Chlorophyta, Chloromonadophyta, Chrysophyta, Xanthophyta, Bacillariophyta, Pyrrhophyta, Phaeophyta, Rhodophyta, Schizomycetes, Myxomycetes,** and **Eumycetes.** Sometimes the Cyanophyta and Schizomycetes are combined into the Phylum **Schizophyta.**

The Bryophyta may be divided into two classes: liverworts and mosses; or into three: liverworts, hornworts, and mosses.

The Pteridophyta and Spermatophyta are often combined into the Phylum **Tracheophyta,** with subdivisions **Psilopsida, Lycopsida, Sphenopsida,** and **Pteropsida,** the last-named group including ferns and seed plants. The Bryophyta, Pteridophyta, and Spermatophyta have been united in the group **Embryophyta.**

There is much structural and paleontological evidence to support these various interpretations. However, these are all man-made classifications aimed at better understanding of plant relationships, and for the purpose of this book, the division of plants into four phyla will serve our understanding.

The remainder of Part II will be concerned with selected representatives of these four phyla, describing their mode of life and their relationships to each other and to the rest of the world.

REVIEW QUESTIONS

1. Describe the life of Linnaeus.
2. What was Linnaeus' contribution to biology?
3. Distinguish between artificial and natural classifications.
4. What has been done in plant classification since Linnaeus' time?
5. Name and distinguish among the four phyla of plants.

GENERAL QUESTIONS

1. Do you think Linnaeus' plan of differentiating a species in no more than twelve words is practicable in English and with the varieties of organisms known today?
2. In naming organisms, scientists sometimes honor other people by using their names, as, for example, *Linnaea*, the twin-flower. Others use mythological names such as *Venus*, the hard-shelled clam. Still others give descriptive names such as *Trifolium* (three-leaf) *pratense* (of a meadow), the red clover. Discuss the relative merits of these principles.
3. The division of plants into four phyla is only one of several schemes current today. Why do not biologists agree on a single scheme?

CHAPTER 13

Thallophyta: Viruses and Bacteria

CLASSIFICATION

The thallophytes are plants which have no distinct vegetative organs such as leaves, stems, and roots. Among the possible ways of subdividing the phylum, the one most commonly used at present is based on the method of obtaining nourishment. Those which do not synthesize carbohydrates out of water and carbon dioxide in the presence of the chlorophylls are called **Fungi.** Those which do perform that synthesis with the aid of the chlorophylls are called **Algae.**

Among the Fungi there is a group of organisms each made up of no more than one cell, not containing a nucleus like that of human cells, but with nuclear material, if present, scattered through the organism. These plants multiply by separating into two or more parts. This latter feature gives them their name: Class **Schizomycetes,** from the Greek for splitting fungi. To this class belong the **viruses** and the **bacteria.**

VIRUSES

Size of Viruses

Viruses are tiny bodies increasing in numbers when and only when they are in the protoplasm of other organisms. Viruses vary in size from about ten to three hundred millimicrons in diameter, and may be spherical, cylindrical, or tadpole-shaped. See Figure 13.1.

Since an object must be at least as long as half the wave length of visible light in order to be visible, these viruses are invisible to the human eye. However, the electron microscope uses electron beams instead of light waves for its image-producing energy source, and these beams may have a wave length of $\frac{1}{100,000}$ that of light. Images of virus particles may be seen and photographed by using such an electron microscope.

Nature of Viruses

The nature of viruses presents a very interesting problem. Like living organisms, they increase in numbers in suitable environments; they act as parasites in causing diseases in plants and animals; they may change their

Fig. 13.1 Electron micrographs of viruses. **A,** Influenza virus magnified 78,570 times. The size of the particles may be judged from the mark indicating one tenth of a micron. **B,** Tobacco mosaic virus magnified 17,000 times. These are rod-shaped particles, often tending to adhere in chains, nets, and sheets. **C,** Crystals of the bushy stunt virus magnified 168 times. **D,** Crystals of necrosis virus magnified 5,200 times. This picture shows the regular arrangement of the individual virus molecules making up the crystal. **E,** Bacteriophage particles magnified 23,250 times. Observe their "all-day sucker" shape. **F,** Bacteriophage particles escaping from a colon bacillus which they have destroyed. Magnification: 49,500 times.

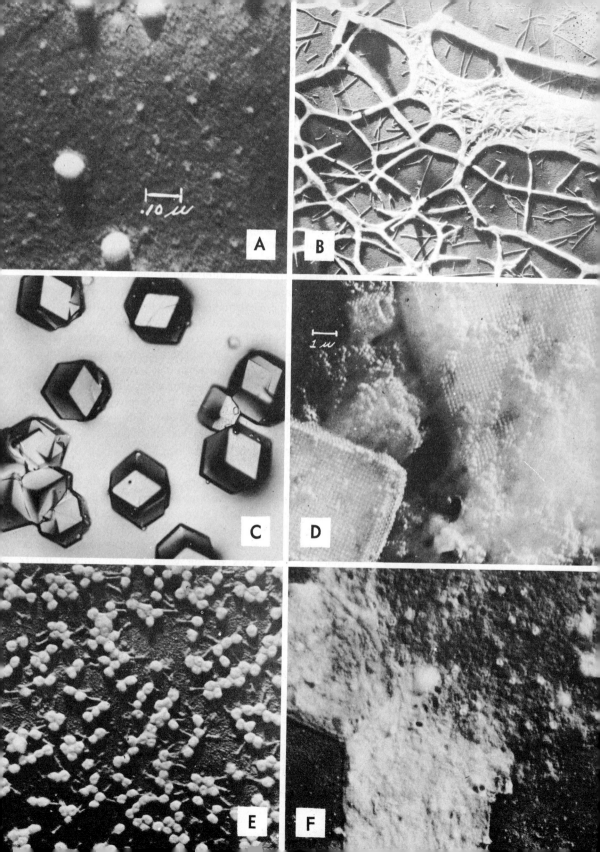

characteristics by mutation, and this change is preserved by heredity through subsequent generations.

Yet, in contrast to our traditional concept of living forms, some viruses have been crystallized, stored in dry containers, kept for some time with no evidence of active metabolism, and yet exhibit their disease-producing and reproductive powers upon reintroduction into living protoplasm of the specific type they parasitize.

Further research into this phenomenon has shown that each virus particle may be a single protein molecule, or it may be a cluster of molecules: some protein, some fat, some carbohydrate. Of those composed of a single protein molecule, some exhibit changed properties — mutations — if one or more amino acids in the molecule are changed: added, subtracted, or altered in proportion.

This change in characteristic expression with a slight change in chemical make-up, together with the particulate nature of the virus and its ability to thrive and multiply within and only within a certain type of protoplasm suggests that viruses may be genes. There is some speculation that the first living organism may have been something very much like a gene or a virus, but independent of additional protoplasm. Or, the virus may be conceived of as a parasite stripped down to the barest of essentials — simply one gene or a group of genes capable of duplication in certain protoplasmic environments.

We may like to think that the virus is autocatalytic in the sense that it manufactures its twin out of the protoplasm in which it acts. Or we may say that the virus stimulates the protoplasm to form more virus particles like the model presented. These are different ways of stating the idea that when the virus particle and the susceptible protoplasm get together, duplicates of the virus particle appear in the protoplasm under the influence of original virus particles.

The closer we approach to the dividing line between living and nonliving matter, the more that line seems to be a mirage which dissolves away into nothingness. Quite possibly men will yet assemble a living organism. We are tempted to believe that life and nonlife differ in degree of complexity, but not in kind.

Virus Diseases

Among the viruses of particular interest to humans, aside from theoretical considerations, are those which cause influenza, measles, mumps, poliomyelitis, rabies, smallpox, chicken pox, yellow fever, and the common cold.

In addition, various animal and plant diseases caused by viruses are of considerable economic importance because of the damage they cause. These include foot-and-mouth disease of cattle and hogs, hog cholera, horse encephalitis, rabies in dogs, and Newcastle disease of chickens, among animals; and tobacco mosaic, peach yellows, dwarfing of onions, curly top of sugar beet, sugar cane gall, potato leaf roll, and tomato streak, among plants.

It is quite possible that some viruses exist which do not cause such conspicuous disease symptoms in the organism which acts as host. But discovery of these must await refinement of technique and the use of some criteria of identification other than such symptoms.

It is apparent that a virus, or any other parasite, which damages its host to the point of destruction has then to find a new host or die. In a sense, the most successful parasites are those which do the least harm to their hosts, and thus enjoy the hospitality of a healthy organism the longest. Using that criterion, such virulent parasites as those of rabies and yellow fever are not as well adapted to parasitic life as the milder viruses of chicken pox and the common cold.

If, indeed, viruses are parasites which have become simplified by the loss of protoplasmic complexity — some stripped to bare protein molecules — they have gained thereby the ability to maintain themselves in a crystalline state with no metabolism, hence no expenditure of energy, and no need for a constant source of supply. When they find themselves in the presence of suitable protoplasm, they reproduce or stimulate the reproduction of themselves, and during this process mutations may occur. Otherwise, for them time has stopped.

BACTERIA

Structure of Bacteria

If viruses may be compared to genes, bacteria may be compared to nuclei. There is about each bacterium a membrane enclosing a mass of protoplasm which has scattered through it granules perhaps comparable to chromatin granules. In some bacteria these granules may be gathered into one body resembling a nucleus.

The bacterial membrane is somewhat like that of a human cell. It is thin, semipermeable, and made of a fatty or fatty-protein substance, probably a sort of emulsion with the fatty material as the continuous phase and the protein in solution in water as the dispersed phase.

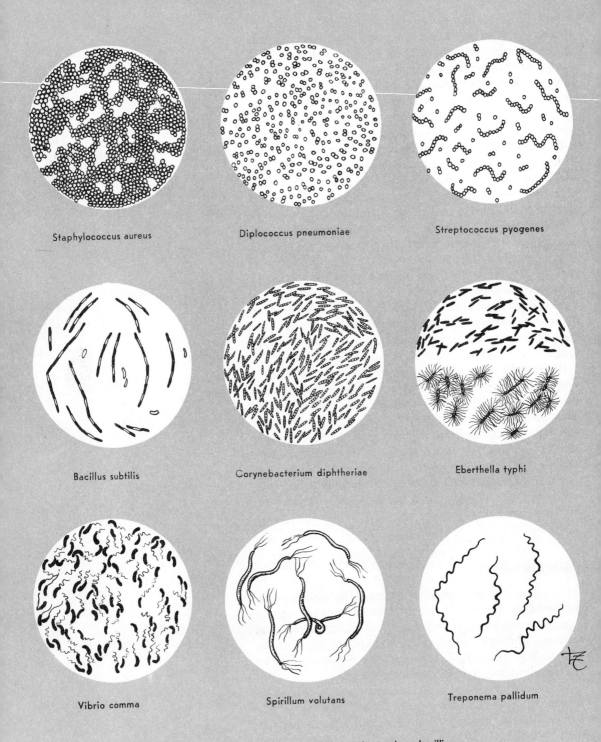

Staphylococcus aureus   Diplococcus pneumoniae   Streptococcus pyogenes

Bacillus subtilis   Corynebacterium diphtheriae   Eberthella typhi

Vibrio comma   Spirillum volutans   Treponema pallidum

Fig. 13.2   Diagrams of shapes of bacteria. First row: cocci; second row: bacilli; third row: spirilla.

Outside this cell membrane is a **cell wall,** typical of plant structure. This cell wall is made of some complex carbohydrate, usually **cellulose** or a **hemicellulose** or **chitin.** A cellulose molecule is composed of several hundred glucose molecules united into one very long strand. These strands may be very closely packed to make a dense substance. Hemicelluloses are a group of substances composed of various simple sugars and acids formed from such sugars united into long chains. Chitin is a similar substance made of the union of many sugar molecules each with an amino (NH_2—) group in its make-up. All of these substances are resistant to solution by most substances with which they are apt to come in contact.

Many bacteria have a slimy layer outside the cell wall. If this is a thick and constant layer, it may be called a **capsule.**

Bacteria vary in size from 0.15 micron to 15 microns in greatest length. They usually conform in shape to one of three types: **cocci** (from the Greek for berries) are spherical or nearly so; **bacilli** (from the Latin for little rods) are slender cylinders; **spirilla** (from the Latin for little coils) are helically coiled, although they may represent only part of one turn of the coil. See Figure 13.2.

Some bacteria possess special organs called **flagella,** Latin for little whips. Each flagellum is somewhat like one of the cilia described in Chapter 4, except that it is longer and not necessarily coordinated with other flagella. It is a slender protoplasmic strand extending out from the bacterium. It is helically coiled, and, by contraction waves, exerts enough force against the medium to push the bacterium along. See Figure 13.3.

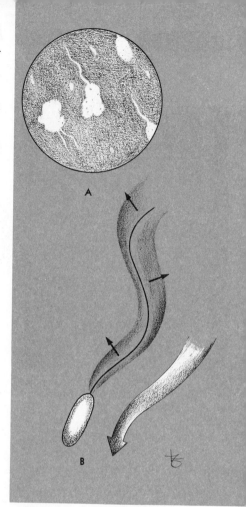

Fig. 13.3   Bacterial flagella: **A,** Appearance, and **B,** Diagram of the action of a flagellum. The bacterium is swimming toward the bottom of the page; the arrows show the direction of push of parts of the flagellum. These pushes result in a funnellike helical path of the bacterium.

Physiology of Bacteria

Some bacteria may attain speeds of fifty to one hundred microns per second. When you realize that this may be many times the length of the bacterium per second, the power of the flagellum becomes apparent. The bacterium in motion is pushed obliquely away from the direction of the flagellum, which therefore acts not only to propel but to steer. Flagella occur in all spirilla, many bacilli, and some cocci.

Reproduction in bacteria is called **fission.** The cell membrane pinches in and divides the bacterium into two.

Bacteria may obtain energy from many different types of chemical reactions. As in the case of humans, they require water, minerals, vitamins, carbohydrates, fats, and proteins.

Fig. 13.4   Above, Root nodules on clover roots. These nodules contain nitrogen-fixing bacteria. Opposite page, Close-up of nodules.

Many of the same minerals necessary for human life are also necessary for bacteria: sodium, potassium, calcium, magnesium, iron, chlorine, phosphorus, and sulfur, and possibly iodine, copper, manganese, zinc, and some others.

Especially important to bacterial life are the B vitamins. Many of these may be manufactured by bacteria, as was mentioned in Chapter 3.

There are a few bacteria which are able to obtain energy from oxidation of inorganic elements or compounds, and hence do not need to be provided with carbohydrates and fats for oxidation purposes. For example, some bacteria oxidize hydrogen sulfide to sulfur and to a sulfate, releasing the energy they need for their metabolism. Other bacteria oxidize ammonia to nitrous acid, and still others change the nitrous acid to nitric acid, both reactions releasing energy which may be used by the bacterium bringing about the changes.

Bacteria that are able to obtain their energy by such means, and the carbon necessary for protoplasmic construction from carbon dioxide, are called **autotrophic,** or self-nourishing bacteria. Many of them use free oxygen in these oxidations, and are hence referred to as **aerobic.** A few may oxidize substances in the absence of free oxygen, for example, oxidizing sulfur by combining it with a nitrate to produce a sulfate and free nitrogen, with the release of energy. Such a bacterium or such a process is said to be **anaerobic.** Nonautotrophic bacteria may likewise be aerobic or anaerobic, or both.

Nitrogen-Fixing Bacteria

The ability of some bacteria to transform ammonia to nitrates is of very great significance, for living organisms other than these **nitrogen-fixing bacteria** and a few algae cannot use nitrogen in the manufacture of proteins. Most plants secure the nitrogen needed in amino acid formation from nitrates. Animals ingest proteins manufactured by plants, either directly from eating these plants or indirectly from some animal which has eaten plants. The animals then break the proteins down into amino acids, and then reconstruct from these their own peculiar proteins.

In addition to this source of nitrates, another group of nitrogen-fixing bacteria may transform atmospheric nitrogen into organic compounds. This group includes both aerobic and anaerobic bacteria, and also a group which forms an association with members of the legume family of seed plants, such as clover, alfalfa, beans, and peas.

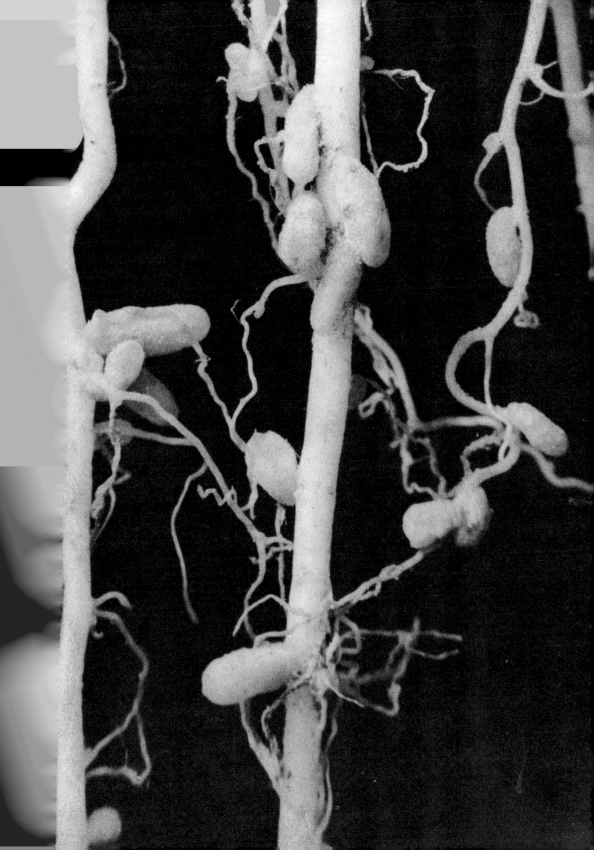

The bacteria invade the roots of such plants, and the plants form nodules in which the bacteria are protected from drying and are provided with many of the substances they need. The legume is able to use the nitrogen compounds formed by the bacteria, so the association is of the mutual benefit type known as **symbiosis,** from the Greek for living together. See Figure 13.4.

In the planning of the use of farmlands, the symbiotic nitrogen-fixing bacteria are of great importance. All crop plants use quantities of nitrogen compounds, and unless the supply is replenished somehow, the soil may become deficient. Nitrogen compounds may be restored either by fertilizers containing adequate amounts of nitrates or by growing a leguminous crop and plowing part or all of it back into the soil.

Saprophytic Bacteria

Autotrophic bacteria constitute a small minority of the types of bacteria. The other kinds must have organic materials to work on in order to survive. These forms may be either parasitic, getting their food from some other living organism, or **saprophytic,** getting their food from some remains of dead plant or animal bodies.

The saprophytic forms, together with some of the other fungi, also play a very necessary role in the life on this planet. They are responsible in large part for the decay of dead bodies of both plants and animals. They restore the substances of those bodies to availability for other living forms. Each saprophyte seems to be limited in the types of substances it can use. It has enzymes which break down one or a few compounds of a decaying body, and other organisms have other enzymes. Eventually, by the collective action of many species, a body may be reduced to water, carbon dioxide, ammonia, hydrogen sulfide, and a few other simple compounds or elements; and these may be used by other plants to reconstruct living protoplasm. At the same time, the saprophytes have obtained energy for their activities, the space formerly occupied by the dead body is again vacant, and the materials hoarded by that body are restored to general circulation. Bacteria are thus not only useful to other organisms, they are essential to the continuation of the variety of living organisms, including humans, inhabiting the earth.

There are other bacteria whose methods of obtaining energy have been made use of by humans. The disposal of sewage and garbage are examples of decay activity of bacteria. The formation of some foods, such as butter, many kinds of cheese, cured meats, fermented beverages, and silage depends upon bacteria. The preparation of linen and hemp by retting, and the tanning of leather involve bacterial action. The formation of many chemicals of industrial and commercial importance is accomplished by controlled bacterial action. Examples of such chemicals are formic acid, acetic acid (as in vinegar), lactic acid, butyric acid, various sugars, ethyl and butyl alcohols, and acetone. Comparatively recently bacteria have been used to produce certain substances called **antibiotics** used in treatment of human and animal diseases. Among those made by bacteria are **tyrothricin** and **subtilin.** The importance of bacteria in manufacturing vitamins in the human digestive tract was mentioned before on pages 71 and 72.

Pathogenic Bacteria

From the viewpoint of human welfare, not all bacteria are beneficial. Some may have little or no direct effect on human life, and a few are quite detrimental. Some cause diseases by secreting toxins which poison some phases of human metabolism. Disease-producing bacteria are called **pathogens.** Among them are the cocci which cause boils, erysipelas, scarlet fever, pneumonia, meningitis, and gonorrhea; the bacilli which cause diphtheria, bubonic plague, tularemia or rabbit fever, food poisoning, typhoid fever, undulant fever, tuberculosis, leprosy, whooping cough, lockjaw, and anthrax; and the spirilla which cause cholera and syphilis. The cavities formed in teeth are due to the action of acids, some of which may be formed by cocci and bacilli in the mouth.

Pathogenic organisms may be acquired by a human due to contact with a person or other animal carrying the bacteria; or by contact with some object, such as a tool or utensil, touched by another infected organism; or by eating food, drinking liquids, or breathing air contaminated by the bacterium. Many pathogenic forms are able to live for some time away from their usual sources of supply if they are kept reasonably moist and in normal temperatures.

Spores

Many species of bacteria are able to form highly resistant bodies called **spores.** Each spore is a condensation of protoplasm within the wall of the bacterium, and is provided with a wall of its own. After the spore is formed, the rest of the bacterium degenerates, and the spore is prepared to

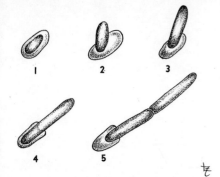

Fig. 13.5 Bacterial spores. Figures 2–5 show spores in successive stages of germination.

withstand drying, temperature changes, and prolonged separation from energy supplies which the vegetative bacterium could not survive. If and when the spore finds itself in a favorable environment, it may dissolve its wall or break out of its wall and resume active metabolism in its vegetative form. Since one bacterium forms one spore which forms one bacterium, it does not accomplish multiplication of numbers, but it does permit the bacterium to weather adverse conditions in an inactive state. Not all kinds of bacteria have been shown to form spores, but those which do include both nonpathogenic and pathogenic forms. See Figure 13.5.

Pasteurization of milk and cooking of many foods accomplish the destruction of most bacteria including most bacterial spores. Some few may survive such treatment. The preservation of food by refrigeration is accomplished not so much by killing bacteria by the low temperatures as by greatly slowing down their metabolic activities and their increase in numbers. This reduces the fermentation and decay which they might otherwise cause.

Unlike the viruses, the bacteria may be grown on nonliving prepared media containing suitable inorganic and organic substances.

RICKETTSIAS

Intermediate between viruses and bacteria are a group of organisms known as **Rickettsias,** named for Howard Taylor Ricketts (1871–1910), an American pathologist who died investigating the cause of typhus fever. Rickettsias fall into the size range characteristic of the largest viruses and the smallest bacteria, varying between 0.2 and 0.5 micron. Some few may attain a length of 2 microns. Rickettsias cannot be cultured apart from living cells, resembling viruses in this respect. But their structure is like that of bacteria. Ordinarily they inhabit lice or ticks, and are transmitted to other animals such as man by the bite of these creatures. Diseases caused by Rickettsias include typhus fever, Rocky Mountain spotted fever, tsutsugamushi disease or scrub typhus, and Q-fever.

ACTINOMYCETALES

One other group of organisms, though usually classified with the bacteria, has some characteristics which are quite distinctive. These belong to the Order **Actinomycetales.** One example, *Mycobacterium tuberculosis*, the organism which causes tuberculosis in man, appears as bacilli, or may occur as very long filaments.

Actinomyces bovis, the cause of lumpy jaw in cattle, may appear as a network of filaments. The whole net is known as a **mycelium** (Greek for fungus meadow), and any one strand is called a **hypha** (Greek for web). These hyphae may fragment into bacilli.

A third example, members of the genus *Micromonospora*, have at the ends of certain hyphae single spores called **conidia**. A related genus, *Streptomyces*, has at the ends of some of its hyphae not single conidia, but long chains of conidia. See Figure 13.6.

The formation of hyphae, mycelia, and conidia is characteristic of many of the fungi other than Schizomycetes, and it is interesting to find organisms among the bacteria having such characters. The Actinomycetales are considered to be Schizomycetes because the hyphae are very slender and thin, like the bacteria and unlike other fungi, and they do not show nuclei as do the other fungi.

SUMMARY

The Schizomycetes include the viruses and the bacteria. They are relatively simple in structure — that is, in visible differentiation. The fact that they carry on metabolic activities shows that there is a complexity not apparent to the eye.

Support is provided by the cell membrane and cell wall. Movement in some forms of bacteria is accomplished by flagella. Others may wriggle slightly, or depend upon external forces for their transportation. Materials for the release of energy and for building the organism are obtained from the environment. Enzymic activity accomplishes the breakdown of some substances and construction of others. Distribution of substances through the body is a matter of diffusion for a Schizomycete. It lives on a molecular plane, so to speak, and distances are not so great as to require a circulatory system. Waste removal is merely a matter of diffusion. Regulation is chemical — vitamins and enzymes control the metabolism. And reproduction is accomplished by fission — splitting of the organism into two.

Insofar as any living organism may be called simple, the Schizomycetes are simple organisms. It may be a reduction of complexity from a previously self-sustaining status, however, rather than a primitive simplicity, for most of them require other organisms, living or dead, as a source of supply. Only a few sulfur-using and nitrogen-using bacteria are independent of other organisms.

An order of increased complexity may be traced from

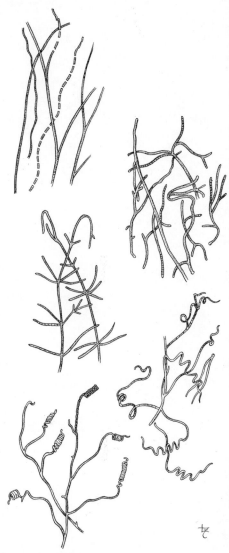

Fig. 13.6 Actinomycetales. Note the very long, filamentous shape of these plants. These are all members of the genus *Actinomyces*.

protein molecules through viruses, Rickettsias, bacteria, Actinomycetales, and other Fungi. This transition is one of steppingstones, however, rather than a connected pathway. Further work may show relationships between these groups of organisms.

REVIEW QUESTIONS

1. Distinguish between Algae and Fungi.
2. Characterize the Schizomycetes.
3. How can viruses be studied if they can't be seen?
4. What is known about the nature of viruses?
5. How do viruses affect humans?
6. What are the characteristics of a "successful parasite"?
7. Describe the structure of a bacterium.
8. Describe the shapes of bacteria.
9. How do bacteria move?
10. How do bacteria obtain energy?
11. What is the importance to humans of nitrogen-fixing bacteria?
12. What industrial uses are made of bacteria?
13. What is the importance of bacteria in medicine?
14. What is a spore?
15. Describe the Rickettsias; the Actinomycetales.

GENERAL QUESTIONS

1. Do the viruses constitute a natural or an artificial taxonomic group?
2. What characteristics would you use to determine whether or not viruses are living organisms?
3. What methods might be used to locate viruses which do not cause disease symptoms?
4. If humans could suspend and renew metabolism as viruses seem to do, would our concept of time be changed?
5. When a bacterium divides into two, are the two daughters of the one? If so, what has become of the mother? If not, do the two partake of one nature? What may be said about individuality in bacteria?
6. Could some bacteria live on the earth if there were no other living organisms there?
7. How would human life be affected if some antibiotic killed all Schizomycetes on the earth?
8. Would cooking and refrigerating of food be necessary if there were no bacteria?
9. How can a scientist be sure that a certain species of bacterium causes a certain disease?
10. What is the significance of the resemblance of Actinomycetales to both bacteria and other fungi?

CHAPTER 14

Thallophyta: Fungi

CLASSIFICATION

Aside from the Schizomycetes, Fungi may be divided into four classes: **Myxomycetes,** or slime fungi; **Phycomycetes,** or seaweed fungi; **Ascomycetes,** or bag fungi; and **Basidiomycetes,** or pedestal fungi.

MYXOMYCETES

Ceratiomyxa

Among the Myxomycetes, one fairly typical example is *Ceratiomyxa fruticulosa.* It grows in decaying wood, as in the trunks of fallen trees. The body is a mycelium, composed of numerous hyphae containing nuclei unseparated by cell membranes. When the mycelium is mature, it pushes hyphae to the surface of the wood, and these hyphae project out as tiny white pillars. On each pillar is formed a spore case, or **sporangium,** containing a nucleus and a little cytoplasm. The sporangium looks like a knob perched at the tip of the hypha. This knob then develops a membrane which separates the knob from the rest of the mycelium. Within the sporangium the nucleus divides by meiosis, forming four nuclei, each containing representatives of half the chromatin granules possessed by the nucleus from which they came. See Figure 14.1.

These sporangia then may be broken off and scattered. Wherever it lands, the sporangium may soften its wall by the action of enzymes developed by the cytoplasm inside. Then, at some point of weakness, the sporangium breaks open, and the cytoplasm with its four nuclei escapes, absorbs water, and swells.

It may elongate into a slender, wormlike form, and then round up again. Eventually the cytoplasm divides into four parts, each surrounding one of the nuclei. These four cells may be called **spores.** Each spore may divide again, by mitosis this time, to form two cells, making a total of eight. These cells then become active, moving about by the same sort of creeping, flowing movement which characterizes the motile white blood corpuscles of humans. In addition, each may develop a flagellum projecting from the anterior end of the cell; this flagellum moves the cell along by its pushing movements against the

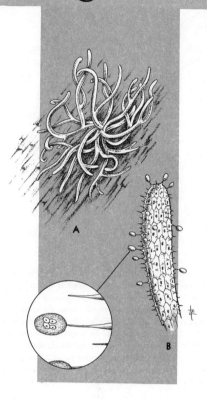

Fig. 14.1   *Ceratiomyxa fruticulosa.* **A,** The method of growth on a piece of wood. **B,** The knoblike tip of a branch bearing spores.

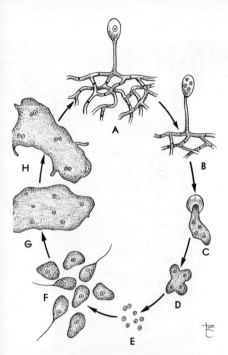

Fig. 14.2 Life cycle of *Ceratiomyxa*. **A,** Mycelium with sporangium. **B,** The sporangium is cut off by a cell wall, and the nucleus undergoes meiosis. **C,** The sporangium breaks open, releasing the ameboid cytoplasm with its four nuclei. **D,** The cytoplasm divides into four spores. **E,** Each spore divides into two cells. **F,** These cells become ameboid; some have flagella. **G,** The cells fuse into one large cytoplasmic mass. **H,** The nuclei gather in pairs and fuse. The mass then ravels out into a mycelium as at **A.**

medium in which the cell lives. The flagellum may be withdrawn into the cytoplasm.

These motile cells grow, and eventually meet and coalesce into a large mass of protoplasm in which the cell boundaries dissolve, leaving the cytoplasm of the various cells confluent. Then the nuclei begin to fuse in pairs. Curiously, of the two nuclei in each pair, one travels through the protoplasm to the other, and the other remains stationary. While there does not appear to be any visible structural distinction between the motile nuclei before fusion, yet this one distinguishing characteristic resembles a feature of human reproduction — separate sexes. The motile nucleus may be considered the male nucleus, and the stationary one the female nucleus.

As in the case of human sperms and eggs, these reproductive elements may be called **gametes,** from the Greek for marriage partners. The nuclei of the fused protoplasmic mass possess the double number of chromatin granules after this union. The mass may move about for a while as a large protoplasmic unit, and then it ravels out into a series of hyphae constituting a mycelium.

The history or life cycle of *Ceratiomyxa*, then, consists of: (1) a mycelium in which the nuclei are **diploid** (having the double number of chromatin granules); (2) development by the mycelium of numerous sporangia in which the nuclei undergo meiosis, producing spores with nuclei that are **haploid** (having the single number of chromatin granules); (3) division of each spore into motile, flagellated gametes with haploid nuclei; (4) fusion of gametes, which restores the diploid number of chromatin granules; and (5) formation of the mycelium with diploid nuclei, like that with which the cycle started. See Figure 14.2.

Alternation of Generations

This type of cycle, in which nuclei are alternately diploid and haploid, is known as **alternation of generations.** This characterizes most plants that will be described in this and later chapters of Part II. The portion of the cycle in which the nuclei are diploid is called the **sporophyte generation;** this begins with the **zygote** formed by the fusion of two gamete nuclei, and ends with the cell about to undergo meiosis in forming spores. The portion of the cycle in which the nuclei are haploid is called the **gametophyte generation;** this begins with the formation of spores and ends with the gametes about to fuse or pair.

PHYCOMYCETES

Saprolegnia

An example of this class is the water mold, *Saprolegnia monoica*. It grows on dead animals, such as insects, floating on water. The mycelium penetrates the animal, getting nourishment from its breakdown of the animal's body. See Figure 14.3.

A sporophyte mycelium may develop sporangia at the tips of some of the projecting hyphae. The sporangium develops a membrane separating itself from the rest of the mycelium. Within the sporangium several nuclei undergo meiosis, producing motile spores. Each spore is a rounded droplet of cytoplasm containing a haploid nucleus and provided with two short flagella at the front end. These spores may swim about in the water, and if they find another suitable bit of a dead animal floating nearby, they may attach to this object and become transformed into gametophyte mycelia.

A gametophyte mycelium may produce gametes in two kinds of structures. One of these is a somewhat contorted hypha, the **antheridium.** The other is a large, swollen, globular hypha, the **oogonium.** The oogonium develops a membrane which cuts its contents off from the rest of the mycelium. The contents divide into a few large masses of protoplasm, each with a nucleus; these are the eggs. An antheridium usually occurs in close proximity to an oogonium; after developing a membrane which separates it from the mycelium, it twists about the oogonium and penetrates its wall. Nuclei in the antheridium migrate into the oogonium, and the first nucleus to encounter each egg fuses with the nucleus of that egg. The zygote forms about itself a heavy wall, and then remains dormant for some time, often for many months. At last, the zygote wall

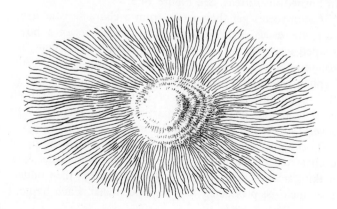

Fig. 14.3 Saprolegnia growing on decaying organic matter. Note the growth of the mycelium away from the center. How do the outer edges obtain nourishment?

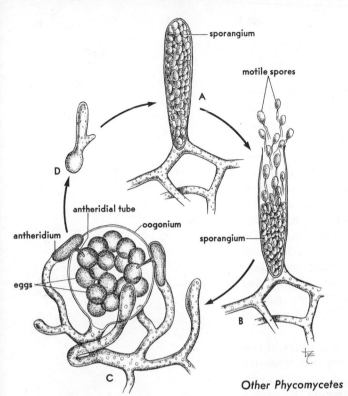

sporangium

motile spores

A

D

antheridial tube

oogonium

antheridium

sporangium

eggs

B

C

Fig. 14.4   Life cycle of *Saprolegnia*. **A,** Mycelium with sporangium. **B,** Motile spores leaving the sporangium. **C,** Mycelium with antheridia and oogonium. **D,** Zygote developing a sporophyte mycelium.

breaks open and the protoplasm pours out to form a new sporophyte mycelium. See Figure 14.4.

Thus the life story is much like that of *Ceratiomyxa:* there is a sporophyte stage including the zygote, the mycelium it produces, and the sporangia which develop on that mycelium; and a gametophyte stage including the motile spores, the mycelia they produce, and the antheridia and oogonia with the gametes developed in them.

In contrast to *Ceratiomyxa, Saprolegnia* has gametes which are readily distinguishable by visible structure, and even develop in distinctive organs. The differentiation of sex has proceeded farther here, but it will be noted that one mycelium is able to produce both kinds of gametes.

Other Phycomycetes

Other examples of Phycomycetes, generally similar in essential characteristics, are: the black bread mold, the downy mildews, and the fungus causing potato rot. It was the potato rot fungus which caused the great potato famine in Ireland in the middle 1840's, which started a great migration of Irish people to America and effected many important changes in the policy of the British government.

ASCOMYCETES

Pyronema

Pyronema confluens is a fungus found on decaying wood in burned-over areas. See Figure 14.5.

Ascomycetes get their name from a characteristic structure, the **ascus.** In *Pyronema* the ascus occurs in a bowl-shaped **ascocarp,** which consists of a wall of hyphae surrounding a cluster of fertile and sterile hyphae. The fertile hyphae bear at the tips chambers cut off from the rest of the mycelium. As a matter of fact, the mycelium itself is divided into chambers by partitions, but there may be several nuclei in any one such chamber.

Two nuclei occur in the chamber, or ascus, at the tip of each fertile hypha in the ascocarp. These two nuclei fuse, making a diploid nucleus. The diploid nucleus then undergoes meiosis, producing four haploid nuclei. Each haploid nucleus divides again to form eight. Each of the eight is surrounded by a bit of cytoplasm, and cut off from the others by a cell membrane. These cells are **ascospores.**

An ascospore may form a mycelium if it finds itself blown or carried to a suitable substrate. The spore wall breaks open, releasing the bit of protoplasm. The haploid nucleus divides repeatedly, and the protoplasm grows by digesting and using some of the vegetable material on which the fungus develops. It finally branches into hyphae forming a mycelium.

The mature mycelium develops two kinds of reproductive organs. The antheridium is a twisting, columnar hypha somewhat like that of *Saprolegnia*. The oogonium is a large, globular structure like the oogonium of *Saprolegnia*, but it has growing out of it a more slender tube, the **trichogyne.** The antheridium and oogonium are separated from the rest of the mycelium by cell membranes.

The antheridium and trichogyne may twist about each other, and the cell membranes break down at a point of contact, allowing the contents of the antheridium to flow into the trichogyne and from there into the oogonium.

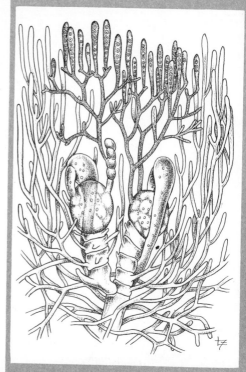

Fig. 14.5   *Pyronema* mycelium. The nuclei are haploid at this stage.

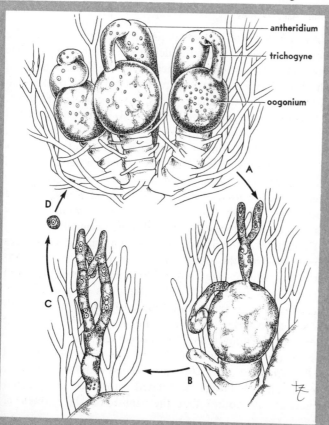

antheridium

trichogyne

oogonium

Fig. 14.6   Life cycle of *Pyronema*. **A,** Antheridia establishing contact with the trichogynes of the oogonia. The cytoplasms mix and the nuclei aggregate in pairs. **B,** From the oogonium grow up hyphae carrying paired nuclei. **C,** These hyphae elongate, each pair of nuclei fuse and then divide by meiosis, forming four nuclei; each of these divides by mitosis, forming a total of eight nuclei. **D,** Ascospore containing one of those eight nuclei. In favorable conditions, this ascospore forms a new mycelium, **A.**

Both the antheridial protoplasm and the oogonium contain numerous haploid nuclei. These nuclei assort in pairs, one from the antheridium with one from the oogonium, but do not fuse yet. From this oogonium grow hyphae containing pairs of nuclei. These hyphae are the fertile hyphae of the ascocarp. The mycelium around the oogonium forms the walls of the ascocarp. The fertile hyphae produce ascospores in the manner described before, and the cycle is repeated. See Figure 14.6.

The fact that the paired nuclei in the oogonium do not fuse until ascospore formation confuses the terminology used in designating the generations, but the sporophyte generation may be thought of as starting with the pairing of the nuclei in the oogonium, even though fusion has not occurred. The meiosis in the ascus marks the end of the sporophyte generation and the beginning of the gametophyte generation. The mycelium is gametophytic, as are the antheridium and oogonium with the nuclei they contain. After the antheridial protoplasm has entered the oogonium and the nuclei have paired off, the sporophyte generation may be said to have begun again.

Other Ascomycetes

As to number of known species, the Ascomycetes are the most numerous of the fungi described in this chapter. The powdery mildews (distinguished from the downy mildews, which are Phycomycetes) are parasitic on many plants such as willow, oak, and cherry trees, roses, clover, and grass.

Various green, blue, and black molds occur on damp and decaying food and clothing. An example is *Penicillium*, named from the Latin for paintbrush because of the strands of ascospores radiating from the top of a fertile hypha. See Figure 14.7. *Penicillium roqueforti* and *Penicillium camemberti* are used in the manufacture of Roquefort and Camembert cheese from milk. *Penicillium notatum* is the manufacturer of the antibiotic substance **penicillin.**

Penicillin was the first of many such antibiotic substances developed from the secretions of various fungi for therapeutic purposes among humans. **Pyocyanin,** first crystallized in 1860, was isolated from the secretions of a bacterium, *Pseudomonas*, in 1899, and found to inhibit the growth of some bacteria. In 1929, the English bacteriologist Alexander Fleming (1881–1955) observed that his cultures of cocci did not grow when the cultures were contaminated by *Penicillium notatum*. He experimented with this discovery, and isolated a group of related substances he named penicillin, and found that they inhibited the growth of

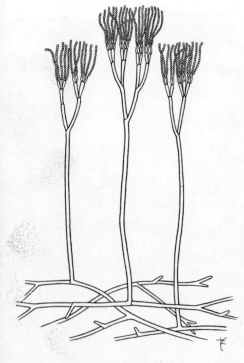

Fig. 14.7   *Penicillium mycelium with spores.*

several kinds of bacteria. He suggested the development of penicillin to be used in helping combat diseases caused by bacteria.

Little progress was made along this line, however, until Rene Dubos (1901–   ) described similar results from the bacterial secretion tyrothricin. Then work on penicillin was revived, and commercial production of this and other antibiotic substances started. Other antibiotics developed since include **tyrocidin** and **gramicidin** from bacteria, and **streptomycin, aureomycin,** and **chloromycetin** from Actinomycetales.

Also included in the Ascomycetes are the morels and truffles, edible fungi considered a very great delicacy. Truffles grow underground in some places. Pigs have the ability to locate these underground fungi by the sense of smell. Some pigs are trained to find them as a dog might find a rabbit hole. The trainer then digs up the truffle, and moves his pig on in search of more. See Figure 14.8.

Parasitic Ascomycetes include the organisms which cause Dutch elm disease; apple scab, leaf spot, and canker; chestnut blight; peach leaf curl; and the ergot disease of such cereals as rye. Ergot produces a substance which is a violent poison to humans. In controlled amounts, it is used in medicine to restrict hemorrhages and aid in childbirth.

One more important group of Ascomycetes includes the **yeasts** and **torulae.** Yeasts are usually one-celled plants, although they may undergo a form of fission called budding, in which a smaller cell is pinched off from a larger one.

Fig. 14.8 Morel (A) and truffle (B). These fungi are considered delicacies. Below, Trained pig hunting truffles.

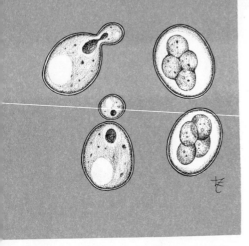

Fig. 14.9 Yeast cells. The ones at the left show asexual reproduction by budding. The ones at the right show sexual reproduction, with the formation of four ascospores from one zygote.

These buds may adhere to the parent cells, and a chain or cluster of several cells may cling together. Two yeast cells may fuse, forming an ascus, which divides into four ascospores by meiosis. See Figure 14.9.

Some yeasts are parasitic in animals such as humans. Other yeasts are saprophytic, living in the presence of carbohydrates from which they are able to get energy by reducing starches to sugar, sugar to alcohol, and alcohol to carbon dioxide and water.

Yeasts are used commercially in producing alcohol and alcoholic beverages, and in baked goods. Bread dough inoculated with yeast will undergo breakdown of starch into sugar and fermentation of the sugar with the production of carbon dioxide gas, which lightens the dough by accumulating in the mass. When the bread is baked, most of the carbon dioxide together with the volatilized water and alcohol escape. This formation and departure of gases gives the bread its characteristic spongy texture. The use of various yeasts imparts particular flavors to the product.

Torulae are yeastlike in structure, but do not cause fermentations. They are considered nuisances in some of the industries involving fermentation, since they may alter the products in undesirable ways.

BASIDIOMYCETES

Puccinia

The remaining class of fungi is the Basidiomycetes. A well-known example is the wheat rust, *Puccinia graminis*. *Puccinia* is named for a professor of anatomy at Florence, Italy, Th. Puccini.

In the spring, mycelia of the wheat rust are found in the leaves of the common barberry bush. The hyphae penetrate among the cells of the leaf, and special hyphae gather in a cluster called an **aecium** on the underside of the leaf. Aecium is the Greek word for injury, and the structure looks like a wound on the leaf. From each hypha in an aecium, an indefinite number of **aeciospores** bud off from its downward-projecting tip. The hyphae have nuclei in pairs like those of the *Pyronema* ascus. Each aeciospore carries one pair of nuclei. See Figure 14.10.

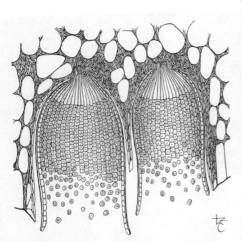

Fig. 14.10 *Puccinia* aeciospores forming on a barberry leaf. What advantages are there to their formation on the lower side of the leaf rather than the upper side?

As the aeciospores mature consecutively, they drop off the hyphae on which they develop, and may be blown about by the breezes. If one of them happens to come in contact with a growing wheat plant, it may infect that plant by breaking out of the spore coat and developing a mycelium in the wheat stem. After a time, hyphae grow to the surface of the stem. The tips of these hyphae bud off little binucleate spores called **uredospores.** These are of an orange-red color similar to iron rust, and their appearance on the wheat stem has given the name **wheat rust** to the disease and the organism causing it. See Figure 14.11.

Uredospores may be blown about by the wind, and if one lands on another wheat plant, it may develop into a mycelium and produce still more uredospores. It is by this means that the fungus may be rapidly distributed throughout a wheat field or a large area of wheat fields.

Later, as the wheat plants approach maturity, the mycelia may produce another type of spores, the **teliospores,** named from the Greek for final spores. These are dark brown or black, and do not reinfect wheat. They still contain nuclei in pairs, one pair to each teliospore. The teliospores are formed in pairs, one pair at the tip of each hypha. See Figure 14.12.

The teliospores remain on the wheat stems or drop off on the ground and remain over the winter. In the spring, each teliospore breaks the spore covering and produces a short hypha. The pair of nuclei in the teliospore fuse, and this diploid nucleus undergoes meiosis, producing four haploid nuclei. The nuclei are distributed along the short hypha, which then develops cell membranes which separate the nuclei. The resulting four cells grow little buds into which the nuclei migrate. The buds separate off from the hypha by membranes, making little **basidiospores,** named from the Greek for pedestaled spores, for they appear to be perched on slender pedestals based on the hypha. See Figure 14.13.

The basidiospores then drift about in the atmosphere. If one lands on a barberry leaf, it may break out of its spore coat and form a mycelium in such a leaf. Subsequent behavior seems to show that each teliospore forms two kinds of basidiospores. Since they are structurally indistinguishable as yet, and since in later sexual unions size and motility of the uniting members are alike, it has not yet been possible to detect which is male and which is female, so they are spoken of as plus and minus strains. Of the four basidiospores produced by one teliospore, two are plus and two are minus. A union between the two may be effected, making possible the formation of aeciospores. There seem to be two ways of accomplishing this union. If mycelia of the two different strains are growing on the same barberry leaf, their hyphae may meet and fuse, and the nuclei assort in pairs, each pair consisting of a plus nucleus and a minus nucleus. These hyphae may then develop into aecia. Or, some hyphae may grow through

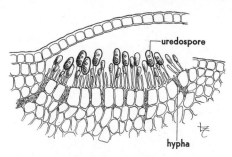

Fig. 14.11 *Puccinia* uredospores forming on a wheat stem. Notice how the epidermis of the wheat stem has been broken and pushed out.

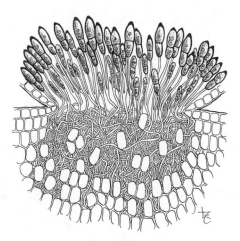

Fig. 14.12 *Puccinia* teliospores, growing from a wheat stem. Note that each hypha bears a double spore.

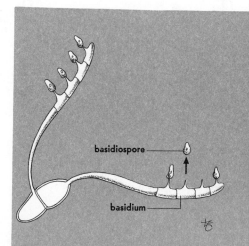

Fig. 14.13 *Puccinia* basidiospores. Basidia grow out of teliospores.

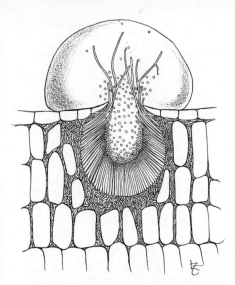

Fig. 14.14 *Puccinia spermatia on a barberry leaf.*

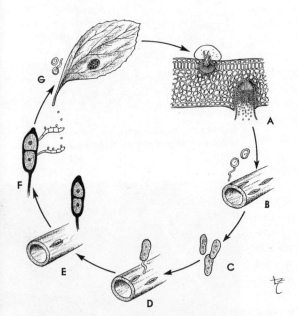

Fig. 14.15 Life cycle of the wheat rust. **A,** Barberry leaf with aeciospores; **B,** Aeciospore infects wheat stem; **C,** Uredospores formed; **D,** Uredospore infects another wheat stem; **E,** Teliospores formed; **F,** Teliospore forms basidia; **G,** Basidiospore infects barberry leaf.

the upper surface of the leaf and bud off from their tips little gametes called **spermatia.** See Figure 14.14. These spermatia occur in little droplets of a sap which attracts insects. If a spermatium of one strain is carried by an insect to contact with a spermatium of the other strain, the spermatia may fuse, and develop a mycelium. This mycelium will be populated with pairs of nuclei. Whenever one nucleus of such a pair divides, the other one does also. These pairs of nuclei remain through the aeciospores and the mycelia in the wheat, finally fusing in the teliospore before the formation of basidiospores. See Figure 14.15.

Here again we have a problem in interpretation of parts of the life cycle. In conformity with the explanation offered in the case of *Pyronema*, we may think of the sporophyte generation starting with the union of hyphae or spermatia in the barberry leaf, producing pairs of nuclei. This stage lasts until the teliospore nucleus undergoes meiosis in the process of forming basidiospores. Basidiospores and the mycelia they form in the barberry leaf, together with the spermatia, constitute the gametophyte generation.

Wheat rust is a matter of great concern to wheat farmers, for the fungus uses much of the food which otherwise goes into grains, and thus lowers the yield of a wheat plant considerably. Attempts have been made to control it by destroying the common barberry plant extensively, so there will be no place for the basidiospores to grow, and the rust cycle may be interrupted. There are a few other plants which may substitute for the common barberry as hosts to the rust. The Japanese barberry is immune, and is not involved in the wheat rust cycle, but the common barberry (known also as American barberry) and the *Mahonia*, or "Oregon grape," are susceptible.

Furthermore, the distance to which uredospores can travel during the growing season of wheat is tremendous, measured in tens and hundreds of miles, so that control of wheat rust is one of the most difficult agricultural problems.

The best solution to date is the one of developing genetic strains of wheat resistant to attacks by wheat rust. Since there are over two hundred known varieties of wheat rust, and possibly others yet to be discovered, the development of wheat strains resistant to every one of these rusts is no easy matter. But care and persistence have produced very successful varieties of wheat. During the summer of 1950, a variety of rust native to Siberia invaded the American wheat fields, causing great loss. Fortunately, strains of wheat resistant to this had already been developed in agricultural stations in this country, and are available for current and future plantings. Further work along this line is in progress, with a view to being prepared in advance for any new threat to wheat production, or other farm products.

Other Basidiomycetes

Several other parasites of cereal grains belong to the Basidiomycetes. Smuts of corn, wheat, oats, barley, rye, and rice take considerable toll of these crops. Rusts other than wheat rust attack apples, pears, peaches, cherries, plums, legumes, white pine trees, and many ornamental plants.

Fig. 14.16 Fairy ring. These are the spore-bearing parts of a mycelium which grows underground. The mycelium spreads in all directions, and periodically sends up these mushrooms at the periphery of the plant. The circular formation gave rise to stories that they sprang up where fairies had danced the night before.

Among the saprophytes in the Class Basidiomycetes are the mushrooms, toadstools, and puffballs. A mushroom is the aerial reproductive structure of a fungus which grows in the ground or in decaying logs as an extensive mycelium. The mushroom consists of a stalk bearing a spreading cap. On the underside of the cap of many mushrooms occur radiating mycelial plates called **gills.** On the surfaces of these gills basidiospores are produced, which are capable of growing new mycelia. Some mushrooms are edible; some are poisonous to humans. There is no easy rule-of-thumb for distinguishing them, and a thorough acquaintance with the characteristics of the edible kinds is advisable before selecting wild mushrooms for the table. See Figures 14.16 and 14.17.

UNCLASSIFIED FUNGI

There are some fungi whose life histories are not known well enough to permit of their assignment to one of the classes described above. Among these are the causes of some diseases of many plants, such as apples, bananas, beans, beets, celery, cotton, potatoes, tomatoes, and watermelons.

Fig. 14.17   Mushrooms. A, The deadly poisonous *Amanita*. It takes an expert to distinguish between all edible and poisonous mushrooms. B, The common edible mushroom.

Other such fungi cause animal diseases, including such human afflictions as thrush, ringworm, athlete's foot, and blastomycosis.

MYCORHIZA

Two types of symbiotic relationships exhibited by fungi and other plants may be mentioned. One type is called **mycorhizal,** named from the Greek for fungus-root. Ascomycetes or Basidiomycetes may surround and penetrate roots of many trees and shrubs, sometimes penetrating root cells, and receive food from the host. They probably aid the host in absorption of water and nitrates.

LICHENS

Another symbiotic relationship is the **lichen,** a composite plant body made of algae or autotrophic bacteria contained in a fungus mycelium. There are many varieties of lichens, but in each case the alga or bacterium is able to manufacture food, whereas the fungus is able to secure water from localities too dry for algae to live in alone. The fungi participating in this relationship are Ascomycetes or Basidiomycetes. Lichens are among the first plants to populate a denuded region, and aid in disintegrating bare rocks. They often are the first kinds of plants to grow on bare rocks and soil, and may be followed later by mosses, ferns, and seed plants. Lichens are of some commercial value as sources of dyes, and are used as feed for animals and food for humans. The manna mentioned in the Book of Exodus may have been the lichen *Lecanora esculenta.* See Figure 14.18.

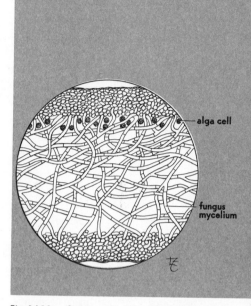

Fig. 14.18   Structure of a lichen. This is an association of alga cells in a fungus mycelium. What contributions does each partner make to the success of the association?

SUMMARY

The fungi described in this chapter have nuclei distinct from the cytoplasm. In general, a mycelium, a protoplasmic body containing several nuclei, is characteristic of these fungi.

Four classes are recognized besides the Schizomycetes described in Chapter 13: Myxomycetes, Phycomycetes, Ascomycetes, and Basidiomycetes. They are all soft-bodied forms, depending for support upon the substrate on or in which they grow. The mushrooms may project away from the substrate a little. Their form is maintained by the turgidity of the hyphae and by somewhat thickened cell walls. There is little active locomotion among the fungi except for the motile spores of such forms as *Saprolegnia.*

Materials are furnished by the host or the dead organic material on which the fungi live. By enzyme action these materials are used in building up the protoplasm of the fungus and in providing energy for its activities. Since few or no cell walls divide the mycelium, rapid distribution of materials within the fungus is accomplished by diffusion and by movement of protoplasm along the hyphae. Wastes are excreted directly through the surface of the body, or are accumulated in a part of the body and discarded as the life cycle proceeds to the next stage. Regulation of processes depends upon environmental stimuli and some chemical action.

Reproduction involves a cycle of forms through which the organism passes. A sporophyte stage is characterized by the possession of diploid nuclei, or haploid nuclei associated in pairs. If the latter is the case, the pairs undergo fusion before meiosis. Meiosis produces four haploid spores, which may produce haploid mycelia with sex organs producing gametes, or the haploid spores may form gametes directly, as in the case of *Ceratiomyxa*. This alternation of generations will be noted in other groups of plants which we shall study in succeeding chapters.

REVIEW QUESTIONS

1. What are the classes of fungi?
2. Describe the structure and life cycle of *Ceratiomyxa fruticulosa*.
3. Explain alternation of generations.
4. Describe the structure and life cycle of *Saprolegnia monoica*.
5. What effects may phycomycetes have on human history?
6. Describe the structure and life history of *Pyronema confluens*.
7. Of what importance to humans are the ascomycetes?
8. Explain the life cycle of the wheat rust fungus.
9. How do humans combat wheat rust?
10. Of what importance to humans are basidiomycetes other than *Puccinia?*
11. Why are some fungi unclassified?
12. Explain mycorhiza.
13. What is a lichen?
14. What is the importance of lichens to human welfare?
15. Why are viruses and bacteria included in the Subphylum Fungi?

GENERAL QUESTIONS

1. How would you differentiate among the classes of fungi?
2. How does *Ceratiomyxa* obtain energy?
3. How sound is the argument that the motile nucleus of the *Ceratiomyxa* protoplasm is male, and the stationary nucleus female?
4. Do humans have alternation of generations?

5. What happens to *Saprolegnia* spores which do not encounter any dead animals? Be detailed as to the specific chain of events.

6. Will our increased concern with forest fire prevention doom *Pyronema* to extinction?

7. How would it change the view of the *Pyronema* life cycle if the gametophyte generation were thought of as extending until the fusion of nuclei?

8. Of what value are antibiotic substances to the plants which produce them?

9. How and where do wild yeasts live?

10. How did the wheat rust fungus come to parasitize two such different plants as wheat and barberry in different phases of its life cycle?

11. Why cannot a uredospore develop on a barberry plant?

12. Some trees and shrubs do not thrive unless they are infected with mycorhiza. Account for this.

13. Would it be possible for a human to put algae and fungi together and make a lichen?

14. What evidence can you suggest which bears on the question as to whether the manna mentioned in the Book of Exodus was a lichen?

15. Why don't Schizomycetes exhibit alternation of generations?

CHAPTER 15

Thallophyta: Algae

PHOTOSYNTHESIS

Algae are thallophytes which contain **chlorophylls.** These chlorophylls are green substances which act as catalysts in the manufacture of sugar (usually glucose) from carbon dioxide and water. In this process, the radiant energy of sunlight is captured and transformed into chemical energy stored in the sugar. Because sugar is formed by synthesis from carbon dioxide and water, using the energy of light, the manufacturing process is called **photosynthesis.**

Photosynthesis with chlorophylls occurs in most plants except fungi. Not only algae, but mosses, ferns, trees, grasses, vegetables, and weeds all make their food photosynthetically. All animals depend, first or last, upon plants for food. When a human eats a beefsteak, he is getting second-hand grass. When he enjoys a fish dinner or clam chowder, he is getting fourth-hand algae. The importance of photosynthesis will be discussed again in Chapter 32.

The chemistry and physics of photosynthesis are not yet completely understood. The manufacture of sugar from carbon dioxide and water involves many reactions. Apparently the energy from the sun is used in separating water into hydrogen and oxygen, with chlorophylls playing a key role in bringing this about. The oxygen is released, and the hydrogen is combined with carbon dioxide or one of its products, and after several intermediate reactions, glucose is produced. Respiration, described in Chapter 4, is essentially the reverse of photosynthesis. In photosynthesis, energy is used in combining water and carbon dioxide, forming glucose and releasing oxygen. In respiration, oxygen combines with glucose, releasing carbon dioxide and water, and giving off energy.

The glucose which a plant manufactures is the basic material from which many other substances are formed. Other sugars, starches, cellulose, and fats are synthesized from glucose. In combination with nitrates, phosphates, and sulfates, glucose is transformed into a great number of kinds of protein by different plants. In fact, all organic substances in nearly all plants and animals originate in the photosynthesis of glucose.

CLASSIFICATION

All of the Algae possess chlorophylls, but they all possess other pigments as well. Some of the carotenes, yellow pigments mentioned in Chapter 3 as the sources of vitamin A, occur with the chlorophyll. Other pigments are associated with certain kinds of algae, and division of the Algae into classes is based on pigment together with many correlated features.

Thus the **Cyanophyceae** have a blue pigment. The **Chlorophyceae** have only the chlorophyll and carotenes in the same proportion as in grass. The **Chrysophyceae** have only the chlorophyll and carotenes, but the yellow carotenes are in a much higher percentage than in the Chlorophyceae, so that the Chrysophyceae appear yellowish, golden, or brown. The **Phaeophyceae** contain an abundance of a brown pigment which hides the chlorophyll. The **Rhodophyceae** contain a red pigment and occasionally some blue pigment as well.

CYANOPHYCEAE

The Cyanophyceae are usually known as the blue-green algae. Like the bacteria, these algae do not have definite nuclei, but the chromatin material is scattered about the plant body. The chlorophyll and blue pigment are also scattered throughout the cell. The plants are one-celled; some of the plants form long, linear chains of cells called **filaments.** These are colonies of individuals rather than cells making up one individual, since each cell is fundamentally self-sufficient and independent of the others.

The only method of reproduction, as among bacteria, is fission. A cell may divide into two cells, thus producing two individuals, and, in the case of a filament, increasing the length of the filament as the two new cells grow. Filaments increase in number by breaking into pieces.

Oscillatoria

One of the more common blue-green algae is *Oscillatoria limosa.* It is found in soil, particularly in greenhouses. It has the ability to swing from side to side slowly, or to creep along a surface. How this is accomplished is not understood. *Oscillatoria* cells form a long, cylindrical filament in which each cell is a short cylinder like a tiny pillbox, except for the terminal ones, which have rounded ends. A thin coating of some gelatinous substance covers the entire filament. Occasionally there will appear a gap

Fig. 15.1 *Oscillatoria.* The individual cells are arranged in a filament held together by a gelatinous coating. One gap is shown at which the filament may separate into two.

in the filament between two cells, and the filament separates into two at this gap. See Figure 15.1.

Other Blue-Green Algae

Other blue-green algae occur in the soil, in rivers and lakes, and a few in the ocean. Some species produce thick, slimy masses along the edges of lakes, swimming pools, or reservoirs. Some species may produce immense populations in quiet water, such as reservoirs, in warm weather. They die, and their decay produces undesirable odors. Control of odor-producing blue-green algae is one of the problems of managers of city water supplies. On the other hand, blue-green algae form an abundant food supply for small animals which in turn are eaten by larger animals, starting a chain of food supply, important in the natural economy of the area. Some blue-green algae join fungi in the formation of lichens. The Red Sea gets its name from the occurrence in it of the red-colored Cyanophycean *Trichodesmium erythraeum.*

CHLOROPHYCEAE

The Chlorophyceae are called green algae. They are much more numerous than the blue-green algae as to number of species, and widely varied in their structure and physiology. One of the most interesting groups of green algae includes a series of genera known as the Volvocine Series, after its most complex member, *Volvox.*

Chlamydomonas

The simplest member of this series is an alga called *Chlamydomonas.* It occurs in small bodies of fresh water and in moist soil. It is a rounded cell, each cell being entirely free; *Chlamydomonas* does not form colonies. See Figure 15.2.

The *Chlamydomonas* cell has a cell membrane and a conspicuous cell wall of cellulose. The cytoplasm contains a nucleus near the center of the cell. At the anterior end of the cell occur two flagella, equal to each other, extending from the cytoplasm into the medium in which the plant lives. At the base of each flagellum in the cytoplasm at the anterior end of the cell is a tiny body connected to the

flagellum

contractile vacuole

eyespot

neuromotor apparatus

nucleus

chloroplast

starch granule

pyrenoid

Fig. 15.2 *Chlamydomonas cell.*

centriole at the edge of the nucleus by a strand. This apparatus is known as the **neuromotor apparatus,** and seems to control and coordinate the beating of the flagella.

The cytoplasm in the center and at the anterior end of the cell contains no chlorophyll. On the sides and at the posterior part of the cell occurs a large structure, the **chloroplast,** which stores the chlorophyll used by the cell. In this body photosynthesis takes place.

In the center of the posterior part of the cell, within the chloroplast, is a structure called a **pyrenoid.** The pyrenoid is concerned in the manufacture of starch from the sugar made by the chloroplast.

Near the front (flagellated) end of the cell, to one side of the bases of the flagella, there is a reddish-orange body, the **eyespot.** This seems to be sensitive to light, and when the plant swims about by means of its flagella, it travels toward the greatest intensity of light. This puts it in position to accomplish photosynthesis whenever light is available. In ponds, therefore, *Chlamydomonas* will occur at the surface of the water during the daytime.

Also at the anterior end, near the bases of the flagella, are two tiny bodies known as **contractile vacuoles.** These contract occasionally, expelling their contents into the surrounding water. It is thought that this is a bailing-out device, important in maintaining an osmotic balance between the cytoplasm of the cell and the water of the environment. The cytoplasm has a much greater concentration of dissolved substances than the fresh water in which the plant lives. Osmotic pressure is therefore built up tending to force water into the cell and to dilute its contents to a level in equilibrium with the medium. As this water accumulates gradually, it is pumped out by the contractile vacuoles. It may be that some waste products which diffuse into the water in the contractile vacuoles are disposed of by their contraction. While the cellulose wall slows down the entrance and exit of substances by diffusion, it does not stop the process, so the timing of contraction of the contractile vacuoles is dependent upon the rate of diffusing of the entering water and in turn the difference in concentration of dissolved substances inside and out of the cell.

Two methods of reproduction occur in *Chlamydomonas:* fission and sexual union. Preceding fission, or asexual reproduction, the cytoplasm of the cell withdraws the flagella into itself. The nucleus undergoes mitosis. The contractile vacuoles disappear. Then the cell divides its contents into two parts, and pinches in two in the middle. Another mitotic

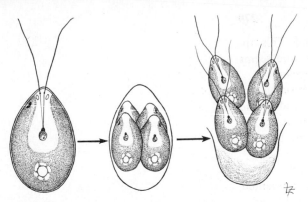

Fig. 15.3 *Chlamydomonas* asexual reproduction. The cell withdraws its flagella, rounds up, divides into four cells, and each develops the organs characteristic of a complete vegetative plant and escapes.

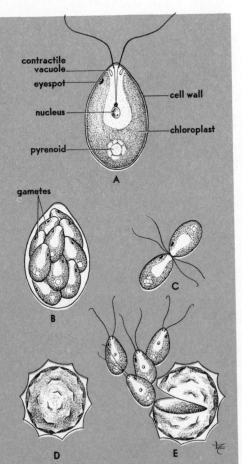

contractile
vacuole

eyespot

nucleus

pyrenoid

cell wall

chloroplast

A

gametes

B

C

D

E

Fig. 15.4 *Chlamydomonas* sexual reproduction. A, Cell before reproduction starts. B, Cell divides into many gametes. C, These gametes unite in pairs, head on. D, The zygote builds a thick, resistant wall. E, Later, the wall breaks open, releasing four vegetative *Chlamydomonas* cells.

division of each daughter nucleus is followed by a division of the two cells into four, this dividing plane being at right angles to the previous one. The cellulose wall encasing the four is stretched, and breaks open, releasing the four cells. Each of these differentiates new organs like those of the cell from which it came — eyespot, contractile vacuoles, flagella, chloroplast, pyrenoid — and secretes a new cellulose wall about itself. It is then ready to continue the vegetative existence of the species (Fig. 15.3).

Each new cell is smaller than the one from which it came, having one fourth the protoplasm. It will grow if it is in a suitable environment, and when it reaches adult size, it may also divide.

Preceding sexual reproduction, a *Chlamydomonas* cell rounds up and withdraws its flagella just as before fission. The cell divides by repeated mitoses into as many as thirty-two tiny cells. These break out of the cellulose wall, reorganize themselves into miniature *Chlamydomonas* replicas, and swim about. These are **gametes,** and further development does not ordinarily take place until they unite in pairs. If two of them chance to meet, they fuse head on, that is, with their anterior ends in contact. The flagella are withdrawn into the cytoplasm, and the nuclei fuse, forming a diploid nucleus. The zygote secretes a heavy, resistant, brick-red wall about itself, and remains dormant within this wall. In this form it may survive unfavorable conditions such as winter or drying. When the environment becomes more suitable for vegetative activity, the cytoplasm absorbs water, swells, and bursts the zygote wall. The nucleus undergoes meiosis, producing four haploid nuclei. Each nucleus is incorporated into one of four cells formed by dividing the zygote cell. Each one of the four new individuals differentiates the usual vegetative structures of a *Chlamydomonas*, and is able to live and grow, and undergo either fission or sexual reproduction again. See Figure 15.4.

The environmental conditions seem to determine whether the cell will reproduce asexually or sexually. One experimenter found that decreasing the salt content of the water by a few hundredths of one percent would stimulate the cell to reproduce sexually instead of asexually.

If we compare the life cycle of *Chlamydomonas* with that of some of the fungi described in Chapter 14, we shall see that the vegetative cell is haploid, and belongs to the gametophyte generation. When gametes unite, forming a zygote, this is the beginning of the sporophyte generation. The sporophyte cell undergoes meiosis, forming haploid cells which we may call spores, and these belong to the gametophyte generation again.

The gametes of *Chlamydomonas* are usually indistinguishable from each other under the microscope, so that it is at present impossible to say that one is male and another female. In some cases there may be a slight difference in size, but this is not consistent enough to warrant a distinction with any great degree of certainty.

Gonium

Another member of the Volvocine Series is *Gonium sociale*. This consists of four cells fastened together in a gelatinous plate. See Figure 15.5. Each cell is like a *Chlamydomonas* vegetative cell, with its two flagella sticking out of one corner of the squarish plate. The four cells have slender cytoplasmic connections with each other. This seems to permit some coordination, so that movement in one particular direction may be accomplished by cooperative beating of the flagella.

At the time of asexual reproduction, the cytoplasmic connections between the cells are broken and withdrawn, and each cell goes through divisions like those in *Chlamydomonas*, producing four cells. The gelatinous plate holding the colony together dissolves, probably due to action of enzymes secreted by the cells, and the four cells produced in each corner build themselves a new gelatinous binder, and become a new *Gonium* colony, so that one colony has changed itself into four colonies.

At sexual reproduction, gametes are produced much as in *Chlamydomonas*. These gametes are indistinguishable in structure, but a gamete from one colony does not unite with another gamete from the same colony, but with one from a different group. The zygote forms a wall as in *Chlamydomonas*. Meiosis occurs. The cell then divides into four cells. These secrete a gelatinous plate about themselves, and become a new colony.

Another species of the same genus, *Gonium pectorale*, has sixteen cells in each colony, all bound together in a flat gelatinous plate, and interconnected by slender cytoplasmic strands. Here, during asexual reproduction, each of the sixteen cells produces a sixteen-celled colony. Since this takes place immediately after cytoplasmic connections are

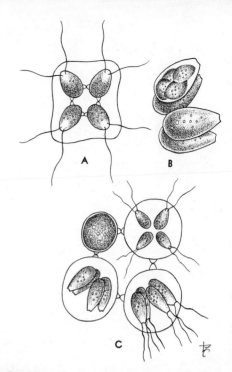

Fig. 15.5   Reproduction in *Gonium*. Each cell reproduces sexually and asexually as a *Chlamydomonas* cell does. **A** shows the vegetative colony; **B**, the process of asexual reproduction in one cell of the colony; and **C**, the process of sexual reproduction in various stages.

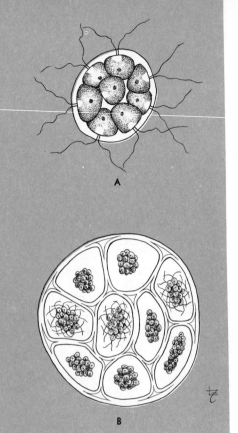

severed, all cells in a colony produce daughter colonies at the same time. During sexual reproduction, which is much like that of *Gonium sociale*, each zygote forms a complete sixteen-celled colony.

Pandorina

Pandorina morum (Fig. 15.6) is a colony of sixteen cells closely packed into a hollow sphere encased in a matrix of gelatinous consistency. The cells are in contact with each other. Each cell is like that of *Chlamydomonas*.

During asexual reproduction, each cell forms a new colony of sixteen cells. As the colony forms, it is a flat plate at first; then it develops a curvature, and the curvature increases until it becomes a sphere.

During sexual reproduction two visibly distinct types of gametes are formed. The male gametes, or sperms, are smaller and more active, whereas the female gametes, or eggs, are larger and more sluggish in their swimming. A male and a female gamete may unite, forming a zygote. The zygote develops a resistant wall. It later will undergo meiosis, and divide into sixteen cells which become a new colony.

Pandorina was so named because the simultaneous release of gametes from so many cells reminded its observer of the escape of hordes of evils from Pandora's box.

Eudorina

Eudorina elegans is a sphere of thirty-two *Chlamydomonas*-like cells. Coordination and differentiation have reached the stage that the individuals in the colony are not all alike. There is an anterior and a posterior end of the colony, and the cells nearer the anterior end are slightly smaller, but the cells nearer the posterior end have smaller eyespots. Cytoplasmic connections occur among the individual cells of the colony. Asexual reproduction is like that in *Pandorina*. In sexual reproduction, the distinction between male and female gametes is even greater than in *Pandorina*. The cells of a male colony each divide into 64 tiny sperm cells. At first these 64 sperms are encased in a plate of gelatinous consistency, and travel together. When they reach the vicinity of a mature female colony they separate, each swimming about until it finds an egg or dies. The female colony makes little change in its structure, the eggs resembling vegetative cells. After the sperm unites with the egg, the zygote may build a wall, undergo meiosis, and divide into 32 cells, forming a new colony.

Fig. 15.6   Reproduction in *Pandorina*. A, Vegetative colony; B, Colony undergoing sexual reproduction.

Pleodorina

Pleodorina illinoisensis is a sphere of either 32 or 64 cells. It is very much like *Eudorina* in the characteristics described, except that at its anterior end it has four cells which are incapable of forming gametes. If you recall Weismann's idea of the separation of germ plasm from somatoplasm, you will see how his followers interpreted this as an early stage in the development of such a distinction. The four sterile cells are the beginning of a body, as distinct from reproductive organs.

Pleodorina californica is another species of the same genus, a sphere of 64 or 128 cells, the anterior half of which are incapable of forming gametes. This seems to represent a further stage in the development of a vegetative somatoplasm.

Volvox

Volvox perglobator is a colony in a hollow sphere consisting of from 500 to many thousand cells (Fig. 15.7A). Each is like a *Chlamydomonas* cell, imbedded in gelatinous material and connected to its companions by cytoplasmic strands. Of these cells, usually not more than a hundred are capable of reproduction. Thus the somatoplasm has far surpassed the germ plasm in numbers of cells in the colony.

In asexual reproduction, one cell divides many times to make a small colony. This buds into the cavity of the large colony, curiously enough with the flagella directed inward toward the cavity of the small colony. When the small colony separates from the wall of the parent colony, the wall of the small colony pushes through the opening at the junction with the parent, and reverses itself so that the flagella now face outwards. But the colony is still within the cavity of its parent colony, and stays there until the parent breaks up. While it is still in the parent colony, a daughter colony may form granddaughter colonies within itself.

In sexual reproduction, the reproductive cells of one colony form large clusters of sperm cells — from 16 to 128 sperms per cluster. These form a little platelike colony which undergoes inversion much as does the daughter colony, and then squirms through the wall of the parent colony to the outside. If it comes in contact with a colony with female gametes, the plate breaks up, releasing the individual sperms.

In the female colony the reproductive cells greatly enlarge,

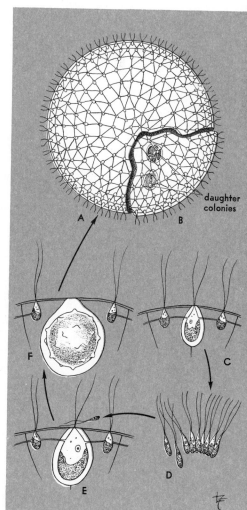

Fig. 15.7   *Volvox.* A, Colony. B, Daughter colonies formed within the parent by asexual reproduction. C, Sperm-forming cell. D, Bundle of sperm cells. E, Egg-forming cell. F, Zygote.

becoming perhaps ten times the size of vegetative cells. They lose their flagella and store food. When such an egg is fertilized by a sperm, a zygote is formed. The zygote develops a wall, and, when suitable conditions occur, undergoes meiosis and develops into a new colony. In the development of the new colony, there are first four haploid cells in a plate, then eight, then sixteen. At this stage the colony rounds up, forming a sphere. Thus the colony goes through stages at which other members of the Volvocine Series stopped. The sphere then continues to increase in number of cells, and undergoes an inversion like the other developing Volvoxes.

Volvox globator differs from *Volvox perglobator* in that it may produce both sperms and eggs in different cells of the same colony.

The Volvocine Series of green algae shows a progressive development of multicellularity, sex differentiation, and distinction between germ plasm and somatoplasm. Some of the pertinent data are summarized in Table 15.1.

TABLE 15.1

VOLVOCINE SERIES

PLANT	NUMBER OF CELLS	FORM OF COLONY	NONREPRODUCTIVE CELLS	GAMETES
Chlamydomonas	1		None	Like
Gonium sociale	4	Plate	None	Like
Gonium pectorale	16	Plate	None	Like
Pandorina morum	16	Sphere	None	Unlike
Eudorina elegans	32	Sphere	None	Unlike
Pleodorina illinoisensis	32 *or* 64	Sphere	Four	Unlike
Pleodorina californica	64 *or* 128	Sphere	Half of the cells	Unlike
Volvox perglobator	500 *or more*	Sphere	All but about 100	Unlike

Other Green Algae

Many green algae are single-celled, and many others form a linear filament of cells, like that of *Oscillatoria*. Still others may form a large, flattened, leaflike body. They occur in fresh and salt water, and even on land, such as the kinds which make a greenish patch on the bark of trees. Some green algae are associated with fungi, forming lichens.

CHRYSOPHYCEAE

Diatoms

The Chrysophyceae, or golden algae, include many forms, chiefly one-celled, with a golden or golden-brown color, and food stored as fat rather than starch. Among the most numerous forms of this order are the **diatoms.**

The name diatom comes from the peculiar form of the cell wall, which is a di-atom or two-part cover like the top and bottom of a pillbox. The cell wall is made of pectin impregnated with a silicon compound. The silicon compounds are usually deposited in patterns, so that characteristic sculpturing and surface markings distinguish many species of diatoms. See Figure 15.8.

Diatoms occur in marine and fresh waters, in the soil, and on rocks. They are the most numerous of algae as to numbers of individuals. One author has stated that a cubic meter of water may contain eight billion diatoms. They may increase in numbers a hundredfold in a week under favorable conditions. They are used as food by many animals, such as protozoa and rotifers, which in turn are eaten by others, such as small crustacea, and so on, forming the basis of a food chain involving many of the inhabitants of the earth.

The silicon compounds deposited in the cell walls of diatoms are not of use to their predators, and quantities of these compounds collect on the ocean floor. If such a deposit becomes raised by geologic changes, it forms diatomaceous earth, which is a commercial product of considerable value to man. Diatomaceous earth is used as an abrasive, as a filter in the manufacture of sugar, as a heat insulation in blast furnaces and boilers, and as a filler in the manufacture of rubber and dynamite.

Some diatoms have the power of locomotion, due to protoplasmic streaming. Tiny longitudinal fissures in the cell walls expose a thin band of cytoplasm to the surrounding water (Fig. 15.9). Cytoplasm moves along these fissures, and friction with the adjacent water moves the diatom along. The cytoplasm moves in one direction on the exposed portion, and flows back in the opposite direction internally. The diatom moves in a direction opposite to that of the cytoplasmic streaming in the exposed fissure. Periodically the direction of this streaming, and hence of diatom movement, may be reversed.

Diatoms may reproduce either asexually or sexually. In asexual division (Fig. 15.10), the nucleus undergoes mitosis, and then the cell swells, pushing apart the two parts of the cell wall. The cell then divides into two, each having a nucleus and one part of the cell wall. In each daughter cell, the one part of the cell wall remaining becomes the cover of the new pillbox, and a new smaller cell wall is built comparable to the bottom of the pillbox. Thus, one of the daughters will be as large as the parent, but the other will be slightly smaller.

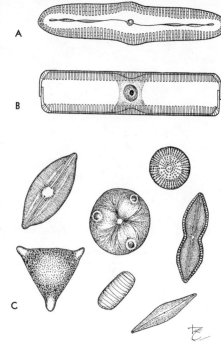

Fig. 15.8 Diatoms showing sample forms and sculpturing. Can you account for the symmetry and the delicate designs? **A** shows top view of one; **B** is the side view of the same one; **C** shows a variety of forms.

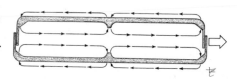

Fig. 15.9 Diagram to illustrate diatom movement. The plant is moving to the right. The smaller arrows indicate the line of movement of the exposed cytoplasm in the fissures and the return of the cytoplasm internally.

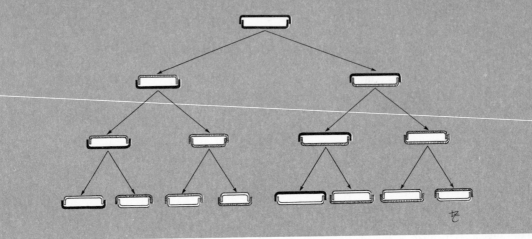

Fig. 15.10 Asexual reproduction in a diatom. When the cell divides, each daughter cell takes with it one half of the pillbox. Then a new part of the pillbox is developed, fitting inside the old one. Thus, one daughter remains the same size as the parent, and one daughter is slightly smaller. This may go on for generations.

However, in many cases, the cell wall is elastic and the daughter cells may grow to normal size. The reduction in size may continue in some forms, however, successive generations showing smaller and smaller individuals. Some of these small forms may discard both halves of the cell wall, swell considerably by absorbing water, and secrete new cell walls fitted to this larger size.

In sexual reproduction, two diatoms are involved. The nucleus of each undergoes meiosis, producing four haploid nuclei. Three of these may disintegrate. The cell walls of the two cells are discarded, and the cells unite. The nuclei fuse, and a new diploid individual is thus formed.

Chrysophyceae are widely scattered over the face of the earth. A few types become nuisances by growing in reservoirs of public water supplies, giving the water an oily "taste." This is actually an odor, and the fats extracted from diatoms have an odor like fats derived from fishes, so that the characteristic "taste" of fish may be due in large part to the fats stored by diatoms.

PHAEOPHYCEAE

Almost all of the Phaeophyceae, or brown algae, are marine. They are especially prominent along rocky shores of temperate and polar oceans. Some seem to be able to thrive in the frigid Arctic regions where sunlight may be very weak during much of the year.

Ectocarpus

Ectocarpus siliculosis is a brown alga found along seacoasts all over the world. It is a highly branched filamentous alga. See Figure 15.11. There is an alternation of generations, some plants having haploid cells, some having diploid cells. There is not a great difference in the vegetative structure of these two types, except that the diploid plant is apt to be larger, more robust, and have bigger cells.

The diploid plant, or sporophyte, bears two kinds of reproductive organs. One is a long, tapering structure divided into chambers by numerous internal partitions. In each chamber develops a motile cell (Fig. 15.12) which may break out and swim away. The motile cell is somewhat pear-shaped with the narrow end directed forward. From the side of the cell, at the level of the greatest girth, project two flagella, a long one directed forward, and a short one trailing behind. The cell contains a chromatophore, carrying the pigments of the cell, and a tiny eyespot near the base of the flagella. The eyespot is sensitive to light, and appears to direct the movement of the cell toward the greatest intensity of light.

This cell may swim about for a while, and then settle down on some object such as a rock, withdraw its flagella, and divide, forming a branching filament. The cell carried a diploid nucleus, and the new plant formed is diploid. This process is, then, asexual, and entirely within the sporophyte generation.

The sporophyte may also bear a shorter, more rounded reproductive organ, the **sporangium.** This is not partitioned into chambers. The nucleus in the sporangium undergoes meiosis, producing four haploid nuclei. After a time these may divide repeatedly, forming many nuclei. Each nucleus with its surrounding cytoplasm may round up into a motile cell much like those previously described, except that the nuclei are haploid. These motile cells may be called spores. They break out of the sporangium, swim about, settle down, and build new filaments like the plant from which they came, except that the cells are haploid and smaller.

The haploid plant may develop many-chambered reproductive organs like those first described for the diploid plant. Each chamber may produce a motile cell which looks like those previously described. These are, however, gametes. A differentiation in sex is recognizable. Some of these gametes move more feebly, and settle down sooner. These are the eggs. The other gametes are more active, and cluster about an egg in considerable numbers. The longer, forward-directed flagellum of each of these sperm cells attaches to the egg. Finally, one such flagellum contracts, drawing the sperm cell to the egg cell. The two cells fuse. The other sperm cells ordinarily swim away. The zygote develops directly into a diploid branched filament.

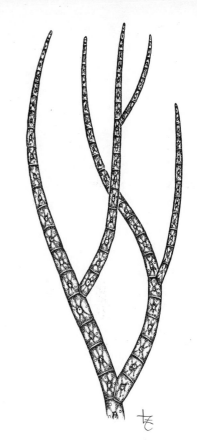

Fig. 15.11   *Ectocarpus branched filament.*

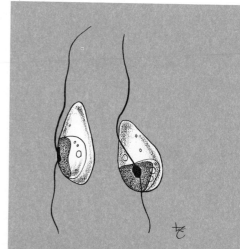

Fig. 15.12   Motile cells of *Ectocarpus.*

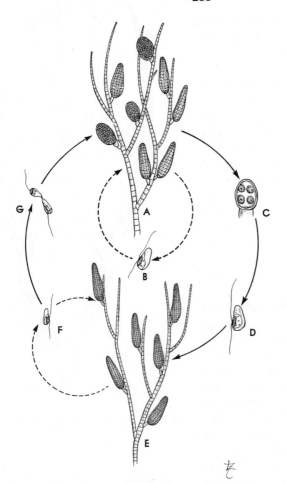

Fig. 15.13 Life cycle of *Ectocarpus.* **A,** Diploid filament with both kinds of reproductive organs. **B,** Motile cell. **C,** Sporangium after meiosis. **D,** Motile spores. **E,** Haploid filament with reproductive organs. **F,** Gametes. **G,** Fusion of gametes, forming zygote.

In some cases a gamete from the haploid plant may develop into a new plant without undergoing fertilization. The new plant is haploid. Thus, in *Ectocarpus*, it is possible for either the sporophyte or the gametophyte to reproduce its own stage without going through the usual alternation. The sporophyte may produce diploid cells which grow into new sporophyte plants; or the gametophyte may produce gametes which fail to be fertilized, and develop into new gametophytes. See Figure 15.13.

Kelps

Other examples of brown algae include many of the seaweeds and kelps familiar to the dweller along a seacoast. Some of these may grow to lengths upwards of 800 feet. Some of these larger forms are used as foods, as fertilizers, and as sources of iodine and potash.

RHODOPHYCEAE

Polysiphonia

The most complex of all the algae are the Rhodophyceae, or red algae. *Polysiphonia violacea* is a red alga found along the seashores in the northern hemisphere. It is a highly branched filamentous form in which the filaments are several cells thick. In a cross section through a *Polysiphonia violacea* filament, you will find one central cell surrounded by four peripheral cells. The central cell maintains a slender, cytoplasmic connection with each peripheral cell around it, and also with the central cells above and below it. Such connections may also develop secondarily between a peripheral cell and the peripheral cells above and below it. Branches arise from peripheral cells. See Figure 15.14.

Growth is carried on chiefly by the cell at the tip or apex of each branch. Such a cell is called an **apical cell.** By repeated division it forms the peripheral cells about itself. One of these may become the apical cell for another branch. The first apical cell has become a central cell, and it elon-

gates with the peripheral cells about it. The central cell
may divide, the cell at the tip of the branch remaining an
apical cell, capable of further division, and the other becoming a central cell which does not divide again. This
type of growth, elongation only at the tips of branches, is
characteristic of plants in all phyla of the Plant Kingdom.

At different stages in the life cycle this same pattern
may consist of diploid cells or haploid cells. In the sporophyte stage the cells are diploid. Certain branches give rise
to sporangia, and these branches usually have five peripheral
cells around each central cell, instead of four. In the formation of a sporangium, one peripheral cell divides by mitosis
to form two cover cells, a spore mother cell, and a stalk
cell. See Figure 15.15.

The spore mother cell divides by meiosis to form four
spores. These break out between the two cover cells, and
drop to the ocean floor. Here, two of them may develop
into male haploid plants and the other two into female
haploid plants.

The male and female plants look much like the sporophyte except for their reproductive structures. The male
plant has short branches on which are formed nonmotile
sperm cells. These cells are produced in large numbers,
and float about in the water after they are released.

The female plant bears ovaries near the tips of its branches.
Each ovary has a protecting wall about the egg cell, and a
trichogyne which reaches through the wall to the outside.
The trichogyne wall is sticky, and sperm cells drifting
against it will stick there. The sperm nucleus is in prophase
stage at this time, and works its way down past the trichogyne nucleus to the egg nucleus, with which it fuses.
See Figure 15.16 on page 290.

The fertilized egg divides repeatedly within the ovary,
forming a cluster of short filaments. The tips of these
filaments form cells which break off, float away from the
ovary through the pore where the trichogyne was, and
settle to the bottom. Here they develop into sporophytes
like those described before. Hence, several sporophytes
may be produced by one zygote.

The red algae differ from other algae by the absence of
any stage capable of independent locomotion, by the red
pigments, and by the special type of starch which serves
them as stored food. This "floridean starch" is a carbohydrate intermediate between starches and dextrins, which
are simpler products of starch decomposition. Red algae
possess the advanced characteristics of apical growth, in

Fig. 15.14   *Polysiphonia* life form.

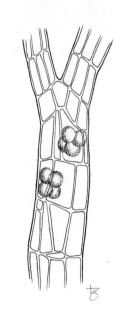

Fig. 15.15   Sporangia of *Polysiphonia*, each forming four spores.

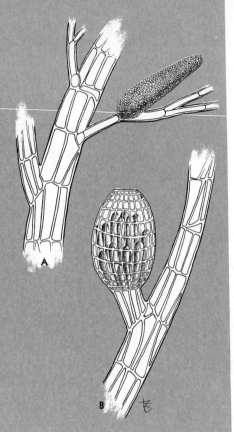

Fig. 15.16 *Polysiphonia* reproductive organs: A, Male; B, Female.

which growth is restricted to certain cells at the tips of branches, and complete differentiation of sexes in the gametophyte generation. The gametes and the organs that bear them are always distinguishable as male or female.

The cell walls of red algae are composed of cellulose on the inside and pectin on the outside. The pectin may be used commercially as agar on which to grow bacteria or fungi, or as a base for jellies, puddings, and soaps.

SUMMARY

The Algae are plants able to manufacture their own foods from carbon dioxide and water with the aid of chlorophyll, which occurs in all algae, and other pigments which are characteristic of the various classes of algae.

Algae are one-celled, or composed of filaments of cells, or in a few cases of plates or hollow spheres of connected cells.

In the simplest class, the blue-green algae, the chromatin material and the pigments are scattered throughout the cell, not gathered into distinct nuclei and chloroplasts. Asexual reproduction occurs by simple cell division and by fragmentation of a filament. Sexual reproduction does not occur.

The green algae are quite numerous and diverse, but they all have distinctive chloroplasts and nuclei. Both asexual and sexual reproduction occur in the green algae. Sexual reproduction shows many variations including the development of distinguishable sexes and the restriction of gamete-formation to certain special cells. The alternation of generations in algae is not necessary to continuation of the species, however, for an alga may reproduce asexually for many generations without the formation of gametes and zygote.

The golden algae are predominantly one-celled, and include the most numerous group of all algae, the diatoms. Both asexual and sexual reproduction occur in these plants, but the alternation of generations is again not compulsory, since asexual reproduction is much more common than sexual.

The brown algae alternate generations as a regular procedure, although the two generations may reproduce their kind without going through the alternate stage under certain circumstances. Here the plant body is much the same whether sporophyte or gametophyte, and it is always many-celled, branched, and filamentous or platelike.

The red algae normally have compulsory alternation

of generations, a highly branched, relatively complex plant body, and an advanced type of reproduction in which independently motile cells do not occur.

The Algae as a group are of great importance to other forms of life, especially in the sea, as a basis for the chain of food organisms reaching from themselves to whales.

REVIEW QUESTIONS

1. Explain photosynthesis.
2. How do algae use the sugar made by photosynthesis?
3. Differentiate among the classes of algae.
4. In what ways are blue-green algae like and unlike bacteria?
5. Describe *Oscillatoria*.
6. Of what importance to humans are blue-green algae?
7. Describe the Volvocine Series. What is its theoretical significance?
8. How do contractile vacuoles operate?
9. Describe diatoms and their reproduction.
10. In what ways are diatoms important to humans?
11. Describe the structure and life cycle of *Ectocarpus*.
12. Describe the structure and life cycle of *Polysiphonia*.
13. Explain growth by apical cell.
14. How do red algae differ from other algae?
15. In what ways are brown and red algae of economic importance to humans?

GENERAL QUESTIONS

1. To what degree are photosynthesis and the breakdown of sugar in human muscle the same process in the opposite direction?
2. Is it possible to prove that photosynthesis has not been going on an infinite length of time? If so, how? If not, why not?
3. Could fungi live if there were no photosynthetic plants on the earth?
4. Chlorophyll and hemoglobin molecules are much alike in chemical structure. Is this fact of any significance?
5. Invent a plausible hypothesis to account for the movement of *Oscillatoria* filaments. How would you go at it to test your hypothesis?
6. What are the advantages and disadvantages of colonial formation as opposed to independent cells as illustrated in the Volvocine Series?
7. How would decreased salt content bring about sexual rather than asexual reproduction in *Chlamydomonas?*
8. In rare cases, a *Chlamydomonas* gamete may grow into a vegetative *Chlamydomonas* cell. What do you suppose happens to the chromosome number in this case?

9. What do you suppose the exact difference is between the *Pleodorina* cells which can produce gametes and those which cannot?

10. What is the significance of the cytoplasmic strands connecting the cells of *Volvox?*

11. How can a daughter *Volvox* colony obtain the energy to form *Volvox* colonies within itself while it is contained within its parent?

12. How are diatoms able to secure silicon for their cell walls?

13. Is there a causal connection between the structural complexity of red algae and the fact that their alternation of generations is compulsory?

14. Are the classes of algae enough alike to be grouped in one subphylum?

15. Is the Phylum Thallophyta a natural group, or a catchall for plants which cannot be classified elsewhere?

CHAPTER 16

Bryophyta

BRYOPHYTE CHARACTERISTICS

Bryophytes are the liverworts and the mosses. Most of them are land plants, though a few float on the surface of fresh water and a few grow attached to stones or roots of trees in streams or shallow ponds where they are partially submerged most of the time. Many bryophyte species grow most luxuriantly in places where the supply of moisture is quite constant, but most species can also survive drying to the point of brittleness. A few aquatic mosses may attain a length in excess of two feet, but most bryophytes are smaller — from one-eighth inch to eight inches.

These qualities, small size and ability to survive drought, help explain why many bryophytes are pioneer plants. A number of species of both liverworts and mosses grow on exposed rocks or soil where wetting and extreme drought may alternate.

All bryophytes have alternation of gametophyte and sporophyte generations. The gametophyte is the familiar green, independent plant. The gametophyte produces gametes which fuse. The zygote develops into a multicellular sporophyte which remains attached to and is either completely or partially parasitic upon the gametophyte. Spores produced by the sporophyte give rise to gametophytes.

Bryophytes have neither roots, stems, nor leaves in the sense that seed plants have these organs. The gametophytes of some liverworts are flat plates called **thalli.** Other liverworts are differentiated into stemlike and leaflike organs. All mosses have stemlike and leaflike parts. None of the bryophytes have the specialized conducting tissues which characterize true stems and leaves. Gametophytes are anchored in place, not with roots but with **rhizoids,** which are slender nongreen filaments only one cell in diameter. The gametophytes of many liverworts and mosses reproduce vegetatively by several means. Indeed vegetative reproduction is more common than sexual reproduction in some species.

LIVERWORTS

In the Middle Ages there was a common belief that all living things were put on earth for the physical or spiritual

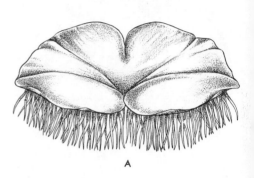

A

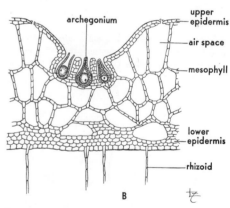

B

Fig. 16.1   *Ricciocarpus* gametophyte. The plant floats on the water with the rhizoids hanging down into the water. **A** represents the entire plant; **B,** a section through the plant to show the arrangement of cells and spaces.

[Figure B labels: archegonium; upper epidermis; air space; mesophyll; lower epidermis; rhizoid]

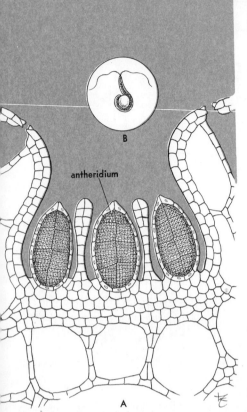

B

antheridium

A

Fig. 16.2 A, *Ricciocarpus* antheridia, imbedded in a depression in the upper surface of the plant. How can sperm cells get out of here? B shows a single sperm cell.

benefit of man. In some cases the intended use was obvious: some animals furnished skins for clothing or meat for food. Some plants furnished fruits or leaves for food, or wood for houses. Other organisms, like flies, snakes, or tigers, were a warning or spiritual chastening to emphasize religious teachings. Still others had no very obvious use, and these were marked by some clue as to their intended purpose. This clue could be deciphered by thoughtful study. Some liverworts have a lobed, rounded shape somewhat like the human liver, so they were thought to yield medicines for the treatment of any disease of the liver. From that circumstance liverworts derive their name.

Ricciocarpus

Ricciocarpus natans (Fig. 16.1) is one of the liverworts which lives on the surface of lakes. Related species live on land.

The gametophyte body of *Ricciocarpus natans* is a lobed plate several cells thick. The uppermost layer of cells is called the **upper epidermis.** The cells here are closely packed, leaving a few pores which open into air chambers below. The cells below the epidermis are more loosely joined, with large air spaces between them. The cells in this layer have chloroplasts in the cytoplasm. This layer may be called the **mesophyll.** And, finally, a basal layer of compactly arranged cells without chlorophyll, the **lower epidermis,** forms the under surface of the plant. This layer is several cells thick. Projecting downward from this basal layer are numerous single-celled rhizoids.

Growth in the gametophyte is carried on by one or more apical cells, much as in the alga *Polysiphonia*, except that a flattened plant body is formed instead of a branched filament. The growth of cells laterally from the apical cells is enough greater than the longitudinal extension that a plate, not a column, is formed.

Each gametophyte may bear both male and female reproductive organs. The male organ is called an **antheridium.** See Figure 16.2. It consists of a football-shaped chamber borne on a short stalk. The whole structure is sunk below the epidermal level in a large pit. The wall of the antheridium is composed of a single layer of large cells. Inside the wall the internal cells multiply, forming large numbers of tiny sperm cells. When the sperm cells are fully formed, the wall of the antheridium breaks open, and the sperms escape.

The female reproductive organ is called an **archegonium.** See Figure 16.3. It is shaped like a flask with a swollen base and a long, narrow neck. It is also sunk into a pit and borne on a short stalk. The wall of the archegonium is one cell thick, and the top of the neck is closed by four **cover cells.** Within the archegonium may be found four **neck canal cells** in the neck, and a **ventral canal cell** and an **egg cell** in the enlarged base of the flask.

Although the antheridia and archegonia are produced on the same plant, the antheridia usually develop earlier, so that sperm cells are ready before the egg cells on the same plant. However, other *Ricciocarpus* plants in the neighborhood may have mature archegonia. Since *Ricciocarpus natans* lives in the water, it is easy for an escaping sperm cell to swim about by beating its two cilia, and perhaps encounter an archegonium. A mature archegonium loses its cover cells, and the neck and ventral canal cells disintegrate, releasing substances which seem to attract the sperm cell. One or more sperm cells may swim down the archegonium neck to the egg cell, but only one sperm cell will fertilize the egg.

The zygote develops immediately into the sporophyte. Repeated mitoses result in a cluster of cells within the archegonial wall. The outermost cells of this cluster form a single-layered sporangium wall. The inner cells are called **spore mother cells.** The entire sporophyte is a sporangium. See Figure 16.4.

Each spore mother cell undergoes meiosis, producing four spores. These spores remain in the sporangium until the gametophyte dies and disintegrates. Any food required for the growth of the sporophyte must be produced and made available by the gametophyte.

When the spores are released by the decay of the gametophyte, each is able to develop by repeated division into a new gametophyte. Thus the cycle is completed — the gametophyte stage includes the haploid spores and the gametophyte with its antheridia and archegonia and their products. When the sperm fertilizes the egg, the diploid zygote initiates the sporophyte stage, parasitic on the gametophyte. The spore mother cells are the last of the sporophyte stage, and when they undergo meiosis, forming haploid spores, the next gametophyte generation has begun.

Anthoceros

Anthoceros laevis is another liverwort, found on moist clay soils. The gametophyte is much like that of *Ricciocarpus* except that there are no air spaces in the mesophyll of

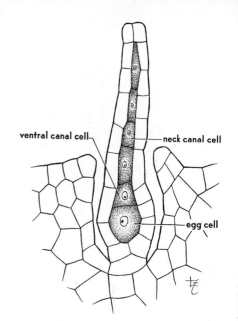

ventral canal cell　　　　　　　　neck canal cell

egg cell

Fig. 16.3　　*Ricciocarpus archegonium.*

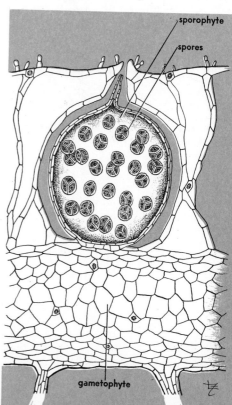

sporophyte

spores

gametophyte

Fig. 16.4　　*Ricciocarpus* sporophyte growing in the gametophyte. How does the sporophyte produce a gametophyte in turn?

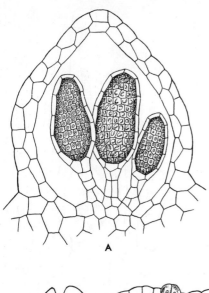

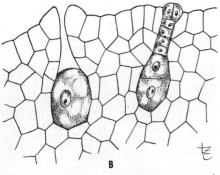

Fig. 16.5 *Anthoceros reproductive organs.* **A,** Antheridia; **B,** Archegonia.

Anthoceros. The basal layer has rhizoids which project down into the soil, and there are some cavities in the basal layer filled with a gelatinous material in which blue-green algae often grow.

The reproductive organs are more deeply imbedded than is the case in *Ricciocarpus.* The antheridia develop in clusters within an antheridial chamber completely covered over by the epidermis. Each antheridium is borne on a short stalk, and resembles a *Ricciocarpus* antheridium in structure, except that its shape is more rounded. The archegonia develop within the mesophyll, but the neck canal is open through the epidermis. Each mature archegonium includes an egg cell, a ventral canal cell, four neck canal cells, and four cover cells. The archegonium wall is continuous with the rest of the gametophyte plant, and is not sharply marked off. See Figure 16.5.

When the sperm cells are mature, they break through the antheridium wall, and the roof of the antheridial chamber breaks open, allowing the sperms to swim out. This happens normally only when the surface of the gametophyte is wet because of dew or rain, and the sperm cells may swim to the necks of archegonia. As in *Ricciocarpus,* the *Anthoceros* neck and ventral canal cells disintegrate, and a sperm may swim through the canal and fertilize the egg.

The zygote develops immediately into the *Anthoceros* sporophyte. The zygote divides repeatedly into numerous cells, and these cells become arranged into a long sporophyte divisible into three parts. The lowest part, still located in the enlarged part of the archegonial chamber, is the **foot.** This grows into close contact with the gametophyte cells and receives water and dissolved inorganic salts and some food from these cells. The intermediate part is a place of rapidly dividing cells which continues to grow for some time. The uppermost part is the **capsule,** a long, cylindrical shoot extending up into the air for an inch or more.

The capsule has a central core of supporting cells surrounded by a cylinder of spore-making cells, which is in turn surrounded by a cylinder of supporting cells. An epidermis covers the whole. In the spore-making cylinder some cells become spore mother cells, while others remain sterile. The spore mother cells undergo meiosis, each forming four spores. When the spores are mature, the top of the capsule splits open, and spores may be scattered by the wind and the rain. The sterile cells in the spore-making cylinder appear to make little partitions or shelves separating the spore mother cells into numerous small groups. See Figure 16.6.

The outer layers of cells in the *Anthoceros* capsule contain chloroplasts, and are capable of producing food by photosynthesis. If the foot were able to develop rhizoids which could penetrate the lower part of the gametophyte plant and establish contact with the soil, the *Anthoceros* sporophyte could conceivably become independent of the gametophyte. In the two remaining phyla of the Plant Kingdom, the sporophyte is independent of the gametophyte. This makes it possible for the ferns and seed plants to attain a much greater size than the bryophytes. The gametophyte must remain small enough to enable the sperm to swim to the egg in a dewdrop. But a sporophyte produces spores without the necessity of providing for fertilization, and a large sporophyte is more effective in increasing the numbers of the plant than a small one. For this reason, botanists who look to the bryophytes for a hint as to how the ferns and seed plants have come about center their attention on *Anthoceros*. As we shall see next, the mosses have tended toward a much more elaborate gametophyte, and have also produced a sporophyte able to provide some of its own food, but the sporophyte in many mosses is farther from the ground and somewhat more specialized in structure.

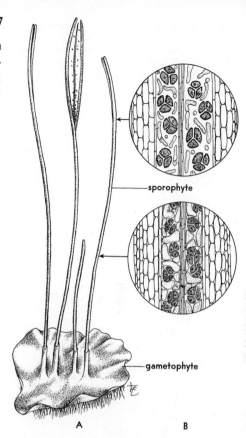

Fig. 16.6 *Anthoceros* sporophyte. A, External appearance. B, Internal structure, showing central supporting column, spore-forming tissue, and outer photosynthetic tissue.

MOSSES

Funaria

Funaria hygrometrica is an example of the mosses. The gametophyte developing from a spore is at first a branched filament of cells joined end to end. The cells possess numerous chloroplasts. At intervals along this filament arise shoots bearing leaflike appendages. See Figure 16.7.

These shoots become the conspicuous moss, and many shoots may come from different parts of the same branched filament, hence from a single spore.

The stalk is anchored into the ground by multicellular rhizoids which may branch. The stalk consists of an epidermis, a cortex, and a central cylinder. The epidermis is a single layer of cells. The cortex is made of large cells capable of storing food and of supporting the weight of the "leaves" and eventually of the sporophyte. The central cylinder is made of smaller, elongated cells which may facilitate the conduction of water through the stalk, though they are not structurally specialized beyond mere elongation.

The leaflike appendages are flattened plates of cells, one cell thick except for a longitudinal thickening down the middle. The cells contain chlorophyll in chloroplasts, and manufacture food. Any one moss gametophyte may con-

Fig. 16.7 *Funaria* filament and leafy shoot. Several of these leafy shoots may grow from any one filament. If the filaments between these shoots die and disintegrate, several individual moss gametophytes may come from one spore.

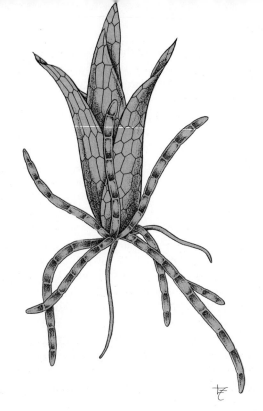

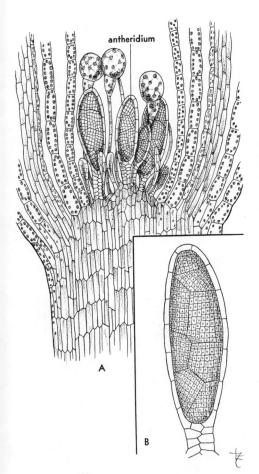

antheridium

Fig. 16.8 *Funaria* antheridia. A, Tip of leafy shoot, showing arrangement of antheridia. B, Structure of one antheridium.

sist of several shoots and the filament from which they grow. If the filament dies, the several shoots become separate individuals.

The sex organs may be borne on the same plant. In *Funaria hygrometrica* the antheridia appear at the tips of shoots first, and the archegonia at the tips of branches of the same shoots somewhat later. In some other mosses, the two kinds of sex organs may be carried on separate plants.

The antheridia are borne in a cluster at the tip of a shoot. The appendages surrounding this cluster bend out away from the antheridia, giving the appearance of flower petals. The resemblance to a flower is heightened by the appearance in the antheridial walls of a bright reddish-orange color. Each antheridium resembles the antheridia of liverworts. It is a long chamber, shaped like a straight-necked summer squash, borne on a relatively long stalk, and enclosed in a wall made of a single layer of cells. Scattered among the antheridia are long filaments of green cells which may protect the antheridia somewhat.

Within an antheridium repeated cell divisions result in the production of a large number of small cells, each capable of becoming a sperm equipped with two cilia. See Figure 16.8.

The archegonia are borne on the tip of a separate branch, but here the leaves surrounding the archegonia do not fold back to resemble petals, but remain upright, partially enclosing the tip. Again there are filaments of green cells growing up among the sex organs.

The archegonia are somewhat like those of liverworts, but much longer. The archegonial stalk is many cells long, and the neck is considerably elongated. The wall of the neck is a single layer thick, and six rows around, all produced from one cover cell which acts as an apical cell. The cover cell is a sister cell to the one which divides to form egg and ventral canal cell. As the cover cell continues to divide producing the neck wall, it also produces the neck canal cells, six in number. These neck canal cells and the ventral canal cell disintegrate early, and the cover cell disappears when the archegonium is mature. See Figure 16.9.

The antheridial wall breaks open when the sperms are mature and when the moss is wet with dew or rain. The sperm cells swim about, and if they come near to the archegonium, the secretions of the archegonium seem to exert a directing influence on the sperm cells, steering them down the neck to the egg. One sperm unites with the egg, forming a zygote.

The zygote develops immediately into the sporophyte plant. Like the sporophyte of *Anthoceros*, the *Funaria* sporophyte consists of a foot, an intermediate part, and a capsule. The foot grows down through the base of the archegonium into the top of the gametophyte shoot, and derives food and water from the gametophyte. The intermediate part elongates very much, pushing the capsule and the upper part of the archegonium about $1\frac{1}{2}$ inches into the air. The upper part of the archegonium breaks away from the rest of the gametophyte, and remains for some time as a dry, shrivelled hood over the top of the capsule.

The capsule itself is a swollen, rounded chamber with a central column of supporting cells, a cylinder of spore-forming cells around this, another cylinder of supporting cells, and a single-layered epidermis. The top of the central column projects out into a domelike lid over the capsule. See Figure 16.10.

The spore-forming cells divide by mitosis and thus produce large numbers of spore mother cells, each of which may divide by meiosis, forming four spores. When the spores are ripe, the lid breaks loose from the top of the capsule and falls off. The tissues at the rim of the opening form long, triangular tongues which are very sensitive to moisture. When the capsule is moist, each tongue dips down into the

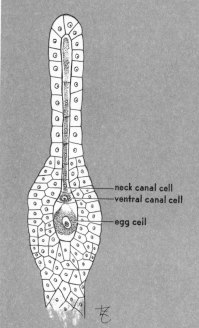

neck canal cell
ventral canal cell
egg cell

Fig. 16.9   *Funaria* archegonium. Notice the very long neck. How can a moss sperm get to the egg?

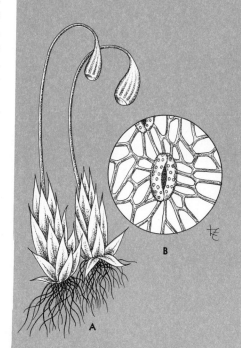

B

A

Fig. 16.10   *Funaria* sporophyte. A, External view. B, Stomata.

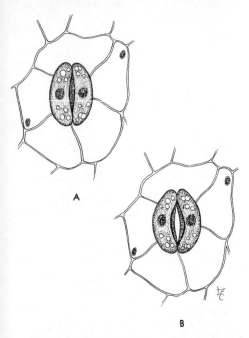

Fig. 16.11 Diagrams to show the operation of stomata. A, Stoma closed; B, Stoma open.

mass of spores, some of which stick to it. When the air and the capsule dry in the wind, the tongues curl upward, lifting the spores into the air, where they may be blown away. If a spore lands on moist soil, it may develop into a filament of green cells and produce new shoots.

The outer layers of the capsule contain chloroplasts, and may manufacture some of the food needed to sustain the sporophyte. In the outer layer of supporting tissue, beneath the epidermis, there are air spaces. These may communicate with the outside through tiny pores in the epidermis known as **stomata.** Each stoma is surrounded by two specialized epidermal cells known as **guard cells.** The guard cell walls next to the stoma are much thicker than the walls on the other sides of the cell. They are slightly incurved toward the center of the cell and away from the stoma. When the cell is turgid, due to accumulation of water and sugar, the thick wall swells and increases its concavity so that the stoma is enlarged. When the guard cell loses water and transforms sugar into starch, the wall shrinks, partially collapsing, and narrowing the stoma. Most stomata are open in the daytime and closed at night. See Figure 16.11.

This action of the guard cells facilitates photosynthesis. When the stomata are open, carbon dioxide may diffuse into the air spaces in the capsule, and excess oxygen may escape. When the stomata are closed, the diffusion in of carbon dioxide decreases, as does the amount of water lost by evaporation through each stoma. Stomata are characteristic of the sporophytes of ferns and seed plants, also.

In the life cycle of *Funaria*, the gametophyte generation begins with the spore, which produces the branched filament from which the shoots grow. The tips of the shoots produce sex organs. Antheridia produce sperms, which swim about in the moisture on the surface of the plant. If a sperm gets to a mature archegonium, it may swim through the neck and unite with the egg, producing a zygote, which begins the sporophyte generation. By cell division and differentiation, the zygote becomes a sporophyte, which is partially parasitic on the gametophyte. The epidermis of the capsule has stomata bounded by specialized guard cells, and the underlying tissue has chloroplasts and large air spaces. The spore-forming tissue produces numerous spores which are thrown out of the capsule by a special device. In some mosses the special device may be different, or even absent. Groups of plants having more complex sporophytes will be discussed in succeeding chapters.

Mosses have little commercial value, except for the peat moss, which is used as fuel and as packing for other plants.

Mosses are valuable, however, as ground cover in preventing erosion, conserving water, and building soil.

SUMMARY

The liverworts and mosses are small plants of no great economic importance. The gametophyte stage is the dominant or conspicuous one, whereas the sporophyte is dependent upon the gametophyte for its support, water, mineral supplies, and some or all of its food. The process of fertilization in bryophytes involves the swimming of a sperm to the egg, and this requires a water pathway from the antheridium to the archegonium. Therefore bryophytes are limited in size and in habitat. Most liverworts and mosses grow on soil and rocks, although a few live in fresh water. Some species grow on bark and some on tree leaves.

The gametophyte may have leaflike organs, and in the case of mosses, stalks with an epidermis, a cortex, and a central cylinder. There are no true roots, but rhizoids, which are one-celled in liverworts, and filaments of cells in mosses.

The sporophyte of *Ricciocarpus* is merely a sporangium, but in most other bryophytes the sporophyte has a foot by which it fastens to the gametophyte, an intermediate part devoted to rapid cell division and elongation, and a capsule. The capsule contains the spore-forming cells together with supporting tissue, photosynthetic tissue, an epidermis, and often some mechanism which releases mature spores. In some bryophyte capsules a specialization occurs among epidermal cells in the form of guard cells surrounding stomata.

While some of the thallophytes are land plants, the majority are aquatic. Among the bryophytes, however, the land habitat is the usual one, and water the exception. In the colonization of any newly exposed land, lichens are often first, soon followed by bryophytes. Frequently, mosses such as *Funaria* are the first plants to become established in areas burned over by forest fires.

But to the botanist interested in variation among the plant phyla, bryophytes are of particular interest as the only land plants in which the gametophyte generation is both independent and predominant and the sporophyte generation is for the most part parasitic on the gametophyte.

REVIEW QUESTIONS

1. Characterize the bryophytes as a plant group.
2. Why are liverworts so called?
3. Describe the structure and life cycle of *Ricciocarpus*.

4. Describe the structure and life cycle of *Anthoceros*.
5. What characteristics of the *Anthoceros* sporophyte suggest a trend toward its independence?
6. Describe the structure of the gametophyte of *Funaria*.
7. Describe the life cycle of *Funaria*.
8. How do guard cells operate?
9. To what extent is a moss sporophyte parasitic on the gametophyte?
10. What is the importance of bryophytes to human economy?

GENERAL QUESTIONS

1. Account for the names: agueweed, birthwort, bloodroot, boneset, bugbane, cankerroot, catchfly, clear-eye, colicroot, coughwort, cramp bark, feverwort, goutweed, headache plant, heal-all, heart's-ease, horse balm, itchweed, lungwort, nailwort, pleurisy root, soapwort, spleenwort, toothache grass, woundwort.
2. How is it possible for such different kinds of *Ricciocarpus* gametophyte cells as epidermis, mesophyll, guard cells, and rhizoids all to be derived from one apical cell?
3. Is there any advantage to the development of antheridia and archegonia at different times on a *Ricciocarpus* plant?
4. The entire *Ricciocarpus* sporophyte is a sporangium. The moss sporophyte includes other structures in addition. Which plan is more efficient judged by weighing the results accomplished against the materials and energy used?
5. If the *Anthoceros* sporophyte foot should penetrate the gametophyte and reach the ground, what additional changes would be necessary for the sporophyte to become independent of the gametophyte?
6. Is there any special significance to the presence of chloroplasts in guard cells and not in other epidermal cells?
7. The beauty of such plants as mosses is widely recognized. To what extent is such natural beauty of economic importance to humans?
8. How do you account for the fact that no bryophytes grow to the size of lilac bushes?
9. What differences are there in structure and physiology between aquatic plants and land plants?
10. Would you consider bryophytes as relatively successful plants?

Pteridophyta

PTERIDOPHYTE CHARACTERISTICS

The *Pteridophyta* possess roots and stems as well as leaves. The gametophyte of most species is capable of independent existence, as in the bryophytes, but the sporophyte is also independent, and is the more conspicuous of the two generations. The pteridophytes include the ferns and some closely allied plants.

POLYPODIUM

Polypodium virginianum is one of the most familiar of the ferns. It is commonly called rock polypody or stone brake because it grows on rocks. It is evergreen; that is, its leaves remain green and attached to the stem for at least two growing seasons. The sporophyte is the large, prominent generation. The gametophyte is a small green plate resembling somewhat the gametophyte of *Ricciocarpus* or *Anthoceros*.

The gametophyte starts as a spore, which by cell division forms a short filament. The gametophyte is formed by repeated divisions of an apical cell at the tip of the filament. It is a flattened, valentine-shaped plate held in place by some one-celled rhizoids. The plant is one cell thick except in the immediate neighborhood of the apical cell at the notch in the valentine. See Figure 17.1.

The gametophyte bears both antheridia and archegonia. The antheridia are formed relatively early, and may be found on the underside of the plant among the rhizoids. Each antheridium is a spherical chamber with a wall one cell thick, and no stalk. A relatively small number of sperm cells are formed within each antheridium, normally about 32. Each sperm cell is a coiled, worm-shaped cell bearing many cilia. See Figure 17.2.

The archegonia form rather late in the development of the gametophyte, and occur on the underside in the thickened area near the apical cell. The archegonium is much like that of the liverworts except that

Fig. 17.1 Fern gametophyte shown from the under surface. The plant is about a quarter of an inch in diameter.

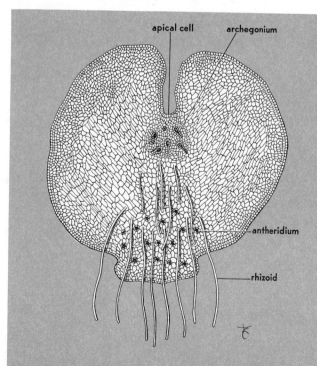

apical cell   archegonium

antheridium

rhizoid

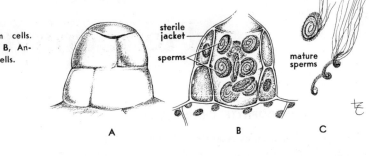

Fig. 17.2 Fern antheridium and sperm cells.
A, Antheridium viewed from the outside. B, Antheridium containing sperm cells. C, Sperm cells.

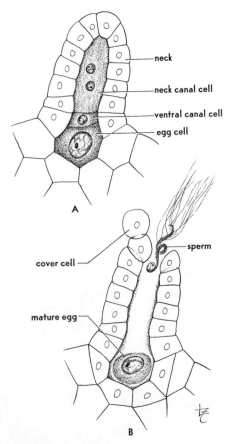

Fig. 17.3 Fern archegonium. A, Mature archegonium. B, Sperm cell entering archegonium.

Fig. 17.4 Development of the zygote into a sporophyte in the fern. A, Zygote in the venter of the archegonium. B, First division of the zygote. C, Second division of the zygote. D, Later stage after several cell divisions. E, Differentiation of parts of the sporophyte.

it has no stalk, and a shorter neck. The cell in the interior of the archegonium divides into a neck canal cell and another cell which soon divides again to form the egg cell and the ventral canal cell. The nucleus of the neck canal cell may divide into two, but the cell itself usually remains undivided. See Figure 17.3.

The neck canal cell and ventral canal cell soon disintegrate. The space between the gametophyte and the soil is usually moist, so that when the sperms are mature and break out of the antheridia, they may swim about in the film of water under the plant. If a sperm reaches the neck of a mature archegonium, it may swim through the neck and fertilize the egg cell.

The zygote is the first cell of the sporophyte generation. It divides into two cells, and then into four. Of these four, one will develop into the foot, one into the temporary root, one into the stem, and one into a temporary leaf. See Figure 17.4.

The foot is a temporary outgrowth which burrows into the gametophyte, where it obtains nourishment until the

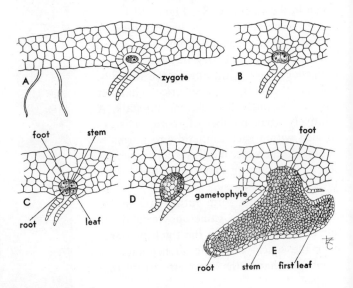

sporophyte plant can supply its own needs. The temporary root and the temporary leaf soon become established,
and the gametophyte may then wither away, and cease to be
a source of supply. Archegonia and antheridia are formed
only under special conditions. If they are not formed, the
gametophyte may live for several years. Also, the gametophytes of some species of ferns reproduce asexually by
means of tiny detachable outgrowths called **gemmae.**

The stem is the only permanent organ developing out of
the first four cells. It elongates and from it develop leaves
and roots. The temporary organs then die.

The structure of the growing and mature fern sporophyte
is more complex than the structure of the bryophyte sporophyte. The roots and stems differentiate structures which
facilitate the transportation of water and food over the
larger plant, and the leaves serve not only as photosynthetic
organs which manufacture food, but also as the site of the
sporangia that produce spores. We shall examine these
structures in some detail.

Stem

The *Polypodium* stem is horizontal, usually growing a
few inches under the surface of the soil. It grows in length
at the tip only, and may branch a few times. The stem tip
is protected by special plates of cells called <u>scales,</u> and by
hairlike filaments growing out of the epidermis. The stem
may live many years, growing in length each year and
developing new leaves and new roots. The older leaves and
roots die at the end of a growing season, and this progressive
death may reach and pass a place of branching. When this
happens, the two separate stems continue to grow. This is a
type of vegetative multiplication not involving special reproductive structures. See Figure 17.5.

The outermost single layer of cells of the *Polypodium*
stem is the epidermis. Next comes a layer called **sclerenchyma,** with cells whose walls are much thickened with
cellulose.

Within the sclerenchyma, and making up most of the
bulk of the stem, is the tissue known as **parenchyma.** This
is composed of large cells with thin walls, which act as
water storage or food depots where excess food manufactured in the leaves may accumulate.

Vascular Tissues

Scattered about in the parenchyma are clusters of cells
known as **vascular bundles.** Each vascular bundle is sur-

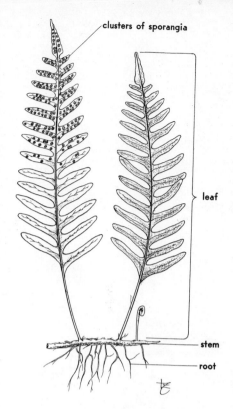

Fig. 17.5   Diagram of fern adult sporophyte.
Which parts extend above ground?

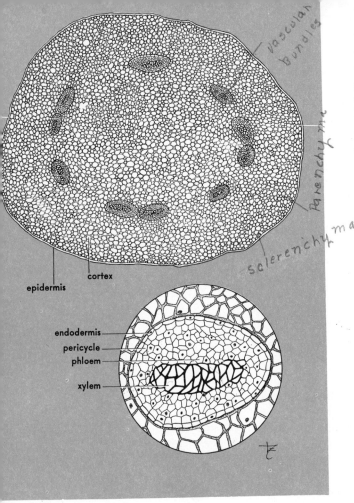

Vascular Bundles

Parenchyma

m a

Sclerenchyma

epidermis

cortex

endodermis

pericycle

phloem

xylem

Fig. 17.6   Microscopic structure of the *Polypodium* stem. Note the scattering of vascular bundles.

rounded by a ring of small cells called the **endodermis**. Within the endodermis is a ring of somewhat larger cells, the **pericycle**. Inside the pericycle and surrounded by an irregular cushion of parenchyma cells are two kinds of cells concerned with transportation. The **phloem** tissue within the cushion carries dissolved substances from one part of the plant to another. The **xylem** tissue carries water from the roots to the stem and leaves. In both the phloem and xylem, cells are connected end to end, forming a continuous branching system throughout the plant. See Figure 17.6.

The phloem cells which are active in transport are very much elongated cells called **sieve tubes**. Their walls are moderately thickened, but where one sieve tube is in contact with another there are groups of perforations known as **sieve plates**. The sieve plates occur at the slanting ends of the cell as well as along the sides, and provide a means whereby the cytoplasm of other phloem cells or of adjacent parenchyma cells may establish contact with the sieve tube. The cytoplasm of the sieve tube lines the wall on all sides and surrounds a large central cavity filled with a solution of inorganic and organic substances. This lake in the middle of the cell is a **vacuole**. Rather early in the elaboration of the sieve tube, the cytoplasm loses its nucleus. The significance of this loss is not well understood at present. One advantage of this loss will be noted later. See Figure 17.7.

Conduction of dissolved substances from one part of the plant to another is carried on largely in the phloem. During the growing season, when the leaves are manufacturing food in considerable quantities, the phloem carries food to the stem and roots. In spring, when new leaves are beginning to grow, food is carried through the phloem to the young leaves. The change in direction may be accounted for by the change in concentrations of food. When the leaf is manufacturing large amounts of sugar, the concentration is higher there than in the stem, so sugar diffuses through the phloem to the stem and roots. In the early spring the concentration of food is greater in the stem than in the growing leaves, so sugar diffuses from the stem to the leaves.

The rate of diffusion may be computed, and it is not always enough to account for the quantities of sugar transported. But the cytoplasm in a phloem cell is in constant rotation, moving up one side, across the top, down the other side, across the bottom, and so on. The presence of a nucleus would slow down this movement, as the nucleus would be bulky and serve as a hindrance to such cyclic movement. But as noted before, the nucleus disappears in a mature sieve tube.

When food is being made in the leaf, the cytoplasm crossing from one side to the other at the top of the sieve tube comes into contact with the sugar-rich cytoplasm of the cell above it, and some of the sugar diffuses through the sieve plate into the cytoplasm. The streaming of the cytoplasm down the side of the sieve tube carries the sugar to the bottom much faster than it could get there by diffusion alone.

When new leaves are beginning to grow, as in early spring, the cytoplasm circulating in a sieve tube in the phloem connecting the stem and leaf comes in contact with concentrated food at its lower end. Food is therefore transported to the growing leaf where sugar is used and is hence in scarce supply. Similarly other substances, such as minerals, may be transported from regions of greater concentration to regions of lesser concentration.

Xylem cells which are active in transport are also much elongated. It is in these cells that water and some dissolved substances are transported from roots to stem and leaves. A developing xylem cell forms a thick wall in which numerous thin areas occur. These thin places are called **pits.** Soon the nucleus and cytoplasm both disappear, leaving only the nonliving cell wall. Such a cell is called a **tracheid.** The tracheids serve not only as a conducting pathway for water but as strengthening and support for the stem and leaf because of their thickened walls. The thin places, or pits, allow for rapid passage of water from one tracheid to another and out of a tracheid into other parts of the plant. See Figure 17.8.

Water Transport

Since the tracheids contain no living protoplasm, they do not actively transport substances as does the phloem tissue. The xylem tracheids are merely inert plumbing, and physical forces lift water from the roots to the leaves.

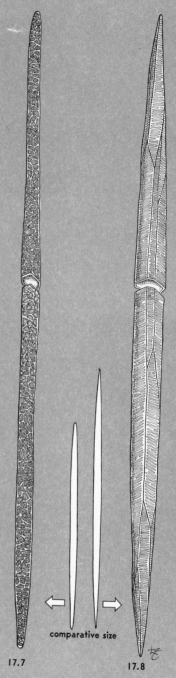

comparative size

17.7   17.8

Fig. 17.7 Fern phloem cell, a sieve tube.

Fig. 17.8 Fern tracheid.

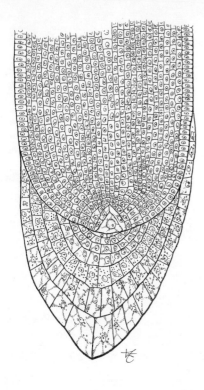

Fig. 17.9   Longitudinal section of fern root.

One force is **diffusion pressure.** The cells of the root contain protoplasm, which is water containing relatively large amounts of salts and organic compounds in both true and colloidal solution. The water in the soil usually contains only small amounts of salts in solution. The diffusion pressure inside the root cells is therefore less than outside these cells, and water enters the root.

Water leaves the plant principally from the leaves, by evaporation. This process is called **transpiration.** Evaporation from leaf cells tends to result in an increase in the proportion of dissolved materials to water, and therefore to a decrease in diffusion pressure.

Cells of the leaf and cells of the root are connected by the water-filled tracheids. Since this is almost pure water, its diffusion pressure is greater than that in leaf cells which have lost water by transpiration. Water therefore diffuses into leaf cells from the tracheids.

The **cohesion** of water, i.e., the tendency for its molecules to remain in close association with each other, can be demonstrated easily. On a waxed surface water piles up in drops, and these drops can be pulled across the surface. Cohesion is the result of the gravitational pull among the water molecules plus the electrical attraction between the positive part of one molecule and the negative part of another.

When water molecules diffuse from the tracheids into leaf cells, they pull other water molecules along. Water molecules cohere along the slender columns of water in the tracheids, all the way to the roots. In *Polypodium* this may be only a foot or two; in some of the largest ferns with thick, vertical stems this may be thirty or forty feet; in the tallest trees it may be more than three hundred feet.

The quantitative relations of these forces in the transport of water through the plant are not yet fully established. In moist environments, some plants exude water through the leaves, indicating hydrostatic pressure in the xylem. If the stem of certain plants is cut across, water containing sugars and other dissolved materials exudes from the cut surface on the part still connected to the roots. Both these phenomena are due to pressure in the xylem tracheids that was built up by the roots. This hydrostatic pressure is called **root pressure.** Though root pressure may be great enough in some species to account for lifting water to the heights of the tallest trees, it cannot be demonstrated in some species, and it cannot account for moving large amounts of water in any species. But lowering of diffusion pressure in the leaves by transpiration increases the pressure difference at the two ends of the xylem tubes, and the cohesion of the water column makes possible the transport of water in response to this pressure difference.

The vascular bundles in the stem of *Polypodium* may divide and branch, some branches uniting with other bundles in the stem to make a loose lattice or network, and some branches turning up into leaves or down into roots.

Roots

The roots of *Polypodium* are numerous, relatively short cylinders growing out all along the stem. The tip of each root has a hardened coat of dead cells something like a thick thimble. This **root cap** protects the growing cells behind it from friction and abrasion against the soil particles. Like the stem, the root grows by the repeated division and enlargement of cells near the tip. Such a growing region is called a **meristem.** In action it resembles growth by an apical cell, except that many actively growing cells are involved, not just one.

The region behind the meristem is made up of cells elongating greatly in the direction in which the root is growing. Still older cells behind these are differentiating into the mature tissues of the root. See Figure 17.9.

The outermost layer of cells in the mature section of the root is the epidermis. Some of these epidermal cells have long, thin-walled projections growing out from them into the soil more or less at right angles to the root. These are **root hairs,** and the surface area of the root exposed to moisture in the soil is very greatly increased by these root hairs. See Figure 17.10.

Within the epidermis is a ring many cells thick, composed of sclerenchyma and parenchyma cells. The vascular bundle is single in each root, continuous with one of the bundles in the stem. The bundle is centrally located in the root, with the sclerenchyma and parenchyma surrounding it. For convenience, the cylinder of sclerenchyma and parenchyma cells is called the **cortex,** and the vascular bundle the **stele.** In a cross section, then, there would be three distinct concentric areas:[1] the outermost epidermis, the intermediate cortex, and the central stele. See Figure 17.11.

The stele is surrounded by an endodermis which is here considered to be the innermost part of the cortex, but by some authors is called the outermost part of the stele. The stele includes a pericycle, some parenchyma cells, phloem cells, and xylem tracheids.

Water is absorbed by the root hairs and other surfaces of the epidermal cells, and diffuses through the cortex, peri-

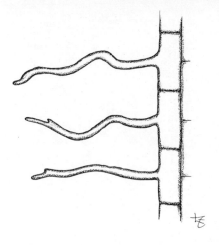

Fig. 17.10   Root hairs.

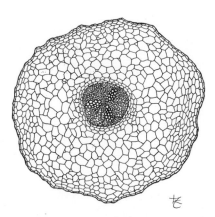

Fig. 17.11   Fern root cross section.

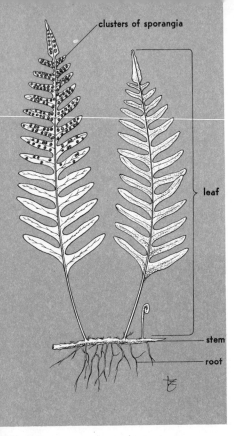

clusters of sporangia

leaf

stem

root

Fig. 17.5 Fern sporophyte, repeated here for the reader's convenience.

cycle, and parenchyma cells to the xylem tracheids. It travels through the tracheids and is transported to the other parts of the root, the stem, and the leaves. Food manufactured in the leaves as sugar is transported by the phloem cells throughout the leaves, stem, and roots. In the stem and roots some sugar diffuses out through the sieve plates to the parenchyma cells of the stele and of the cortex, where enzymes may transform the sugar into starch, much as liver cells do in the human. Starch is a storage form of carbohydrates, and later, when sugar concentration is low, it may be transformed into sugar by enzyme action, and transported by way of the phloem cells throughout the plant, where it may be used as a source of energy for the metabolic activities of the plant.

Leaves

The leaves of *Polypodium virginianum* are very slow in developing. It may take two or three years in some cases after a leaf starts to form before it even appears above ground. But once it reaches the light it develops rapidly, unrolling like a long carpet and stretching up into the air. The main stalk of the leaf is called a **petiole,** and the flattened expansions on either side constitute the **blade** of the leaf. The blade of a *Polypodium* leaf is highly lobed, the margin repeatedly cutting in almost to the middle of the leaf, and then swinging out again around a fingerlike leaflet, and cutting in again. See again Figure 17.5.

The petiole and central shaft of the leaf are bounded by an epidermis and contain a cortex of sclerenchyma and parenchyma cells, and a stele which is a continuation of one of the vascular bundles of the stem.

The blade of the leaf is flattened, and contains branches of the vascular bundle known as **veins.** The pattern of veins is characteristic. Each leaflet has a main vein passing down the middle of the leaflet, and branches on each side. Often the side branches fork into two soon after they leave the main vein, and one or both of these may fork into two again. The veins diminish in size and disappear as they approach the edge of the leaflet. Each vein includes xylem tracheids and phloem cells.

The leaf is covered above, around the margin, and below by a single layer of epidermal cells. Especially on the under surface of the leaf the epidermis contains stomata bounded by guard cells, much like those of the capsule of some moss sporophytes. The guard cells are the only epidermal cells normally having chloroplasts.

Between the upper and lower epidermis of the leaf is the **mesophyll.** This is a loosely arranged tissue composed of large, thin-walled cells containing chloroplasts. Many air spaces are located in the mesophyll, and open through the stomata to the air outside the leaf. The cells bordering the air spaces are coated with a film of water in which gases may be dissolved, facilitating the exchange of carbon dioxide, oxygen, and water between the leaf and the surrounding atmosphere.

When the guard cells are open, carbon dioxide diffuses into the air spaces in the leaf. Carbon dioxide will dissolve in the water film, and diffuse into the mesophyll cells. Using the energy from sunlight, these cells manufacture sugar from the carbon dioxide and water in the presence of chlorophyll. The sugar may be used immediately for energy; or it may be transformed into starch and stored in the cell in which the sugar was made; or it may diffuse out to another cell and be transported by phloem cells to another part of the plant where it may be used or stored; or it may be transformed into some other product such as protein, fat, or cellulose. Proteins require, in addition to sugar, a supply of nitrogen, and perhaps other elements. These may be absorbed by the roots and transported to all cells, where proteins may be built.

When the sugar is used for energy, carbon dioxide and water are produced. The evaporation of excess water through the leaf stomata is continuous unless the relative humidity of the air surrounding the plant is close to 100%, or the plant is submerged in water. Evaporation is, of course, more rapid when the stomata are wide open than when they are closed. Most of this water lost comes from the soil through the roots. The carbon dioxide produced by the plant is used in photosynthesis during the day, but at night it diffuses out of the leaf.

Sporangia

The leaves of *Polypodium* also bear the reproductive organs, the sporangia. The sporangia occur on the underside of the leaflets in little clusters, the clusters appearing in two rows on each leaflet, one on each side of the main vein about halfway between the vein and the leaflet margin. Every leaflet is capable of bearing sporangia.

Each sporangium has a long stalk. The sporangium wall is made of a single layer of cells. Most of these cells have thin walls, but one column of wall cells, the **annulus,** has its inner and side walls much thickened, but its outer walls

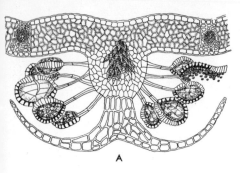

A

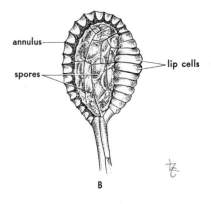

annulus —

spores —

— lip cells

B

Fig. 17.12 Fern sporangia. Note the thickenings in the walls of some cells. A, Cluster of sporangia. B, One sporangium.

thin. The annulus nearly encircles the sporangium. At one side of the sporangium the annulus ends in two small, thin-walled cells known as the **lip cells.** See Figure 17.12.

Within the sporangium wall is a layer of parenchyma cells which store food used later by the spore mother cells. The spore mother cells fill the center of the sporangium. Usually there are sixteen of these in each sporangium. They grow in size, absorb food from the now disintegrating parenchyma cells, and undergo meiosis, each dividing into four spores.

When the spores have been formed, the wall cells of the sporangium begin to dry out and shrink. The annulus cells with their thick walls resist this shrinkage more than do the other cells. The point of greatest weakness appears to be between the two lip cells and here the sporangium wall splits open. The spores are then exposed to the air, and begin to dry.

Continued drying causes even the annulus cells to lose water through their outer walls, and while their other walls remain intact, the outer walls shrink, pulling the part of the sporangium opposite the stalk back so that the split in the sporangium becomes progressively wider. The thick walls of the annulus develop a considerable tension such as might be found in bending an India rubber cane. This tension resists the bending back of the sporangium more and more, but the cohesion of the water still in the annulus cells prevents release of the tension until the tension is so strong that it overcomes the cohesion of the water column in the annulus. Then the sporangium snaps back together, throwing some of the dried spores out into space like a catapult.

If dew replenishes the water content of the annulus cells, and another drying period ensues, the process may be repeated. The broken part of the sporangium wall will gradually draw back as the water in the annulus cells evaporates until the tension of the thick walls overcomes the cohesion of the water, and the sporangium will snap shut again, throwing spores into the air where they may be blown about by the wind. See Figure 17.13.

Life Cycle

The spores which land on suitable ground may form a small filament, the apical cell of which develops the gametophyte as was described at the beginning of this chapter. The gametophyte forms egg and sperm cells, and these unite to form a zygote. The zygote develops a sporophyte which is at first dependent upon the gametophyte for nourishment, but soon makes contact with the soil by means of a temporary root and begins to manufacture food in its temporary leaf. Soon the sporophyte becomes independent of the gametophyte and the more permanent roots and leaves develop.

Moss and Fern Sporophytes

This sporophyte is much more complex than the sporophyte of the moss. However, the moss sporophyte has some characteristics which are more highly developed in the fern. The moss capsule has a central supporting column, a cylinder of spore-forming cells containing some sterile cells, and an outer wall of supporting and photosynthesizing cells. Stomata occur in the epidermis.

It is possible to imagine a series of changes by which a fern sporophyte could have evolved from a moss sporophyte or from the sporophyte of *Anthoceros*. But fossil forms intermediate between bryophytes and ferns are unknown, and in addition fossils of fernlike plants are known from rocks much older than the rocks from which bryophyte fossils have been found.

However it came about, the development of an independent sporophyte containing vascular tissues made large land plants possible. Since the sporophyte does not bear gametes which must unite before the cycle may go on, it is not limited by the need for a sperm to swim to an egg in a drop of water. Each reproductive element — a spore — produced by the sporophyte is able to develop by itself if it finds a favorable environment. Hence, the larger the sporophyte the more spores it can produce.

The independent gametophyte, however, remains small, and since it supports the early growth of the sporophyte, any one gametophyte can produce but few sporophytes, often one or none. Therefore the possibilities of any considerable increase in numbers of ferns are chiefly in the development and dissemination of spores by the sporophyte plants.

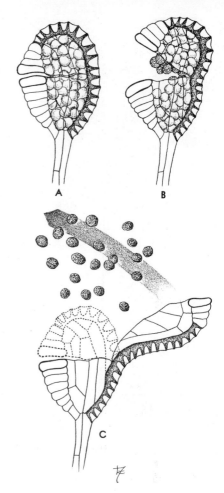

Fig. 17.13 Breaking of sporangium and catapulting of spores. In **A**, the sporangium splits open at the lip cells. As the cells of the annulus dry, the split is widened, as in **B**. When the annulus bends back as far as in **C**, the tension on the thick walls is suddenly released by the breaking of the cohesion of the water column, and the upper part of the sporangium snaps back into place (dotted figure), throwing spores into the air.

OTHER FERNS

In some ferns the sporophyte plant is much larger than that of *Polypodium*. The tree ferns of the tropics, for example, may have an upright stem thirty or forty feet high. See Figure 17.14 Fossil members of the Phylum Pteridophyta have been found whose stems were over one hundred feet high. See Figure 17.15. These plants lived many millions of years ago, and flourished abundantly in marshy areas. With the passage of time there was a great accumulation of dead and fallen plants buried in the muck of the marshes. Anaerobic decay broke down the organic substances into simpler compounds. Later movements of the earth's crust squeezed these deposits with tremendous pressures, and forced most of the gases out of them, reducing them to little more than masses of carbon. These constitute the deposits we now mine as coal. The heat we release in burning coal today represents energy from the sun captured by photosynthesis and stored in pteridophytes millions of years ago.

OTHER PTERIDOPHYTES

Many of these fossil trees, although pteridophytes, were not in the strict sense ferns. They belong instead to one or another of several fernlike groups. They had small leaves, with sporangia on their upper surfaces, instead of the typi-

Fig. 17.14 Tree fern in Hawaii, about thirty feet tall.

Fig. 17.15 Artist's restoration of fossil Pteridophyta. Some of these sporophytes attained heights of over one hundred feet. The remains of these plants form most of the coal deposits found in the earth today.

cal fern characters — large leaves with sporangia on the undersides of the leaves.

Selaginella

One of the living genera of fern allies, *Selaginella*, has some 500 species scattered throughout the world. One of these is the so-called resurrection plant. This curls its branches into a ball when it dries, and unfolds and spreads its branches when moistened. It performs this action even after the plant is dead, hence the name.

Selaginella apoda is one of the most common species of *Selaginella* in the United States. The sporophyte has a highly branched stem spread out on the top of the ground. The leaves are tiny, growing out from the stem in four longitudinal rows. Little roots develop much as do those of *Polypodium*. They may branch. See Figure 17.16.

The structure of the stem is much like that of the *Polypodium* root. There is an epidermis, a cortex of parenchyma and sclerenchyma cells, and a stele or vascular bundle surrounded by endodermis and including pericycle, phloem, and xylem, but usually no parenchyma cells. Branches from the vascular bundle come off only at the points of entrance into roots or leaves.

The roots of *Selaginella* are also much like *Polypodium* roots in structure. Sometimes the endodermis layer around the stele is not easily recognizable.

The leaves are much like those of *Polypodium* except for their great difference in size. The *Selaginella* leaf has an upper and a lower epidermis and a mesophyll. The lower epidermis has numerous stomata. The cells of the mesophyll have few, but relatively large, chloroplasts. The vegetative life of *Selaginella* is like that of *Polypodium*. Growth is by repeated divisions of apical cells. The leaves manufacture food, which involves combining water brought from the roots through the xylem tracheids with carbon dioxide diffusing into the mesophyll through the stomata. The food may be used for energy, made into some other substance used by the plant, or carried in phloem cells to the stem or roots where it may be used or stored in the form of starch.

The leaves at the tips of the stem branches are smaller and do not spread as much as the ones farther back along the stem. These terminal clusters of leaves bear the sporangia. In *Polypodium* all leaves are able to develop sporangia, but in *Selaginella* the ability to produce spores is localized in the leaves near the stem tip. Such a cluster of special sporangium-bearing leaves is called a **strobilus.**

Fig. 17.16   *Selaginella* sporophyte. In general appearance it resembles one of the more leafy liverworts.

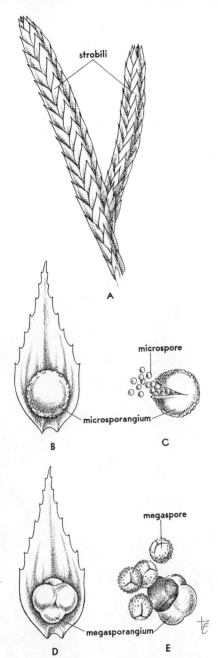

Selaginella Reproduction

The sporangia are of two kinds. One, called the **mega-sporangium,** develops at the angle between the stem and one of the lower leaves of the strobilus. The other, the **micro-sporangium,** develops at the angle between the stem and one of the upper leaves of the strobilus. Upper in this case means closer to the tip of the stem, although the strobilus may lie along the ground. See Figure 17.17.

In *Selaginella apoda,* a strobilus may have several mega-sporangia and several microsporangia, one sporangium growing in the axil of each strobilus leaf. The micro-sporangium has a short stalk, and a sporangium wall composed of a single layer of cells. Within the sporangium develop the spore mother cells, usually sixteen in number. Each spore mother cell undergoes meiosis, producing four spores. This makes sixty-four spores for each micro-sporangium. These **microspores** begin to develop gameto-phytes within the microsporangium. This is unlike the spores of bryophytes and ferns, which are shed before they continue their development.

The microspore divides into two cells, one of which is a vegetative cell, and does not ordinarily divide again. The other is a reproductive cell, and produces by repeated division an antheridium composed of a single-layered wall and a few hundred sperm cells. Sometime during this development within each spore, the microsporangium breaks open, and the gametophytes are shed, still encased within the spore wall. They may blow or roll onto the ground, or come to lie among the leaves of the strobilus. See Figure 17.18.

Meanwhile, in the megasporangia, **megaspores** have been forming. The megasporangium is much like the micro-sporangium except that it may be a little larger. But of the sixteen spore mother cells, normally only one undergoes meiosis, and the others degenerate and are used as food by the one remaining. The four megaspores derived from one spore mother cell develop within the megasporangium.

The megaspore nucleus divides repeatedly. The resulting nuclei are at first scattered throughout the spore cytoplasm, but growth pressure causes the spore wall to crack open at one point, and the nuclei migrate to the part of the cytoplasm thus exposed. Cell membranes then form, so that at this stage the gametophyte consists of a mass of cells at the end of the spore where the split occurred and a non-cellular mass of stored food in the rest of the spore. See Figure 17.19.

Fig. 17.17 *Selaginella* strobilus. **A,** Unopened strobilus. **B,** Microsporangium. **C,** Microspores. **D,** Megasporangium. **E,** Megaspores. Which of these are sporophyte structures and which game-tophyte?

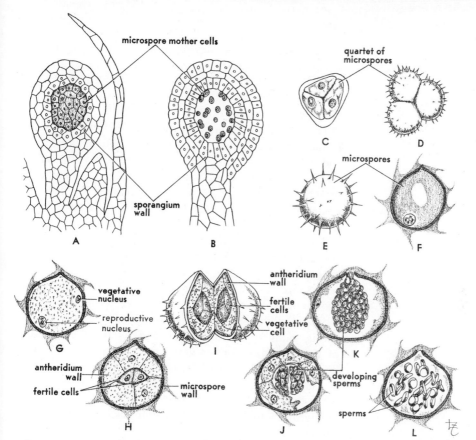

Labels in figure: microspore mother cells; quartet of microspores; sporangium wall; microspores; vegetative nucleus; reproductive nucleus; antheridium wall; fertile cells; vegetative cell; antheridium wall; fertile cells; microspore wall; developing sperms; sperms

A B C D E F G H I J K L

Fig. 17.18 Development of the *Selaginella* microspore. How much of the male gametophyte is reproductive tissue?

One or more of the cells at the surface may begin the formation of archegonia. Each archegonium consists of an egg cell, a ventral canal cell, and a neck canal cell, all bounded by a rather indefinite archegonium wall. The megasporangium is usually broken open at this stage, but the four gametophytes remain within it still.

The sperm cells may break out of the microspore wall when they are mature and when there is enough moisture. The sperm cell has two cilia, like the bryophyte sperm, but unlike the fern sperm. It may swim in the moisture available. A sperm may enter an archegonium in an open megasporangium, and swim in to the egg. The canal cells have disintegrated. The sperm unites with the egg, forming a zygote.

The zygote may start to develop into a new sporophyte immediately, although still within the archegonium of the gametophyte which is, in turn, still within the megasporangium of the old sporophyte. The first division of the zygote produces a **suspensor cell** and an **embryo cell.**

The suspensor cell elongates and may divide a few more times. Its growth pushes the embryo cell into the gametophyte, where it has access to the food stored there.

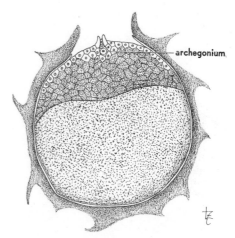

archegonium

Fig. 17.19 *Selaginella* female gametophyte. How much of this is reproductive tissue?

The embryo cell divides repeatedly, developing a young stem with two temporary leaves at the tip. These two leaves are called **cotyledons.** Just beyond the cotyledons the stem branches into two, and these branches continue to grow by the repeated division of their apical cells.

The stem tends to grow at right angles to the suspensor. In the opposite direction are gradually differentiated a foot and a temporary root. The foot does not develop far and seems to be of no great importance to the developing embryo. The root may begin to differentiate its cells into epidermis, cortex, and stele in continuation of these regions in the stem. See Figure 17.20.

All of this development may take place in the tissues of the gametophyte within the megasporangium. The new sporophyte is large enough now to spill out of the old megaspore wall. The embryo may remain in the megasporangium during the winter, and be released when the old sporophyte strobilus degenerates. The embryo in the spring gains access to the ground by the disintegration of the tissues of former generations, and the root grows downward into the soil, while the stem grows along the surface of the ground. New leaves and new roots develop, while the temporary ones gradually disappear. The embryo now grows into a mature sporophyte, such as was described earlier.

The production of two different kinds of spores, each developing into a distinct kind of gametophyte, is characteristic of the seed plants to be described in the next three chapters, but it is not found in the bryophytes and occurs in only certain genera among the pteridophytes. The microspore develops into a gametophyte which produces only sperms, and therefore is called a male gametophyte. It has only one vegetative cell and only one antheridium, in contrast with the gametophytes of liverworts, mosses, and ferns which have many vegetative cells and both antheridia and archegonia. The megaspore of *Selaginella* forms a female gametophyte consisting of several vegetative cells and one or more archegonia.

Neither gametophyte develops chloroplasts or becomes independent of the sporophyte. The female gametophyte of some species of *Selaginella* may form a few rhizoidlike filaments, but these do not reach the ground and do not supply the gametophyte with water and minerals.

The two kinds of gametophytes and the dependence of the gametophytes on the parent sporophyte are characteristic of seed plants. The development of the embryo sporophyte within the megasporangium is carried even further in seed plants, where the megasporangium remains closed during early embryonic development. This closed megasporangium with the developing embryo inside constitutes the seed. If the megasporangium of *Selaginella* were to close over the developing embryo and protect it over a dormant period, *Selaginella* would be classified as a seed plant. Rare instances of this have been reported in *Selaginella*.

SUMMARY

In the pteridophytes we see the sporophyte generation as the dominant stage, and the gametophyte as a small but independent plant in the fern, but as a much reduced parasite in the case of *Selaginella*. We find the development of specialized tissues carried to a considerable degree in the sporophyte. Especially notable is the vascular system consisting of phloem and xylem tissues.

With the development of dominant sporophytes with transportation systems, there are greatly increased possibilities for growth and variation. Among present-day plants these potentialities culminate in the seed plants, which we shall study next.

REVIEW QUESTIONS

1. Distinguish between bryophytes and pteridophytes.
2. Describe the gametophyte of *Polypodium*.
3. Describe the life cycle of *Polypodium*.
4. How can a fern sporophyte multiply vegetatively?
5. Describe the structure of a *Polypodium* stem; root; leaf.
6. Trace the conduction of water and of food through a fern.
7. Explain the forces involved in raising water into a fern leaf.
8. Describe a *Polypodium* sporangium. How does it disperse spores?
9. What are the advantages to a plant of an independent sporophyte?
10. What is coal?
11. Describe the structure and life cycle of *Selaginella*.
12. How does *Selaginella* resemble a seed plant?
13. Compare the degrees of independence of gametophyte and sporophyte generations in *Funaria*, *Polypodium*, and *Selaginella*.
14. What structures are found in pteridophytes but not in bryophytes?

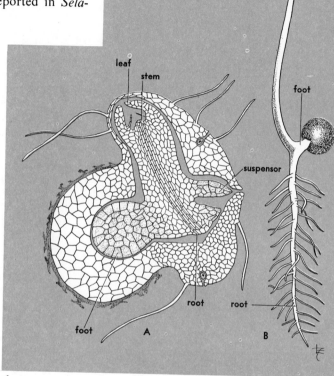

Fig. 17.20 *Selaginella* embryo sporophyte. **A,** Still within the gametophyte. **B,** Establishing its independence.

GENERAL QUESTIONS

1. How do the gametophytes of *Ricciocarpus* and *Polypodium* differ from each other?

2. Does the need for greater efficiency bring about the loss of a nucleus in a sieve tube? If so, what is the chain of events involved? If not, how do you account for the loss of the nucleus?

3. If the osmotic concentration in a fern root is greater than that of the water in the ground around it, how is a fern able to absorb the inorganic salts it uses?

4. Does the evaporation of water from a fern leaf suck up water from the roots?

5. In what ways are the circulatory systems of ferns and humans alike? In what ways are they different?

6. Why is there disagreement as to whether the endodermis belongs to the cortex or to the stele?

7. Why are the leaflets of a fern not considered separate leaves?

8. Does the type of spore-dispersal used by *Polypodium* affect the geographic distribution of the plant?

9. Evaluate the hypothesis deriving the fern sporophyte from the moss sporophyte.

10. Is coal being formed now?

11. What is the significance of the similarity in structure between the *Polypodium* root and the *Selaginella* stem?

12. Which is more advantageous, the large leaf of *Polypodium* or the small leaf of *Selaginella?*

13. *Selaginella* has two kinds of spores, and *Polypodium* has but one kind. Is *Selaginella* an advanced form and *Polypodium* primitive?

14. Would it be possible to have trees without xylem and phloem?

15. Why are plants like *Selaginella* distinguished from ferns?

CHAPTER 18

Spermatophyta — Gymnospermae

SPERMATOPHYTE CHARACTERISTICS

The Spermatophyta are characterized by roots, stems, and leaves, all interconnected with a vascular system; they are also characterized by seeds, which are embryos contained within closed megasporangia. The Spermatophyta include most of the plants with which the majority of us are familiar — trees, shrubs, flowers, herbs, and so forth. There are two subphyla here. One is the **Gymnospermae,** with seeds exposed: the megasporangium occurs at the junction of the stem and a strobilus leaf, as in *Selaginella.* The other subphylum is the **Angiospermae,** with seeds covered: the leaf at the angle of which the megasporangium develops wraps around the megasporangium and completely encloses it in a structure called the **ovary.**

PINE

Pinus strobus, the eastern white pine, is one of the most widely known gymnosperms. It has been logged extensively for timber and is much used for reforestation. The tree may grow to a height of a hundred feet or more, and have a diameter near the base of the stem of three feet or more. The leaves are long and needlelike, borne in bundles of five on short twigs. The root system is highly branched. See Figure 18.1.

Stem

The stem is somewhat different in structure from that of a fern. See Figure 18.2. The young stem shows a division into epidermis, cortex, and stele, differentiating from the embryonic cells at the stem tip. The epidermis is a layer of cells which persists for a time, but is later lost.

The cortex contains sclerenchyma cells, and at some distance from the epidermis there is a layer of small, undifferentiated cells called the **cork cambium.** The cork cambium is made of cells like those of the meristem, or growing tip. By repeated divisions these cells form a layer

Fig. 18.1A   White pine sporophyte. Compare this with the sporophyte of *Anthoceros.* Also see Fig. 18.1B on page 322.

of cells called **cork** just outside the cork cambium. The cork cells have in their walls a fatty substance known as **suberin,** which is nearly impermeable to air and water. The cork cells soon die, and their walls become compressed by the pressure of growth from the inside, making a tough, resistant layer which protects the tree stem from drying and from injury. The layers of cortex and epidermis outside the cork are shut off from their source of water and food supply, and soon die. Then this cork layer becomes the outer garment of the tree.

The pine stele also differs from the fern stele. There is no endodermis, but a pericycle is present. The phloem lies around the outside of the cylinder of xylem. In the very center of the stem there may be a few parenchyma cells in a column called the **pith;** as the stem grows older, the pith is relatively reduced. Between the phloem and xylem cells is a thin cylinder of small cells called the **vascular cambium.** This cambium is also a continuation of undifferentiated cells from the meristem at the stem tip down through the rest of the tree trunk.

The vascular cambium cells divide repeatedly, some of them remaining as cambium cells, some becoming phloem cells on the outside of the cambium cylinder, and some becoming xylem cells on the inside of the cambium cylinder. This secondary accumulation of phloem and xylem cells adds on to the primary vascular tissues differentiated out of the stem tip, and allows for growth in diameter of the stem after the meristem area has moved on up.

The pressure built up by division and growth of cambium cells is exerted throughout the stem. The xylem cells have walls heavily thickened with cellulose, and resist the pressure very well. But the phloem and cortex cells are squeezed between the expanding xylem and the resistant cork, and many of them are crushed as growth continues. The thick-walled sclerenchyma cells of the cortex can resist the crushing to some extent, and the younger, more active phloem cells and cork cambium and vascular cambium cells are able to survive. Older phloem cells and parenchyma cells succumb to the increasing pressures.

The activity of vascular cambium cells is not uniform throughout the year. During the spring, when metabolic activity is accelerated after a dormant period, the cambium forms large, active phloem and xylem cells which soon undergo their characteristic changes. During the summer and fall the xylem cells continue to be built, but at a slower rate, and they are progressively smaller. Then, during the winter, no xylem is formed at all. The following spring,

Fig. 18.1B White pine sporophyte. This tree grew up surrounded by other trees in a forest. The tree in Fig. 18.1A on page 321 grew up in an open field. Can you explain why the forms are different?

large tracheids are formed again, fitting against the outside of the small ones built the previous fall. This process produces the **growth rings** visible to the naked eye in a section through the stem. If such a section is magnified until the individual tracheids become visible, the succession of yearly additions to the xylem is evident.

These growth rings may be used to find out the age of a stem. Generally, one ring is formed for each year that part of the stem has been growing. Unusual external conditions may change this pattern, however, as when damage by fire, drouth, or parasites may prevent the plant from growing during a year. An unfavorable environment in the middle of the growth season followed by a resumption of growth may produce two rings in one year.

Comparison of the growth rings of several trees from different areas is possible, and the nature of the environment over a large area may be determined for many past years by comparing the nature and amount of growth for a given year with that of other years in several tree trunks. Scientists investigating this phenomenon are even able to date certain events by the rings of tree trunks associated with those events. Some of the redwood stumps along the Pacific coast of the United States have nearly 2000 growth rings.

Most of the xylem and phloem cells are very long in the vertical direction. Some groups of cells are elongated horizontally, though, forming supply lines to the stem itself at different levels. These horizontal bundles are called the **vascular rays,** which are also shown in Figure 18.2. Rays are initiated by the cambium and, once started, continue to elongate as long as the tree grows. As the tree grows in diameter, the rays get farther and farther apart. New rays are regularly initiated at the cambium, resulting in a rather even distribution of rays throughout the stem. Therefore, the larger the stem, the more rays there will be; and the length of any one ray is an index of how long it has been in existence.

One other type of stem structure is typical of the pine. Vertical channels of considerable size, lined by a single layer of parenchyma cells, are called **resin ducts.** These carry the resin secreted by the duct cells. The significance of this

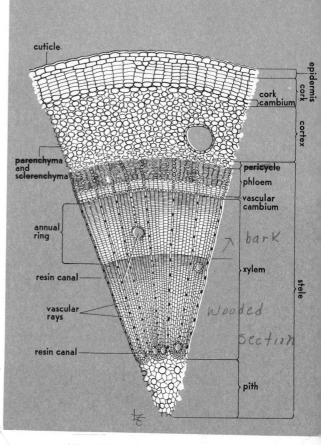

Fig. 18.2   Microscopic structure of a pine stem.

resin is not known. It may serve as a protection to the plant against its enemies; it may be a wound-closing aid; it may be stored food; or it may be a water-conservation aid.

The pine stem branches in such a way that the tip of the vertical trunk is the dominating meristem, the side branches never being as long or as fast-growing as the vertical axis. The branches are formed from embryonic cells in leaf axils near the stem tip, so that the lower branches are older and longer than the upper ones, giving a conical form to the entire tree. See again Figure 18.1.

Roots

The roots are highly branched and run deep into the ground. They secure water and mineral substances from the soil, and anchor and support the plant.

The growing tips of the roots are like those of ferns, with a root cap, meristem, region of elongating cells, and mature region of differentiated cells. Root hairs are present on the younger parts of the root. The mature tissues are much like those of the stem, except that pith is absent, and the tracheids are thinner-walled. The epidermis is replaced in older roots by cork, which is usually thinner than that of the stem. The stele, as in the stem, makes up the bulk of the mature root. In older stems, the cork may form in the phloem layer, cutting off the cortex and pericycle.

As in the stem, some storage takes place in the older xylem cells. Various organic substances accumulate in the xylem and form a rigid, supporting column in the roots and stems. The xylem then loses its capacity for conducting water readily, and is known as **heartwood** in contrast to the younger **sapwood** surrounding the heartwood, and still active in transporting water.

In both stems and roots the xylem tissue is the wood of the tree, and what is usually called bark is made up of the thin cambium, phloem, and the thick cork layer, with pericycle and cortex in younger portions.

Leaves

The leaves of the white pine are long, narrow, thickened needles. In cross section they are triangular. The epidermis has a thick outer coating of **cutin,** a waxy substance which greatly reduces water loss from the leaf. Stomata are deeply sunk into the leaf. The epidermis covers a few layers of sclerenchyma cells which stiffen the leaf. The mesophyll is within the sclerenchyma, and consists of loosely packed cells with infolded cell membranes. An endodermis encloses the vascular column, in which are the xylem and phloem cells and a surrounding layer of parenchyma. See Figure 18.3.

The leaves of a pine tree may live for two years or more, and then are shed. Each year a new set of leaves grows, and the set that grew two or three years previously is lost, so that there is no period in the life of a normal pine tree from seedling to death in which it is devoid of leaves. Because of this it belongs to the group of trees commonly known as evergreens.

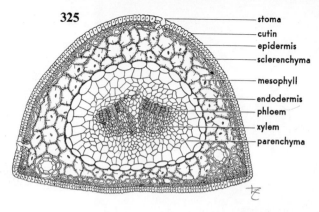

Fig. 18.3   Pine leaf cross section, showing microscopic structure. How is the leaf adapted to slow down evaporation of water?

Reproduction

As in *Selaginella*, the reproductive organs are borne in special clusters of leaves at the tips of stems. These are called **strobili,** or cones, and for this reason all the cone-bearing gymnosperms are called **conifers.** In the white pine each strobilus produces either microsporangia or megasporangia but not both, although the same tree may have both kinds of strobili.

The strobilus producing microsporangia (Fig. 18.4) is a tightly packed cluster of leaflike structures, each with a short stalk and a broadened blade on the underside of which occur two microsporangia. Each microsporangium has a wall composed of one layer of cells, and a lining of nutritive cells. In the middle of the sporangium the cells multiply, forming numerous spore mother cells. The spore mother cells undergo meiosis, each producing four haploid spores. Each spore inflates its wall into two gas-filled balloonlike wings. See Figure 18.5.

The nucleus of the spore divides into two, one flattening out against the wall and degenerating rapidly. The other nucleus divides into two again, one flattening out against the wall and degenerating also. These two degenerating nuclei correspond to the one vegetative cell of the *Selaginella* male gametophyte. The remaining nucleus represents the antheridial cell. It divides into two. One is cut off by a cell membrane in the direction of the vegetative cells. This cell is called the **generative cell.** The remaining nucleus and the remaining cytoplasm become the **tube cell.**

Development may stop at this point, and no further significant changes may occur until the following year. At that time the leaves of the strobilus may open out, exposing the microsporangia. The sporangium walls may dry and

Fig. 18.4   A, A cluster of pollen strobili, *Pinus*. B, Longitudinal section of pollen strobilus showing microsporangia.

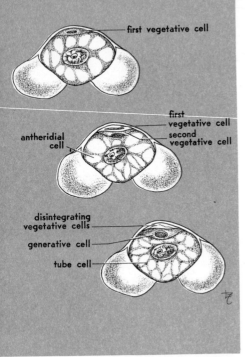

first vegetative cell

first vegetative cell
second vegetative cell

antheridial cell

disintegrating vegetative cells

generative cell

tube cell

Fig. 18.5 Development of the male gametophyte of a pine. Two vegetative cells appear and disintegrate. The single antheridial cell then divides into a generative cell and a tube cell. How does this compare with the male gametophyte of *Selaginella*?

break open, and the male gametophytes, now called **pollen grains,** are exposed to the air, and may be blown about by the wind.

Those pollen grains which happen to land in a strobilus having mature female gametophytes of the white pine may carry on reproduction. Others will be lost and eventually disintegrate. The chances of a single pollen grain being blown into a suitable strobilus are very small, but the species is preserved because millions of pollen grains are produced.

The strobilus bearing megasporangia is much larger and more conspicuous than that producing microspores. See Figure 18.6. It is the familiar pine cone. Each leaflike part of the strobilus becomes quite thick and woody. On the upper side of its base, where it is connected to the axis of the strobilus, there occur two megasporangia. Each megasporangium is a thick, swollen mass of cells, most of which store food. This food-storing tissue is known as the **nucellus.** A coat develops around the megasporangium enclosing it completely except for a small opening at the base of the leaf. This coat is called the **integument,** and the small opening is the **micropyle.**

In the middle of the megasporangium one cell enlarges conspicuously. This is the megaspore mother cell. Like its representative in *Selaginella*, it is the only one which undergoes meiosis. Of the four megaspores produced by this process in the white pine, the three nearest the micropyle degenerate, and the fourth develops into the female gametophyte. This development into the female gametophyte normally does not occur until the year after the megaspore is formed.

When the gametophyte does start to develop, it derives its energy from food in the nucellus. The megaspore nucleus divides repeatedly, forming a number of nuclei. These nuclei acquire areas of cytoplasm marked off by cell membranes, and become gametophyte cells. Most of these cells absorb food from the nucellus, and store it in themselves. At the end of the female gametophyte nearest the micropyle two archegonia form. These are simpler than the archegonia of bryophytes and pteridophytes. The neck is very short, and there are no neck canal cells at all. There are an egg cell and a ventral canal cell, but the latter degenerates very soon after it is formed.

When the female gametophytes are mature, the leaves of the strobilus spread away from each other, and pollen grains blowing through the air may sift down between them, coming to rest at the leaf stalk in close contact with the micropyle end of the megasporangium.

The pollen grain contains at this time two shriveled vegetative cells, a generative cell, and a tube cell. The tube cell, if it comes into contact with the nucellus of the megasporangium through the micropyle, begins to digest some of the nucellus. This produces a pathway called the **pollen tube** leading toward the female gametophyte. The building of this tube may take another year.

While the tube is being built, the generative cell follows along behind, and divides into two cells, a **stalk cell** and a **body cell,** names reminiscent of parts of the antheridium of mosses and ferns. The stalk cell takes no part in the process of fertilization. The nucleus of the body cell divides again, forming two sperm nuclei within the one cell.

When the pollen tube reaches the female gametophyte at the neck of an archegonium, the tube cell breaks apart, and the body cell with its two sperm nuclei moves into the archegonium. One sperm nucleus unites with the egg nucleus, forming a zygote. The other sperm nucleus and the remains of the tube cell are digested by the female gametophyte and added to its stored food supply.

The zygote develops immediately into a sporophyte embryo. The nucleus divides into two, then four, then eight, then sixteen. These sixteen nuclei are grouped at the end of the egg cell opposite the micropyle. They are arranged in four tiers of four cells each. See Figure 18.7. The tier farthest from the micropyle starts to form four embryos. The next tier elongates very much, forming a **suspensor,** which pushes the embryos into the stored food in the gametophyte.

Of the four embryos, one surpasses the others, which then degenerate. This one soon begins to differentiate into recognizably different structures. These are the **radicle,** which will become the first root of the new tree; the **hypocotyl,** which will become the base of the stem; the **plumule,** which is the first bud, destined to form the remainder of the stem and the leaves; and several **cotyledons.**

The integument has by this time closed over the micropyle, and the structure of the seed is complete. The integument makes the seed coat. Under this is a thin layer which is all that is left of the nucellus. The integument and nucellus belong to the old sporophyte generation. The food supply of the female gametophyte fills the space between nucellus and embryo. The gametophyte generation and the old and new (embryo) sporophyte generations all contribute to the making of the seed.

The strobilus axis now grows out in such a way that the cone hangs down. The integument of each seed grows a

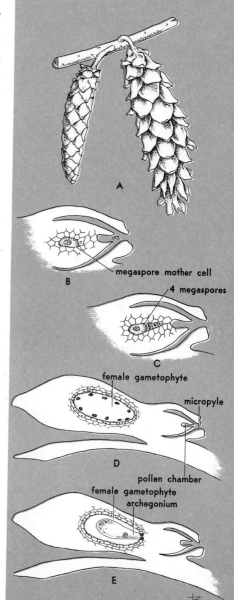

Fig. 18.6   Pine strobilus with megasporangia. A, Mature strobili, one closed, one open. B–E, Developing gametophyte. B, Megaspore mother cell. C, Meiosis, producing four megaspores of which three degenerate. D, Remaining megaspore divides to form the cells of the female gametophyte. E, Archegonium in the gametophyte.

flattened vane or wing at the end farthest from the cone axis. The seeds now break loose and drop out, where a breeze may catch the expanded vane and blow the seed as it settles to the ground. The seed normally lies dormant for a year, and then, if it is in a favorable location, absorbs water, splits open the integument, and begins to grow again. The hypocotyl elongates, pushing the radicle down into the ground. The cotyledons furnish the growing sporophyte with food until it expands the plumule and forms leaves which carry on photosynthesis. Then the sporophyte continues to grow, if the environment is still favorable, forming a new white pine tree.

Comparison of this story with the life cycle of *Selaginella* shows a great deal of similarity, but also three outstanding differences. In the pine, the cambium layer provides for renewal of vascular tissues and great increase in size. Secondly, the pine uses a method of fertilization which does not require the sperm to swim to the egg, and hence gets away from the limitations imposed by the size of a dewdrop. Thirdly, the embryo is completely enclosed by an integument, and may remain dormant for a time before developing into the mature sporophyte.

There are other differences, of course, such as the separation of microsporangia and megasporangia into separate strobili, and the reduction in archegonia, but the three listed in the previous paragraph represent potentialities for variation and efficiency which have made the seed plants the dominant plants of the earth.

OTHER GYMNOSPERMS

Other gymnosperms have much the same sort of life cycle. Many other cone-bearing trees are familiar — spruces, hemlocks, yews, tamaracks, junipers, firs, cypresses, and cedars. The cycads are sometimes referred to as "potted palms," and are cultivated for decorative purposes. The

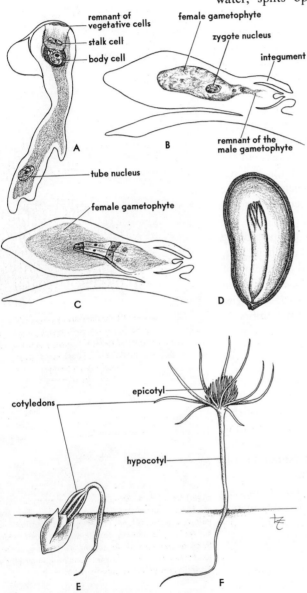

Fig. 18.7 Formation and development of the pine embryo. **A,** Pollen grain developing a tube. **B,** Union of sperm and egg nuclei, forming a zygote nucleus. **C,** Sixteen-cell stage. **D,** Embryo in the seed. **E,** Germinating seed. **F,** Seedling.

maidenhair tree, *Ginkgo biloba*, is a beautiful plant which nearly became extinct a few hundreds of years ago, but was preserved by Buddhist priests in the gardens of Chinese monasteries. It has since been transplanted to other countries, including the United States, and seems to thrive under cultivation.

One other curious group of gymnosperms, the **Gnetales,** shows some characteristics which resemble the angiosperms, and may suggest the direction of transition toward that group. The Gnetales have carried differentiation of the xylem a step further than the pine. The tracheids may unite end to end, breaking down the cross walls which separate them, producing a much longer tube called a **vessel.** This facilitates the transportation of water even more than the separate tracheids.

Secondly, the strobili of Gnetales may bear both microsporangia and megasporangia, with the microsporangium-bearing leaves below and outside of the others. This is similar to the condition in the angiosperm flower.

Thirdly, no archegonia are formed. In the development of the female gametophyte from the megaspore, many nuclear divisions take place, but no cell partitions are formed, and any nucleus in the female gametophyte may serve as an egg nucleus.

Lastly, the development of the embryo from the zygote eliminates the stage of free nuclear division. After each nuclear division in the embryo, cell partitions occur, so that the embryo is cellular from the first.

The Gnetales are shrubs or small trees, with broad, rather than needlelike leaves. This is also a characteristic of many angiosperms, but is found in some other gymnosperms as well. See Figure 18.8.

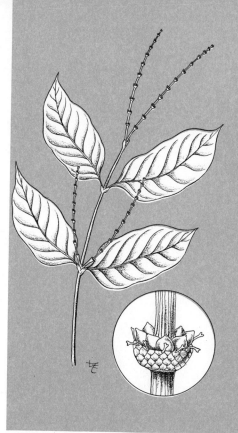

Fig. 18.8   *Gnetum.* Branch showing leaves; enlargement of "flower," showing globular megasporangia, slender microsporangia, and imbricated leaves comparable to petals and sepals.

SUMMARY

The Gymnosperms develop cambium layers which renew sporophyte tissues. They form seeds, which enable the species to endure a long period of unfavorable environment in a dormant state, and emerge from dormancy with an abundance of stored food when conditions are better. They are not dependent upon a water medium for fertilization. And in the Gnetales, some of the developments characteristic of the angiosperms have occurred.

Many of the gymnosperm trees are of great economic importance as sources of lumber, paper, and turpentine, and as landscape decoration. They are among our most valuable natural resources.

REVIEW QUESTIONS

1. Characterize Spermatophyta; Gymnospermae; Angiospermae.
2. Describe the structure of a pine sporophyte.
3. How does a pine tree trunk grow in diameter?
4. Explain the formation of growth rings.
5. How is the characteristic shape of a tree developed?
6. Describe the reproductive cycle of the pine.
7. How long does it take for a pine tree to produce a pine seedling from the time megaspores are formed?
8. Trace the changes in archegonial cells from bryophytes through gymnosperms.
9. Compare and contrast the life cycles of pine and *Selaginella*.
10. Describe *Ginkgo;* describe the Gnetales.

GENERAL QUESTIONS

1. How does a cambium cell in the stem of a pine tree get oxygen?
2. In grafting one stem on another, the cambium layers are fitted together. What is the importance of this?
3. How much can be told of the past environment of a pine tree by studying a cross section of its trunk?
4. Compare and contrast the structure of a pine stem and of a pine root.
5. If you were trying to show that pine trees were derived from *Selaginella*, how would you derive a pine leaf from a *Selaginella* leaf?
6. Justify the statement that the two degenerating nuclei of a pine male gametophyte correspond to the vegetative cell of *Selaginella*, and the remaining nucleus to the antheridial cell.
7. Would it be possible for more than one embryo to develop in one pine seed?
8. Why does not a pine seed develop as soon as it strikes the ground?
9. Why aren't the Gnetales included with the angiosperms?
10. What changes in human life would occur if all gymnosperms were destroyed?

CHAPTER 19

Spermatophyta — Angiospermae Dicotyledoneae

ANGIOSPERM CHARACTERISTICS

The Spermatophyta, or seed plants, are divided into two groups, as you have read, according to whether or not the seed is enclosed in the modified leaf supporting it. In the Angiospermae the megasporangia are enclosed in such modified leaves, producing an **ovary** in which the seeds develop.

The Angiospermae are further divided into two groups, the **Dicotyledoneae** (commonly called **dicots**) and the **Monocotyledoneae** (commonly called **monocots**), depending upon whether the seed has two cotyledons or one. The dicots are those in which two cotyledons are formed in each seed.

APPLE

Pyrus malus, the apple tree, is an example of the dicots. It is a tree native to Europe and Asia, but introduced into North America as a cultivated plant. See Figure 19.1.

Stem

The stem of the apple plant is much like that of the white pine. The epidermis found on the very young stem is later cut off from its source of supply by the developing cork. The cork cambium in the apple stem comes originally from cells of the epidermis which divide, producing an inner cork cambium layer next to the outer epidermis.

The cortex contains parenchyma cells and sclerenchyma cells. There is no endodermis. The older parts of the stem have the cortex partially crushed between the expanding xylem area and the hardened cork.

The stele is much like that of the pine, with a pericycle, a phloem layer, vascular cambium, xylem increasing in diameter, and vascular rays. Parenchyma cells occur scattered throughout the phloem and xylem layers.

Fig. 19.1 Apple tree in bloom. How does the tree compare in form with a pine tree? A tree fern?

In the phloem are found not only the phloem cells with sieves in the walls, but parenchyma cells, sclerenchyma cells, and **companion cells.** The companion cells are sisters to the sieve tubes, each prospective sieve tube dividing and forming a cell with sieves and one or more companion cells. The companion cell is much smaller, and there may be a linear column of several companion cells adjacent to one sieve tube. The companion cell retains its cytoplasm and nucleus, and does not develop a large internal vacuole as does the sieve tube. It retains cytoplasmic connections with the sieve tube through perforations of wall between them.

The xylem cells form not only tracheids but vessels. Parenchyma cells are interspersed about the conducting structures. Sclerenchyma cells in the form of long, thick-walled fibers strengthen the wood. There are no resin ducts in the apple stem. See Figure 19.2.

Root

The root of the apple tree is not greatly different in structure from that of the pine. The root cap at the tip of each growing root branch protects the meristem. There

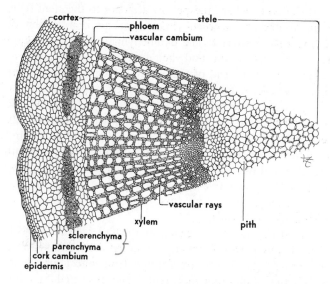

Fig. 19.2   Section of apple stem.

is an elongating region, and a mature region. Root hairs are prominent in the newer areas of the root. A cork layer cuts the epidermis off from the older parts of the root. The cortex has parenchyma and sclerenchyma cells; in younger parts, an endodermis. The stele is like that of the stem.

Leaf

The leaf of an apple tree is broad and flat, in contrast to the needlelike leaf of the white pine. There is an epidermis on both the upper and lower sides of the leaf, as well as around the margin. The stalk of the leaf, or petiole, is also enclosed in an epidermis. Stomata occur much more frequently in the lower epidermis than in the upper epidermis. Guard cells are the only cells of the epidermis which contain chloroplasts.

The mesophyll may be divided into two parts because of the arrangement of its cells. The portion just under the upper epidermis is composed of a compact array of columnar cells in three tiers, and is called the **palisade layer.** Between the palisade layer and the lower epidermis the mesophyll cells are scattered, loosely packed, and interspersed with air spaces connected to the outside through stomata. This is called the **spongy layer.** See Figure 19.3.

Veins form by branching from the vascular bundle which separates from the stele of the stem, passes through the petiole, and up the middle of the leaf blade. These veins have xylem and phloem cells and some sclerenchyma cells. They subdivide within the mesophyll of the leaf, being distributed in a network to all parts of the blade.

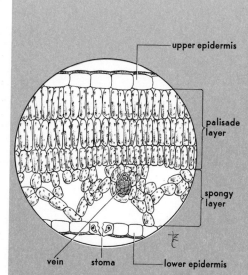

Fig. 19.3   Microscopic structure of an apple leaf. What gives strength and stiffness to the leaf?

At the point where the petiole attaches to the stem there is an absence of sclerenchyma cells. This is a section of comparative weakness. The parenchyma cells in this region have dense cytoplasm, and their turgidity gives strength to the petiole. At the end of the growing season, however, the parenchyma cells here lose some of their turgidity, and the cells on either side of the section harden their walls. Winds and frost may further weaken the area, which is eventually held only by the vascular bundle passing through it, and finally even this breaks, so that the leaf drops off, carrying with it stored waste products. The hardened cells left on the stem form a protective scar over the place where the leaf was attached, preventing loss of fluids and entrance of pathogenic organisms.

This shedding of all leaves in the fall is characteristic of most angiosperms which live more than one year. In the spring, new leaves are formed from **buds,** which are branch tips containing meristem tissue protected by over-lapped small leaves with hardened exteriors.

Physiology

The vegetative activity of an apple plant is not greatly different from that of other plants we have studied in the last two chapters. The roots absorb water and dissolved salts. These are carried to other parts of the plant by the xylem tracheids and vessels. In the leaf, the mesophyll and guard cells manufacture sugar from the water and carbon dioxide. The sugar may be used for energy, converted into other substances, or transported through the phloem to other parts of the plant body, where it may be used or stored. Growth continues both at stem and root tips, and in stem and root diameters by means of the cambium layers. The older phloem cells and the cortex parenchyma cells are crushed by the expanding xylem, so that in an older part of the stem, for example, almost all of the thickness of the stem is in the xylem layer.

Flower

The reproductive organs of the apple plant are found in a special structure, the **flower.** The flower consists of a part of a stem bearing four different kinds of flower parts, thought by some biologists to be modified leaves. The stem of the flower, itself, does not undergo elongation, so that the four kinds of leaves are attached to the stem almost at the same level. The stem is thickened and slightly rounded at the tip, constituting a **receptacle.** On this receptacle the four kinds of leaves are arranged in circles or whorls. See Figure 19.4.

The lowest whorl of flower parts, the **calyx,** is made of a ring of five **sepals.** Each sepal is somewhat like a normal leaf in structure except that it is much smaller. In the flower bud of the apple plant the sepals make the outer, protective coat. When the flower bud opens, the sepals spread out, but never completely separate from each other, remaining fused together at the base.

The next whorl of parts, the **corolla,** is made of a ring of five **petals,** which make the conspicuous, showy part of the flower. They, too, are somewhat leaflike in structure except that they do not have chlorophyll, as do sepals, but are colored white or pink. They are much larger than the sepals, and alternate with them in position.

Next to the petals are the **stamens,** which occur usually in three whorls; there may be twenty or more stamens in one flower. Each stamen consists of a slender stalk, the **filament,** supporting two tiny sacs, the **anthers.** Each anther has two chambers in it. These chambers are microsporangia, capable of developing microspores.

In the center of the flower are the **pistils.** There is a circle of five of these, but they are all united at the base into one body, the ovary. The apple ovary is encased in the fused parts of the sepals, so that the other flower structures appear to branch out beyond it. From the top of the ovary arise the separate parts of the five pistils. Each has a stalk called the **style,** surmounted by an expanded knob called the **stigma.** Within the ovary are the megasporangia, here called **ovules.**

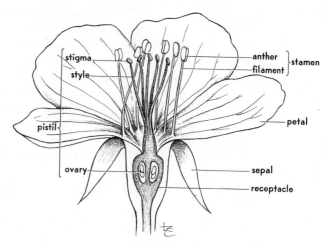

Fig. 19.4 Apple flower. Which parts contain reproductive tissues?

Reproduction

In the process of reproduction, the anthers form microspores, which in turn become pollen grains. The ovules form megaspores, which produce egg nuclei. The pollen grain is transported, usually by insects, to the stigma, from which its nuclei gain access to the ovule. The fertilized egg forms the embryo which becomes incorporated into a seed. Thus far the story is much like that of the pine. There are differences in the details, as we shall see now.

In the anther, repeated division of internal cells produces a considerable number of spore mother cells, each of which may undergo meiosis, forming four microspores. Each

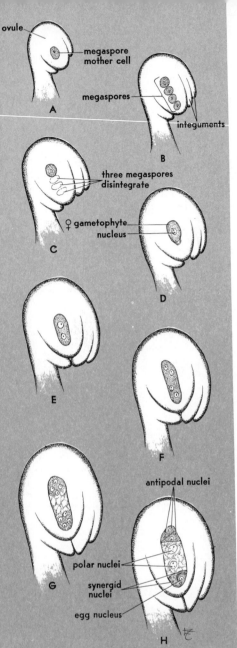

ovule

megaspore
mother cell

A

megaspores

integuments

B

three megaspores
disintegrate

C

♀ gametophyte
nucleus

D

E

F

antipodal nuclei

polar nuclei

G

synergid
nuclei

egg nucleus

H

Fig. 19.5 Typical development of female game-tophyte. **A,** Ovule with megaspore mother cell. **B,** Four megaspores. **C,** Three megaspores disinte-grate. **D,** The fourth megaspore enlarges. **E,** Its nucleus divides. **F,** Each daughter nucleus divides. **G,** A third nuclear division occurs. **H,** Mature female gametophyte.

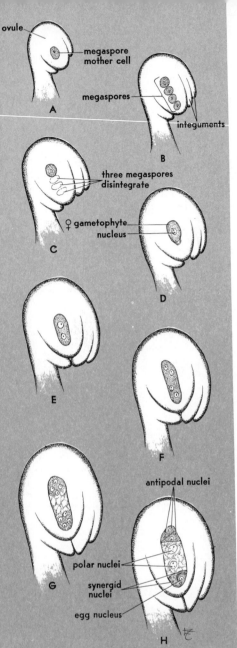

microspore nucleus divides into two: a tube nucleus and a generative nucleus. The generative nucleus divides again into two sperm nuclei. Then the microspore cytoplasm secretes a wall about itself, and the male gametophyte thus formed is a pollen grain. It is much reduced from the condition found in the white pine, where there are two vegetative cells and a stalk cell formed in addition to those described for the apple. Thus, the gametophyte stage is only a tiny bit of cytoplasm containing three nuclei. One might compare the apple gametophyte with the large bryophyte gametophyte. The entire apple male gametophyte is no more than 28 microns in diameter.

In the ovary, each of five parts contains two ovules. The ovule consists of two integuments open at one end (the micropyle) and a mass of inner cells, one of which becomes the megaspore mother cell. This divides by meiosis into four megaspores. Three of these disintegrate, and the fourth gives rise to the female gametophyte.

The cytoplasm of the megaspore increases greatly in size. The nucleus divides into two, one passing to each end of the elongated cell. Each nucleus then divides twice more, so that there are four nuclei at each end of the cell. One of the four from each end passes to the middle of the cell. These two nuclei are called the **polar nuclei.** The three at the end away from the micropyle are called **antipodal nuclei.** Those at the micropyle end are the **egg nucleus** and two **synergid nuclei.** See Figure 19.5.

The egg nucleus is now ready for fertilization. The pollen grains are released from the anther by the breaking of its wall. The pollen is transported by insects which rub against the anthers and pick up the pollen grains on their hairs. Some of these pollen grains may come in contact with the stigma of a pistil. If the tissues of the stigma belong to the same species of plant as the pollen grain — in this case, if both come from apple plants — the pollen grain enzymes begin to digest an opening into the stigma. The tube nucleus goes first, and the rest of the protoplasm of the male gametophyte follows along through the broken walls of the pollen grain and the stigma. The pollen tube continues to digest its way through the style into the ovary, and to the micropyle of an ovule. See Figure 19.6.

When the pollen tube with its three nuclei reaches the protoplasm of the female gametophyte, the membranes break down at the area of contact, and the male gameto-phyte protoplasm flows into the female gametophyte. The tube nucleus is pushed to one side, takes no further active part in the process, and soon degenerates.

The two sperm nuclei enter the female gametophyte cytoplasm. One unites with the egg nucleus, forming the zygote nucleus. The other passes to the two polar nuclei in the middle of the gametophyte and fuses with these two, making the **endosperm nucleus,** which now has three sets of chromosomes. Such a nucleus is called **triploid.**

The synergid and antipodal nuclei degenerate, leaving the gametophyte protoplasm to the zygote and endosperm nuclei. The zygote nucleus divides repeatedly, each such division being accompanied by the formation of cell membranes, so that cell division and separation go on with nuclear division. The endosperm nucleus also divides repeatedly, forming cells which absorb the substance of the gametophyte and become a food storehouse which supplies the embryo during germination of the seed. The endosperm cells are triploid and large, but since they are all destroyed during the growth of the embryo into a seedling, the triploidy is not preserved in the mature plant.

The two integuments of the ovule, or megasporangium, meet at the micropyle, enclosing the embryo and endosperm. The embryo, endosperm, and integuments now constitute a seed.

Fruit

Meanwhile, the ovary, partly buried in the receptacle of the flower, becomes completely enclosed by the great enlargement of the receptacle, which becomes the fleshy part of the apple fruit. If you examine the end of an apple opposite the stem, you will find the remains of sepals, stamens, and styles. If you cut an apple crosswise through the middle and look at the cut surface, you can distinguish the five parts of the ovary in the center, each with two seeds if all ten ovules have been transformed into seeds. The remainder of the fruit is the receptacle, and the boundary between stele and cortex may be found, as well as the epidermis, or "skin" of the apple, with its waxy cuticle on the outside. See Figure 19.7.

The animals, including deer, foxes, woodchucks, opossums, and man, that find the apple fruit edible are agents in the distribution of the apple seeds, so that the opportunities for disseminating the species are greatly increased because of the formation of a fleshy fruit and indigestible seed coats.

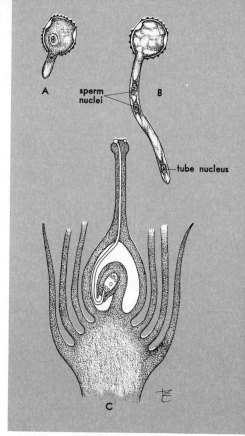

Fig. 19.6 Development of the pollen tube **A,** Formation of tube and reproductive nuclei. **B,** Further development of tube; two sperm nuclei formed. **C,** Penetration of the pistil by the pollen tube. The tube has entered the female gametophyte.

Fig. 19.7 Apple fruit. **A,** Vertical section. **B,** Horizontal section. The parts you eat are derived from what parts of the flower?

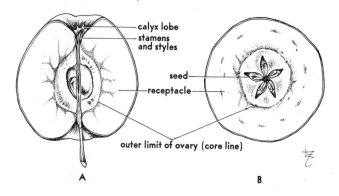

OTHER DICOTS

Many other angiosperms have a similar type of fruit formation and benefit by such distribution of seeds. Others develop hooks on their seeds or fruits, and these often catch on passing animals and are carried to new locations. Examples are sticktights, beggar's-ticks, and cockleburs.

Other fruits are very light and possess devices which catch the wind, which may transport them for some distance. Examples are the dandelion, milkweed, and cottonwood. Still others float and may be transported for great distances by streams or ocean currents.

Some fruits include only the ovary and its seeds; these are represented by the grape, tomato, orange, peach, cherry, olive, bean pod, buckwheat, acorn, and chestnut. Others include ovary and receptacle; these are represented by the apple, pear, watermelon, pumpkin, and cucumber. Still others include one receptacle with several ovaries, such as the raspberry, blackberry, and strawberry. And finally there are those which are formed by the coalescence of ovaries from several separate flowers, such as mulberries, figs, and pineapples.

The apple is fairly representative of angiosperms with respect to its reproduction, but there is some variation in details. For example, in some plants all four megaspores in one ovule may persist for a time, one forming the egg, the synergids, and one polar nucleus, while the other three form antipodal cells, later contributing the second polar nucleus. In others, the synergids may be fertilized as well as the egg, or antipodal cells may form embryos parthenogenetically. Even the egg cell may form a parthenogenetic embryo upon occasion. And the food-storing cells of the ovule have been known to initiate embryo formation in oranges and raspberries.

In some cultivated plants such as navel oranges, seedless grapes, bananas, and pineapples, a fruit may develop without the formation of seeds. Such a phenomenon is called **parthenocarpy.** Parthenocarpy may be induced in other plants by application of chemicals such as naphthoxyacetic acid to the pistil, producing seedless tomatoes, watermelons, cucumbers, and squashes.

There is some variation, too, in the actual structure of seeds. A grapefruit seed may carry several embryos. The stored food in the castor bean, the morning-glory, the coconut, and many monocotyledons other than the coconut, such as grains, is in the endosperm. The stored food in peanuts, lima beans, walnuts, and acorns is in the cotyledons. The seed coat may be thin, as in peas; or thick and hard, as in Brazil nuts; or fibrous, as in cotton, in which the seed coat fibers provide humans with textiles.

SUMMARY

The dicotyledonous angiosperms differ from the gymnosperms in several characteristics. The phloem develops companion cells, and the xylem produces vessels. Flowers are the characteristic reproductive branches of the sporophyte. The male gametophyte consists only of a pollen grain with three nuclei. The megasporangia are enclosed in an ovary, and the female gametophyte develops no archegonia. The seeds are enclosed in the ovary, and sometimes additional structures, forming a fruit. The formation of a triploid endosperm nucleus is peculiar to the angiosperms.

Angiosperms resemble gymnosperms in a great many general characteristics. Many angiosperms are trees, but most are herbs, and do not develop a woody xylem. These herbs are often limited to one growing season per generation (annuals), growing from seed in the spring and producing seed in the fall, then dying. Some may live two years (biennials), some many years (perennials).

The variety of dicots is tremendous. Except for the grasses, grains, conifers, and palm trees, most of the seed plants with which the average person is familiar are dicots. Some of these of particular interest to humans will be discussed in later parts of this book. There is a great deal of variation in the details of structure, metabolism, and reproduction of dicots. For the purposes of this chapter, however, it may be said that a large majority of these familiar plants, the dicots, live and reproduce much like the apple plant.

REVIEW QUESTIONS

1. How do dicots and monocots differ?
2. Describe the structure of an apple sporophyte.
3. How do leaves separate from an apple tree in the fall?
4. Describe the physiology of an apple plant.
5. Describe an apple flower.
6. Describe reproduction in the apple plant.
7. From what stem and flower structures do the various parts of an apple fruit develop?
8. What devices do angiosperm fruits exhibit which facilitate distribution?
9. How do other fruits differ from the apple in their structure?
10. Distinguish between a tree and an herb.

GENERAL QUESTIONS

1. In what ways do pine and apple leaves differ? Which is more efficient?
2. How can a leafless apple plant survive the winter?
3. Is it justifiable to speak of flower parts as modified leaves?
4. Compare a flower to a moss sporophyte capsule and to a *Selaginella* strobilus.
5. Compare the female gametophyte in *Ricciocarpus*, moss, fern, pine, and apple.
6. Of what advantages to an apple plant is the succulence of its fruit?
7. What determines the kind of fruit an angiosperm will develop?
8. What are the advantages of seeds over direct development of a zygote into a mature sporophyte?
9. What, if any, is the significance of the triploid nature of endosperm?
10. What characteristics of angiosperms do you think account for their great measure of success as land plants?

CHAPTER 20

Spermatophyta — Angiospermae Monocotyledoneae

MONOCOT CHARACTERISTICS

The monocot embryo in the seed possesses as a rule only one cotyledon. There are other characteristic differences between monocots and dicots. In most monocot stems the stele is composed of many separate vascular bundles, each with xylem and phloem, but no cambium. As a rule, the leaves have their veins running parallel to each other, rather than radiating out in a network. The flower parts are generally in twos or threes or multiples of three rather than in fives, as in the apple and many other dicots, or in fours, as in some other dicots.

CORN

One of the best known monocots is *Zea mays*, maize, or corn. See Figure 20.1. In Europe, the term "corn" refers to cereal grains generally; in the United States the term usually refers to maize. The sporophyte of corn lives through one growing season, produces seeds, and dies. The absence of cambium is no great disadvantage, since growth does not continue year after year in any one individual.

Stem

The stem of the corn plant conspicuously shows the presence of **nodes** and **internodes.** The nodes are levels at which the tissues are much denser than elsewhere, and from which branches such as roots, leaves, and flowers arise. An internode is the length between two consecutive nodes; the tissue here, particularly in the center of the stem, is much less compact and gives rise to no branches or leaves. It is a part of the stem which undergoes great elongation. See again Figure 20.1.

In cross section, the corn stem has an outer layer of epidermis, underlain by some sclerenchyma cells. There is

Fig. 20.1 *Zea mays,* corn.

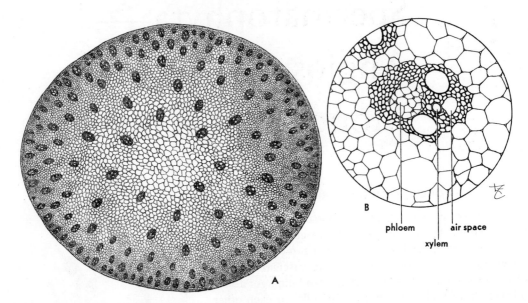

Fig. 20.2 Corn stem microscopic structure. A, Cross section of entire stem. B, Enlargement of one vascular bundle.

no topographic separation of cortex from stele, but within the epidermis and sclerenchyma is a column of soft parenchyma tissue, in which are embedded many small vascular bundles. Each bundle consists on the outside of heavy-walled sclerenchyma and on the inside of a layer of phloem nearer the epidermis and a layer of xylem nearer the center of the stem. Vascular bundles are smaller and closer together near the outside of the stem. The phloem is made of sieve tubes and companion cells; the xylem has tracheids, woody fibers, and vessels. There is no endodermis. The pericycle cells are like the parenchyma cells, and it may be difficult to distinguish between them. See Figure 20.2.

Roots

The roots of the corn plant are relatively short compared with those of other plants of the same size. The roots are numerous slender cylindrical columns branching through the soil. Some of the corn roots called "prop roots" branch from nodes on the stem several inches above the level of the ground and slant down through the air until they reach the soil, then spread out underground. See Figure 20.3.

The internal structure of the corn root is much like that of the young root of an apple tree. There is an epidermis, a loosely packed cortex of parenchyma and sclerenchyma cells, an endodermis, a pericycle, vascular bundles arranged in a cylinder, and a central mass of parenchyma cells.

Leaves

The leaves of the corn plant are very long, slender, thin blades without petioles. The base of the leaf may form a sheath around the stem for some distance above the node of its origin, but then the leaf grows away from the stem, appearing like the blade of a thin, flexible sword.

The epidermis of the corn leaf has a waxy layer. The stomata are more numerous in the lower than in the upper epidermis. The mesophyll is not differentiated into palisade and spongy layers, the entire mesophyll appearing spongy.

Flowers

The corn plant bears two kinds of flowers, each having one type of reproductive organ. The tassel of the corn is a collection of staminate flowers, whereas the ear of corn is a group of pistillate flowers, arranged usually in double rows.

In the tassel, flowers are usually grouped in bundles of two, and the bundles in turn in groups of two, one fastened immediately to the branch and one rising above it on a short stalk. See Figure 20.4.

Each bundle is enclosed by protective leaflike parts. Each flower has three stamens and the beginning of a pistil, which ordinarily does not develop far. Occasionally pistils will develop to maturity in the tassel, and even contribute to the production of seeds there. But normally pistils in the tassel remain undeveloped. Each stamen consists of a filament bearing two anthers. Each anther is divided into two chambers, within which microspore mother cells divide by meiosis, forming microspores. These microspores become pollen grains much as did the microspores of the apple. Two leaflike parts in the flower represent sepals, but no petals appear. The vein entering the receptacle of a flower divides into branches leading to the protecting parts, the three stamens, and the two sepals. An extra vein branch may indicate that there was once a third sepal, but this is speculative. See Figure 20.5.

The developing ear of the corn plant carries the pistillate flowers, which are grouped in pairs of bundles, each bundle composed of two flowers. But only one of the two flowers in each bundle develops very far. In this occur the pistil and three rudimentary stamens. The stamens remain undeveloped normally, although exceptionally they may mature. Sepals and petals are not apparent in the fully developed pistillate flower. The pistil is composed of an ovary and a very long style which is the silk of the corn ear. All along the style except near the ovary are tiny

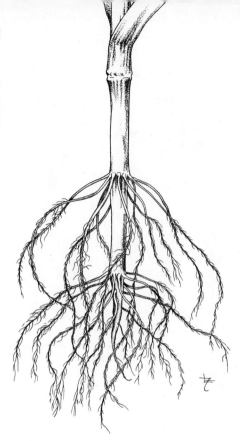

Fig. 20.3   Corn roots. Note how they come off from the nodes of the stem. Can you determine where the ground level came on this plant?

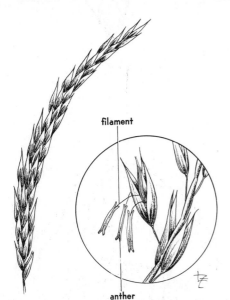

Fig. 20.4 Corn staminate flowers. **A,** Individual flowers on a branch of the tassel. **B,** Detail of one staminate flower.

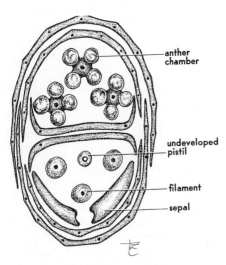

Fig. 20.5 Cross section of one staminate flower of corn. How does this flower compare with an apple flower?

cellular hairs which act as stigmas and receive pollen grains. See Figure 20.6.

Within the ovary only one megasporangium forms. The single megaspore mother cell divides by meiosis. Of the four resulting megaspores, three disintegrate, and the fourth produces the female gametophyte by repeated nuclear divisions. This gametophyte is like that of the apple except that more than three antipodal nuclei may form.

Reproduction

When the pollen grains are mature, the anthers break open, and the wind blows the pollen grains about. Those which come in contact with the silk may adhere and form pollen tubes leading through the style to the ovary. Here one sperm nucleus unites with the egg nucleus, forming a zygote, and the other sperm nucleus unites with the two polar nuclei, forming an endosperm nucleus. The integuments around the ovule do not develop as completely as in the apple; the outer integument degenerates and the inner integument fuses to the ovary wall, so the resulting kernel of corn is really a fruit, not merely a seed. This type of fruit is called a grain.

The zygote nucleus divides repeatedly, forming the nuclei of the cells of the embryo. The first division results in two cells, one of which forms a suspensor, and the other the embryo. The embryo grows until it consists of a hypocotyl and its outgrowths, the single cotyledon, the plumule, and the radicle. The plumule is a bud protected by a sheath, and may differentiate into a meristem region surrounded by some beginning leaves. The radicle is also protected by a sheath, and may form the beginnings of branch roots.

The endosperm cells absorb and store food in the megasporangium. The main portion of the endosperm is sugary or starchy, but the outer layer stores protein.

The cotyledon, in turn, digests and stores some of the food of the endosperm. The resulting fruit in the condition in which it remains dormant is shown in Figure 20.7. The bulk of the grain is endosperm.

Only one grain develops from each pistillate flower, and since only one flower of each bundle of two passes beyond the rudimentary stage, each flower bundle produces but one grain. The flower bundles occur in pairs, however, so that an ear which receives an adequate sprinkling of pollen on its silk will produce grains in paired rows.

If one of these grains is planted the following year, the fused ovary wall and integument will burst as the grain absorbs water and swells, and the embryo, drawing on its cotyledon and upon the endosperm for food, expands its radicle into a root and its hypocotyl into a stem, and unfolds its plumule into stem and leaves.

OTHER MONOCOTS

The other cereal plants, the grasses, reeds, and sedges, are all monocots. Among the gaudier monocots are the lilies, the irises, and the orchids. The bamboos are grasses which are widely used by peoples in southeastern Asia and elsewhere. Sugar cane is a grass from which is derived much more than half the world supply of sugar. Most of the monocot trees belong to the palm family. Date and coconut palms are among the most valuable economic plants of the tropics.

SUMMARY

Monocots differ from dicots generally in possessing one cotyledon in the seed, in having the vascular bundles of the stem scattered, in parallel venation of the leaves, and in having flower parts in twos or threes. Not all of these characteristics are universal in monocots, but they are representative.

The corn plant is an annual. Its stem has conspicuous nodes and internodes. The leaves have no palisade tissue.

Corn flower clusters are of two kinds, tassels and ears. The tassels bear flowers with mature stamens and undeveloped pistils. Pollen grains develop here, and drift through the air to the ears. Ears bear flowers with mature pistils and undeveloped stamens. The silk of the ear is made up of the styles of the pistils.

The process of fertilization resembles that in the apple. The fruit is a grain, having the inner integument fused to the ovary wall.

The grasses are the most important food plants of many of the higher animals, including man.

REVIEW QUESTIONS

1. Describe the structure of a corn stem; of a corn root.
2. Compare and contrast a leaf of corn and a leaf of apple.
3. Describe the structure of a staminate flower of corn.
4. Describe the structure of a pistillate flower of corn.
5. Describe reproduction in the corn plant.
6. Define a grain.
7. In a corn grain, what generations are represented?
8. How does a corn seed become a seedling?
9. Describe some monocots other than corn.
10. Of what importance are monocots to humans?

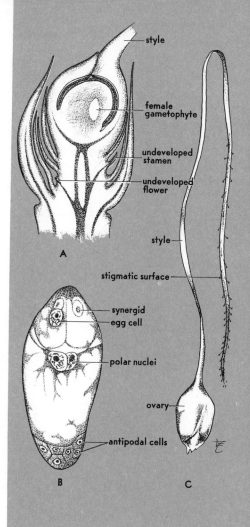

Fig. 20.6 Corn pistillate flower. **A,** Vertical section through one developed flower. **B,** Detail of the corn female gametophyte. **C,** Pistil of the corn flower. The style is a strand of corn silk.

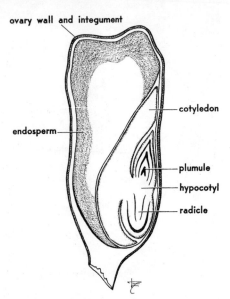

ovary wall and integument

endosperm

cotyledon

plumule

hypocotyl

radicle

Fig. 20.7 Structure of the corn fruit. What is the more common name for this fruit?

GENERAL QUESTIONS

1. Are there advantages for a plant in the possession of stem nodes and internodes?
2. In the corn staminate flower, what could the extra vein branch indicate if not an absent third sepal?
3. What do you suppose causes three of the four megaspores in a corn ovary to disintegrate?
4. Compare the processes of seed formation and the structure of a seed in pine, apple, and corn.
5. What changes would have to be made in corn if it were to become a perennial plant?
6. How do you account for the occasional appearance of ovaries in a tassel or of pollen chambers on an ear?
7. How is hybrid corn obtained?
8. Apple flowers have petals, and are insect-pollinated; corn flowers have no petals, and are wind-pollinated. Is there a causal connection between the presence or absence of petals and the type of pollination?
9. Trace through the plant kingdom the relative dominance of sporophyte and gametophyte generations.
10. Does increased complexity in plants mean increased efficiency? Does it mean increased success?

Summary to Part II

FUNGI

To summarize the variation in the entire plant kingdom: The plants may be arranged in four phyla. The Thallophyta include those plants without leaves, stems, or roots. Some, the Fungi, have no chlorophyll, and therefore are unable to carry on photosynthesis. They depend, except for a few of the bacteria which gain energy by oxidizing inorganic substances, upon the organic materials prepared by other living organisms.

Among the viruses and bacteria, reproduction consists of duplication of molecules and fission into two similar individuals. In the other fungi nuclei appear, and reproductive cycles involve the alternation of two generations. The gametophyte generation has haploid nuclei and produces gametes. These gametes unite in pairs, and their nuclei pair and fuse to produce diploid zygote nuclei. The sporophyte stage begins with this zygote and includes the formation of spore mother cells. These undergo meiosis, producing haploid spores which are the initial members of the next gametophyte generation. It is this alternation which we have followed in its variations through the remainder of the plant kingdom.

ALGAE

In the Algae, chlorophyll appears, in association with other pigments. These plants are able to produce their own food by photosynthesis and subsequent enzymic reactions. The algae show a great variety from the blue-greens in which nuclear material and pigments are scattered throughout the individual cells to the red algae which not only have nuclei and chloroplasts but a complex plant body made of branched filaments and multicellular reproductive organs.

Alternation of generations does not occur in blue-green algae, and is not a regular cycle in the green and golden algae. In the green algae we traced the Volvocine Series, finding an example of an increase in differentiation between the sexes and of an increase in differentiation between germ plasm and somatoplasm. In the brown algae alternation of generations is the regular procedure, but exceptions are possible. In the red algae alternation proves to be the only method of continuing the species.

The algae form the basis of the food chain in the ocean and in fresh water. The accumulations of diatoms, especially, are known as the meadows of the sea, for they form the browsing grounds of aquatic animals (small and large). The fungi play an indispensable role in breaking down dead bodies of plants and animals, restoring the chemical elements in these bodies to availability for new living organisms.

BRYOPHYTES

The bryophytes are a less conspicuous group, limited in size by the dependence of the sporophyte on a gametophyte which is small enough to allow its sperms to swim to its eggs in a film of water. The bryophytes are primarily land plants, and are often among the first to gain a foothold on a denuded area. The sporophytes of some have the ability to photosynthesize, but none are rooted in the ground, depending for water and some food upon the gametophyte to which they are attached.

PTERIDOPHYTES

The pteridophytes have sporophytes which become independent of their gametophytes, and increase considerably in size. In some, as the ferns, the gametophyte is also free and independent. In *Selaginella* the gametophytes become and remain dependent for their supplies upon the sporophytes. In fact, *Selaginella* comes very close to developing true seeds, which are sporophyte embryos completely encased in the megasporangium wall of the preceding sporophyte generation.

SPERMATOPHYTES

The seed plants may be divided into the gymnosperms in which the seeds are exposed and the angiosperms in which the seeds are enclosed in ovaries. The seed plants are the most conspicuous plants on land, as the algae are in the water. They are the most numerous, the dominant group. The gymnosperms include many of the most abundant and economically important members of our forests. The angiosperms include most of the food plants of man and the feed of the land animals. Some of these are trees, some shrubs, some herbs. Both the pteridophytes and the spermatophytes exhibit a vascular system of xylem and phloem tubes capable of conducting water and food throughout the large plant body. The seed plants, except the monocots, have a vascular cambium which allows for replenishment of these vascular tissues with continued growth in diameter of their stems and roots. The leaves of many seed plants may be lost and replaced. Thus, many seed plants may live and grow for many years, developing great size.

The swimming sperm has been done away with in the coniferous gymnosperms. The archegonium disappears in the Gnetales. The male gametophyte is reduced to three nuclei and their surrounding cytoplasm in dicots, and the female gametophyte to eight nuclei and their surrounding cytoplasm in many plants of the same group. This represents a great decrease from the dominant gametophyte of the mosses.

Finally, the monocots differ from the dicots in the reduction of cotyledons from two to one in the seed, in flower parts from fives or fours to threes or twos, in stele from a ring of vascular bundles to a scattering of small bundles in the stem, and a change from a network of veins to parallel veins in the leaves.

OTHER CLASSIFICATIONS

In the introduction to Part II, alternative classification schemes were mentioned. It was pointed out that the Phylum Thallophyta includes such diverse plants that many botanists believe it should be divided into several phyla.

The viruses and bacteria are called Phylum Schizomycetes.

Because they have no discrete nuclei and their reproduction is by fission only, the Schizomycetes and Cyanophyceae are sometimes combined into the Phylum **Schizophyta.** Otherwise, the blue-green algae may be considered a separate phylum.

The Class Myxomycetes is elevated to a phylum.

The remaining fungi are put in the Phylum **Eumycetes.**

The Chlorophyceae are divided into several phyla.

The **Euglenophyta** almost all have one or two flagella, all have a food-getting system consisting of a mouth and a system of vacuoles, and all reproduce by longitudinal fission. Most Euglenophyta have chloroplasts, and these organisms store food in the form of the carbohydrate **paramylon.**

The Phylum **Chloromonadophyta** also includes motile forms with two flagella, one flagellum directed forward, the other usually trailing. Most of the chloromonads have chloroplasts containing the yellow pigment xanthophyll as well as chlorophyll. Food is stored as fats and oils in these organisms. Reproduction is by longitudinal fission.

The group recognized in Chapter 15 as Chrysophyceae is sometimes made a separate phylum, or even divided into three classes or phyla: **Xanthophyta** with yellow-green chloroplasts; **Chrysophyta** with brown chloroplasts and no capsule; and **Bacillariophyta** with brown chloroplasts and a two-valved, silicious capsule.

The **Pyrrhophyta** include brown forms which store starch. This includes such organisms as dinoflagellates, desmokonts, and cryptomonads, all usually one-celled motile forms.

The **Chlorophyta** include the remainder of the green algae, such as the members of the Volvocine Series. They have green chloroplasts and store starch.

The Phaeophyceae and Rhodophyceae have been called distinct phyla: **Phaeophyta** and **Rhodophyta.**

Division of the bryophytes into classes varies. One point of view combines such forms as *Ricciocarpus* and *Anthoceros* into one class, the liverworts. Another group of scientists separates those like *Ricciocarpus* into one class and those like *Anthoceros* into another. The mosses constitute a distinct class in either case.

The vascular plants are now commonly united into the Phylum **Tracheophyta.** This is then said to have four subphyla; or the Tracheophyta may be called a division with four phyla:

The **Psilophyta** include a few living forms and some fossil ones whose characteristics have given rise to the idea that these are ancestors of all vascular plants, and represent the link between the algae and the ferns and seed plants. This subject is further discussed in Part IV.

The **Lycopsida** include such forms as *Selaginella*.

The **Sphenopsida** include the horsetail rushes and their allies, many of which were plants which formed our present-day coal deposits.

The **Pteropsida** include the ferns and seed plants.

UNITY IN DIVERSITY

Throughout the plant kingdom we recognize innumerable variations, but these may be gathered into a story showing continuity in the more fundamental features of structure, metabolism, and reproduction. The significance of this continuity will concern us in Part IV, but we shall first consider the story of continuity amid variation in the animal kingdom.

PART III

THE ANIMAL KINGDOM

DIFFERENCES BETWEEN ANIMALS AND PLANTS

It is not difficult to distinguish between a human and an apple tree. The human moves about from place to place under his own power. He is unable to manufacture his own food from inorganic materials. He responds much more quickly than the tree to stimuli coming from his environment. He does not, like the apple tree, have cellulose cell walls. He has an active excretory system, as the apple tree does not. He carries male and female reproductive organs in separate individuals, while the apple tree is neither male nor female.

Euglena

But when we try to devise a scheme to classify every living thing as either a plant or an animal, we encounter difficulties. Particularly in the one-celled forms it is not easy to assign each living organism to one kingdom or the other. One of the standard treatises on one-celled animals described a group of creatures such as *Euglena* (see Figure III.1) through a few editions, and then discarded the group entirely in a later edition, holding that they were plants and not animals. *Euglena* is somewhat like *Chlamydomonas*, except that it does not have a cellulose wall and does not have the same type of reproduction. *Euglena* forms two new cells by fission but has no sexual form of reproduction. It has two flagella fused together except at the base. It has chloroplasts and an eyespot. Yet, if *Euglena* is kept in a dark place for some time, it loses its chlorophyll. Does it thereby change from being a plant to being an animal? If it is restored to the light, it develops chlorophyll. Has it become a plant?

Astasia

A close relative of *Euglena*, *Astasia*, is shaped much like *Euglena*, but never develops chlorophyll. *Euglena* and *Astasia* move about and respond to stimuli much as does *Chlamydomonas*. *Euglena* and *Astasia* do not have cellulose walls. Which characteristics shall we use in classification

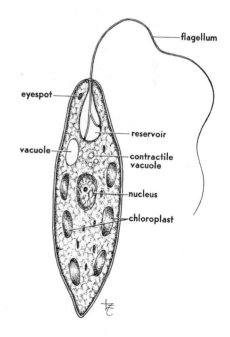

Fig. III.1 *Euglena*. This is a one-celled organism. What characteristics of *Euglena* are plantlike and what ones animal-like?

of these forms? If we use photosynthesis as a strictly plant characteristic, we must put the entire group of Fungi in the animal kingdom. If we use locomotion as a strictly animal characteristic, we must call oysters and barnacles plants, and motile bacteria and the members of the Volvocine Series animals. If we use cellulose walls as a strictly plant characteristic, we would have to place the Tunicates, which are marine organisms now classified in the phylum to which humans belong, among the plants, for they possess cellulose. If we use the possession of a distinctive excretory system as our basis, we shall eliminate from the animal kingdom many of the simpler creatures like amebas, sponges, and corals.

The fact is that we find no sharp separation of living organisms into animals and plants, any more than we found a sharp distinction between living viruses and nonliving protein molecules. As far as we have been able to determine to date, nonliving forms can be arranged so that they grade into living forms, and plants can be arranged in a series that will grade into an animal series.

In the following eight chapters we shall investigate some selected representatives of the animal kingdom to find out about their variety of structure, physiology, reproduction, and natural history.

REVIEW QUESTIONS

1. In what general ways do humans and apple trees differ?
2. In what ways is *Euglena* plantlike? In what ways is it animal-like?
3. How do *Euglena* and *Astasia* differ?

GENERAL QUESTIONS

1. Set up a series of criteria for distinguishing all plants from all animals.
2. Is *Astasia* more animal-like than *Euglena?*
3. What is the significance of the difficulty in distinguishing between living and nonliving forms and between plants and animals?

Protozoa

The name *Protozoa* comes from the Greek for "first animals." **Protozoa** are one-celled, in contrast to the adults of other phyla of animals. Members of the Phylum Protozoa are divided into four classes depending upon the presence and nature of their organs of locomotion. The Class **Flagellata** includes those which move by means of one or more flagella. The Class **Sarcodina** includes those which move only by temporary projections of the cytoplasm called **pseudopodia,** or false feet. The Class **Ciliata** includes those which have many short hairlike projections of cytoplasm called **cilia.** These cilia are coordinated in their beating. The Class **Sporozoa** includes those which have no special organs of locomotion.

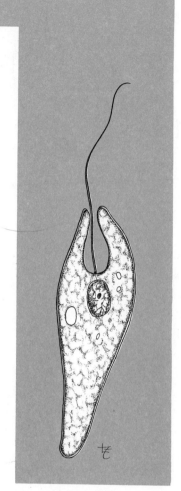

Fig. 21.1   *Astasia.* This animal is similar to *Euglena* in many respects, but *Astasia* does not possess chlorophyll.

FLAGELLATA

Astasia

Among the flagellates we find the organisms most closely resembling the algae. The fresh-water forms *Euglena* and *Astasia* belong to this group. *Astasia klebsi* is a long, tapering form shaped much like *Euglena*. See Figure 21.1. Unlike *Euglena*, *Astasia* has no chlorophyll. The cell is surrounded by a flexible **pellicle,** an elastic membrane which keeps the animal to its normal shape much of the time, while allowing some bending and twisting. At the anterior end of the body is a double flagellum united into a single strand. At the anterior end also is a cavity called the **gullet,** open to the outside, through which food passes into the cytoplasm. *Astasia* depends upon other living organisms for food, eating diatoms and other algae, bacteria, and protozoa. It is in turn eaten by larger animals.

The tip of the flagellum is sensitive to contact, and the borders of the gullet are sensitive to chemical substances, making a sort of sense of taste and smell. A piece of food is taken into the gullet, and then the membrane lining the gullet recedes into the cytoplasm for a short distance. The water in the gullet follows the recession of the membrane, carrying the food organism with it. Then the membrane closes around the food and locks it into a little lake of water separate from the gullet. This little lake with the organism inside is called a **food vacuole.** See Figure 21.2.

Into this food vacuole the cytoplasm of *Astasia* secretes enzymes. These digest the food, and the soluble products of digestion may be absorbed through the vacuole wall into the organism. Technically, the food vacuole is part of the water in which the Astasia lives, and not an internal organ, just as the cavity of a man's stomach is part of the outside world.

Undigested parts of the food organisms, such as diatom shells, are retained within the food vacuole until the vacuole passes to the surface of the body and empties out by a process like vacuole formation, but in reverse. The edge of the vacuole touches the limiting membrane around the cytoplasm. The water in the vacuole breaks through, establishing contact with the water outside. The vacuole membrane then contracts, forcing out the contents of the vacuole. The vacuole membrane finally smooths off and becomes one with the cell membrane. Several food vacuoles may be present in *Astasia* at any one time.

Astasia possesses a contractile vacuole like that of *Chlamydomonas*. In *Astasia* it empties into the gullet.

Reproduction in *Astasia* involves mitosis and cell division. The nucleus divides into two; then the cell splits longitudinally. Each resulting cell organizes itself into an adult *Astasia* equipped with all the usual structures.

There is no sexual reproduction in *Astasia* as far as has yet been discovered. In an unfavorable environment, however, the animal may round up, secrete a more resistant membrane about itself, and remain dormant for a time as a **cyst**. When the environment becomes more suitable for growth, this cyst may break open, releasing the active *Astasia*.

Contrasted with simple algae like *Chlamydomonas*, *Astasia* differs in the absence of chlorophyll and of a cellulose wall. *Astasia* also lacks sexual reproduction. Contrasted with complex animals such as man, *Astasia* carries on all its necessary metabolic activities within the borders of one cell. Food-getting, digestion, and elimination involve the gullet and the food vacuoles. Excretion and oxygen-getting are carried on by diffusion through the outer cell membrane. Circulation is taken care of by diffusion within the cell. Support is provided by the pellicle, and locomotion by the flagellum. *Astasia* has no nervous system; impulses may pass through the whole cell. Thus, from a structural viewpoint, *Astasia* is a very much simpler animal than the human. From a physiological viewpoint, *Astasia* is simpler than man as an organism, but if it is to be compared to any one cell of a human, it is much more complex.

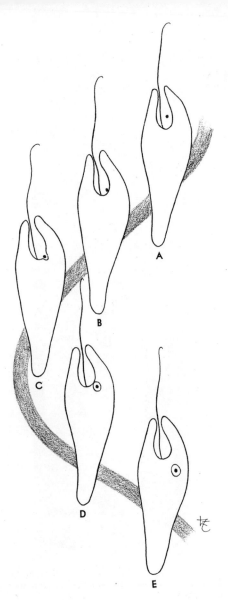

Fig. 21.2   Stages in the formation of a food vacuole.

Some investigators believe that it is misleading to consider *Astasia* one-celled, because this leads us to compare it with one cell of a human. Instead, *Astasia* should be thought of as an entire organism whose body is not divided into separate cells. From a physiological viewpoint this is a helpful concept. From a structural viewpoint *Astasia* has the characteristics we associate with single cells: cell membrane, cytoplasm, and a nucleus.

If you recall the discussion of the Volvocine Series, you may see how the nature of cells changes in passing from one-celled to many-celled forms. The simplest colonies are groups of independent similar cells. In more complex colonies, the cells are differentiated from each other, some being specialized as reproductive cells, some as vegetative cells. In even more complex plants and animals the reproductive cells are further specialized into sperms and eggs and cells associated with them, and the vegetative cells are further specialized into epidermis, or xylem, or blood, or muscle cells, etc. This specialization involves adaptations to greater efficiency in one type of action, and reduction in capacity for other types of action, a sort of division of labor among cells comparable to the division of labor in a human society. One man produces food, another operates a transportation or communication device, still another combats disease, and so forth. In *Astasia*, however, specialization is confined to the various parts of one cell.

Other Flagellates

Among other flagellates of especial interest are those which live in association with other animals. Some, such as the **trypanosomes,** are parasitic. For example, one form of sleeping sickness in man is caused by trypanosomes. The flagellates are transmitted from one host to another by the **tsetse fly,** a native of Africa. The fly sucks blood for its food, and may swallow some trypanosomes if it takes blood from an infected human or other animal. In the stomach of the fly the parasites undergo structural changes, and then migrate to the fly's salivary glands. From here they may be transmitted to another victim of the fly. The parasite may live in many of the larger game animals of tropical Africa. If it gets into the blood of a human, it causes fever and anemia. It may invade the cerebrospinal fluid, and there its secretions act as toxins on the central nervous system, gradually poisoning the system until the human loses consciousness, and eventually dies unless the parasites are destroyed. See Figure 21.3.

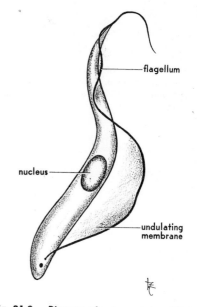

Fig. 21.3   Diagram of a trypanosome. This is a very graceful swimmer, but its secretions may bring on sleeping sickness. It is transmitted by the African tsetse fly.

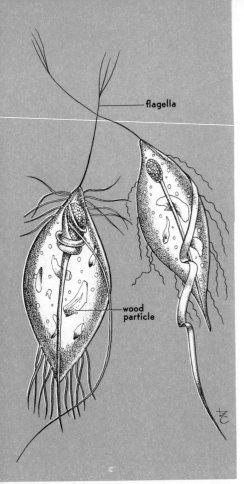

flagella

wood
particle

Fig. 21.4 Hypermastigina. These flagellates live in the digestive tracts of termites and are able to ingest and digest wood. Would a termite starve without Hypermastigina? How do the flagellates get into newborn termites?

Leishmania is another parasitic flagellate. One species causes the oriental disease called kala azar, an affliction involving damage to the lymph nodes, liver, and spleen. Another species of the same genus causes Oriental sore.

A number of genera in the group **Hypermastigina** inhabit the intestines of termites and cockroaches. The Hypermastigina are able to digest cellulose, an ability which generally does not occur among animals. The insect host eats wood, the flagellate digests it, and both host and guest absorb the digested products and use them as sources of energy. This type of collaboration between two different kinds of organisms in which each requires the presence of the other for the accomplishment of a process beneficial to both is called **symbiosis.** See Figure 21.4.

SARCODINA

Sarcodina are more nearly like the flagellates than are the other protozoa. Some flagellates have pseudopodia in addition to their flagella.

Ameba

Ameba proteus is one of the best known of the Sarcodina. The word *Ameba* comes from the Greek for "change," and *Proteus* was a character in Greek mythology who could change his shape readily. Both names refer to the type of locomotion by pseudopodia, resulting in continually different body forms. See Figure 21.5.

Ameba has no definite pellicle, but the cytoplasm of the cell is differentiated into an outer, thin, gelatinous **ectoplasm,** and an inner, less viscous **endoplasm.** In movement by pseudopod formation, a localized area of the ectoplasm becomes liquefied, perhaps because of the secretion of acid at this point. The fluid endoplasm is under some pressure from the contractility of the ectoplasm, and flows into the area of liquid ectoplasm, causing a lobelike swelling to form here. The sides of the lobe become gelatinous again, and eventually the advancing front of the lobe also gels. Then the pseudopodium stops spreading, and soon a new pseudopodium is started at another area. Sometimes several pseudopodia may be active at one time. Usually only the tips of the pseudopodia are in contact with the surface on which the ameba is moving, so that it seems to walk on stilts. See Figure 21.6.

Ameba is sensitive to chemical substances at any point of its surface. In some cases it seems to be able to distinguish not only between food and other substances, but even between kinds of food, judging from its reactions in the presence of these stimuli. Acceptable food stimulates the production of pseudopodia which surround the food particle and take it into a food vacuole like that of *Astasia*. Digestion occurs by the action of enzymes secreted into the food vacuole, and undigested wastes are left behind as the vacuole moves to the surface and opens out.

Ameba proteus also has a contractile vacuole. Marine amebas lack this structure. The salt concentration of sea water is about equivalent to that of the marine ameba's cytoplasm, so that there is no flooding of this cytoplasm by water pouring in due to osmotic pressure, and no stimulus for constant bailing out.

Ameba absorbs oxygen by diffusion from the surrounding water, and excretes carbon dioxide and nitrogenous wastes by diffusion from its cytoplasm.

Reproduction is by mitosis and cell division. A spindle forms within the nucleus, chromosomes develop and are arranged on an equatorial plane, and then separated to the two poles of the spindle. Then the ameba pinches into two, each with one of the daughter nuclei. Sexual reproduction has not been observed in *Ameba proteus*.

Ameba is able to form a cyst by rounding up and secreting a heavy, resistant wall about itself. This cyst protects the ameba during times of unfavorable environment. When the surroundings are more nearly normal, the cyst wall breaks open, and the ameba escapes, returning to a more active life.

Ameba is sensitive to several stimuli. It reacts to the presence of food by movements which almost seem to be attempts at capture. It varies these attempts with the nature of the food, advancing directly on nonmotile forms, but surrounding and trapping moving prey. It moves away from most mechanical contact with objects other than food, from media different in their chemical concentrations from the one the ameba is in, and from extremes of temperature or light. No differentiated structure has been found associated with the conduction of impulses through the ameba. Sensitivity and conduction of impulses are characteristic of the whole body of the ameba.

Other Sarcodina

Endameba is a genus of parasitic Sarcodina. Several kinds live in the digestive tract of humans, but only one is seriously harmful. *Endameba histolytica* is the cause of amebic dysentery, a disease characterized by the destruction of the

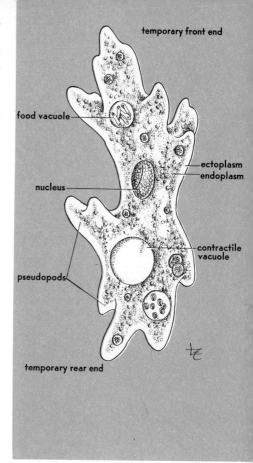

Fig. 21.5   *Ameba*. This one has found food-hunting good.

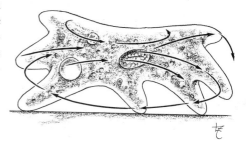

Fig. 21.6   Movement in *Ameba*. The arrows inside the animal show the pathway followed by the streaming cytoplasm. The arrows below show how the animal moves its stiltlike pseudopodia, as if it were turning handsprings.

lining of the intestine and the formation of abscesses in various parts of the body.

Some of the Sarcodina form shells about themselves. See Figure 21.7. Especially striking are the internal skeletons secreted by the marine **Radiolaria.** See Figure 21.8. The

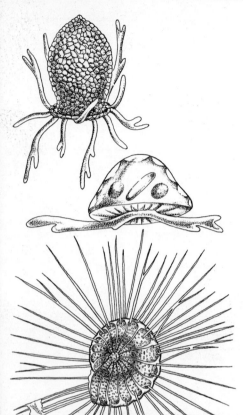

Fig. 21.7   Shelled amebas.

Fig. 21.8   Radiolarian skeletons.

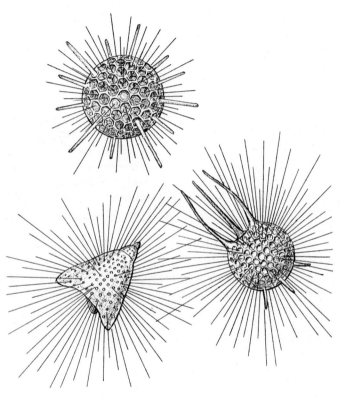

Foraminifera are another group of shelled Sarcodina. These are very numerous in the ocean, and their castoff shells constitute a considerable portion of the ocean floor, especially in the shallower seas. In some of the uplifted parts of the ocean floor, now geological formations on land, the Foraminiferan shells constitute valuable guides as to the age and nature of the deposit, because they vary in shape from one formation to another, and are present in such numbers as to be a convenient reference clue. They are especially used as indicators of oil-bearing strata, and the geologist who knows well the kinds of Foraminiferan shells is invaluable to the oil prospector. See Figure 21.9.

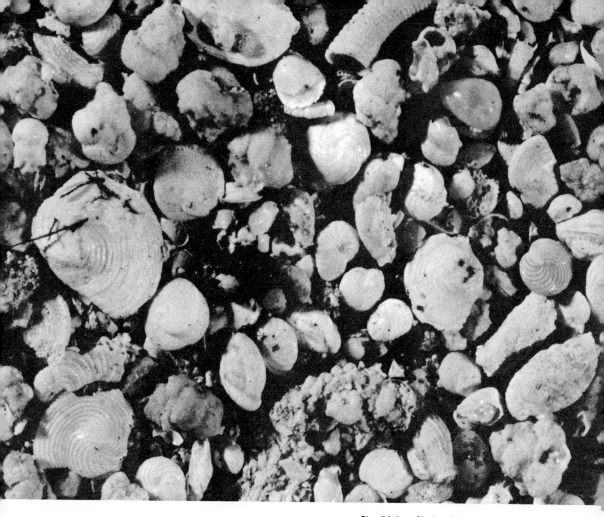

CILIATA

Paramecium

The Ciliata are somewhat more specialized than the Flagellata or Sarcodina. The most commonly studied example is *Paramecium*. We shall consider the species *Paramecium caudatum*. See Figure 21.10.

Paramecium has a fairly firm pellicle which is flexible enough to bend when pushed against some solid object, but elastic enough to maintain the definite shape of the animal after contact with the object is released. The pellicle is marked by many shallow depressions, looking like a honeycomb. From the center of each depression emerges a cilium. The cilia are in longitudinal rows, and the bases of the cilia are connected by strands which carry impulses facilitating the coordination of ciliary beat. These strands converge to a mass, the **motorium,** at the edge of a broad groove in the body of the paramecium. The motorium is

Fig. 21.9   Shells of Foraminifera, marine sarcodinans.

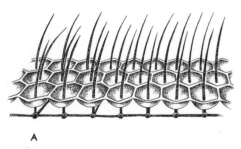

contractile vacuole

food vacuole

vegetative nucleus
reproductive nucleus

oral groove

undigested food
being eliminated

gullet

contractile vacuole

cilium

trichocyst

pellicle

Fig. 21.10 *Paramecium*. This is one of the more complex of the Protozoa.

the center of coordination of the beat. Waves of contraction pass along the cilia from the front of the paramecium to the back. See Figure 21.11.

In the borders of the depressions in the pellicle are tiny openings through which the **trichocysts** may be exploded. The trichocysts are tapering, rounded columns just under the surface of the animal. Upon stimulation by mechanical contact or some chemicals a trichocyst may erupt, shooting out a long, fine filament. Such a filament helps anchor the paramecium during feeding, acting as a mooring line. It may also be a weapon of defense against some of the animal's predators.

The paramecium has two contractile vacuoles, one near either end. Each vacuole has a permanent pore through which it expels water. Further, each vacuole is associated with a radiating series of canals through which water flows into it. The posterior contractile vacuole normally contracts a little more often than the anterior one, probably due to water entering the posterior end of the animal through the gullet as well as diffusing through the pellicle.

The gullet is at the posterior end of the long, slightly helical **oral groove** in one side of the animal. Food particles such as bacteria are swept by ciliary currents along the oral groove and into the gullet. Here they are incorporated into food vacuoles as in *Astasia*. The food vacuoles are carried through the cytoplasm in a definite pathway, and digestion is carried on as in *Astasia*. Digested products are absorbed into the cytoplasm. Undigested remains are eliminated at a definite spot near the posterior end of the paramecium.

Paramecium caudatum has two kinds of nuclei, a vegetative nucleus and a reproductive nucleus. The reproductive nucleus is much the smaller, and is located in a slight concavity in the vegetative nucleus, near the center of the animal's body. The vegetative nucleus regulates the ordinary metabolic activities of the cell, and the reproductive nucleus is involved in reproduction.

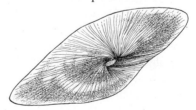

A

B

C

Fig. 21.11 Movement in *Paramecium*. **A,** Enlarged portion of the body surface, showing cilia penetrating the cuplike depressions. The cilia are connected at their bases by a network of fibers which have a center in the motorium. **B,** Motorium and connecting fibers. **C,** Pattern of ciliary contraction. Waves pass along the cilia. Each cilium beats strongly and recoils gently.

Fission

Asexual reproduction is by fission into two cells. The reproductive nucleus undergoes mitosis. The vegetative nucleus seems merely to divide into two parts without going through the mitotic stages. Then the paramecium divides transversely, each half getting one vegetative nucleus and one reproductive nucleus. Then each half builds the additional structures characteristic of a mature paramecium such as another contractile vacuole, and the part of the oral groove which went to the other half. Thus reproduction is completed, and each new organism may grow to adult size again. See Figure 21.12.

It is uncertain whether *Paramecium* ever forms a cyst; it is surely not at all common or typical.

Sexual Reproduction

Sexual reproduction involves the temporary cytoplasmic union of two paramecia, an act known as **conjugation.** Two animals swim side by side, their oral grooves apposed, and then the membranes at the area of contact open up, allowing the cytoplasm of one to be in communication with the cytoplasm of the other. This bridge of cytoplasm maintains the two animals in the form of Siamese (or parabiotic) twins for several hours. During this time or soon thereafter, the vegetative nucleus of each cell breaks down and dissolves away into the cytoplasm.

Then the reproductive nucleus in each animal divides by meiosis, forming four haploid nuclei. Of these four, three degenerate. The remaining one divides by mitosis, forming a larger, female nucleus and a smaller, male nucleus.

The male nucleus from each animal passes through the cytoplasmic bridge and unites with the female nucleus of the other animal, forming a diploid zygote nucleus in each paramecium. After this, the two paramecia may separate, the membrane of each cutting through the cytoplasmic bridge, enabling the two animals to swim away from each other.

The zygote nucleus in each animal then divides by mitosis three times, producing eight nuclei. Four of these become vegetative nuclei and four reproductive nuclei. Then the animal divides into four organisms, each with one vegetative nucleus and one reproductive nucleus. Each paramecium then develops the structures characteristic of the adult, and sexual reproduction is complete. See Figure 21.13.

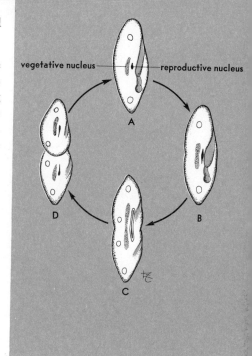

vegetative nucleus — reproductive nucleus

Fig. 21.12   *Paramecium asexual reproduction.*

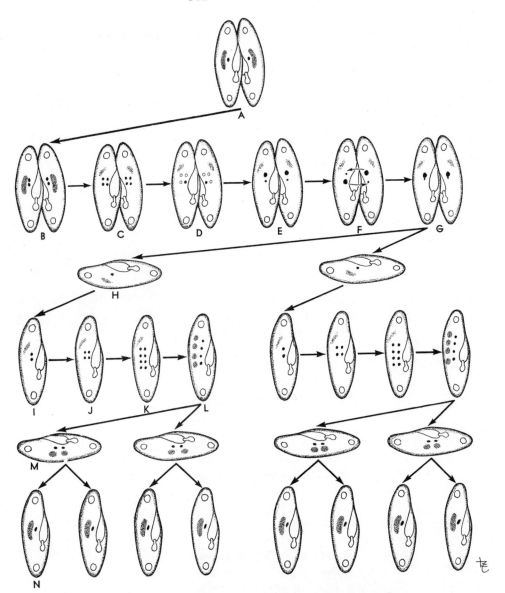

Fig. 21.13   Conjugation in *Paramecium*. A, Two paramecia join. **B,** The reproductive nucleus of each divides into two, as the vegetative nucleus of each begins to degenerate. **C,** Each animal has four reproductive nuclei. **D,** Three of these disappear in each paramecium. **E,** The remaining one divides into a large and a small nucleus. **F,** The smaller nuclei are interchanged. **G,** The small nucleus of one unites with the large nucleus of the other. **H,** The two conjugants separate. **I,** The zygote nucleus divides into two. **J,** Four. **K,** Eight. **L,** Four of the eight enlarge, forming vegetative nuclei. **M,** The paramecium divides into two. **N,** Four paramecia from each of the original conjugants.

Potential Immortality

In the first decade of this century, biologists discussed the question whether one-celled animals had periods of youth, maturity, old age, and death as did the more familiar many-celled animals. In many-celled animals, an individual starts out as a single cell which divides repeatedly, forming an adult organism composed of many cells. Some of these cells eventually slow down in their division rate, gradually become more sluggish in their metabolism, and finally degenerate to and below the lower limit of efficiency necessary to maintain life.

Some biologists held that similar events happen among Protozoa: Following sexual reproduction, the cells divide rapidly, although they do not remain together forming a large, many-celled organism, but separate and become distinct individuals. After a time the division rate slows down, and unless sexual reproduction intervenes to start a new series of cells, the old series will grind to a halt and die after a few hundred cell generations.

Other biologists believed that protozoa are potentially immortal, that division can go on indefinitely without the necessity of sexual reproduction to renew the youth of the series of cell generations.

In order to test this matter, Lorande L. Woodruff, on May 1, 1907, started to watch an individual *Paramecium aurelia*, a species related to *Paramecium caudatum* but somewhat smaller in size, different in shape, and having normally two reproductive nuclei instead of one, in addition to the vegetative nucleus. The *Paramecium aurelia* individuals were separated from each other after each asexual reproduction so that conjugation could not occur. Then the number of cell divisions was carefully recorded.

Exactly eight years later, May 1, 1915, there had been 5071 cell generations without intervening conjugation and without, as far as Woodruff could ascertain, any decrease in vitality as indicated by division rate. The number of cell generations per year was between 600 and 700. Within any one year, it might fluctuate up or down from month to month, but by the year it was fairly steady. Woodruff published his results, maintaining that they supported the idea of potential immortality, at least for *Paramecium aurelia*.

Endomixis

On the advice of an older scientist Woodruff did not abandon his daily observations, and within a few months

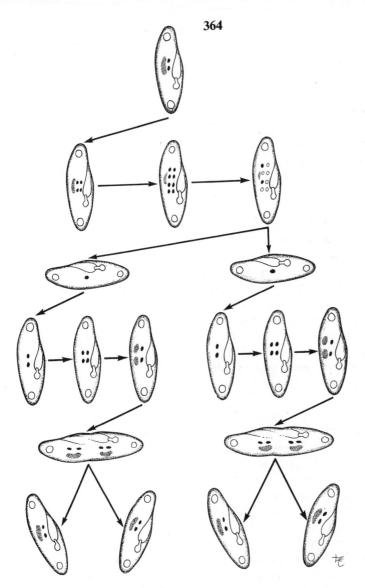

Fig. 21.14 Endomixis in *Paramecium* according to Woodruff. Compare with Fig. 21.15.

he discovered the method of reproduction which he called **endomixis.** It is a sort of short-circuited form of sexual reproduction in which only one individual is involved. As Woodruff described it, the vegetative nucleus disintegrates and each reproductive nucleus divides twice, producing four. Of these four, three disappear. Each remaining nucleus goes to one of the two cells into which the paramecium divides. Within the new paramecium, the nucleus divides twice more, forming four. Two of these become

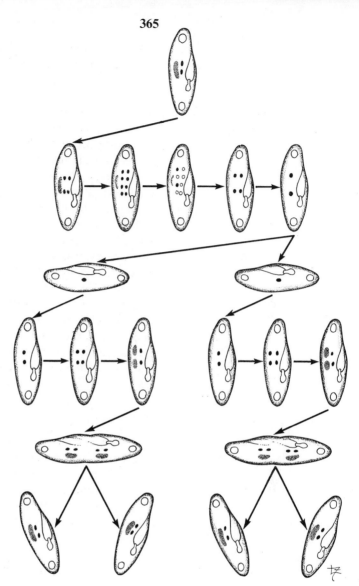

Fig. 21.15 Endomixis in *Paramecium* according to Diller. Compare with Fig. 21.14.

vegetative nuclei. The other two divide again, forming four reproductive nuclei. Then the paramecium divides again, resulting in two animals each with one vegetative nucleus and two reproductive nuclei. See Figure 21.14.

A later paper by William F. Diller, Jr., gives a different account of the process. Diller says that after each reproductive nucleus divides twice, and three of the four nuclei degenerate, the remaining one divides again, forming two gamete nuclei, which unite, forming a zygote nucleus.

After this, repeated nuclear and cell divisions produce daughter paramecia as before. See Figure 21.15.

Whatever the details of the process are, the discovery of endomixis again raised the question of the necessity of sexual reproduction for long-continued life in *Paramecium*. For endomixis was supposed by some to supply a rejuvenation comparable to that which results from conjugation. But Woodruff found other forms of protozoa which did not undergo endomixis, and which could yet divide indefinitely without conjugation, so it seems that if environmental conditions are maintained suitable, some animals, at least, never grow old. Whether in the more complicated animals and plants a limited lifetime is a necessary result of complexity is not yet certain. Cells of complex animals may be kept alive indefinitely if removed from the body to a nutrient medium kept under aseptic conditions. This process is known as **tissue culture.** Connective tissue cells, for example, live in tissue cultures if they are transferred to fresh medium every few days. A piece of chick heart was put in tissue culture in 1912. Thirty-five years later, cells derived from this tissue were still thriving, although no chicken has been known to live so long.

Other Ciliata

A very few of the ciliated protozoa are parasitic. Some species live in the intestine of frogs, one in the skin of a fish. Some invade the digestive tracts of horses and cows, and similar animals. *Balantidium coli*, normally an intestinal parasite of the pig, may infect humans, causing serious illness. Most ciliates are free-living; there is a wide variety of form.

SPOROZOA

Plasmodium

All sporozoa are parasitic. None have locomotor organs. Many have a life cycle in which they alternately parasitize two kinds of hosts. The best known examples belong to the genus *Plasmodium*, members of which cause malaria in humans and other animals. *Plasmodium vivax* is the cause of benign tertian malaria in humans. The animal is transmitted to humans by the bite of mosquitoes of the genus *Anopheles*.

An infected mosquito may have *Plasmodium* organisms in its salivary glands, and when it bites a human the organisms are carried into the blood of the human. *Plasmodium* at that time is a long, slender organism known as a **sporozoite.** Each sporozoite burrows its way into a red blood corpuscle and rounds up. It digests the cytoplasm of the corpuscle and enlarges into a **trophozoite,** which soon fills the corpuscle.

Then the trophozoite nucleus divides repeatedly, producing from 16 to 24 nuclei. This division process starts about 36 hours after the sporozoite entered the corpuscle. Then the trophozoite undergoes cell division resulting in one cell for each nucleus formed. These new cells are called **merozoites.**

The merozoites break out of the red corpuscle about 48 hours after the sporozoite entered the corpuscle. Some toxin secreted by the *Plasmodium* is released at the same time, but the amount is so small that the effect on the host is not noticeable.

The merozoites enter other red corpuscles and begin to digest the corpuscle cytoplasm, being transformed into new trophozoites. These form more merozoites, which in turn break out after another 48 hours, and invade still other corpuscles. Each time, the number of corpuscles attacked becomes greater, until after about ten or twelve days the amount of toxin released when the merozoites break out of the corpuscles is enough to bring on in the host symptoms of chills and fever.

These symptoms recur every two days, since the cycles of invasion and breaking out go on about simultaneously. Of course, the host's white corpuscles are active and combat the spread of the infection by devouring some merozoites during the short time they are exposed between breaking out of one corpuscle and entering another.

About 18 days after the parasite entered the human blood there appear two new cell types, derived from trophozoites. One, slightly smaller than the usual trophozoite, is called a **microgametocyte;** the other, slightly larger than the trophozoite, is a **megagametocyte.** These, when released from red corpuscles, do not enter other corpuscles, but are carried around in the blood plasma until they are destroyed by white corpuscles, or until they are swallowed by another Anopheles mosquito drawing blood from the human.

In the mosquito's stomach these gametocytes are transformed into gametes. The microgametocyte forms four or eight sperm cells, and the megagametocyte forms one egg. If a sperm unites with an egg, the resulting zygote burrows into the wall of the mosquito's stomach and divides, forming several thousand sporozoites. The sporozoites migrate through the body of the mosquito to the salivary glands after from ten to twenty days, and are in position to be transmitted to another human by the bite of the mosquito.

Two other species of *Plasmodium* affect humans. *Plasmodium malariae* causes quartan fever, which is much like tertian except that the cycles of merozoite release occur every three days instead of every two. *Plasmodium falciparum* causes malignant tertian fever in which the cycles recur every two days, but the infected corpuscles tend to form clumps and block the blood capillaries, causing serious complications, especially if the blocked capillaries are in vital organs.

Other Sporozoa

Other Sporozoa cause coccidiosis in many animals, red dysentery in cattle, and other diseases, notably blood diseases of several animals.

SUMMARY

The Protozoa include a highly diversified assembly of species, having in common the possession of a body not divided into separate cells. The usual interpretation is that the body consists of one cell. Dobell and some others prefer to consider the Protozoa noncellular, that is, comparable to the bodies of other animals except that separation of the body into cells does not occur. But the structure and cell division of Protozoa is so much like the structure and cell division of cells of other animals that the Protozoa are generally thought of as one-celled.

Protozoa are small in size compared with most other animals. Food may be absorbed through the cell membrane, as in *Plasmodium*, or taken in through a special organ, as in *Astasia* and *Paramecium*. Digestion is by enzymes, as in all organisms. Excretion and supply of oxygen is by diffusion through the cell membrane. In fresh-water forms, contractile vacuoles help prevent dilution by osmotic pressure. *Paramecium* has a coordinating neuromotor mechanism. Reproduction is by fission and in some forms, such as *Paramecium* and *Plasmodium*, by formation and fusion of gametes. Some protozoa are parasitic. Free-living protozoa live in both fresh and salt water, and some in damp soil. They are very numerous, and form an important link in the chain of food organisms between bacteria and algae on the one hand and larger animals on the other.

REVIEW QUESTIONS

1. Differentiate among the classes of Protozoa.
2. Describe the structure of *Astasia*.

3. How does *Astasia* secure its food?
4. How does *Astasia* reproduce?
5. What is a protozoan cyst?
6. Compare *Astasia* with a human white blood corpuscle.
7. Describe trypanosomes; leishmanias; Hypermastigina.
8. Describe the structure, physiology, and behavior of an ameba.
9. What are endamebas? radiolaria? foraminifera?
10. Describe the structure and physiology of *Paramecium*.
11. Describe reproduction in *Paramecium*.
12. Explain the idea of potential immortality of protozoa.
13. What is tissue culture?
14. What ciliates are parasitic?
15. Describe the life cycle of *Plasmodium vivax*.

GENERAL QUESTIONS

1. How does *Astasia*, with no nervous system, secure food and form cysts?
2. List the characteristics of protozoa which make them seem to be cellular, and those which make them seem to be non-cellular.
3. Is a human body a colony of cells?
4. Did the symbiosis of Hypermastigina and termites arise gratuitously?
5. Can the behavior of an ameba be explained on physical principles such as surface tension and osmotic pressure?
6. How does it happen that the shells of certain species of foraminifera are associated with oil-bearing strata?
7. Are the paramecium motorium and its branches parts of a nervous system?
8. Compare sexual reproduction in *Paramecium* with sexual reproduction in corn.
9. Evaluate the idea of potential immortality of protozoa.
10. Does the association of different kinds of cells into a complex organism destroy their potential immortality?
11. By assigning estimated probabilities to the survival of individuals at each stage of the *Plasmodium vivax* life cycle, and considering the rate of increase of individuals, determine whether you would predict that the species will increase, hold its own, or decrease in numbers.
12. Is there a causal connection between the absence of locomotor structures in Sporozoa and their parasitic habit?
13. Is the Phylum Protozoa as diverse a group as the Phylum Thallophyta? Should the Protozoa be broken into several phyla?
14. Why cannot protozoa be as large as cats?
15. What kinds of protozoa would you expect to find in damp soil?

CHAPTER 22

Coelenterata

METAZOA

In contrast to the Protozoa, consisting of animals whose bodies are composed of one cell only, all other animals have bodies composed of many cells. These many-celled animals are called **Metazoa.** Within the Metazoa two general divisions are recognized, the radial and the bilateral animals. The radial animals are radially symmetrical about a linear axis; that is, any plane passed through that central axis would divide the animal into two approximately equal halves. See Figure 22.1.

In contrast, the bilateral animals are symmetrical with respect to a median plane; that is, only one plane passed through the central axis would divide the animal into two approximately equal halves. Man is a bilaterally symmetrical animal. If a plane passes through the middle of his spinal column and through the middle of his breastbone, it would divide his body into similar, though not identical, right and left halves. But if the plane passed at any other angle, the two parts it divided would not be similar.

PORIFERA

In the sense used in this book, two phyla of animals are radially symmetrical: **Porifera** and **Coelenterata.** There are members of other phyla which become radial after having passed through bilateral stages, but they are here classed with the bilateral group.

The Porifera, or sponges, are not far beyond the colony stage of development and are not particularly typical of the chain of progressive specialization which may be traced through the animal kingdom. Hence, the sponges will not be discussed extensively in this book. The reader interested in them is encouraged to consult other accounts which describe this group more fully.

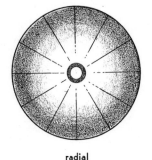

radial

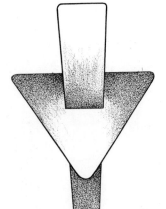

bilateral

Fig. 22.1   Radial and bilateral symmetry.

COELENTERATA

The Coelenterata are aquatic animals; many live in the ocean, a few in fresh water.

Hydra

The most frequently studied coelenterate is the freshwater hydra. In Greek mythology, Hydra was a fabulous creature that had the ability to grow two new heads wherever one head was cut off. The ability to restore lost parts possessed by the coelenterate now called hydra is described on pages 375–376.

The hydra commonly used in laboratories is *Pelmatohydra oligactis*. It consists of a hollow cylinder with tentacles at one end. The wall of the cylinder is composed of two layers of cells. The cylinder narrows to the base, which secretes an adhesive substance that temporarily fastens the animal to a solid surface. See Figure 22.2.

The hollow cavity in the cylinder is called the **gastrovascular cavity,** since it serves both as a digestive chamber and a circulatory medium. The cavity extends into the tentacles.

The body and tentacles are extremely contractile and extensible. There may be a variable number of tentacles, normally about five or six in young hydras, more in older ones. The tentacles are spread out in the water in which the animal lives; they capture prey and force it into the mouth, which opens through the top of the cylinder into the gastrovascular cavity.

The two layers of cells forming the wall of the body and tentacles are comparable to the two layers of cells formed in the early development of a human embryo. But the hydra cells are fully differentiated cells, whereas the human embryonic layers will elaborate further in later development. The outer layer of hydra cells, comparable to ectoderm, is called **epidermis;** and the inner layer of hydra cells, corresponding to endoderm, is called **gastrodermis.** Between the epidermis and gastrodermis is a thin, noncellular gelatinous material called **mesoglea.** It supports the body and holds the cells of the two layers together. (Figure 22.3.)

The majority of the cells of the epidermis and gastrodermis possess the characteristics of both epithelial and muscular tissue. They are tightly packed together, leaving no open spaces. They have large nuclei, and are able to secrete and excrete, digest, assimilate, and respire. The part of the cell next to the mesoglea is expanded parallel to the mesoglea layer, and contains contractile fibers like those of a visceral muscle cell of a human. The fibers of the epidermal cells run longitudinally and those of the gastrodermis cells run in a circular direction. Their contractions are coordinated by a relatively simple nervous system so that when the circular fibers contract, the hydra body and tentacles are reduced in diameter and greatly increased in length; when the longitudinal fibers contract, the body and tentacles are shortened in length and increased in diameter. See Figure 22.4.

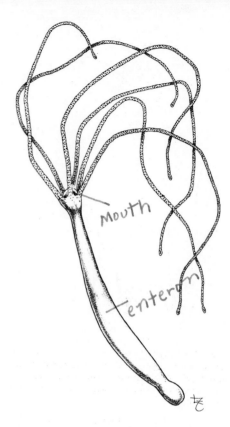

Fig. 22.2   *Hydra. This is a fresh-water animal.*

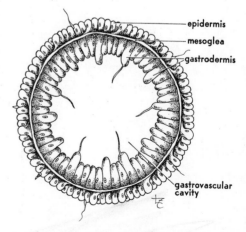

Fig. 22.3   Cross section through the body of a hydra. The body is composed of two layers of cells surrounding the gastrovascular cavity. Compare this with a human gastrula.

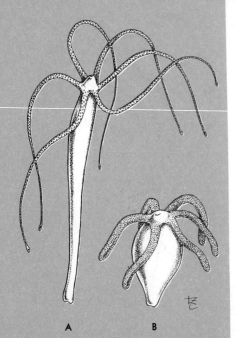

Fig. 22.4 *Hydra* may elongate or contract. Figure A shows a hydra in a normally elongated position. Figure B shows the form resulting from contraction after stimulation by some disturbance in the environment.

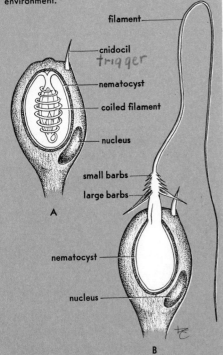

Fig. 22.5 *Hydra* nematocysts. A, Unexploded. B, Exploded.

The hydra nervous system is made of nerve cells each with several projections. These projections form synapses with projections of other cells, the whole system forming a netlike sheath at the bases of the epidermis cells on the outer side of the contractile fibers. The nerve cell projections are not distinguishable into dendrites and axons, since impulses may go in any direction through a cell. A few nerve cells are scattered among the gastrodermal cells also. There is some concentration of nerve cells at the mouth and at the base of the cylinder.

Sensory cells occur in the epidermis and in the gastrodermis. A sensory cell may have a protoplasmic hairlike projection especially sensitive to touch or to other stimuli. Projections from the base of a sensory cell go to contractile fibers or to synapses with nerve cells.

Scattered through the epidermis are the **mesenchyme** cells. These are relatively undifferentiated cells which may become more specialized cells. Some of them begin to form structures called **nematocysts.** As the development of a nematocyst proceeds, the mesenchyme cell forming it migrates to the outer edge of the epidermis. A nematocyst is a weapon somewhat resembling a harpoon in its action. It consists of a slender, hollow tube, sometimes with an expanded base, coiled up within the mesenchyme cell. A special projection, the **cnidocil,** protrudes beyond the margin of the epidermis. The wall of the cell, including that of the cnidocil, is normally impervious to water, so that no osmotic pressure is built up between the water outside and the more concentrated gelatinous material inside. But if some stimulus such as bending of the cnidocil on contact with another organism or the presence of acids in the water makes the cell wall more permeable, water enters the cell, exerts great pressure on the coiled thread, and explodes it into the surrounding medium. In being extruded from the cell, the nematocyst turns inside out, often revealing spines. The hollow tube of the nematocyst may be open at the far end, allowing the passage of a substance called **hypnotoxin,** which may paralyze small animals struck by the nematocyst. See Figure 22.5.

Several varieties of nematocysts have been described, all like the one discussed in the previous paragraph with minor variations. Those in a hydra are not dangerous to an organism as large as man, but some of the other coelenterates such as the Portuguese man-of-war (see Figure 22.6) may release enough potent toxin to cause severe pain, skin lesions, and prostration.

In the gastrodermis the cells are large, and many are

Fig. 22.6 Portuguese man-of-war. The animals in this colony grow on the long streamers hanging down from the float. A swimmer getting tangled with this colony may suffer severe injury.

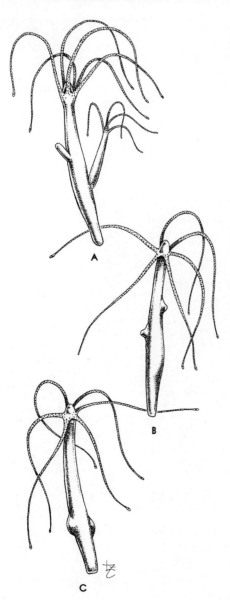

equipped with flagella, usually two to a cell. Many gastrodermal cells secrete mucus or enzymes which aid in the swallowing and digestion of food. Some mesenchyme cells and nerve cells occur in the gastrodermis, although not as abundantly as in the epidermis.

Food consists of animals captured by the tentacles aided by nematocysts. Tentacles force the food into the gastrovascular cavity through the expansible mouth. Insect larvae, small crustacea, even young fish and tadpoles may be eaten by hydras. Gastrodermal cells release enzymes into the cavity and digestion takes place. Digested products are absorbed and diffused to all cells of the body. Undigested remains are forced by contractions of the body back through the mouth to the outside.

Because all cells are exposed to water either outside of the body or in the gastrovascular cavity, exchange of oxygen and carbon dioxide and excretion of other wastes may occur directly through the cell membranes to the outside world. There is no special circulatory system; diffusion distributes food materials through the gastrovascular cavity and through the gastrodermis and mesoglea to the epidermis.

Reproduction in Hydra

Reproduction may be either asexual or sexual. In asexual reproduction, a small outpouching occurs in the wall of the hydra near the base of the cylinder. This outpouching, called a **bud,** is formed of both epidermis and gastrodermis, and a bay of the gastrovascular cavity extends into it. The bud grows into a small cylinder, and eventually begins to develop tentacles at the far end. Finally the bud takes on the appearance of a small hydra and separates off from the parent hydra; the opening into the gastrovascular cavity of the parent seals off, forming a base on the young hydra and normal wall cells on the large hydra. See Figure 22.7A.

In sexual reproduction, the hydra may develop either male or female reproductive organs or, in a few species, both. The male organs, or testes, are concentrations of mesenchyme cells between the epidermis and the gastrodermis. These concentrations cause the epidermis over them to bulge out into conspicuous mounds. See Figure 22.7B. Numerous sperm cells are formed by repeated mitotic divisions followed by meiosis. When the sperm cells are mature, they break through the epidermal covering and escape into the water.

Fig. 22.7 *Hydra* reproduction. **A,** Asexual reproduction by the formation of buds. **B,** *Hydra* with testes. **C,** *Hydra* with ovaries.

The female organs, or ovaries, develop in a similar position between the two cell layers. See Figure 22.7C. If a hydra is hermaphroditic, forming both testes and ovaries, the testes occur near the tentacles and the ovaries near the base. The mesenchyme cells in an ovary fuse with each other, forming a large cytoplasmic mass, the future egg, with one remaining functional nucleus. The other nuclei are digested and stored as food. The cell now undergoes meiosis, producing an egg and small polar bodies. When the egg is mature, the epidermis over it breaks open, exposing the egg.

The egg will die unless fertilization (union with a sperm cell) occurs. A fertilized egg will divide into many cells, which become arranged into two layers, ectoderm and endoderm. A thin, chitinous shell forms around the embryo. The embryo then drops off the parent and adheres to any solid object it contacts. After a period of several weeks the shell breaks open, releasing a young hydra with gastrovascular cavity and sprouts which elongate into tentacles.

Regeneration

The mesenchyme cells are able to replace lost or damaged cells, a process called **regeneration.** If a piece of a hydra is removed, it may be restored by differentiation of mesenchyme cells and shifting of other cells to fill the gap. If a hydra is split into two or more parts, each may rebuild a hydra provided the pieces are not too small. A piece $\frac{1}{6}$ of a millimeter in diameter is large enough to form the basis for a complete hydra. A piece of tentacle alone may not regenerate, but if a bit of the cylinder is included, a complete animal may be produced.

The first man to record a series of investigations on the regenerative powers of a hydra was Abraham Trembley, working from 1740 to 1744. He found that if the animal were split part way down the cylinder from the mouth to

Fig. 22.8   Regeneration in *Hydra*. In the upper row, a piece has been cut out of the middle of the hydra, and stages in its regeneration are shown. In the lower row, a hydra is slit down the middle as indicated by the dotted line. Regeneration results in a two-headed hydra. One of these is split, as indicated by the dotted line; and this forms two heads from one, and so on.

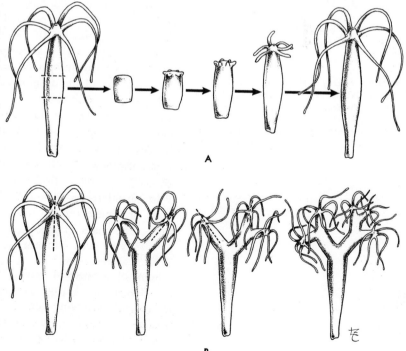

A

B

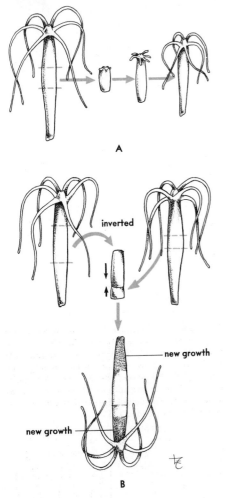

A

inverted

new growth

new growth

B

Fig. 22.9 Polarity in *Hydra*. **A,** A piece cut out of the middle of a hydra develops a head at the end nearer the original head. **B,** If two pieces are grafted together with their polarities in opposite directions, the larger piece dominates the smaller. What would happen if both pieces were the same size?

near the base, it would grow into a Y-shaped piece having two mouths and two sets of tentacles. Each of these may be split, and Trembley succeeded in producing a seven-headed hydra. See Figure 22.8B. He was also successful in grafting hydras and parts of hydras together into weird and unnatural shapes. He tried turning hydras inside out by pushing the base up through the mouth. Such animals restored normal shape by inverting themselves as soon as they were released. Then Trembley turned one inside out and prevented its re-inverting itself by pushing a bristle through it. The hydra later appeared to have restored its normal cellular arrangement. The gastrodermis and epidermis cells migrated back into their usual positions, passing each other on the way.

If hydras are squeezed through a fine mesh such as the silk bolting cloth used in sifting flour, the individual pieces are too small to regenerate separately. But if the pieces are collected into a heap, the gastrodermis cells initiate a process of aggregation which results in a reorganized hydra.

Polarity

One characteristic of regeneration in hydras deserves especial mention. If a slice is cut out of a hydra transversely, the end nearer the mouth forms a new mouth and tentacles, and the end nearer the base forms a new base. See Figure 22.9A. This feature is referred to as **polarity.** Something about the organization of the body affects its cells in such a way that there is a predisposition toward developing specific structures in specific places. This is comparable to the regulation of the development of new structures in the embryo of the animal.

If two slices are cut out of the same or different hydras and grafted together with the directions of their polarities opposite to each other (e.g. with the cut ends nearer the mouth placed together), one piece will dominate the other; normally the larger piece or the one nearer the original mouth will be dominant. See Figure 22.9B.

OTHER COELENTERATES

Obelia

Some of the coelenterates have a more complex life cycle than the hydra. Many have an alternation of generations somewhat resembling that in plants. The marine animal *Obelia*, for example, has an asexual stage composed of a colony of hydralike individuals connected by a branching two-layered tube of cells and bearing special reproductive individuals which bud off **medusae**. A medusa is an independent individual that breaks off and swims about. It has epidermis and gastrodermis, but the mesoglea is very much thicker than the cell layers, and changes the form of the organism without changing its fundamental structure. The medusa bears either testes or ovaries. Sperm cells and eggs are shed into the water. The zygote develops into a solid mass of cells of which the outer ones (ectoderm) are ciliated. This mass of cells is a **planula,** a larval stage which swims about and eventually settles down and develops into a new colony. See Figure 22.10.

Some biologists think that the hydras have lost the medusa stage from their life history, and are therefore a degenerate stage of coelenterate development. Yet this type of alternation of generations is not found in phyla of animals other than the coelenterates, and seems to involve complications which are a hazard and a handicap in a world where competition for available food and danger from predators require the greatest possible efficiency to ensure survival.

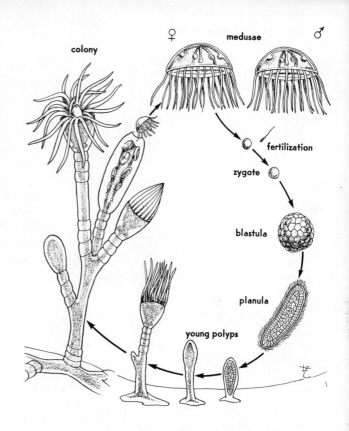

Fig. 22.10   Life cycle of *Obelia*. The colony at the left produces medusae by asexual budding; each medusa forms sperms or eggs, and these unite in the sea water. The zygote forms a swimming larva, which later settles down on a solid surface and forms a new colony.

Jellyfish

Some of the jellyfishes are examples of coelenterates which have medusa stages as the normal form, and lack any stage resembling a hydra.

Corals

The sea anemones and corals, like hydras, have no medusa stages. Corals are individual or colonial forms which secrete a hard platform or sheath around their bases. As the organisms grow, reproduce, and die, new individuals build on the bases of the old, and an accumulation of hard, calcareous material is built up. Corals live in relatively shallow marine waters, often along seacoasts or islands. Over thousands of years, immense masses of coral platforms are built, forming reefs and atolls. The Great Barrier Reef, along the northeast coast of Australia, is over 1200 miles long, between 10 and 90 miles wide, and about 180 feet deep.

Fig. 22.11 Several species of corals off the shore of one of the Bahamas.

Such reefs are a boon to coastwise shipping, since the waters between the reef and the shore are much more placid than the seas outside the reef. See Figure 22.11.

Many islands are formed when coral masses are raised above the level of the ocean. A large number of the Pacific islands are so built. Some limestones and marbles owe their origin to ancient deposits from coral colonies.

SUMMARY

The coelenterates represent a stage more complex than one-celled forms, having bodies composed of two layers of cells about a central gastrovascular cavity. Many coelenterates possess certain specialized features not found in other animal phyla, such as the plantlike alternation of generations and the nematocysts. They have certain primitive features such as radial symmetry, the noncentralization of the nervous system, and the union of epithelial and muscular components in one cell. They have characteristics which will be more fully elaborated in other phyla, such as a digestive cavity into which enzymes are secreted, and special reproductive organs which form eggs and sperm cells. And finally they possess characteristics common to all Metazoa, such as undifferentiated mesenchyme cells and division of labor among specialized tissues.

REVIEW QUESTIONS

1. Define: Metazoa; radial symmetry; bilateral symmetry.
2. What are porifera?
3. Describe the structure and physiology of a hydra.
4. Describe reproduction in a hydra.
5. Explain regeneration.
6. What is polarity?
7. Describe an *Obelia* colony.
8. Describe alternation of generations in *Obelia*.
9. What are jellyfish?
10. Describe corals; of what economic importance are they?

GENERAL QUESTIONS

1. What advantages does radial symmetry confer upon an animal? What advantages does bilateral symmetry confer upon an animal?
2. What part of a sponge animal is the commercial sponge?
3. Is there a valid distinction between the terms "gastrodermis" and "endoderm"?
4. If humans possessed nematocysts, in which organ system would you include them?
5. How does it happen that some cells in a hydra differentiate into specialized cells, and some cells remain undifferentiated mesenchyme?

6. What causes the epidermis and gastrodermis cells to migrate to their normal positions when an inverted hydra has a bristle through it?
7. Compare and contrast alternation of generations in *Obelia* and fern.
8. Contrast trichocysts and nematocysts.
9. Is there a causal relation between radial symmetry, the lack of centralization in the nervous system, and the capacity of nerve cells to carry impulses in any direction?
10. If coral animals are marine, how can coral atolls appear above the ocean surface?

CHAPTER 23

Platyhelminthes and Nemathelminthes

BILATERAL METAZOA

The bilateral animals have developed a greater degree of complexity than the radial animals. The two layers of cells, epidermis and gastrodermis, are separated by a third, intermediate cell mass, developed from an embryonic cell layer called **mesoderm,** in the bilateral forms. The nervous system is somewhat more differentiated, having a concentration of cells in one place, and fibers connecting this with other parts of the body. In addition to the distinction between ventral and dorsal sides, the ventral being that which has the mouth, bilateral animals have distinct anterior and posterior ends. The anterior end is usually that end leading the way in locomotion; the concentration of nerve cells is near the anterior end, and specialized sense organs are more common at the anterior end than elsewhere. With increased complexity of the body due to the differentiation of the intermediate mass of cells, additional organ systems appear. Muscle fibers become separated from epithelial cells and form muscle cells. An excretory system develops, and in some animals special circulatory and respiratory systems arise. Reproductive cells enter the intermediate cell mass and are organized into reproductive organs with ducts and other accessory structures. Increasing specialization of cell structure and activity characterizes bilateral animals; this differentiation may often be traced back to the very early embryonic development of the animal from a zygote.

This chapter is concerned especially with two phyla of animals representing the simplest of the bilateral groups: the flatworms, or **Platyhelminthes,** and the roundworms, or **Nemathelminthes.**

PLATYHELMINTHES

Classes of Flatworms

Among the flatworms are recognized three classes. The **Turbellaria** possess an epidermis which is usually ciliated; they all have a digestive tract. The **Trematoda** have no cellular epidermis, but a secreted sheath, the **cuticle;** they also have a digestive tract. The **Cestoda** have neither epidermis nor digestive system, but have a cuticle like that of the Trematoda. The Turbellaria are almost all free-living animals, inhabiting the oceans, fresh water, and moist land. The Trematoda, or flukes, and the Cestoda, or tapeworms, are all parasitic on other animals.

TURBELLARIA

Planaria

Dugesia tigrina, the common fresh-water planaria, is a representative of the Turbellaria. It is a long, narrow, flattened animal, rather heavily pigmented in splotches, living in warm ponds and rivers. See Figure 23.1.

Adults are from half an inch to an inch long. The anterior end is distinguishable as a head, with a rounded snout, and a triangular projection, the **auricle,** on each side. The body is long, with a tapering, pointed posterior end.

Epidermis

The epidermis consists of a single layer of cuboidal cells. Cilia characterize the cells on the ventral surface, the lateral edges, and the lateral portions of the dorsal surface. By means of the beating of these cilia the animal glides over solid objects or along the underside of the surface of the water in which it lives. As in *Paramecium*, a system of fibers connects the bases of the cilia in each cell, and aids in coordinating the ciliary beating. Numerous glands secrete mucus onto the surface of the epidermis. This mucus furnishes a heavy medium in which the cilia beat, and protects the epidermis from friction against hard surfaces.

Digestive Cavity

The mouth is located at about the middle of the ventral surface; it is lined with epithelium and possesses muscle fibers which open and close it. The gastrovascular cavity of the planaria is divided into a **pharynx,** into which the mouth opens, and a lobulated intestine.

The pharynx is a highly muscular, cylindrical structure which may be protruded through the mouth to the outside of the body; moved about in grasping food; and retracted within the body again.

The intestine branches from the anterior end of the pharynx. One lobe extends anteriorly and two lobes posteriorly. Each lobe has blind pouches projecting laterally from

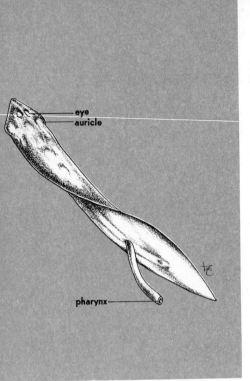

Fig. 23.1 Shape of *Dugesia*. The pharynx is shown extended.

it. See Figure 23.2. The lining of the intestine is composed of tall, columnar cells with rounded ends projecting into the intestinal cavity.

Mesodermal Tissues

Between the epidermis and the digestive tract is the intermediate mass of cells, largely connective tissue. This connective tissue has interlacing fibers, fibroblasts, and mesenchyme cells. This tissue serves to aid in the distribution of digested food and dissolved gases and in the excretion of waste products. It also stores food substances. A planaria may go without food for many months, in which case the connective tissue practically disappears.

Running through the connective tissue are muscles and excretory and reproductive organs. Pigment granules are distributed about the connective tissue, giving a mottled appearance to the planaria. A thin sheet of connective tissue fibers, the basement membrane, separates the intermediate mass of cells from the epidermis and from the gastrodermis.

At the outer border of the connective tissue, between it and the basement membrane, there are two bands of muscle fibers, an outer band with fibers running circularly around the animal, and an inner band with fibers running longitudinally. Traversing the connective tissue more deeply are dorsoventral, transverse, and longitudinal muscle fibers. See Figure 23.3. These muscles may be used in locomotion and in turning.

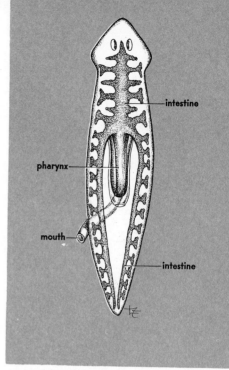

Fig. 23.2 *Dugesia* digestive system. The mouth opens into a protrusible pharynx, which leads to the three-lobed intestine. How do waste materials get out of the intestine?

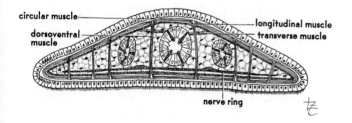

Fig. 23.3 *Dugesia* musculature. Cross section showing some of the muscles. When the animal turns itself over, which muscles does it use?

Nervous System

Just external and just internal to the two bands of muscles near the epidermis are two networks of nerve fibers. The nerve cells of which these fibers are branches are associated with each other by synapses. The inner network is much more conspicuous than the outer. The inner network has two parallel condensations, the right and left ventral

Fig. 23.4 Nervous system of *Dugesia*. There are two conspicuous ventral nerve cords connected by rings and giving off branches. At the anterior end is the brain, connecting the two cords and having branches from the head. Contrast this with the nervous system of *Hydra*.

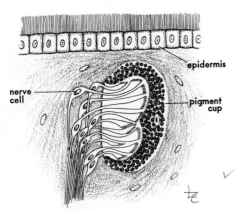

Fig. 23.5 Structure of the *Dugesia* eye. The nerve cells have dendrites imbedded in the pigment cup. These dendrites are sensitive to light. The dendrites respond to light impulses with nerve impulses which pass through the nerve cells to the brain of the planaria.

nerve cords, running longitudinally from the anterior to the posterior end of the animal. At regular intervals branches of these ventral nerve cords form rings running transversely around the animal just within the muscular layers. Near the anterior end the ventral nerve cords connect to a two-lobed enlargement called the **brain.** The brain and ventral nerve cords are supplied with especially numerous connections to parts of the head. See Figure 23.4.

The epidermal cells are sensitive to touch. A special strand of cells along each auricle samples the water as cilia drive it over the surface. The finding of food and avoidance of harmful substances is facilitated by these areas on the auricles. The anterior tip of the head and the tip of the pharynx are also sensitive to food substances, but only on contact; the auricles thus have a sense of smell, and the head and pharynx a sense of taste.

The head also bears two light-sensitive bodies, the eyes. Each eye has nerve endings of a bulbous type in the hollow of a heavily pigmented cup of cells. See Figure 23.5.

Muscular locomotion ceases when the brain is removed, unless strong external stimuli are applied to the body. The waves of muscular contraction are coordinated by the nervous system. If the ventral nerve cords are cut, muscular locomotion occurs only in the part of the animal in which the nerves are still connected to the brain.

In addition to receiving sensory impulses from the eyes and auricles and to affecting muscular movement, the brain seems to have some slight capacity for learning. Experiments on a Turbellarian show that normally light stimulates movement and darkness stimulates quiescence. An animal was put in the light; every time it started to move, it was touched on the anterior end of the head and stopped. The more this was carried on, the less often did the animal attempt to move in the light. Animals with brains removed continued to try to move regardless of the interference at the anterior end of the head.

Excretory System

The so-called excretory system consists of a network of tiny tubules in each lateral half of the animal. The tubules open to the surface through many fine pores scattered about in the epidermis. Terminal branches of the tubules in the intermediate mass of cells end in **flame cells.** Each flame cell is a deep, cup-shaped structure with long, flickering cilia projecting from the base of the cup into the cavity between the walls of the cup. See Figure 23.6.

The flame cells and tubules collect and force out the excess water diffusing into the animal. In this respect they resemble the contractile vacuoles of fresh-water Protozoa. Marine Turbellaria have an excretory system much less elaborate than fresh-water flatworms, or in some cases none at all. In marine flatworms some waste products are washed away by the water leaving the excretory system through pores in the epidermis. Other waste products are diffused out by epidermal cells, or by gastrodermal cells into the digestive tract from which they are eliminated through the mouth.

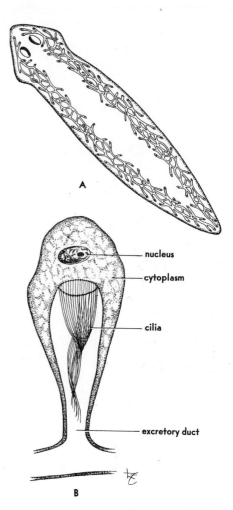

Reproductive System

In the planaria, the full complement of reproductive organs appears only when a period of warm weather follows an extended time of cold, such as spring and early summer. At other times the reproductive organs are much reduced.

A pair of ovaries is found near the anterior end of the animal in the connective tissue layer. These are relatively small. Each ovary is separated by a thin membrane from a chamber just behind it, the **seminal receptacle.** From here a long oviduct reaches to the single **copulatory chamber** near the posterior end. Many small **yolk glands** open into each oviduct along its path.

In addition to the two oviducts, the copulatory chamber receives two sperm ducts. Each sperm duct branches out to connect with many testes. The copulatory chamber has one opening to the outside.

At the time of sexual maturity, two flatworms may come together with the copulatory chambers apposed. The sperm ducts end in a bulblike projection, the **penis,** which may be extended from one worm into the copulatory chamber of the other, releasing sperm cells. These sperm cells travel up the oviducts to the seminal receptacles. Each worm thus supplies the other with sperm cells; cross-fertilization is thus accomplished, even though one animal produces both sperms and eggs.

As the eggs mature, they break through the membrane into the seminal receptacle and are there fertilized. The fertilized eggs pass down the oviduct, receiving yolk cells as they go. In the copulatory chamber a capsule is formed, enclosing several eggs and many yolk cells. This capsule passes to the outside and is fastened to some solid object such as a rock by a short stalk secreted by the walls of the copulatory chamber. After several weeks the eggs hatch into tiny worms resembling the parents except in size and sexual maturity.

Fig. 23.6 Turbellarian excretory system. **A** shows the pattern of the tubules and flame cells. **B** shows the structure of one flame cell. How does this compare with the human excretory system?

Asexual Reproduction

A planaria also may reproduce asexually. During the summer, when the animal grows to a certain size, the posterior end may adhere to some solid surface such as a rock, and the anterior end continue swimming. Then the planaria pulls into two at a transverse plane just behind the pharynx. Each piece then differentiates replacements for the structures it lost, and two smaller worms result from the fission of one large worm.

Regeneration

The ability to form lost parts readily is also demonstrated in restoration of wounded animals. This ability to regenerate or restore lost or damaged structures may be shown by a variety of experiments. If an animal is cut into two approximately equal parts, each will heal the cut surface by contraction of muscles, bringing the edges of the wound toward each other, and by the gliding of epidermal cells across the break, closing the wound. Then each part builds the structures it lost. Rebuilding is accomplished partly by extension of organs already there, such as the intestine or the nerve cords, and partly by the differentiation of mesenchyme cells which migrate to the wound area in considerable numbers.

Like hydras, planarias retain polarity. A transverse cut through a planaria produces two pieces; the anterior piece will develop a new tail at the cut surface; the posterior piece will form a new head at its cut surface. If a small section is cut out of the planaria, it will usually grow a head at the most anterior part left, and a tail at the most posterior part. A very small piece cut out of the side of an animal may form a head at the cut surface rather than the anterior end. See Figure 23.7.

Exposure to X-rays before cutting will diminish or inhibit regeneration. It is known that mesenchyme cells are especially sensitive to X-rays, and it is probable that damage to the mesenchyme is responsible for the loss of regenerative ability after X-radiation.

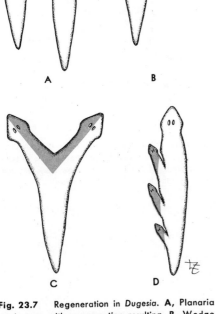

Fig. 23.7 Regeneration in *Dugesia*. **A,** Planaria cut in two, with regeneration resulting. **B,** Wedge cut from a planaria, with regeneration resulting at the cut edge. **C,** Planaria split part way down the middle, with regeneration following. **D,** Planaria with diagonal slits cut into the side, and regeneration resulting.

TREMATODA

The trematodes, or flukes, are all parasitic animals, most of which possess suckers by which they adhere to their hosts. Flukes have a cuticle, but no epidermis. Unlike the cestodes, they do have digestive tracts.

Liver Fluke

Opisthorchis sinensis, the Chinese liver fluke, is one example of the Trematoda. Adult worms live in the smaller bile passages in the liver of humans or other mammals. Unless it clogs one of the larger bile ducts, one fluke may not cause serious damage. But often an infected human or animal may have many flukes — up to a hundred or more. One human was found to have 21,000 liver flukes.

The Chinese liver fluke tapers toward the anterior end, which has a sucker at the tip. The posterior end is somewhat more rounded. See Figure 23.8.

About a quarter of the way back from the anterior end, on the ventral surface, is a second sucker. This sucker is a cuplike depression with very muscular walls. By applying the edge of the cup to some object such as the wall of a bile passage, and retracting the center of the sucker by muscles, the fluke gets the effect of a suction cup which is not easily dislodged.

The cuticle is fairly thick; it is a protein secreted by mesenchyme cells. Layers of circular, longitudinal, and diagonal muscles lie just inside the cuticle, but these are thin and weak. The adult worm fastens onto liver tissues and does not move about much.

The nervous system is much like that of the planaria in structure. A brain just behind the front sucker is connected to two ventral longitudinal nerve cords, which have lateral branches supplying various parts of the body. Aside from those of the sense of touch, the fluke has no well-developed sense organs.

The mouth is located in the center of the anterior sucker. The mouth opens into a muscular pharynx, which in turn leads to a short esophagus. The esophagus opens into a pair of intestinal lobes. Each lobe runs almost the entire length of one side of the animal, and ends blindly. There are no side branches such as those in the planaria. See again Figure 23.8.

A pair of excretory tubules runs through the anterior two thirds of the body, collecting wastes from flame cells on a limited number of branches of the tubules. These two tubules unite into a common tube which passes along the midline through the posterior third of the animal and empties by a pore at the posterior end.

Reproduction in Liver Flukes

In the Chinese liver fluke, as in most trematodes other than the blood flukes, reproductive organs of both sexes

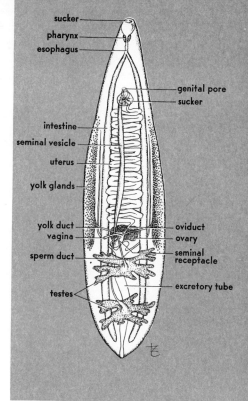

Fig. 23.8   Structure of *Opisthorchis sinensis*.

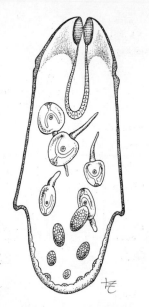

Fig. 23.9 *Opisthorchis* redia. Cercariae are developing inside.

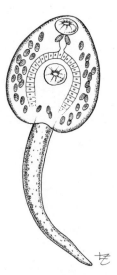

Fig. 23.10 *Opisthorchis* cercaria. The head will develop into the adult fluke, and the tail will be lost.

occur in one animal. There is a pair of much-branched testes near the posterior end of the body. The two sperm ducts leading from these run forward, unite, and enlarge into a **seminal vesicle,** which empties through a genital pore just anterior to the second sucker.

The single, lobed ovary is located somewhat anterior to the testes and is much smaller than a testis. The oviduct leaves the ovary and turns forward, soon enlarging into the uterus. The oviduct is connected also to the seminal receptacle, a storage chamber which receives sperm through a short vagina leading in from the dorsal surface. The oviduct also receives two yolk ducts, one collecting from the numerous scattered yolk glands on each side of the animal. The uterus coils back and forth throughout the middle of the body, and finally empties at the same genital pore which serves as an outlet for the sperm duct.

Normally a fluke does not fertilize itself. When two mature flukes come together, the sperm cells of one are transferred from its sperm duct to the vagina of the other, and are stored in the seminal receptacle. Then, as the ovary releases eggs into the oviduct, these eggs are fertilized, receive yolk material, and pass into the uterus. Here a shell is deposited around the egg and yolk, now an embryo, since the fertilized egg is undergoing cell divisions.

The embryos released from the genital pore enter the bile duct of the host, from which they reach the intestine and are eventually shed with the feces. If the embryos reach the river either in sewage or by being deposited there or washed into it, the embryos may be eaten by certain kinds of snails. Within the snails, an embryo escapes from its shell and burrows through the intestinal wall into the tissues of the snail; here the embryo develops into several larvae called **rediae.** See Figure 23.9.

A redia is an elongated larva with a cuticle, muscle layers, and connective tissue. There is a mouth at the anterior end. The mouth opens into a short pharynx, which leads to a simple, saclike intestine. A few flame cells open into short excretory tubes, which empty through pores. A small brain in the region of the pharynx is connected to nerve trunks. Within the connective tissue of the redia develop a number of more complex larvae called **cercariae.** See Figures 23.9 and 23.10.

Each cercaria has an oval body somewhat like that of an adult fluke, and a long tail with membranous fins. The body has a cuticle with some spines projecting from it. Muscle layers underlie the cuticle. Two suckers occur; the mouth opens through the anterior sucker. The mouth leads into a pharynx, which opens into a two-lobed intestine. Flame cells lead to a pair of excretory tubes, which unite into a common bladder at the posterior end of the body, opening by two pores in the tail. The nervous system consists of a brain and two ventral nerve cords with branches. Two kinds of glands occur in the connective tissue: cyst-forming glands near the cuticle and penetration glands just posterior to the pharynx.

The cercaria wriggles out of the snail and swims in the water by means of its tail. If it finds a fish of certain species in the carp family, it may work its way into the skin of that fish. The penetration glands secrete a substance which softens the scales of the fish, and the tail pushes the body of the cercaria into the fish's flesh. The cercaria tail drops off, and the body becomes enclosed in a cyst secreted by the cyst-forming glands. There the young worm remains until the fish dies. If the flesh of the fish is eaten by some animal such as a human, a dog, or a cat, the fluke is released in the host's intestine, and crawls up the bile duct to its home in the liver, where it becomes sexually mature.

Animals which eat raw fish infected with the fluke may get many parasites. Even cooking the fish does not insure protection, for it has been found that some Opisthorchis cysts survive roasting or boiling for fifteen minutes.

In China and some neighboring countries, where human feces are used as fertilizer in flooded rice fields, the incidence of liver fluke infection is quite high. Attempts to destroy the worm usually take the form of doing away with the snails which serve as hosts to the rediae.

Other Trematodes

Among other trematodes parasitic in man are intestinal flukes, lung flukes, and blood flukes. The intestinal fluke cysts are found on edible water plants. Lung fluke cysts occur in crabs. Blood fluke cercariae attack humans directly, boring into the skin of a man wading or swimming in the water. Rice field workers are particularly susceptible to infection with blood flukes.

CESTODA

Pork Tapeworm

All adult cestodes, or tapeworms, are parasitic in the intestines of vertebrates. One of the best known tapeworms is *Taenia solium*, the pork tapeworm, parasitic in humans. An adult Taenia may be ten feet or more in length. It consists of a small anterior knob, the **scolex,** a short slender

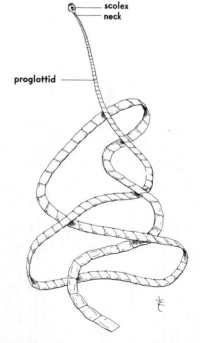

Fig. 23.11   *Taenia solium.* This tapeworm may reach a length of ten feet in the human intestine.

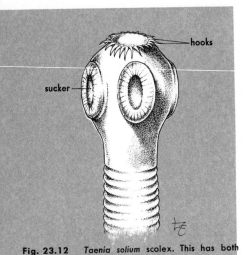

Fig. 23.12 *Taenia solium* scolex. This has both hooks and suckers by which it may be attached to the intestinal lining of its host.

Fig. 23.13 Nervous system of *Taenia*. There are ten longitudinal nerve trunks bound together by cross connections in each proglottid.

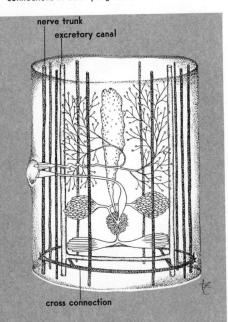

neck, and a series of gradually enlarging segments known as **proglottids.** See Figure 23.11.

The scolex has four muscular suckers placed at ninety-degree intervals around the equator of the scolex. Anterior to the suckers is a ring of spines. See Figure 23.12.

The neck is short, and somewhat narrower than the scolex. Proglottids develop at the posterior end of the neck, so that the smallest and youngest proglottids are the anterior ones nearest the neck, whereas those farther back are older and larger. Each proglottid contains a complete set of male and female reproductive organs. These mature as the proglottid gets older, and after fertilization of the eggs, the zygotes accumulate in an old proglottid. These proglottids full of embryos eventually separate from the posterior end of the worm and are passed from the digestive tract of the host with the feces. Thus old proglottids are constantly being lost at the posterior end of the body, and new ones added at the neck.

There is no epidermis, but the tapeworm has a cuticle. As in the flukes, the circular and longitudinal muscle layers immediately underlie the cuticle. The inner organs of the tapeworm are packed in connective tissue containing mesenchyme cells. Muscles traverse this connective tissue.

The nervous system consists of a brain in the scolex from which a few nerves go to the rest of the scolex and ten longitudinal nerve trunks pass through the neck and proglottids just inside of the muscle layers. Two of these trunks are ventral, two are dorsal, and three run along each lateral side. Tapeworms have no special sense organs. See Figure 23.13.

Tapeworms have no digestive tract. Since they live in the digestive tract of their host, their food is digested and ready for them to absorb directly into their tissues.

The excretory system has flame cells which are connected to excretory tubes running the length of the animal. There are two ventral tubes near the lateral margins of the body, and two much smaller dorsal tubes also near the sides of the body. The ventral tubes have cross connections near the posterior border of each proglottid. In the first formed proglottid at the posterior end of the animal, the two ventral excretory tubes join into a bladder which empties by one pore. When this proglottid is shed, the two ventral tubes open separately at the places where they were broken off by the loss of the end proglottid. The dorsal tubes do not reach to the posterior end of the worm. In the scolex the dorsal and ventral tubes are connected by a network of excretory vessels.

Reproduction in Tapeworms

The reproductive systems in each proglottid reach maturity as the proglottid gets older and farther from the neck. The testes are numerous, scattered throughout the connective tissue in the proglottid. Ducts from these testes collect into a single sperm duct, which empties by a genital pore at one side of the proglottid.

The single bilobed ovary is near the posterior end of the proglottid. The short oviduct connects with a vagina coming from the same genital pore which received the sperm duct. The oviduct also receives the duct from the yolk gland and the duct from the shell gland, and then passes anteriorly into the uterus. See Figure 23.14.

Sperm cells from the testes may fertilize eggs from the same proglottid, eggs from a different proglottid of the same worm, or eggs from a different worm. The sperm cells are transferred from the sperm duct through the genital pore to the vagina. At the junction of the vagina and the oviduct the sperm and egg cells meet and a zygote is formed. A yolk cell and a shell are added, and the embryo is pushed into the uterus. This is a blind sac which extends longitudinally forward in the proglottid and, as it accumulates embryos, branches laterally with up to ten branches on each side. As the uterus expands, the other reproductive organs degenerate, until the proglottid contains little else in its connective tissue except the swollen uterus. In this condition the proglottid breaks off and passes to the outside with the feces of the host. See Figure 23.15.

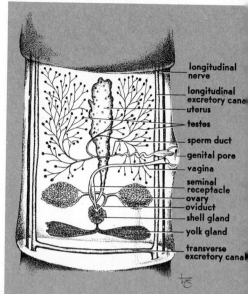

longitudinal nerve
longitudinal excretory canal
uterus
testes
sperm duct
genital pore
vagina
seminal receptacle
ovary
oviduct
shell gland
yolk gland
transverse excretory canal

Fig. 23.14 Mature proglottid of *Taenia solium*. Each proglottid has both male and female reproductive organs. Can one proglottid fertilize itself?

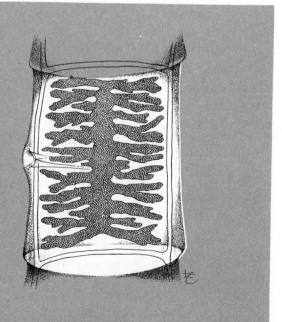

Fig. 23.15 *Taenia solium* ripe proglottid, ready to be separated from the worm. The proglottid contains young embryos.

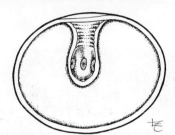

Fig. 23.16 *Taenia solium* cysticercus. The young worm is encased in the capsule. When the capsule is dissolved away, the young worm turns inside out, bringing the suckers and hooks into position to fasten to the lining of its host's intestine.

The embryo forms a mass of cells carrying six hooks and having a pair of flame cells. If a pig swallows the proglottid, or the embryo after the tissues of the proglottid have disintegrated, the embryo sheds its membranes in the pig's intestine. It then squeezes through the intestinal wall of the pig, and travels through the circulatory system to some muscle. Here it leaves the circulation and forms a **cysticercus** in the pig's muscle.

A cysticercus is an enlarged larva in which a fluid-filled cavity develops. Into this cavity the wall projects at one place, forming a scolex with its suckers turned toward the inside. See Figure 23.16.

If a human eats meat from an infected pig, he may swallow a small cysticercus. If the worm has not been killed by thorough cooking, the scolex will become everted so that the suckers and hooks are on the outside, and such a worm may fasten to the wall of the host's intestine and begin to form proglottids. The walls of the larval cavity in which the scolex was originally contained may be shed as the proglottids develop.

The pork tapeworm may do little serious harm in the human except for the possibility of blocking the intestine because of its mass or allowing other infections to get started because of the damage done to the intestinal wall by its hooks. However, if a man infects himself with the larvae, the development of cysticerci in some tissues such as the eye produces serious damage. Perhaps the presence of larval tapeworms in pigs was partly responsible for the opposition of ancient Jews and Egyptians to the eating of pork.

NEMATHELMINTHES

Characteristics of Roundworms

The roundworms include both free-living and parasitic forms. They are relatively inconspicuous but very numerous. One authority has suggested that if all the earth and its inhabitants except for roundworms should suddenly vanish, yet the hills and valleys, rivers and lakes, plains and seas, even the plants and animals would be present as roundworm-filled ghosts, and a nematologist could identify the former living organisms and the type of terrain from the roundworms present. It has been estimated that half a million species of roundworms occur, of which less than ten thousand are now known.

Roundworms have a cylindrical body tapered at each end. The body is long, but not segmented. The number of cells seems to be definite and limited for the animals in this phylum, each organ or tissue having a specific normal number of nuclei. (The digestive tract is a one-way affair, having a mouth at the anterior end and an anus at or near the posterior end of the animal.) The tract is surrounded by a body cavity which is not, strictly speaking, a celom, for it is bounded externally by mesodermal structures and internally by the endodermal intestine rather than entirely by mesodermal derivatives.

Ascaris

While many of the roundworms are less than a milli-meter in length, a few are much larger. The forms parasitic in mammals are usually larger than free-living forms. One of the largest, *Ascaris lumbricoides*, may serve as a con-venient example of the roundworms because of its size, although it is not as typical as a smaller, free-living form would be.

Ascaris lumbricoides is parasitic in the intestines of humans and of some other mammals. There is some question whether the Ascaris found in pigs is the same species or not. There are no apparent structural distinctions in human and pig ascarides, but the eggs from the worm in the human will not develop in the pig, and vice versa. Whether this indicates a physiological difference important enough to make separate species, or whether it is a transitional stage toward differentiation into species is a matter of individual opinion at present.

Ascaris has separate sexes. The male worms may reach a length of ten inches, and the female worms may be as much as fifteen or sixteen inches long. The anterior end of an Ascaris is marked by three rounded lips, one dorsal and the others ventrolateral. The posterior end of the female tapers nearly to a point. The anus is just anterior to that point on the ventral side. The posterior end of the male ascaris is curved in a semicircle, with the anus on the ventral side not quite at the tip of the worm. See Figure 23.17.

The surface of the body is very smooth, covered with a cuticle. The cuticle has an outer, horny layer very resistant to digestive enzymes, and an inner layer of connective tissue fibers. Internal to the cuticle is an epithelial layer of proto-plasm containing many nuclei but not divided into separate cells by cell membranes. This **syncytium** bulges into longi-tudinal cords in the middorsal, midventral, and midlateral lines, making four conspicuous bands. Between these bands

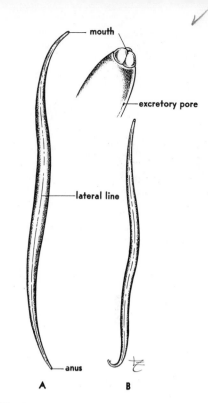

A   B

Fig. 23.17   *Ascaris.* A, Female; B, Male.

round worms in library.

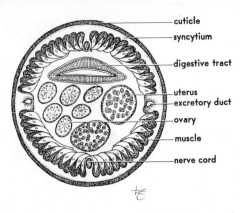

cuticle
syncytium
digestive tract
uterus
excretory duct
ovary
muscle
nerve cord

Fig. 23.18 Cross section through the body of *Ascaris*. The body cavity is not a true celom.

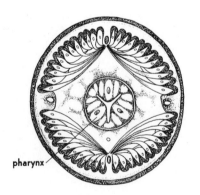

pharynx

Fig. 23.19 Cross section through *Ascaris* in the pharynx region. Notice the muscles in the pharynx wall.

are the four longitudinal muscle bands, two dorsolateral and two ventrolateral. See Figure 23.18.

Near the anterior end is a nerve ring associated with several clusters of nerve cells, or ganglia, encircling the pharynx. From this ring nerves extend forward to the anterior tip of the worm. A main ventral nerve trunk extends posteriorly from the nerve ring along the ventral syncytial cord. This ventral nerve trunk has several ganglia. In the lateral and dorsal syncytial cords occur other nerve trunks. The two lateral ones carry sensory fibers, and the dorsal one motor fibers. Ventrolateral and dorsolateral nerves are also connected to the nerve ring.

Motor impulses go to the longitudinal muscle bands through the ventral and dorsal nerve trunks alternately, so that when the dorsolateral muscles are contracting the ventrolateral muscles are not, and vice versa. Thus the movements of the animal are in a dorsoventral plane.

Nerve endings in the skin are usually at thin places in the cuticle, and pores through the cuticle allow for sensitivity to chemicals as well as touch.

The digestive tract consists of a mouth, pharynx, intestine, rectum, and anus. See Figure 23.20A. The intestine is the only part not lined with cuticle.

The pharynx is muscular and contains a few glands. Its wall is thickened in three places corresponding to the lips, so that the cavity of the pharynx is a three-rayed space. See Figure 23.19.

The intestine occupies most of the length of the body. Its wall is composed of a single layer of gastrodermis. It digests and absorbs food obtained from the host.

The rectum is relatively short. In males it receives the reproductive canal, and the anus serves as an outlet for undigested materials and for sperm cells as well. In the females the reproductive outlet is separate from that of the digestive tract.

The excretory system consists of a tubule in each lateral syncytial cord and a network connecting these two tubules near the anterior end. From this connecting network a canal runs to an excretory pore in the midventral line near the anterior end of the body. Wastes diffuse into the tubules from the body cavity.

Reproduction in Ascaris

The male reproductive system consists of a single very long coiled tube. See Figure 23.20B. The first part of the tube is the testis, very slender. It has a large cell near the tip from which sperm cells are budded off. The sperm cells are amebalike in their movements. They pass along the sperm duct, which appears like a slightly larger continuation of the testis. The sperm duct eventually enlarges a little more into the seminal vesicle, which leads in turn to the rectum. Associated with the sperm outlet are two spicules. These are modifications of the cuticle operated by muscles and serving during copulation to spread open the walls of the female reproductive pore.

The female reproductive system consists of two long coiled tubes. See Figure 23.20C. The first part of each tube is a very slender ovary. This opens into a slightly enlarged oviduct. Eventually the oviduct leads to the somewhat thicker uterus. The uterus is a storage place of sperm cells which fertilize the eggs arriving there. The uterus also adds yolk and a shell to each fertilized egg. The two uteri unite into a short common portion which leads to the cuticle-lined vagina. The vagina is also short, and opens to the outside through a midventral pore about a third of the way back from the anterior end of the worm.

A female ascaris may lay as many as 200,000 eggs a day. The eggs are shed into the intestinal cavity of the host, and reach the outside world in the feces. The eggs develop in the open, still enclosed in the egg shell, forming tiny worms. If these are swallowed by a suitable host, they crawl through the host's intestinal wall into the blood stream, and travel through the liver and heart to the lungs. Here they leave the blood vessels and enter the lung cavity. Then they make their way up the trachea, into the pharynx, and down the esophagus, through the stomach, and back to the intestine again.

In the early development of an ascaris embryo, some cells are destined to become reproductive tissues. These retain the full complement of chromosome material. Others lose portions of the chromatin during mitosis, and these form the other tissues of the body. The number of cells in each structure, such as a muscle band or a nerve ganglion, is definitely established in early embryology, and mitoses stop except for the reproductive system. In later growth the cells may enlarge considerably, but do not divide again.

Ascaris, like other roundworms, has no cilia. It also has no chitin except for the shells of the eggs. These egg shells, especially the fatty coats, are so resistant that they are not only unaffected by enzymes of the host, but also are not penetrated by some of the most virulent poisons, such as 12% formalin, saturated mercuric chloride, 9% sulfuric

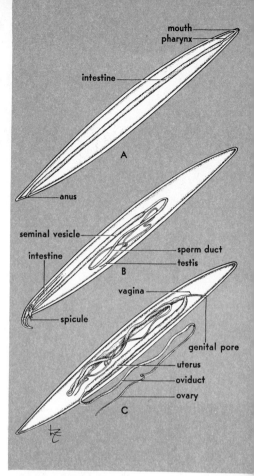

Fig. 23.20   *Ascaris* digestive and reproductive systems. **A,** Digestive tract; **B,** Male reproductive system; **C,** Female reproductive system.

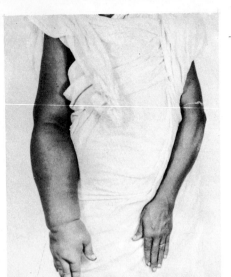

Fig. 23.21 Filarial elephantiasis of arm (*Wuchereria bancrofti*).

acid, or 14% hydrochloric acid. They need the stimulus of an alkaline medium, such as is found in the host intestine, in order to hatch.

Other Parasitic Roundworms

Other parasitic roundworms attacking humans include hookworms and pinworms in the intestine, guinea worms under the skin, trichina worms in muscles, and filarias in the lymph vessels. The filarias are transmitted by mosquitoes, and congregate in lymph vessels, which they may block off completely. This prevents normal drainage of fluid back into the blood system, and the vessel and the tissues around it may swell enormously, producing a condition known as elephantiasis. See Figure 23.21.

SUMMARY

The flatworms are considerably more complex than the coelenterates. The mesoderm, an intermediate layer of cells between ectoderm and endoderm, differentiates into connective tissue, muscles, excretory tubes, and reproductive organs. The symmetry is bilateral, not radial. The nervous system forms centralized organs, and special sense organs occur.

The parasitic habit has been developed to a high degree in flatworms, correlated with a great increase in reproductive organs and decrease or loss of epidermis, digestive system, and sense organs. Parasitic worms have little capacity for locomotion, but they have organs of attachment to the host.

Roundworms have a body cavity and a digestive system open at both ends, with parts of the tract specialized and performing particular operations on the materials passing along in one direction only. The skin has both a cuticle and an epithelium below the cuticle. The early distinction between reproductive and other tissues, and the limitation of numbers of cells are especially interesting characteristics of roundworms.

The roundworms are one of the most numerous and widespread groups of animals on the face of the earth. Some are adapted to life in the ocean, some to fresh water, some to soil, and some as parasites in a wide variety of plants and animals. If success is measured in terms of numbers of individuals, numbers of species, and adaptations to many habitats, the roundworms are among the most successful groups of animals.

REVIEW QUESTIONS

1. In what ways are bilateral metazoa more complex than radial metazoa?
2. Differentiate among the classes of flatworms.
3. Describe the structure, physiology, and reproduction of a planaria.
4. Describe regeneration in a planaria.
5. Describe the structure, physiology, and life cycle of the Chinese liver fluke.
6. Describe the structure, physiology, and life cycle of the pork tapeworm.
7. Describe the distribution of roundworms.
8. Describe the structure, physiology, and reproduction of *Ascaris lumbricoides*.
9. Describe parasitic roundworms other than *Ascaris*.
10. What structural differences distinguish roundworms from flatworms?

GENERAL QUESTIONS

1. How do the fibers connecting the cilia of planarias differ from those of paramecia?
2. Is the auricle of a planaria a sense organ?
3. Is the mesoderm of a planaria comparable to the mesoglea of a hydra?
4. Of what advantage to a planaria are its eyes?
5. What is learning? Is learning in planarias and in humans different only in degree?
6. One writer has suggested that the brain of animals is an organ whose function is inhibition. Is this valid?
7. Correlate the degree of complexity of the reproductive systems, the number of offspring produced, and the parasitic or nonparasitic habit of the animal — in a hydra, a planaria, a liver fluke, a tapeworm, an ascaris, and a human.
8. Would it be possible for a Chinese liver fluke to fertilize itself?
9. Assuming that all offspring survived to maturity, which would produce the most animals in one generation: a fluke which laid 40,000 eggs a year for 20 years, each egg producing 8 rediae and each redia producing 10 cercariae; a tapeworm giving off 5 proglottids a day for 15 years, with 10,000 embryos per proglottid; or an ascaris which lays 200,000 eggs a day for 10 years?
10. What is, in general terms, the effect of the parasitic habit on the structure and physiology of the parasite?

CHAPTER 24

Annelida

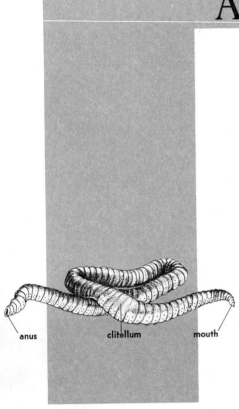

anus   clitellum   mouth

Fig. 24.1 Earthworm. Notice the clear external evidence of segmentation.

CHARACTERISTICS OF ANNELIDS

The Annelida, or segmented worms, have a more fully developed segmentation than tapeworms. In tapeworms, serial repetition of organs was largely confined to the reproductive system. In annelids the serial repetition of organs includes the nervous, excretory, and reproductive systems as well as some other structures.

In addition to segmentation, annelids differ from the animals previously described in Part III in having a true celom surrounded by mesodermal tissues, and by having a specialized, closed circulatory system.

Earthworm

Annelids live in the ocean, in fresh water, in soil, and as parasites in other animals. The most familiar annelid is the earthworm, variously called angleworm, redworm, and fishworm. *Lumbricus terrestris* is frequently called the night crawler. It may be from several inches to a foot or so in length, and about a quarter of an inch in diameter. The body is divided into from a hundred to over a hundred and fifty segments. See Figure 24.1.

The first segment contains the mouth, which is overhung by a sort of porch roof called the **prostomium,** a projection forward of the dorsal part of the first segment. The last segment contains the anus.

A cross section through an earthworm shows that the animal consists of a body wall, a celom with organs in it, and a digestive tract. See Figure 24.2.

The body wall has a cuticle, quite thin, and kept moist by the secretions of glands which open to the outer surface. Underneath the cuticle is the epidermis, a single layer of columnar cells. Internal to this is a layer of muscle fibers arranged circularly around the worm. Still deeper is a thicker layer of muscle fibers arranged longitudinally. Separating the longitudinal muscle layer from the celom is a thin membrane, the **peritoneum.**

Setae

Eight bristles called **setae** project through the skin in each segment except the first and the last. The setae occur in pairs, a pair on each lateral side and another pair on each ventrolateral corner. The setae have special small bundles of muscle fibers which may project or retract them. When the earthworm crawls, it uses both layers of muscles and the setae.

By projecting the setae in the posterior segments of the body, it anchors that end in the soil. Contraction of the circular muscles elongates the body, and since the posterior end is anchored, the anterior end is pushed ahead. Then the anterior setae are projected, and the posterior setae retracted. The longitudinal muscles now contract, shortening the body, thus drawing the posterior end forward. Then the posterior setae are projected, the anterior setae withdrawn, and the circular muscles contracted again. This pushes the anterior end ahead. By constant repetition of these movements, the earthworm burrows through the soil.

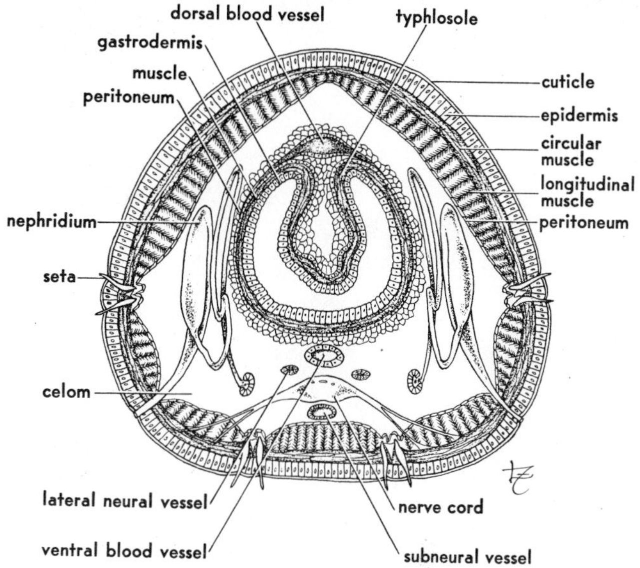

Fig. 24.2 Diagram of the cross section of an earthworm. How does the structure compare with that of *Ascaris?*

Celom

The celom is divided into chambers by **septa** at the segment boundaries. These septa cross the celom from body wall to digestive tract dorsally; ventrally they are incomplete, so that the celom in one segment is in open communication with the celom in the next. The celom is lined with mesodermal peritoneum on all sides.

Digestive Tract

The digestive tract runs straight through the animal from mouth to anus. Various parts of it are specialized in structure and perform particular actions.

The mouth cavity occupies the first three segments. As the animal crawls through the soil or on top of the ground, the mouth is open and takes in dirt and decaying organic matter, such as leaves and roots.

The pharynx, occupying the next two segments, is very muscular. Both circular and radial muscles are associated with the pharynx. The radial muscles run from the pharynx to the body wall; when they contract, the cavity of the pharynx is enlarged, making room for soil taken in at the mouth. When the circular muscles in the pharynx wall contract, they compress the pharynx, forcing the contents back into the esophagus. See Figure 24.3.

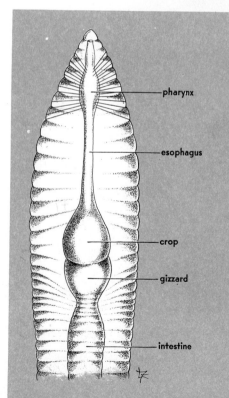

Fig. 24.3 Digestive tract of the earthworm. The intestine extends through the remaining segments, over a hundred, to the anus.

The esophagus runs from segment 6 through segment 14. It is a relatively narrow tube bearing a series of glands which secrete calcium salts into the cavity of the esophagus. This may help to neutralize the humic acids taken in with the soil.

In the next two segments the digestive tract greatly enlarges into a **crop,** a storehouse which holds the accumulated food until it may proceed further.

Behind the crop is the **gizzard,** a very muscular chamber occupying segments 17 and 18. Here the food is ground, the muscular movements of the gizzard wall rubbing the vegetation against the sand grains and reducing it to a fine rubble.

From the gizzard to the anus the digestive tract is called intestine. The lining surface is greatly increased by a fold of the intestinal wall, the **typhlosole,** hanging down from the dorsal wall. See again Figure 24.2.

In the intestine the food is digested and absorbed. Waste products and undigested material are passed out of the anus. These waste products are usually deposited on the top of the ground, and this bringing of organic wastes and finely divided materials to the surface enriches agricultural land considerably. It has been estimated that in good soil there may be 50,000 earthworms to the acre, and these deposit an inch of soil every five years. In time rocks on the surface will be buried beneath this accumulation of topsoil. The presence of burrows in the ground also helps aerate the soil, and keeps it drained. The earthworm is the most valuable animal on the farm. Its activities are of incalculable value in increasing the production of plant crops.

Circulatory System

Absorbed food is diffused partly into the celom, from which it may reach other parts of the body, but also partly into the circulatory system. The circulatory system is a series of tubes containing blood. The plasma is colored red because hemoglobin is dissolved in it. The corpuscles are comparable to the white corpuscles of a human.

Capillaries in the wall of the intestine carry blood which takes up digested food. These capillaries unite into a pair of **intestinal veins** in each segment which has part of the intestine. See Figure 24.4. The intestinal veins leave the lateral sides of the intestine and carry blood to the **dorsal blood vessel,** a median longitudinal vessel running along the dorsal wall of the digestive tract. The dorsal blood vessel acts as a heart. Its walls are muscular, and pulsate,

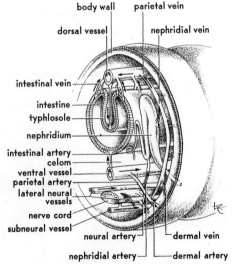

body wall   parietal vein
dorsal vessel   nephridial vein
intestinal vein
intestine
typhlosole
nephridium
intestinal artery
celom
ventral vessel
parietal artery
lateral neural vessels
nerve cord
subneural vessel
neural artery   dermal vein
nephridial artery   dermal artery

Fig. 24.4 Earthworm circulatory system. Section through the middle of the body, showing the vessels given off by and coming to the dorsal and ventral vessels in each segment. The arrows show the direction of movement of the blood in the vessels.

driving the blood anteriorly by a sort of peristaltic action. Valves prevent backflow into the veins.

In segments 7, 8, 9, 10, and 11 there are five pairs of **aortic arches** running down the sides of the esophagus, carrying blood from the dorsal blood vessel to the **ventral blood vessel.** The ventral blood vessel is a median longitudinal vessel underneath the digestive tract. Blood flows posteriorly in this vessel, except for the short portion anterior to the seventh segment, in which blood runs anteriorly, passes out branches to the esophagus, pharynx, and mouth cavity, and to the body wall, and from there to the dorsal vessel and back to the aortic arches again.

In the region behind the aortic arches, the ventral blood vessel gives off **intestinal arteries** to the digestive tract. The dorsal blood vessel also gives off intestinal arteries into the typhlosole. Blood from both these kinds of intestinal arteries is distributed by capillaries to the intestinal tissues, and then this blood is picked up by intestinal veins which have already been traced.

In each segment the ventral blood vessel also gives off a pair of **parietal arteries.** Each parietal artery lies in the septum at the anterior end of the segment, and divides into three branches. One is the **dermal artery,** carrying blood to the body wall. The capillaries from the dermal artery are very near the surface. Since the cuticle is constantly kept moist, the earthworm loses carbon dioxide and gets oxygen through its skin. If oxygen in the ground is scarce, perhaps because a rainstorm has flooded the worm's burrow and it has exhausted the oxygen dissolved in the water, the worm will come to the surface. This accounts for the appearance of earthworms after a heavy rain.

A second branch of the parietal artery is the **nephridial artery** going to one of the excretory organs. The blood passing through capillaries from the nephridial artery salvages useful materials from the products about to be excreted, much as do the blood vessels running along the kidney tubule in a human.

The third branch of the parietal artery is the **neural artery,** which passes to the ventral nerve trunk. The neural arteries empty into **lateral neural vessels,** one running longitudinally along each side of the nerve cord. Capillaries from these supply the nerve cord. Blood then is collected into a single longitudinal **subneural vessel** below the nerve cord. **Parietal veins,** one pair in each segment, run through the septum from the subneural vessel to the dorsal blood vessel, picking up **dermal veins** and **nephridial veins** on the way.

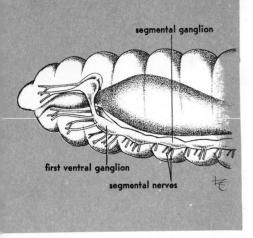

Fig. 24.5 Nervous system of the earthworm. The head is at the left. The nervous system continues through the remaining segments of the worm as is shown at the right. Each segment after the first three receives three pairs of nerves.

Nervous System

The ventral nerve trunk runs from the fourth segment to the posterior end of the body. In each segment the cord swells into a pair of fused ganglia from which three pairs of nerves go to the body wall. One pair is near the anterior end of the segment, the other two near the posterior end. The ganglia in the fourth segment are crowded toward the posterior end of the segment by a fused mass at the anterior end of the segment. This mass represents the combined ganglia of the first three segments, and it is connected by nerves with those segments. It also is connected with a pair of trunks, one running dorsally and anteriorly around each side of the pharynx. These **circumpharyngeal trunks** give off branches which extend along the digestive tract, and then the trunks pass into a pair of ganglia in the third segment dorsal to the pharynx. These ganglia are connected by nerves with the prostomium. See Figure 24.5.

The skin contains numerous sense organs, some sensitive to touch, some to light. Those sensitive to touch are especially numerous at the anterior and posterior ends of the worm. Those sensitive to light are scattered along its dorsal side, chiefly at the anterior and posterior ends.

The cellular makeup of the nervous system is much like that of the human. The ganglia contain cell bodies, and the nerves contain dendrites and axons of sensory and motor nerve cells. Three long nerve fibers run in the dorsal part of the ventral nerve trunk. Possibly these carry impulses through the length of the body, resulting in contraction of muscles throughout the animal on occasion of strong stimulation.

Excretory System

The excretory system consists of a pair of organs called **nephridia** in each segment except the first three and the last one. Each nephridium has a funnel opening into the celom of the segment ahead of it. The neck of the funnel passes through the septum and leads to the main body of the nephridium, which is a slender tube looping up and down three times. The last loop enlarges slightly into a bladder and empties through a pore in the ventrolateral body wall.

The funnel is ciliated on its inner surface, and the beat of the cilia produces a current, drawing the celomic fluid into the nephridium. As the fluid passes along the nephridial tube, the nephridial capillaries carry blood close enough to withdraw some water and dissolved substances from the celomic fluid. The wastes are concentrated in the bladder and passed to the outside through the pore.

Reproductive System

Earthworms are hermaphroditic, but not self-fertilizing. The reproductive organs are collected in segments 9 through 15. In segments 9 and 10 are two pairs of spherical sacs called **sperm receptacles.** Each receptacle opens through a tiny pore in the groove at the posterior end of its segment.

In segments 10 and 11 are two pairs of much larger, lobed structures, the **sperm reservoirs.** Each one of the pair in segment 10 has two lobes passing dorsally, and each one of the pair in segment 11 has one somewhat larger lobe passing dorsally. Near the anterior median corner of each of the four reservoirs is a small glove-shaped testis. This produces sperm cells which are stored in the reservoir. Also in each reservoir is a sperm funnel which leads to one of the two sperm ducts running from the reservoirs to the outlets on the ventral side of segment 15. See Figure 24.6.

There is one pair of ovaries, located near the midventral part of the celom in segment 13. In the posterior wall of that segment are a pair of funnels leading to the short oviducts which open to the outside in the ventral wall of segment 14. See again Figure 24.6.

When the sperm cells are mature, an earthworm must find another earthworm if copulation is to take place. Two worms come together head on, and lie along each other with the head of one reaching about to the **clitellum,** a swollen, glandular band, of the other. A secretion from the clitella and from other skin glands makes a viscous coat around the anterior ends of the two worms and helps hold them together. Then sperm cells are released from the sperm ducts of one and are stored in the sperm receptacles of the other. After each worm has received a supply of sperm cells from the other, the two worms separate.

Later, when the eggs are mature, the clitellum secretes another viscous coat over the anterior end of the worm. The worm then begins to back out of the viscous coat by wriggling. Eggs are deposited in the coat from the openings of the oviducts on segment 14, and sperms are deposited from the sperm receptacles in segments 9 and 10. Then as the earthworm finally pulls all the way out, the viscous capsule closes up and forms a sort of cocoon. In this cocoon the eggs are fertilized and develop into tiny earthworms. The cocoon is then broken open, and the young worms are released. They are much like their parents, but smaller and with immature reproductive organs.

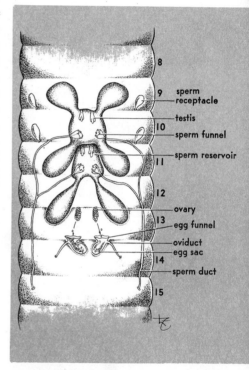

Fig. 24.6   Reproductive systems of the earthworm. The earthworm possesses both male and female systems, each in its distinctive segments; but earthworms ordinarily do not fertilize themselves.

OLIGOCHETA

The earthworm belongs to the Class **Oligocheta,** characterized by having only a few setae on each segment, a relatively simple anterior end, hermaphroditism, and direct development of the embryo into the adult form without a larval stage. Most oligochetes live on land, but a few inhabit fresh water or the ocean.

POLYCHETA

A second class of Annelida is the Class **Polycheta.** Polychetes are mostly marine, although a few live in fresh water or on land. The head is more specialized than in the oligochetes; prominent paired lateral locomotor organs are present in each segment, bearing many setae; separate sexes occur; and there is a larval stage.

Neanthes

Neanthes virens, the sandworm, is a representative of the polychetes. *Neanthes* is about the same size as *Lumbricus*, or slightly larger. It lives in the floor of the ocean near the tide level. Its burrows are lined with mucus, and it stays in the burrow most of the time except during sexual reproduction, protruding the anterior end of the body out of the burrow when feeding. See Figure 24.7.

The prostomium of the sandworm bears a pair of slender **tentacles** and a pair of large, fleshy lobes called **palps.** The first segment bears four pairs of slender projections called **cirri.** The tentacles, palps, and cirri are special sense organs. In addition, the prostomium bears on its dorsal side two pairs of eyes and a pair of olfactory pits.

Each segment except the first and the last bears a pair of lobed paddles, the **parapodia.** These are lateral outgrowths serving as locomotor organs. Each parapodium bears many setae, two of which are quite enlarged and buried in the parapodium, acting as a stiffening support for the fleshy, finlike appendage. Muscles attached to these large setae help operate the parapodium.

The last segment, surrounding the anus, has no parapodia, but has a pair of sensory cirri.

The body wall is much like that of the earthworm, except that the longitudinal muscles are gathered into four bundles like those of *Ascaris*, rather than making a complete cylindrical sheath.

The celom is like that of the earthworm. Incomplete septa result in interconnecting chambers.

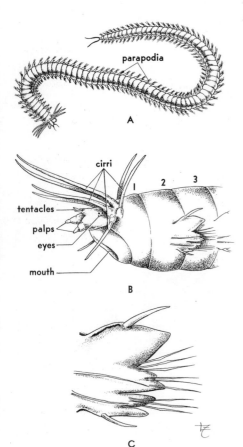

Fig. 24.7 *Neanthes.* **A,** External view of the entire worm. **B,** Detail of the head. **C,** Detail of a parapodium. In what ways does the external appearance of this animal differ from that of an earthworm? How are these differences correlated with their habitats?

The digestive tract is composed of the same layers as that of the earthworm. The chambers into which it is divided are quite different, however. The lining of the pharynx bears some hardened, toothlike prominences, two of which are much larger than the others. The pharynx can be everted through the mouth, and then these two very large prominences act as pincers in grasping food and drawing it into the digestive tract when the pharynx is retracted. See Figure 24.8.

The short esophagus bears two lateral blind pouches, the **ceca,** and then passes directly into the intestine, which occupies most of the length of the body. There is a short, cuticle-lined rectum in the last segment, opening to the outside through the anus.

The circulatory system is like that of the earthworm. The dermal artery supplies the parapodium, which increases the surface exposed to dissolved oxygen in the water, and thus acts as a gill. Nephridia, in all segments except the first and last, carry on excretion.

The ventral nerve trunk runs anteriorly into the first segment. A pair of trunks run from the anterior end of the ventral nerve trunk around the digestive tract to the dorsal ganglia in the prostomium. This dorsal pair of ganglia send nerves to the sense organs of the prostomium.

The reproductive organs are seasonal in appearance. During the breeding season, the celom wall in some of the posterior segments of the animal produces either ovaries or testes, and the eggs or sperm cells are discharged into the celomic cavity. From here they may be passed out of the body through the nephridia, or the posterior end of the body may separate off from the rest, swim about in the water, then disintegrate, releasing the reproductive cells.

Eggs are fertilized in the sea water. The zygote develops into a ciliated larva known as the **trochophore.** See Figure 24.9. This has an outer ectodermal layer, a digestive tract running from a mouth on the ventral surface through a short esophagus, an enlarged stomach which has a right-angle bend, a straight intestine, and a posterior anus. Flame cells and excretory tubes occur. The surface is marked by a band of cilia around the equator, and other bands curving about the posterior half. These bands are called **trochs,** which gives rise to the name of the larva. At the top of the animal, a tuft of long cilia marks the site of a sense organ.

HIRUDINEA

A third class of Annelida, the **Hirudinea,** includes the leeches. These are fresh-water forms, or in a few cases

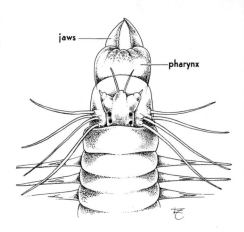

Fig. 24.8 Neanthes with the pharynx protruded, showing the jaws.

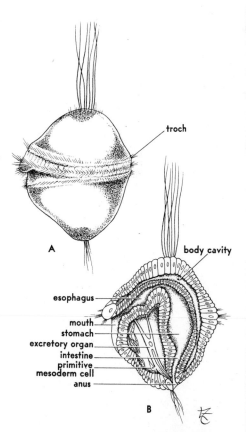

Fig. 24.9 Trochophore larva: **A,** External view; **B,** Internal view.

marine or land forms. Some suck the blood of other animals; some devour smaller animals. Leeches do not have setae or locomotor appendages.

The medicinal leech, *Hirudo medicinalis*, has often been used for withdrawing blood from humans. It may be three or four inches long, rather broad, and somewhat flattened.

Its body wall is like that of other annelids except that each segment has four grooves running around it in addition to the ones which mark the anterior and posterior boundaries of the segment, so that at first glance it appears to have five times as many segments as the internal anatomy shows are really there.

The mouth is located in a sucker at the anterior end of the worm. It contains three hardened clawlike prominences, one dorsal and two ventrolateral, with which it pierces the skin of its victim. The pharynx secretes a substance, **hirudin,** which prevents the clotting of blood, and keeps the blood flowing from the wound until the leech has filled its digestive tract and releases its sucker. The pharynx is very muscular, and pumps blood into the remainder of the tract. Behind the pharynx is the extensible, many-lobed crop in which blood may be stored. One filling may provide the leech with nourishment enough to last for many months. A short stomach behind the crop leads to a still shorter intestine, and this through the rectum to the anus at the edge of the large posterior sucker at the posterior end of the animal.

The celom is largely filled with connective tissue, and the cavity is limited to a space above and another below the digestive tract. Two lateral longitudinal blood vessels force blood about by pulsating, but the system is open, and blood escapes into the celom and penetrates the dense connective tissue.

The excretory and nervous systems are like those of other annelids.

The reproductive system is like that of the earthworm. The leech is hermaphroditic. Ten pairs of testes occur, the ten on each side opening into a sperm duct which leads to the seminal vesicle. The seminal vesicles lead to a single muscular penis. Glands in the penis secrete a viscous material which carries many sperm cells at once.

A pair of ovaries lead to oviducts which unite into one vagina. At the time of copulation, sperm cells are exchanged, and then each worm after separation from the other secretes a gelatinous sheath from its clitellum and deposits in the sheath its eggs and the sperm it received from the other leech. Then it withdraws from the sheath, which becomes a cocoon. The fertilized eggs later hatch into small leeches like the parents. There is no larval stage.

A few other types of worms, not fitting in any of the three classes described in this chapter, are sometimes classed as Annelida. These are doubtful in their relationships to annelids, relatively rare, and not important for the purposes of this chapter.

SUMMARY

In Annelida each segment is almost a duplicate of each of the others. Some differentiation occurs at the anterior end of the body. The digestive and reproductive systems are not uniform in every segment. But most of the other structures are serially repeated.

A definite celom is established in the annelida, although it is reduced in leeches.

A circulatory system also characterizes annelids.

Compared to the roundworms, the annelids show more differentiation of the one-way digestive tract into specialized portions.

The nervous system is more specialized than that of flatworms and roundworms, with ganglia on the ventral nerve trunk in each segment, except where a few ganglia have fused into one mass, as at the anteriormost end of the ventral nerve trunk in the earthworm.

Excretion is accomplished by ciliated tubes supplied with blood vessels. This is a transitional state between the flame-cell-and-tube system of the flatworms and the kidney tubules of humans.

The trochophore larvae of the Polycheta will be discussed further in connection with the larvae of other animals whose adults are quite different from the polychetes, but whose larvae greatly resemble the annelid trochophore.

REVIEW QUESTIONS

1. How do annelids differ from flatworms and roundworms?
2. Describe the anatomy of an earthworm.
3. How does an earthworm travel?
4. How do earthworms benefit a farmer?
5. Differentiate among the classes of annelids.
6. Describe the structure of *Neanthes*.
7. How does a sandworm reproduce?
8. Describe a trochophore.
9. Describe the structure and physiology of a leech.
10. What characteristics are common to all classes of annelids?

GENERAL QUESTIONS

1. Both the body wall and the digestive tract of an earthworm have circular and longitudinal muscles, with the latter nearer the celom. Is there an advantage to this arrangement?

2. In an earthworm the intestine is relatively long; in the leech the intestine is relatively short. How is each advantageous to its possessor?

3. What changes would be necessary to change an excretory system from the flatworm to the earthworm type? From the earthworm to the human type?

4. Would it be possible for an earthworm to fertilize its own eggs?

5. How is the structure of the head correlated with the habitat in the earthworm and the sandworm?

6. Would it be possible for earthworms and leeches to have trochophore larvae?

7. Physicians were at one time commonly called leeches. Account for this.

8. Is the human a segmented animal?

9. Compare the earthworm and human circulatory systems.

10. The earthworm nerve ganglia start in the third segment, the sandworm ganglia in the first segment. What is the significance of the difference?

Arthropoda

Page 40 9

© LakeHouse

CHAPTER 25

Arthropoda

CHARACTERISTICS OF ARTHROPODS

The Arthropoda are segmented, but the segments are specialized and differentiated to a much greater degree than in Annelida. The arthropods have paired lateral appendages which are jointed. These appendages also are differentiated from each other. Furthermore, the arthropods have a much thicker outer covering than the annelids, a heavy coat of chitin which acts as a suit of armor. The celom is reduced or combined with the circulatory system, somewhat as in the leech.

There are more species of arthropods known to biologists than of all other kinds of living organisms put together. This creates quite a problem for the student of classification. However, this great variation may be sorted into six classes: the **Onychophora**, the **Chilopoda**, the **Diplopoda**, the **Crustacea**, the **Insecta**, and the **Arachnida.**

ONYCHOPHORA

The Onychophora are a small class with only a few species in it, but of great theoretical importance because its members seem to be intermediate between annelids and arthropods.

Peripatus Distribution

Peripatus is the best-known genus of the Class Onychophora. Several species are found in the West Indies, Central America, and South America, and some related genera occur in South Africa, the East Indies, Australia, and New Zealand. The animals are land forms, living in warm, moist places under rocks and logs. They cannot exist in salt water. The small number of forms and their extremely wide distribution over the continents and islands of the earth are accounted for by the hypothesis that Onychophora are the remnants of a very ancient, widespread group.

Peripatus Anatomy

Peripatus is a wormlike animal, about 5 cm. long, with paired lateral appendages. See Figure 25.1. The appendages are not jointed, unlike those of all other arthropod classes. Yet, like arthropods and unlike annelids, the ends of the *Peripatus* appendages bear claws.

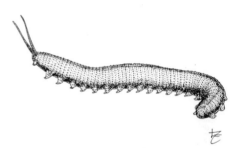

Fig. 25.1   *Peripatus.* This animal has characteristics of both annelids and arthropods. How can you account for this?

The body wall is like that of an annelid, having a cuticle, an epithelial layer, a circular muscle layer, and a longitudinal muscle layer. But the cuticle has in it a thin deposit of chitin, unlike the cuticle of annelids but like that of other arthropods.

The *Peripatus* head is composed of three segments fused, intermediate between annelids, which have no such fusion, and other arthropods, whose heads are fusions of six segments. The head bears the mouth armed with a pair of **mandibles** like those of other arthropods. The anterior part of the digestive tract is lined with chitinous cuticle. The middle part, or intestine, is quite straight, and digests and absorbs its food, chiefly insects. The posterior end of the digestive tract is a rectum, lined with chitinous cuticle and opening to the outside through the anus at the posterior tip of the animal.

The celom is much reduced, and combined with the blood system, as in other arthropods. There is a dorsal contractile blood vessel, the heart, with openings in its sides which take in blood, and other openings at the anterior and posterior ends from which blood is pumped out.

The dorsal ganglia are, even in minute details, very similar to the dorsal ganglia of the annelid *Neanthes* described in the previous chapter. A nerve trunk runs from each dorsal ganglion down the side of the digestive tract to the ventral nerve trunk on that side. The two ventral nerve trunks are widely separated in *Peripatus*, unlike either annelids or other arthropods. The trunks have ganglia segmentally arranged as do the annelids. A pair of antennae like those of other arthropods project anteriorly from the head; they are sense organs sensitive to touch, and each bears an eye and an olfactory organ on the dorsal side of its base.

Excretion is carried on by nephridia like those of annelids and unlike the excretory organ of any other arthropod; in these nephridia occur the only cilia to be found in arthropods.

Respiration is carried on by some chitin-lined tubes, the **tracheae,** projecting into the body from the surface and branching and rebranching throughout the body. Air penetrates these tubes, and movements of the body create pressures which aid in circulating the air. Such respiratory organs are unknown in annelids, but are common in arthropods.

Reproduction is not like that of either the annelids or the arthropods. Sexes are separate. The male has a pair of convoluted testes leading to sperm ducts. The sperm ducts have enlarged seminal vesicles for storing sperm cells. The two sperm ducts unite into a common duct which leads to the outside near the posterior end of the animal. Sperm are deposited at the reproductive pore of the female, or anywhere on her skin. The sperm cells seem to be able to penetrate the skin and find the eggs if they are not placed at the genital opening.

In the female there is a pair of ovaries, each leading to an oviduct. Each oviduct enlarges into a uterus. Fertilized eggs develop in the uteri and are supplied with nourishment by the mother. The two uteri unite into a single vagina, also opening near the posterior end of the animal. The young *Peripati* find their way out of the vagina at an advanced stage of development.

It will be seen that the curious assortment of characteristics, some annelid, some arthropod, some peculiar to the Onychophora, make this group a difficult one to classify, but a fascinating subject for speculation.

CHILOPODA

The Class Chilopoda includes the centipedes. See Figure 25.2. These, too, are long (up to 20 cm.), clearly segmented animals, somewhat flattened dorsoventrally. The chitin layer is quite thick on these animals, with thin, flexible strips at the anterior and posterior borders of segments, allowing for movement of one segment with respect to the next.

The centipede head consists of six segments fused together. It bears a pair of long, jointed antennae and a pair of eyes, each of which may consist of several small facets. There is a pair of powerful **mandibles,** two-jointed appendages on the sides of the mouth. They tear up the insects and spiders used for food. There are also on the head two pairs of appendages called **maxillae.** The second pair are fused at the base, forming a lower lip to the mouth.

The first segment behind the head has a specialized pair of appendages, the **maxillipeds,** each of which is jointed into six spans. The last span is a claw, which bears the opening of a duct from a poison-secreting gland.

The remaining body segments, except the first and the last two, each bear a pair of six-jointed legs with a single claw on the tip of each leg. The entire centipede may consist of from 15 to 173 segments.

The body wall does not have the layers of musculature characteristic of annelids and onychophores. Muscles are specialized, running from the chitinous wall of one segment to that of the next and from span to span in the appendages.

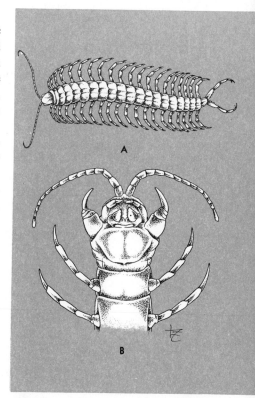

Fig. 25.2   Centipede. A, General appearance. B, Head appendages. How does the centipede resemble annelids? How does it resemble *Peripatus*?

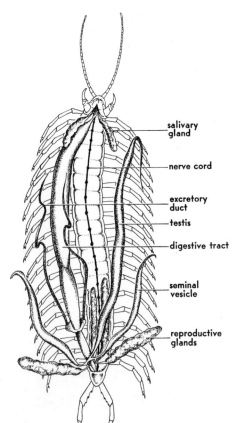

salivary
gland

nerve cord

excretory
duct

testis

digestive tract

seminal
vesicle

reproductive
glands

Fig. 25.3   Centipede internal anatomy. How does
this compare with *Peripatus*?

The muscle fibers are striated in contrast to the visceral
type of fibers found in worms.

The digestive tract is straight. See Figure 25.3. The mouth
cavity receives the ducts of a pair of large salivary glands.
The esophagus opens into a stomach, which leads to the
intestine. The rectum opens to the outside through the
anus near the posterior end of the body.

Like other arthropods except onychophores, centipedes
have no nephridia. A pair of long tubules, the **Malpighian
tubules,** run through the body absorbing wastes, and empty
into the digestive tract at the place where the intestine
passes into the rectum.

The circulatory system has a long, dorsal heart with
lateral openings to receive blood and terminal branches
from which blood is forced into the body tissues.

Respiration is by tracheae like those of *Peripatus.*

The nervous system is like that of *Peripatus* except that
the two ventral nerve cords are much closer together.

Sexes are separate. The testis or ovary is usually single,
with the reproductive duct receiving accessory glands and
opening to the outside near the posterior end. Eggs are
laid and hatch directly into young centipedes.

DIPLOPODA

The Class Diplopoda includes the millipedes. See Figure
25.4. In these there is a head composed of six fused segments, followed by four single segments, and then the
rest of the body consists of a long series of segments (from
10 to 100 or more) partially fused in twos. Each double
segment carries two pairs of legs.

The head bears a pair of antennae and two many-faceted
eyes. A pair of powerful mandibles is used to shred the
vegetable matter which is the food of the animal. There is
one pair of maxillae, the bases of which fuse to make a
lower lip.

The internal structure is much like that of the Chilopoda.
The chitin may be rather heavily calcified. Special scent
glands in millipedes may be a protection against some
enemies. The reproductive openings are in the ventral
wall near the anterior end (between the second pair of legs)
in millipedes. The developing zygote passes through a
stage in which only three pairs of legs are present, as in
adult insects. See Figure 25.5.

CRUSTACEA

The Class Crustacea includes primarily marine and
fresh-water forms, although a few live on land and a few

Fig. 25.4   Millipede. Notice the two pairs of
legs on each of most of the segments.

are parasitic. The head consists of six segments fused. The body shows greater specialization than that of the Ony-chophora, Chilopoda, or Diplopoda. The anterior segments of the body behind the head are collectively called the **thorax,** and may show some fusion, even in some crustacea partially combining with the head to make a **cephalothorax.** The posterior segments of the body usually remain distinct and constitute the **abdomen.**

Crayfish

One of the most familiar of the Crustacea is the crayfish. There are several common species of crayfish, all much alike in structure. See Figure 25.6.

Fig. 25.5   Millipede larva showing three pairs of legs, as in insects.

Crayfish Head

The crayfish head has a pair of **compound eyes** borne on stalks. Each compound eye is constituted of some 2500 very long, slender pyramids with squarish bases. The base is at the surface of the eye, and the apex at the beginning of a nerve fiber. Only an object directly in front of the base of the pyramid will cast a shadow on the apex, for the sides of the pyramids are bordered with pigment cells which absorb all light not passing straight down the center. Since each pyramid is slanted slightly differently from the adjacent ones, the surface of the eye is very strongly curved, and objects over a wide range may be seen even if the eye is not moved. By moving the eyestalks, the crayfish may see in almost any direction.

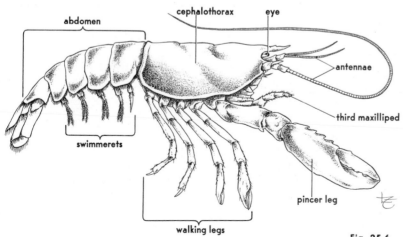

Fig. 25.6   Crayfish. Note the differentiation of structure in the different segments. The head and thorax are somewhat fused together.

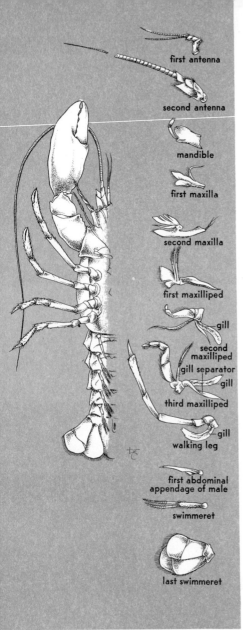

first antenna

second antenna

mandible

first maxilla

second maxilla

first maxilliped

gill

second
maxilliped

gill separator

gill

third maxilliped

gill

walking leg

first abdominal
appendage of male

swimmeret

last swimmeret

Fig. 25.7 Appendages of the crayfish. These are constructed on a common plan, but modified in such a way that they are adapted to specialized actions.

The image formed by the compound eye is like a newspaper illustration — composed of regularly spaced dots of varying degrees of light and dark. The smaller the pyramids, the more detailed is the image. Even a very slight movement of an object is instantly apparent, since the shadow will shift from one pyramid or group of pyramids to another.

In addition to the stalked eyes, the crayfish head bears two pairs of antennae. The crustacea are the only arthropods having more than one pair of antennae. The first pair of antennae are of moderate length and are two-branched. The second pair are much longer, but unbranched. The antennae are sensitive to touch and to chemicals.

At the bases of the first antennae are a pair of sense organs called **statocysts.** Each statocyst is a sac open to the outside through a small pore. In the lining of the sac are sensory hairs. Sand grains get into this sac as the crayfish moves about, and the force of gravity causes the grains to press on the hairs. By this means the crayfish has a sense of equilibrium or orientation in the gravitational field comparable to that of humans with the static equilibrium sense of the inner ear.

The lining of the sac is shed periodically when the entire chitinous coat molts. This process of molting allows the animal to grow. The tissues absorb water and swell. Then a new chitinous coat is secreted, and the tissues may release some of the imbibed water and have room for growth. After each molt, the crayfish must acquire more sand grains in its statocysts. One investigator provided a newly molted crustacean with iron filings instead of sand, and when these were installed in the statocyst, the animal responded to a magnetic field just as it normally would to gravitation. If the magnet were held above the animal, it traveled ventral side up.

The crayfish possesses a pair of strong mandibles and two pairs of maxillae. The maxillae do not make the lower lip. See Figure 25.7.

Thoracic Appendages

On the thorax there are eight pairs of appendages. The first three pairs are called maxillipeds, getting progressively larger from anterior to posterior pair. Then there are the largest appendages of the body, the pincer legs, each armed at the tip with two powerful claws working against each other. The remaining four pairs are called walking legs. The first two of these four pairs bear small pincers, and the last two bear single claws.

Abdominal Appendages

The appendages of the abdomen are quite different. Those of the first abdominal segment of the male crayfish are modified, contorted rods used during copulation. The next four pairs of appendages are called swimmerets. They are two-branched paddles bearing stiff hairs which increase their sculling efficiency. The sixth pair is a much broader pair of swimmerets, called **uropods,** each composed of two wide, rounded plates which combine with the flattened median extension of the abdomen to make a powerful swimming flap at the posterior end of the body.

In the female the abdominal appendages are like those of the male except that the first pair is a pair of reduced swimmerets, not modified copulatory appendages.

Locomotion

In locomotion, the crayfish may crawl along the bottom of the river or on land by means of its walking legs; it may swim forward in a leisurely manner by beating its smaller swimmerets; or it may swim backward very quickly by a sudden contraction of the muscles which pull the posterior flap ventrally with a powerful stroke.

The chitinous covering is fused over the dorsal side of the head and thorax, but the plates of the abdominal segments have thin places between them, so that the abdomen is flexible. Thin places also occur between the separate spans of the appendages, so that they may be moved on each other.

The abdominal segments and the appendages are operated by specialized muscles.

Digestion

The food of the crayfish consists of other animals. The mouth is small, and the appendages around the mouth are used in tearing the prey into small pieces. The mouth leads by way of a short esophagus to the large stomach. See Figure 25.8. Imbedded in the wall of the stomach is a complicated series of chitinous thickenings and muscles known as the **gastric mill.** This mill grinds the food much more finely than the appendages did. The food passes through the mill except for objects which are not reduced by the grinding, and these larger pieces are returned to the outside through the mouth.

In the stomach the food is exposed to secretions of the pair of large digestive glands at either side of the stomach and intestine. These glands secrete enzymes, digest and absorb most of the food, store some of it, and take an active

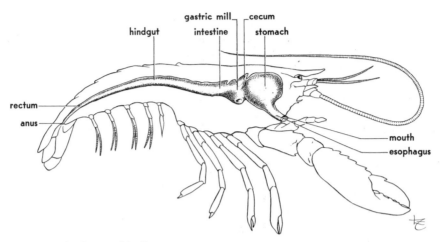

Fig. 25.8 Digestive system of a crayfish. How does this compare with the digestive system of an earthworm? Can you correlate structural differences with differences in diet?

part in excretion. The ducts of these glands open into the digestive tract just behind the stomach. Another small pouch, the cecum, extends dorsally and anteriorly at this point. Then the digestive tract continues as the hindgut, which runs through the rest of the thorax, the abdomen, and enlarges into a rectum just before emptying at the anus on the ventral side of the last segment.

The mouth, esophagus, and stomach are lined with chitin, as are also the hindgut, rectum, and anus. The chitin is shed with the armor on the outside of the body at each molt. Only the short portion of the digestive tract between the stomach and the hindgut, together with the cecum and the digestive glands, are devoid of chitin. These are comparable to the intestine in other arthropods and in annelids.

Respiration

At each side of the thorax, in a space between the chitinous coat and the body wall, occur a series of gills. See Figure 25.9. These are feathery, branched extensions of the bases of the last two maxillipeds, the pincer leg, and the next three walking legs, as well as of the wall of the thorax. A paddlelike extension from the second maxilla beats back and forth at the anterior end of the space, maintaining a current of water past the gills. This is the respiratory system. No tracheae occur.

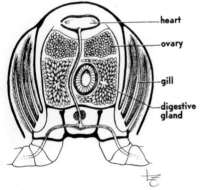

Fig. 25.9 Gills of the crayfish. The gills are attached to the bases of appendages and are moved when the appendages move. Although partly protected by the exoskeleton, the gills have access to the water below.

Circulation

Circulation is a little more complex in the crayfish than in the arthropods previously described in this book. See

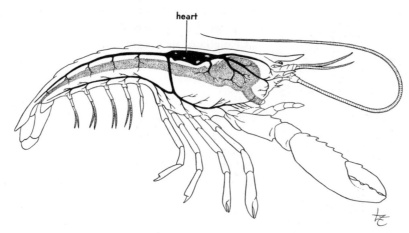

heart

Fig. 25.10   Circulatory system of the crayfish. The heart is dorsal and pumps blood into the arteries. From the arteries the blood flows into the body tissues and is returned by sinuses through the gills to the heart.

Figure 25.10. The heart is an irregularly shaped dorsal tube with openings in the side through which blood enters. Several arteries leave the heart, carrying blood to various parts of the body. Three go to the head and anterior end of the digestive tract; two to the digestive glands; one to the dorsal part of the abdomen; and one ventrally, which divides into an anterior and a posterior branch. Blood leaving these arteries passes freely into the tissues, collecting later in an open space, or sinus, in the ventral part of the thorax. Hydraulic pressure forces the blood from here through spaces in the gills back to the region around the heart. The heart admits the blood by way of its lateral openings and pumps it out through the arteries again. Valves at the various inlets and outlets of the heart prevent reversal of the direction of blood flow.

Excretion

Excretion is carried on by the digestive glands and by the gills, but also by a pair of **green glands** anterior to the stomach. Each green gland consists of an opening from the diminished celom, a long, much-coiled tubule well supplied with blood capillaries, and a storage bladder which opens to the outside at the base of a second antenna.

Nervous System

The dorsal ganglia or brain of a crayfish is somewhat larger than those of annelids or onychophores. Branches from the brain supply the eyes and antennae. Nerve trunks run from the brain around the esophagus to the ventral nerve trunk. Branches from the connective trunks pass along the esophagus to the stomach. The anterior ganglion pair of the ventral trunk are the fused ganglia of the last five of the six head segments. Behind these the ventral nerve trunk swells in each segment to include the fused pair of ganglia of that segment.

Endocrines

In each eyestalk is located a **sinus gland,** which is endocrine in its action. Its hormones regulate pigmentation, including distribution of pigment in the compound eyes in bright or dim light, molting, blood sugar level, heart rate, growth of the ovaries in the female, and some other activities.

Reproduction

Sexes are separate in crayfishes. The male has a pair of testes just ventral to the heart, leading by a pair of sperm ducts to·openings at the bases of the last pair of walking legs.

The female has a pair of ovaries, often fused in the midline, just ventral to the heart. The oviducts open to the outside at the bases of the second of the four pairs of walking legs. A sperm receptacle occurs between the last two pairs of walking legs in the female. Sperm placed by the male in this receptacle may remain there for months. When the female lays eggs, she lies ventral side up, and curls the abdomen up over the posterior part of the thorax. The eggs are passed out of the oviduct, fertilized by the sperm cells from the sperm receptacle, and fastened to the swimmerets by a viscous secretion. The embryos develop here for some time, even after hatching.

In their early stages, the young crayfish look like the parents, though much smaller. This is not true of all Crustacea, some of which go through a larval stage known as a **nauplius,** which metamorphoses into an adult of quite a different appearance. This is illustrated in Figure 25.11.

OTHER CRUSTACEA

Some of the adult Crustacea have structures which are unlike those of the more typical forms. Barnacles, for example, attach themselves permanently to some solid object like a rock, secrete a limy shell of several plates, and gather food by sweeping the water with appendages resembling a rake or a net. *Sacculina* is a parasite on crabs which loses all semblance of arthropod form in the adult stage and resembles the mycelium of a fungus. Only by studying the development of *Sacculina*, which has a recog-

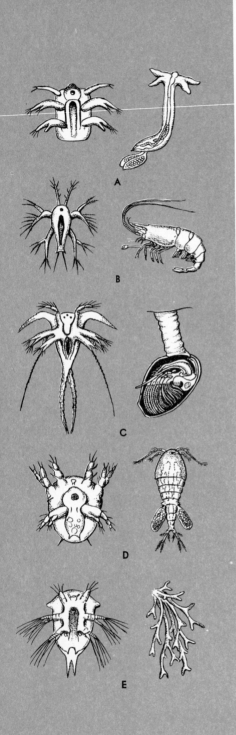

Fig. 25.11 Crustacean nauplii and adults. **A,** *Lernaeocera,* a fish parasite. **B,** A shrimp. **C,** A barnacle. **D,** The fresh-water *Cyclops.* **E,** *Sacculina.*

nizable nauplius larva, were scientists able to discover its crustacean nature.

The hermit crabs somewhat resemble the crayfish in structure except that their abdomens have only a soft cuticle, not as hard and protective as the calcified chitin on the anterior part of the body. They seek out empty snail shells and back into these, fitting the abdomen into the space formerly occupied by the snail. As the hermit crab grows, it becomes too large for its rooms, and it hunts around for a larger apartment. When it finds a shell that might be suitable, it explores the shell with its antennae. If it is satisfied, it pulls its abdomen out of the old shell, and backs quickly into the new one.

Among the most numerous of aquatic animals is a group of crustacea known as **copepods.** They eat algae and protozoa in great numbers and are eaten in turn by fishes and whales, forming an important link in the chain of food organisms from the smallest to the largest predators. They are small in size but are present in tremendous numbers. They also act as intermediate hosts to many of the parasites of other animals, parasites such as the fish tapeworm and the guinea worm which attack man.

INSECTA

The largest of all classes of animals in number of species is the Class Insecta. The insects are of small to moderate size (less than a quarter of a millimeter to more than a quarter of a meter). Various species are adapted to an astounding variety of habitat niches. While each species has become quite specialized and associated with only a limited habitat, the insects as a group have penetrated almost every cranny of the earth.

One genus of bugs lives on the surface of the ocean, often at great distances from land. The brine fly lives in the Great Salt Lake. Some insects inhabit deserts. One fly larva lives in petroleum pools. Some ants grow fungi in underground caverns, and use the plants for food. Bees use the nectar and pollen of flowers. Termites devour their way through wood. The larvae of bark beetles confine their diet to the cambium layer of trees. Aphids suck the juices from leaves. Some insects devour books. The wax moth eats the comb of honeybees. Clothes moths eat wool, silk, and feathers. One of the relatives of the clothes moth feeds on the yeasts growing on corks in wine cellars. The dung beetle and the housefly larva live on the bacteria and fungi growing on excrement. The larvae of some lacewings are parasitic on fresh-water sponges. *Strepsiptera* are internal

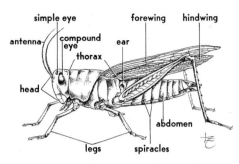

simple eye
antenna
compound eye
forewing
hindwing
ear
thorax
head
abdomen
legs
spiracles

Fig. 25.12 Grasshopper. This is one of the larger insects, and it retains many primitive characteristics typical of all insects.

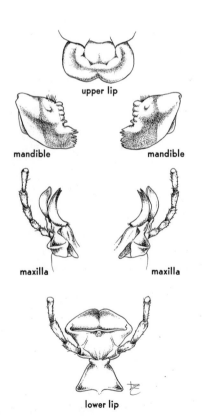

upper lip

mandible   mandible

maxilla   maxilla

lower lip

Fig. 25.13 Mouth parts of the grasshopper. The jaws work from side to side in insects.

parasites of wasps. Dragonflies capture and eat other flying insects. The ant lion builds a trap in the sand and captures ants. The mosquito sucks the blood of mammals and other animals. Botfly larvae live in the digestive tract of horses. Assassin bugs attack bedbugs and devour second-hand the blood the bedbugs obtained from humans. Except for the ocean, there is scarcely a place on the surface of the earth that insects have not colonized.

The body of an insect is divided into a head of six fused segments, a thorax of three fused segments, and an abdomen of a variable number of separate segments. The head and the thorax bear jointed appendages, but the abdomen does not. The thorax also usually bears wings, a feature found in only one other phylum of animals.

Grasshopper

Among the largest of living insects is the grasshopper, *Romalea microptera*, with a length of two to three inches. See Figure 25.12. The head bears a pair of large compound eyes built into the dorsolateral corners of the head, not on stalks. Three small simple eyes occur on the front of the head, as well. The grasshopper has one pair of jointed antennae, about half as long as the rest of the body. A pair of stout mandibles helps the grasshopper chop up the leaves which constitute its food. There are two pairs of maxillae, of which the second pair has fused in the midline to make the lower lip of the mouth. See Figure 25.13.

The thorax has three segments. Each segment bears a pair of jointed legs ending in claws, two claws on each leg. Each of the last two thoracic segments bears a pair of wings. The first of the two pairs of wings is a thick, leathery pair which protect the more membranous, folded, hind wings when the insect is not flying. In flight the second pair is extended and unfolded, forming vanes of considerable surface area strengthened by radiating tracheal tubes. Contractions of thoracic muscles cause these wings to pump up and down, propelling the animal through the air with powerful strokes.

The abdomen of the grasshopper has eleven segments. The first is partially fused with the thorax, and the last few may show some tendency to fuse.

The external armor is chitinous, but not calcified like that of the crayfish. Muscles inside the skeleton operate parts of this armor on the rest (as in moving the wings), or they operate one part of an appendage on the next part.

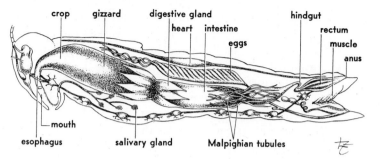

Fig. 25.14 Digestive tract of a grasshopper. How does this compare with the digestive tracts of annelids? Of humans?

The digestive system has a mouth cavity which receives secretions from a pair of salivary glands. See Figure 25.14. The esophagus leads into a crop, or temporary storage place, which leads to the gizzard, a very muscular grinding organ lined internally with chitinous thickenings which macerate and strain the food. Next comes the intestine, which receives secretions from four pairs of two-lobed digestive glands. Both digestion and absorption take place in the intestine. The intestine and glands are the only parts of the digestive tract not lined with chitin. The intestine opens into the hindgut, which narrows as it proceeds posteriorly, until it opens into the enlarged rectum, which empties by way of an anus at the posterior end of the body.

Respiration is carried on in tracheae. These are open to the outside by a series of ten paired pores, one pair on each of the last two thoracic and first eight abdominal segments. Movements of the abdomen help propel the air through the tracheae. See Figure 25.15.

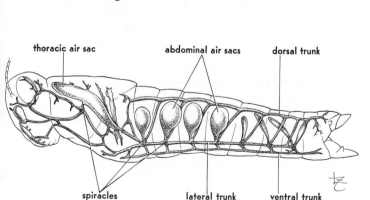

Fig. 25.15 Respiratory system of a grasshopper. Air is pumped in and out by movements of the body. How do insecticidal dusts kill insects?

The circulatory system is like that of centipedes. A long, narrow, dorsal, tubular heart has openings in the side which receive blood and openings at each end through which blood is expelled. The blood is worked through the tissues and the celom by muscular movements of the insect, and eventually is returned to the heart.

Excretion is accomplished by many pairs of long Malpighian tubules which empty into the digestive tract at the region where the intestine passes into the hindgut.

The nervous system resembles that of other arthropods. The brain, dorsal to the esophagus, is made of three pairs of ganglia fused together. These are the ganglia of the first three of the six head segments. Nerve trunks pass around the esophagus, giving off branches to the digestive tract, and then meet ventrally at the beginning of the ventral nerve trunk. At this junction is a mass consisting of three pairs of ganglia fused, representing the ganglia of the last three head segments.

The ventral nerve trunk consists of paired cords running back through the thorax and abdomen, and knotted together at intervals by ganglion masses. Each thoracic segment has a pair of fused ganglia in it. The last thoracic segment has in its fused ganglia the ganglia of the first abdominal segment as well. The second abdominal segment has the fused ganglia of the second and third segments. The fourth, fifth, and sixth segments each have a pair of fused ganglia representing that particular segment. The seventh segment has a mass representing a fusion of the ganglia of the last five abdominal segments. See Figure 25.16.

In addition to the senses of sight represented by the five eyes, of touch on the antennae and other parts of the body, and taste in the mouth, grasshoppers have a sense of hearing. On each side of the first abdominal segment is a large opening covered by a thin tympanic membrane supplied by sensory nerves.

Sexes are separate in grasshoppers. The male has a pair of testes, and a pair of sperm ducts receiving the secretion of accessory glands and uniting into a common duct which opens at the posterior end of the body.

The female has a sperm receptacle opening off the vagina, which receives the sperm at the time of copulation. There is a pair of ovaries which form long, cylindrical eggs. The two oviducts lead to the common vagina. Eggs pass along the vagina, are fertilized by sperm cells from the sperm receptacle, and are deposited in small burrows in the ground. The egg hatches into a recognizable grasshopper

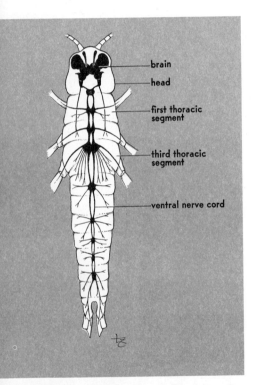

brain
head
first thoracic segment
third thoracic segment
ventral nerve cord

Fig. 25.16 Nervous system of a grasshopper. How does this differ from the nervous system of an earthworm? Of a human?

like its parents except that the head is disproportionately large, reproductive organs are immature, and the wings do not yet appear. Several molts interspersed with periods of growth ensue before maturity is reached. See Figure 25.17.

Hormones seem to be important in controlling growth and molting. Certain cells in the brain secrete hormones without which metamorphosis into the adult does not occur. Just posterior to the brain is a pair of small glands, the **corpora allata,** which secrete a hormone retarding maturity in grasshoppers and to some extent opposing the metamorphosis hormone. It has also been shown that the corpora allata regulate fat metabolism in grasshoppers and other insects.

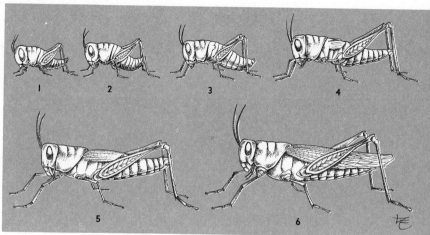

Fig. 25.17 Developmental stages of a grasshopper. Note the changes in bodily proportions in succeeding stages.

OTHER INSECTS

About a million species of insects have been described, and there may be many more yet unknown to biologists. The scientific problems involved in classifying these and studying their characteristics are tremendous.

Insects play a very important role in human economy: Some insects are essential to the pollination of many species of seed plants. Some insects such as the honeybee and the silk moth produce substances of commercial value. Shellac, some dyes, and several other chemicals are derived from insects. Many animals live wholly or partly on a diet of insects.

Insects damage and destroy many plants, some of which are our most important crop plants. Some insects cause diseases; others carry organisms which cause diseases of humans and other animals. Others, such as the termites and the clothes moths, damage materials useful to humans. Some insects are used in combating the spread of others. An Australian ladybug is used in controlling the spread of a destructive scale insect.

Because of their size, their high reproductive rates, and other special biological characteristics, insects are well suited to certain types of scientific study. On page 229 the use of *Drosophila* for genetics studies was mentioned. Cockroaches, grasshoppers, caterpillars, and beetles are widely used in the study of embryology and physiology.

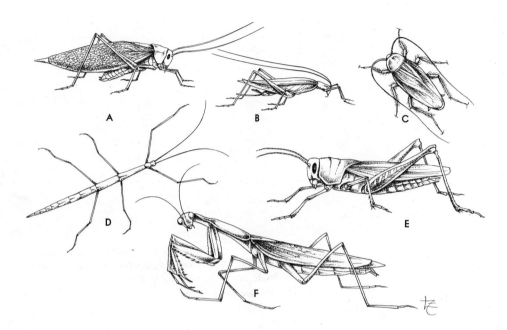

Fig. 25.18 Kinds of Orthoptera. **A,** Katydid. **B,** Tree cricket. **C,** Cockroach. **D,** Walking stick. **E,** Locust. **F,** Praying mantis.

Orthoptera

Grasshoppers, locusts, crickets, cockroaches, praying mantises, and walking sticks belong to the insect Order **Orthoptera.** See Figure 25.18. The reproductive powers of some of these animals are remarkable. Sailors of many years ago would open a barrel of ship's biscuits and find instead a barrel of cockroaches.

Migratory locusts in swarms may completely strip vast grain fields. An English scientist once recorded a locust swarm covering about 2000 square miles of territory in Egypt. By various computations he estimated that the total weight of locusts was about 42,850,000,000 tons. Since each locust weighed about $\frac{1}{16}$ of an ounce, this represented quite a few locusts. These are somewhat like the devastating grasshoppers of this country.

Such quantities of insects make abundant food for predators, such as birds. These predators accordingly increase greatly in numbers, so that they threaten the continuance of the locusts. Locusts then decrease markedly during the next few years. This decrease in prey starves many of the predators, which themselves then decrease in number. With fewer enemies, the locusts again increase, and a cycle recurs, with the predators a year or two later in phase.

Many Orthoptera, such as the crickets, are able to make a chirping noise by rubbing one part of their chitinous coats on another part. Some people can recognize different species of insects by their particular calls. The rate of intermittent chirping, like most other insect activities, is increased with a rise in temperature, and in one species, the number of chirps a cricket emits in fifteen seconds, added to 38, gives the temperature of the cricket in degrees Fahrenheit.

The praying mantis is a predator on other insects. It stands on the branch of a shrub or tree in an attitude similar to a person folding his hands in prayer. If a passing insect comes within reach, the mantis swings out his long legs and seizes the prey, tears it apart, and eats it. The mantis has been the subject of many a sermon on hypocrisy.

Walking sticks are shaped like tree twigs. They are leaf-eaters, and apparently the resemblance to twigs makes them more difficult to find by their enemies. Even in color these insects resemble their environment. They are green in spring and early summer and turn grayish brown in the fall.

Thysanura

The silverfish, Order **Thysanura,** has no wings. It is common in some attics and basements and in some libraries, where it devours such things as the paste in the bindings of books.

Ephemerida

The May fly, Order **Ephemerida,** is curious in that its egg hatches into an aquatic larva, which lives for a year or more in the water, then metamorphoses into an aerial adult which has no mouth and does not eat. It lives for a half hour or more, up to about three days, reproduces, then dies. See Figure 25.19.

Fig. 25.19   May fly. Left, Larva. **Right,** Adult. The adult lives only a very short time, but it takes a year to produce another generation.

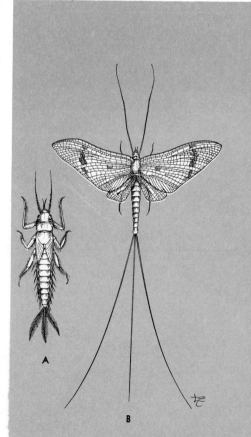

A

B

Hemiptera

Insects generally and even other kinds of animals are sometimes inaccurately called bugs. To the biologist, the term *bug* refers to an insect of the Order **Hemiptera** only. Included in this order are many of the insects of particular concern to the gardener and farmer, whose crops they injure or destroy. They include the water bugs, leaf bugs, bedbugs, chinch bugs, squash bugs, and stinkbugs. See Figure 25.20F–M.

Homoptera

Somewhat similar are the **Homoptera,** an order including the cicadas, of which the seventeen-year locust is an example; the scale insects that infest fruit trees; and the aphids, called plant lice or ant cows. See Figure 25.20N–R. The aphids suck the cell sap from plants, and are often attended by ants, which devour a sweetish secretion produced by the aphids. Aphids have an ability to reproduce by the development of unfertilized eggs, a phenomenon known as **parthenogenesis.** After many parthenogenetically produced generations, sexual aphids may be produced. The zygotes from such individuals develop into aphids which reproduce parthenogenetically.

Lepidoptera

Some insects undergo a much more complex life cycle than the grasshopper. The Order **Lepidoptera** includes the moths and butterflies. The egg of such an insect hatches into a caterpillar, an animal superficially somewhat like *Peripatus.* The caterpillar devotes its time to eating, usually devouring leaves. After a while the caterpillar becomes a **pupa.** In moths the pupa is enclosed in a cocoon spun by the caterpillar. In the pupa a remarkably extensive metamorphosis takes place. The larval structures are very greatly altered and new ones are developed. After a time, the adult moth or butterfly emerges from the old pupal skin. See Figure 25.20A–E.

Diptera

Members of the Order **Diptera** are different from the other insects in that the second pair of wings is reduced to tiny stalked knobs. Flies, mosquitoes, and gnats belong to this group. *Drosophila,* on which so much work in genetics has been done, is a dipteran. See Figure 25.20S–Y.

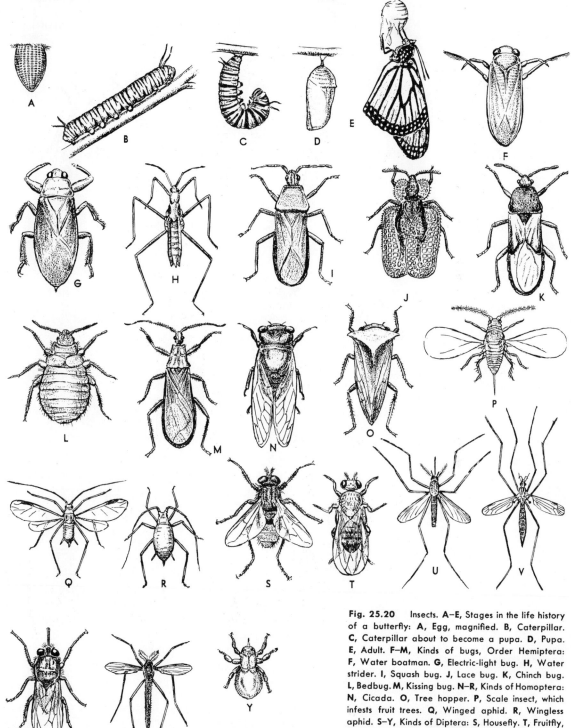

Fig. 25.20   Insects. **A–E,** Stages in the life history of a butterfly: **A,** Egg, magnified. **B,** Caterpillar. **C,** Caterpillar about to become a pupa. **D,** Pupa. **E,** Adult. **F–M,** Kinds of bugs, Order Hemiptera: **F,** Water boatman. **G,** Electric-light bug. **H,** Water strider. **I,** Squash bug. **J,** Lace bug. **K,** Chinch bug. **L,** Bedbug. **M,** Kissing bug. **N–R,** Kinds of Homoptera: **N,** Cicada. **O,** Tree hopper. **P,** Scale insect, which infests fruit trees. **Q,** Winged aphid. **R,** Wingless aphid. **S–Y,** Kinds of Diptera: **S,** Housefly. **T,** Fruitfly, *Drosophila.* **U,** Mosquito. **V,** Crane fly. **W,** Tsetse fly, which carries the trypanosome causing African sleeping sickness. **X,** Midge. **Y,** Sheep tick.

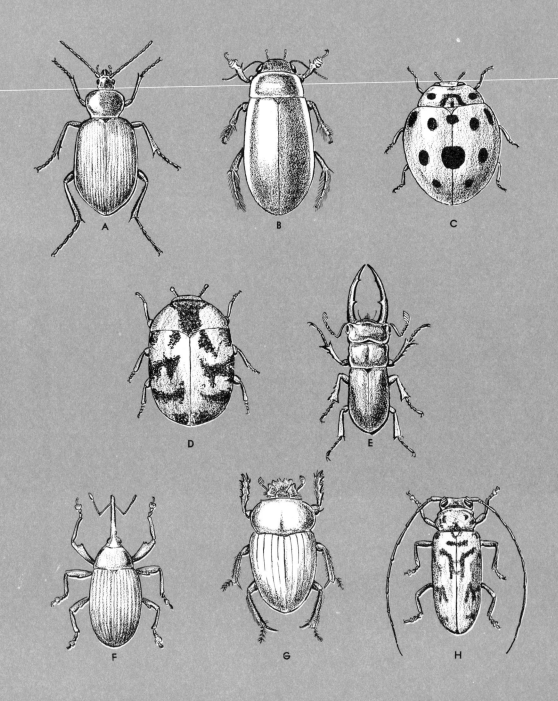

Fig. 25.21 Kinds of beetles. **A**, Ground beetle.
B, Diving beetle. **C**, Ladybird. **D**, Carpet beetle.
E, Stag beetle. **F**, Cotton boll weevil. **G**, Scarab
beetle. **H**, Long-horned beetle.

Coleoptera

The most numerous order of insects is the **Coleoptera,** or beetles. See Figure 25.21. This includes the ladybug, firefly, June bug, and others. The names are often inappropriate. The June bug is a beetle which puts in an appearance in May. The ladybugs are beetles, about half of them male. The firefly is a beetle able to produce a cold light at the posterior end of the abdomen. The larva of this beetle is also able to produce light; this larva is called a glowworm. The significance of light production is uncertain. It is thought that it enables the two sexes to find each other. This does not account for the light production in the larva, or in many other luminescent organisms such as bacteria. Nor does the presence of luminescence in the larva and the bacteria disprove the idea that it helps adult fireflies find each other. Much more study is needed to clarify the phenomenon.

SOCIAL INSECTS

Some members of the Order **Isoptera** (termites) and the Order **Hymenoptera** (bees, wasps, ants) are organized into a complex society. Among termites, for example, some individuals, the royalty, have reproductive organs, and some, the soldiers and the workers, do not. There seem to be degrees of royalty, the primary royalty consisting of males and females with fully developed wings, which have a nuptial flight, start a new colony, and break off their wings. The queen becomes an animated egg factory. Her abdomen greatly enlarges because of the growth of her ovaries. She is one of the few insects that grow continuously without further molting. As can be seen in Figure 25.22, the chitinous thickenings protecting her abdomen are widely separated. Some termite queens are said to produce eggs at the rate of one a second for thirty years. The termite king remains much smaller, and does little except contribute sperm cells to the eggs.

A secondary royalty consists of potentially reproductive males and females, with partially developed wings. In case of the loss of the primary royalty, members of the secondary royalty are pressed into service. A tertiary royalty exists, in even less mature condition than the secondary. Its members do not reproduce unless all of the primary and secondary royalty of a colony are destroyed.

Among the infertile forms are the soldiers and workers, which have no functional reproductive organs and no wings. The soldiers are provided with huge mandibles and

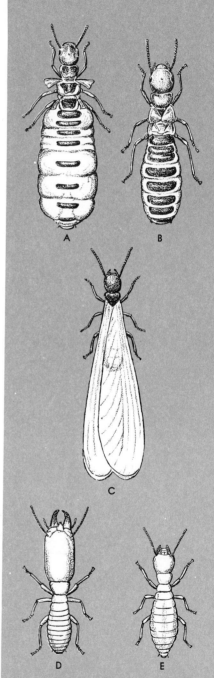

Fig. 25.22 Kinds of termites. **A,** Queen. **B,** King. **C,** Winged royalty. **D,** Soldier. **E,** Worker. What structural differences among these are adapted to their special activities?

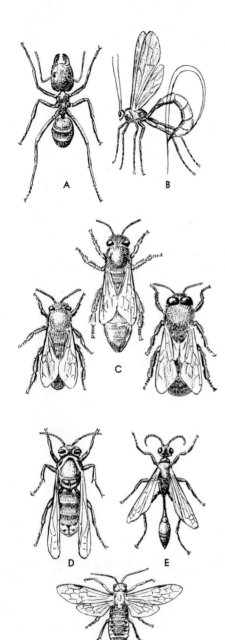

Fig. 25.23 Kinds of Hymenoptera. **A,** Ant soldier. **B,** Ichneumon fly. **C,** Honeybee worker, queen, drone. **D,** Hornet. **E,** Mud dauber wasp. **F,** Sawfly, or rose slug.

protect the colony against invaders. The workers care for the other members of the colony, provide food, tend the developing eggs, and build and maintain the chambers and corridors in which the colony lives. The eggs develop into immature adults of one caste or another without going through differentiated larval stages. The workers infect newly hatched termites with the Hypermastigina (page 356) necessary for the digestion of wood which is the termites' food.

The bees and ants tend more toward a matriarchal society. Males are reproductive individuals only. Among the bees, for example, one queen represents the female royalty. A few drones are the males. The other members of the colony are all immature females, called workers. They collect food and process it into honey, care for the queen, and watch over the developing eggs. The eggs pass through a larval stage, become pupae, and metamorphose into adults. The amount and nature of the food fed the larva determine whether the female will develop into a worker or a queen.

The sex of the bee is determined by its chromosome status. Unfertilized eggs develop into males; fertilized eggs become females. The queen-to-be has a nuptial flight in which she is pursued by drones, and the sperm cells of one drone are transferred to a sperm receptacle over which the queen has control. By opening the receptacle during egg laying, she permits fertilization, which results in females. By keeping the receptacle closed during egg laying, she prevents fertilization, producing males. Since the male is thus haploid (page 262), normal meiosis does not take place in the formation of sperm cells. See Figure 25.23.

ARACHNIDA

The last class of Arthropods to be described in this chapter is the Arachnida. A few unusual forms are sometimes put in additional classes of the phylum, but they will not be further considered here.

The Arachnida include spiders, scorpions, ticks, and other animals. The head and thorax are usually united into a cephalothorax. No antennae or mandibles occur.

Spiders are the most common arachnids. See Figure 25.24. They have six pairs of appendages on the cephalothorax. The first is a pair of **chelicerae,** each with a claw at the tip. Near the end of the claw is an opening of the duct from a poison gland. The second pair of appendages is the **pedipalpi.** These are leglike in form, but have no terminal claws. They serve as sense organs, and in males assist in transferring sperm cells to the females. The remaining four pairs of appendages are walking legs, each with two or three claws at the tip.

The junction between cephalothorax and abdomen is a very narrow stalk. The abdomen is relatively large, without much external evidence of segmentation. Near the posterior end are short, modified appendages, the **spinnerets,** which bear the outlets of the silk glands. The spider may use the silk to spin webs helpful in the capture of prey, in the transfer of sperm from the sperm duct to the pedipalpi, in protecting developing eggs, in molting, or in other activities.

The food of spiders is the fluids of other animals, especially insects. The spider's mouth is very tiny. A captured insect is punctured with the chelicerae and digestive enzymes are poured into the hole. After the soft tissues of the prey are liquefied, the fluid is pumped into the spider's digestive tract by the muscular activity of the sucking stomach. See Figure 25.25.

Food moves from the mouth through the chitin-lined short esophagus and sucking stomach into the intestine. Five pairs of blind sacs branch off the intestine in the cephalothorax, one pair running anteriorly and fusing dorsally to the esophagus, and the other four pairs radiating into the bases of the walking legs.

The intestine then passes into the abdomen, and branches into a finely divided cluster of tubules which fill most of the abdominal cavity. The main trunk of the intestine passes toward the posterior end of the body and empties into the chitin-lined hindgut. At the rectum there is a storage pouch for waste materials which bulges out dorsally from the hindgut. The anus is at the posterior end of the abdomen.

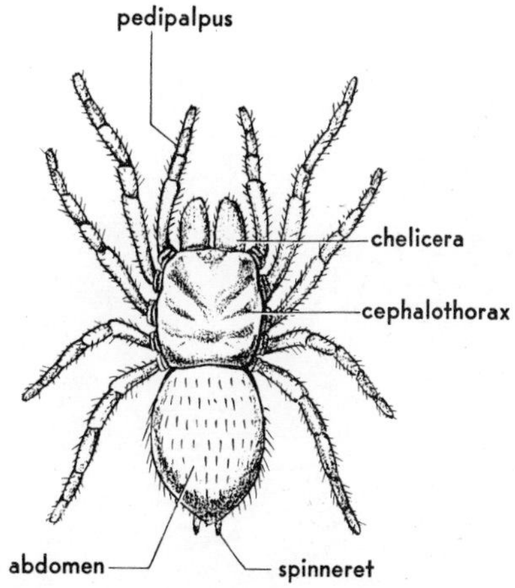

Fig. 25.24   Spider. How do spiders resemble and differ from insects?

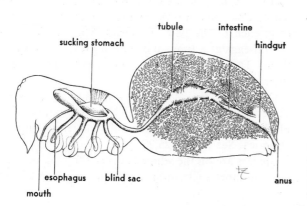

Fig. 25.25   Digestive tract of a spider. The food of a spider is liquefied before it is drawn into the tract by the sucking stomach. It may be stored in the pouches in the cephalothorax and digested in the tubules in the abdomen.

A pair of Malpighian tubules, somewhat branched, serves as the excretory system of the spider. The tubules open into the digestive tract at the junction of intestine and hindgut.

Respiration is accomplished by tracheae opening on the ventral side of the abdomen, and also by a special infolding of the anterior abdominal wall on the ventral side, a structure called the book lung, because the cavity is penetrated by flat sheets of tissue resembling pages in a book. See Figure 25.26. The book lungs are considered to be tracheae of a shape different from the other tracheae of the spider.

Circulation is much like that of other arthropods; there is a dorsal, tubular heart. Blood enters the heart through lateral openings and leaves through anterior and posterior openings.

The nervous system consists of a large mass in the ventral part of the cephalothorax, with a pair of anterior extensions around the esophagus to the brain. Nerves extend from this mass to various parts of the body. This represents a much greater condensation than in the other arthropods. The embryos of spiders show a pair of ganglia in each body segment, but during development these coalesce.

Sense organs include four pairs of simple eyes on the dorsal anterior part of the cephalothorax, hairs sensitive to touch, and openings sensitive to chemicals.

Sexes are separate in spiders. The male has a pair of testes and a pair of sperm ducts. The sperm ducts empty into a common seminal vesicle. When the sperm cells are mature, the male spins a web, and deposits the sperm in this web. Then the pedipalpi pump the sperm cells into cavities in their tips.

The female has a pair of sperm receptacles into which the sperm cells may be placed by the male pedipalpi. The sperm receptacles open into the vagina, which receives an oviduct from each of the pair of ovaries. The female usually lays several eggs at a time, and spins a protective cocoon about them. The embryos hatch into small spiders resembling their parents.

Only a very few of the many kinds of spiders are poisonous enough to harm humans. The large tarantulas and the black widow females are the only dangerous ones in North America. See Figure 25.27.

Spiders are on the whole beneficial to man because of the large number of harmful and annoying insects which they destroy.

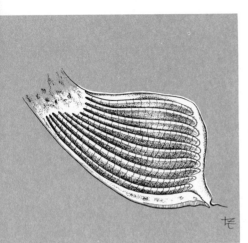

Fig. 25.26 Diagram of a spider book lung. Air enters and leaves through the opening at the lower right. Blood vessels are distributed through the "leaves" of the book, and gas exchanges may take place through the thin walls.

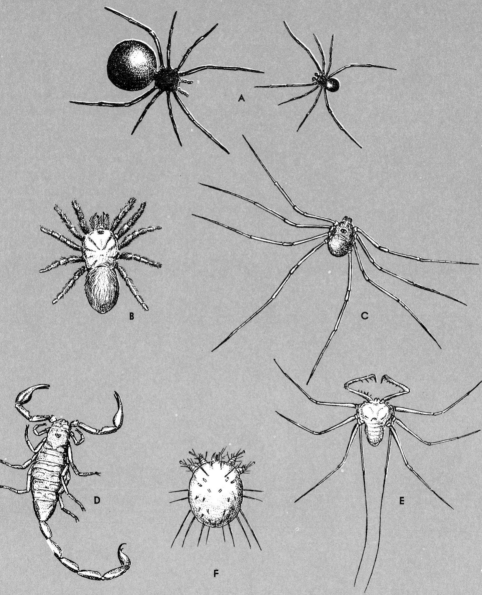

Fig. 25.27 Kinds of arachnids. **A,** Black widow female and male spiders. **B,** Tarantula. **C,** Harvestman, or granddaddy longlegs. **D,** Scorpion. **E,** Whip scorpion. **F,** Itch mite.

SUMMARY

The arthropods are the most numerous and diversified of all the animal phyla. They are characterized by segmentation, differentiation of the organs and appendages of their various segments both in structure and in action, and fusion of some segments.

Arthropods are characterized by a very resistant armor with joints allowing some flexibility of movement. The celom is combined with the circulatory system. The nervous system, especially in Arachnida, has a concentration of ganglia. Growth involves molting, in which the chitinous armor is shed periodically.

With the Arthropoda we have reached the end of a line of increasing specialization. This line passes through the Protozoa, Coelenterata, Platyhelminthes, Nemathelminthes, Annelida, and Arthropoda. In the next three chapters will be discussed three other prominent phyla in the animal kingdom — the Mollusca, the Echinodermata, and the Chordata. These have characteristics peculiar to themselves and efforts to place them in series with the line we have followed thus far have been futile. Their relation to the animals described in Chapters 21–25 constitutes a fascinating challenge to the biologists of today.

REVIEW QUESTIONS

1. Characterize the Arthropoda.
2. Differentiate among the classes of arthropods.
3. Compare and contrast *Peripatus* with other arthropods and with annelids.
4. Describe a centipede.
5. Describe a millipede.
6. Describe a crayfish.
7. Describe other examples of crustacea.
8. Describe a grasshopper.
9. Describe examples of several classes of insects.
10. Of what economic importance to humans are insects?
11. Describe insect societies.
12. Describe a spider.
13. Of what importance to humans are arachnids?
14. What are the advantages and disadvantages to an arthropod of its chitinous armor?
15. Compare the behavior of arthropods with that of the animals previously described in Part III.

GENERAL QUESTIONS

1. Account for the widespread distribution of *Peripatus*, considering that it cannot live in salt water.
2. Would it be feasible to classify *Peripatus* as an annelid?

3. Does the internal development of young *Peripati* indicate a close similarity to the human?
4. Some biologists combine centipedes and millipedes into one class; others believe the centipedes resemble the insects, and the millipedes the arachnids. Is either of these views sound?
5. If the experimental crayfish with iron filings in its statocysts were released in the Mississippi River, would its future behavior be changed because of the iron filings?
6. Are the appendages of a crayfish all variations on one pattern?
7. Write a journalistic account of a crayfish molt.
8. Contrast circulation in earthworm and crayfish.
9. What is the significance of the greater similarity among crustacean larvae than among their adults?
10. Compare the adaptation of structure to habitat in crayfishes and grasshoppers.
11. Is it just to accuse the mantis of hypocrisy?
12. Why do you suppose parthenogenesis is not more common than it is among animals?
13. Compare and contrast human and insect societies.
14. If possible, observe a spider spinning a web, and write an account of the process.
15. What characteristics of arthropods make them so successful in increasing their numbers and variety?

Mollusca

CHARACTERISTICS OF MOLLUSCS

The molluscs are unsegmented, bilaterally symmetrical animals. Some live in the ocean, some in fresh water, and some on land. They have the same internal and environmental problems, and the same kind of organ systems as other complex animals. Their bodies are soft, a fact from which the name **mollusc** is derived. They have a fleshy covering, the **mantle,** over the body and separated from other parts of the body by a **mantle cavity.** Many secrete a limy shell about themselves.

Molluscs are usually divided into six classes:

I. Solenogastres: wormlike animals with small mantles and mantle cavities.

II. Amphineura: chitons, primitive types with a shell composed of eight dorsal plates.

III. Scaphopoda: with long, conical shells.

IV. Pelecypoda: clams, with a shell composed of right and left parts.

V. Gastropoda: with spiral shells or no shell at all.

VI. Cephalopoda: also with spiral shells, or with a reduced internal skeleton. See Figure 26.1.

The first three classes are small groups of theoretical interest, but not common enough to be well known.

PELECYPODA

Clams

In general structure, clams are much alike, although shape may vary considerably. The following discussion applies to either fresh-water clams such as *Anodonta grandis*, or marine clams such as *Venus mercenaria*.

Mantle

The mantle of a clam is much more extensive than the body. It forms a very loose cloak over the animal, fastened to the body along the middorsal line. The mantle is symmetrically divided into right and left sides. Each side secretes one **valve** of the limy shell.

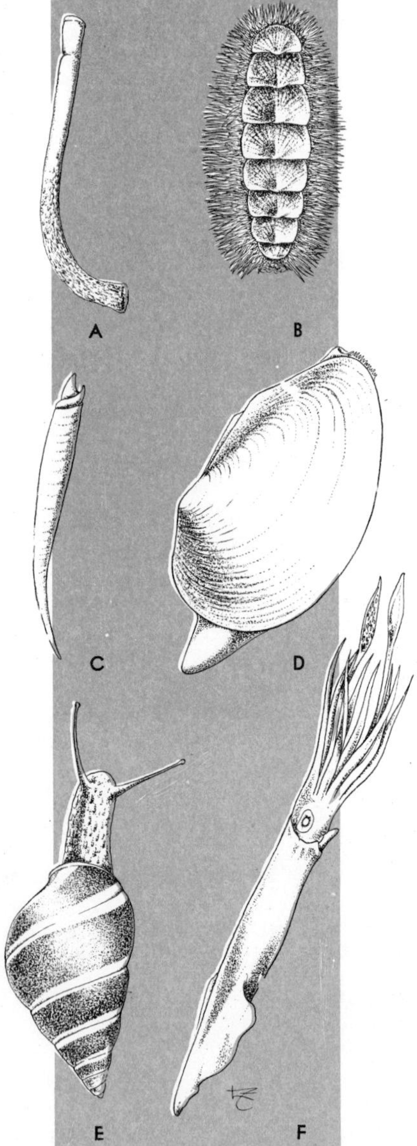

Fig. 26.1 Some kinds of molluscs. **A,** Solenogaster. **B,** Amphineuran, a chiton. **C,** Scaphopod, or tusk shell. **D,** Pelecypod, or clam. **E,** Gastropod, or snail. **F,** Cephalopod, or squid.

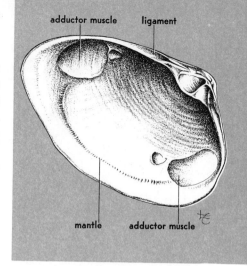

Fig. 26.2   Clam shell structure. How does a clam close the shell? How does it open the shell?

Shell

The two valves are connected dorsally by an elastic ligament which tends to pull the dorsal edges of the valves together, and thus separate the ventral edges. This action is opposed by two powerful **adductor muscles** running from one valve to the other at the anterior and posterior ends of the body. See Figure 26.2.

Growth of the mantle along its ventral margin is followed by secreted additions to the valves ventrally, and growth lines are often apparent concentrically arranged about the earliest part of the shell, which is called the **umbo.**

The outermost layer of the shell is a horny material which is resistant to the acids and salts in the water, and partly protects the limy parts from being dissolved. Beneath this is a crystalline layer of calcium carbonate in which the crystals are little prisms perpendicular to the horny layer. The innermost layer of the shell is a series of thin sheets of calcium carbonate parallel to the horny layer, and called the **pearly layer.** If any object such as a parasite or a grain of sand gets between the mantle and the shell, the mantle deposits thin layers of calcium carbonate around the object, and the result is a pearl. Pearl culture is accomplished by the deliberate introduction of some object under the shell of a clam by an interested human. After some time, the clam is opened, and the pearl-incrusted object removed. See Figure 26.3.

Siphons

The clam is usually partly buried in the bottom of the river or ocean in which it lives. The posterior end of the clam protrudes above the bottom. Two slitlike openings occur between the sides of the posterior end of the mantle. These are the **siphons,** concerned with the circulation of water through the mantle cavity. The linings of the siphons are ciliated and create water currents in at the ventral siphon and out at the dorsal siphon.

Foot

Within the mantle cavity is the body of the clam. The body is much smaller than the cavity. A large, muscular lobe projecting ventrally and anteriorly from the body is called the **foot.** This is used in the slow, ponderous locomotion of the clam. The adductor muscles relax, allowing the valves to be separated ventrally. Then the foot is extended as a sort of spearhead into the sand or mud ahead. Blood is forced into the tip of the foot, causing it to swell into a knoblike anchor. Then muscles in the foot contract,

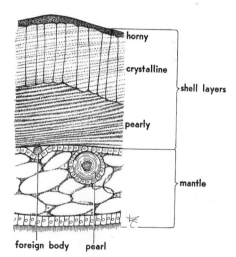

Fig. 26.3   Formation of a pearl. The outer surface of the mantle is very sensitive. If a foreign body happens to become wedged between the mantle and the shell, the mantle secretes a pearly layer over the foreign body. This may smooth any rough edges, but it does not remove the irritant; so the mantle continues to secrete pearl around the object as long as the mantle is alive and able to respond.

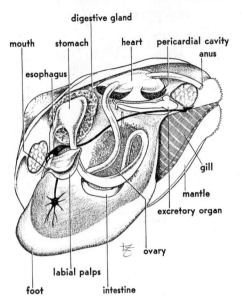

digestive gland

mouth   stomach   heart   pericardial cavity
                                    anus

esophagus

gill

mantle

excretory organ

ovary

labial palps

foot   intestine

Fig. 26.4   Digestive tract of a clam. How does food reach the mouth?

drawing the rest of the clam up toward the anchored foot. Then the foot is extended again, swells, getting a "foothold," and pulls the body forward once more. This is a very laborious means of travel. However, since the clam is well protected from its enemies, and since its food consists of small organisms drawn into the mantle cavity with the water currents, speed does not seem to be important.

Food-Getting

On each side of the body there are two very large folds, the **gills.** The surfaces of the gills are ciliated. As the water drawn in through the ventral siphon sweeps over the gills, larger particles drop to the bottom of the mantle cavity and are passed out of the shell. Smaller particles which might have a food value are caught in the film of mucus on the gills and carried to the mouth by ciliary action.

Digestive Tract

At the anterior end of the body, there are two folds on each side of the mouth. These folds, or **labial palps,** are also ciliated, and aid in passing food into the mouth. The food travels through a short esophagus into the enlarged stomach. See Figure 26.4.

The stomach is almost completely surrounded by a digestive gland which secretes enzymes into the stomach by way of ducts. These enzymes contribute to the breakdown of proteins and fats.

In some species of clams there is a special organ, the **crystalline style,** developed in a little pouch off the stomach. This is a rodlike structure containing an enzyme which is involved in carbohydrate digestion. This rod grows in the pouch and rubs against a hardened part of the stomach wall, grinding off particles of enzyme into the food.

The stomach opens into the intestine, which turns ventrally and coils about in the base of the foot. Then it curves dorsally again and passes through the small celom, over the posterior adductor muscle, and empties into the dorsal siphon by way of the anus.

Gills

The gills constitute the chief part of the clam's respiratory system. Each gill is fastened at its dorsal margin, dips down into the mantle cavity, and folds back up along itself to attach again to the dorsal margin. On each side of the body, the outer gill is attached by one dorsal edge to the mantle and by the other dorsal edge to the inner gill. The inner gill is attached here to the outer gill, dips down, and returns to a dorsal attachment to the body. See Figure 26.5.

Each gill surface is penetrated by numerous tiny pores through which water is passed by ciliary action from the outside of the gill fold to the central cavity of the gill. Water from these central cavities is forced out through the dorsal siphon. Thus, a great deal of gill surface is exposed to the water, and exchange of carbon dioxide and oxygen occurs.

Nephridia

Ventral to the part of the intestine which passes through the celom are the two excretory organs, or **nephridia.** Each nephridium opens into the celom by a ciliated funnel. The funnel leads to a slender tube lined with secretory cells. This tube enlarges into a bladder, which empties posteriorly into the cavity of the dorsal siphon. See Figure 26.6A.

Circulatory System

In the celom and surrounding the intestine is the heart. This consists of a pair of lateral auricles connected to a single median ventricle. When the ventricle contracts, it forces the colorless blood out the two ends into the anterior aorta and the posterior aorta. Each aorta sends branches to the mantle, and then empties the rest of the blood into the body tissues. Pressure exerted by the heart and bodily movements forces the blood through the body, although it is not contained in closed vessels here. The blood collects

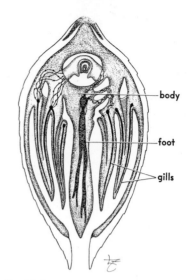

Fig. 26.5   Arrangement of the gills in a clam.

Fig. 26.6   Clam excretory, circulatory, and nervous systems. **A,** Excretory and circulatory systems. Vessels shown in white are arteries, and vessels shown in black are veins. **B,** Nervous system. Three pairs of ganglia and the connecting nerve cords shown in black.

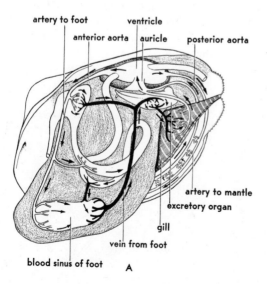

artery to foot · ventricle · anterior aorta · auricle · posterior aorta · artery to mantle · excretory organ · gill · vein from foot · blood sinus of foot

A

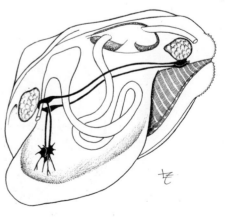

B

in a sinus ventral to the celom, and passes by way of veins along the nephridia and through the gills. From here the blood, together with that returning from the mantle, passes to the auricles. This blood, well aerated, empties into the ventricle, and is forced out the aortae again. See again Figure 26.6A–B.

Nervous System

The nervous system is relatively simple. Three pairs of ganglia occur. One is just posterior and ventral to the anterior adductor muscle, dorsal to the esophagus. This pair sends nerves to the mantle and nerve trunks to each of the other two pairs of ganglia.

The second pair of ganglia is in the base of the foot and helps regulate foot movements. In close association with these second ganglia is an equilibrium organ consisting of a small chamber containing a limy pebble secreted by the clam. The position of the pebble pressing against the chamber walls stimulates a nerve impulse by which the clam is sensitive to its position with respect to gravity.

The third pair of ganglia is just ventral and anterior to the posterior adductor muscle. Associated with these ganglia is a patch of epithelium sensitive to chemical stimuli in the water coming in the ventral siphon. See Figure 26.6B.

Reproduction

The reproductive organs are carried in the base of the foot. There is a pair of testes or a pair of ovaries which, during the breeding season, enlarge and surround the loops of the intestine in this region. Each reproductive organ opens by means of a tiny pore near the opening of the nephridium on that side.

Fig. 26.7 Trochophore larva, A, and glochidium, B, of a clam.

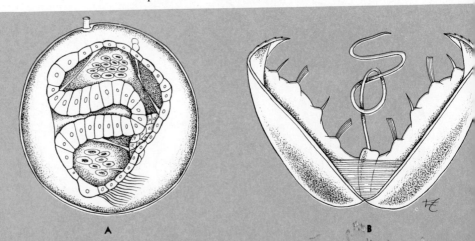

A   B

In marine clams, the sperms and eggs are shed into the sea water. Fertilized eggs develop into trochophore larvae resembling those of polychete annelids. These develop eventually into mature clams.

In fresh-water forms, the sperm cells are swept out the dorsal siphon of the male and into the ventral siphon of the female. The fertilized eggs collect in the gills of the female, and pass through the early embryonic stages there. After several months the young clams, called **glochidia,** leave the parent and continue existence if they happen to encounter a fish. They live as parasites on the skin or gills of the fish for several weeks, then drop off and become independent adult clams. The swimming trochophore larva and the parasitic glochidium accomplish wide distribution of their respective species. See Figure 26.7.

Other Pelecypoda

The Class Pelecypoda to which the clam belongs includes also oysters, scallops, and other forms used as food by humans. The shells of some of these animals have been used as poultry feed and as a source of buttons. Pearls have a commercial value dependent upon size and color. One pelecypod, *Teredo*, uses its shell to burrow into wood; it may cause damage to wharf pilings, wooden boats, and other structures. See Figure 26.8.

Fig. 26.8   Kinds of pelecypods. **A,** Fresh-water clam. **B,** Marine clam. **C,** File shell clam. **D,** Rock-boring clam. **E,** Jackknife clam.

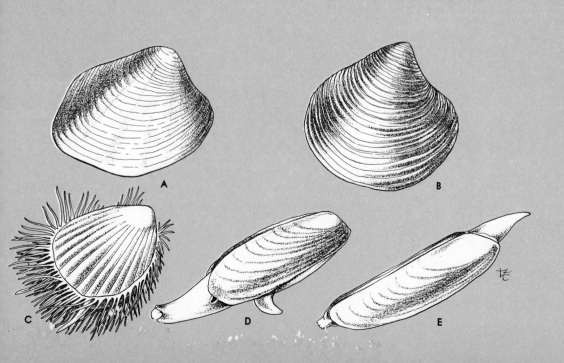

GASTROPODA

The Class Gastropoda includes the snails and slugs. Snails have a one-piece shell, often spirally coiled. Some species live in salt water, some in fresh water, and some on land. Snails have a much more highly developed head than clams. The snail head bears eyes at the tips of tentacles. The foot is a broad, flattened projection which secretes a band of mucus on which the snail travels, beating its way along the mucus by cilia on the foot. Many snails are hermaphroditic. Aquatic snails have a trochophore larva.

The slugs are without shells and are not spirally coiled. Otherwise they resemble snails. See Figure 26.9.

Both snails and slugs harbor parasites. Some of these parasites are intermediate stages which may be passed on to another host. For example, one oriental snail harbors the larva of a fluke whose adult parasitizes birds. The eggs of the fluke are dropped with the feces of birds. If some of these eggs get on a leaf which the snail eats, the fluke larva develops within the snail, and migrates to the tentacle. Here the larva enlarges, and develops brightly colored stripes. The tentacle twitches as a result of the irritation caused by the fluke larva. This brightly colored, twitching object attracts the attention of birds, and a bird may bite off the tentacle or eat the whole snail, thus becoming infected with the parasite.

Fig. 26.9   Kinds of gastropods. **A,** Marine snail shell. **B,** Fresh-water snail shell. **C,** Land slug. **D,** Marine shell-less snail. **E,** Sea hare.

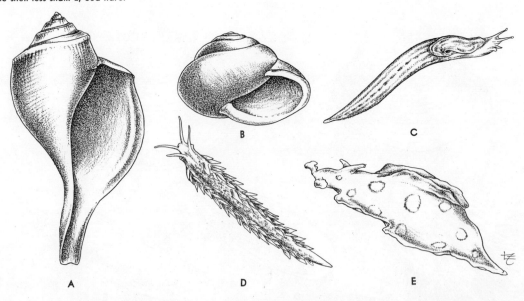

A   D   E

CEPHALOPODA

The Class Cephalopoda includes the squids, octopi, and nautili, all marine animals. The nautilus has a spiral shell with chambers added on to it as the animal grows. This habit is described in Oliver Wendell Holmes' familiar poem, "The Chambered Nautilus."

The Chambered Nautilus

This is the ship of pearl, which, poets feign,
    Sails the unshadowed main —
    The venturous bark that flings
On the sweet summer wind its purpled wings
In gulfs enchanted, where the Siren sings,
    And coral reefs lie bare,
Where the cold sea-maids rise to sun their streaming hair.

Its webs of living gauze no more unfurl;
    Wrecked is the ship of pearl!
    And every chambered cell,
Where its dim dreaming life was wont to dwell,
As the frail tenant shaped his growing shell,
    Before thee lies revealed —
Its irised ceiling rent, its sunless crypt unsealed!

Year after year beheld the silent toil
    That spread his lustrous coil;
    Still, as the spiral grew,
He left the past year's dwelling for the new,
Stole with soft step its shining archway through,
    Built up its idle door,
Stretched in his last-found home, and knew the old no more.

Thanks for the heavenly message brought by thee,
    Child of the wandering sea,
    Cast from her lap, forlorn!
From thy dead lips a clearer note is born
Than ever Triton blew from wreathed horn!
    While on mine ears it rings,
Through the deep caves of thought I hear a voice that sings:

Build thee more stately mansions, O my soul,
    As the swift seasons roll!
    Leave thy low-vaulted past!
Let each new temple, nobler than the last,
Shut thee from heaven with a dome more vast,
    Till thou at length art free,
Leaving thine outgrown shell by life's unresting sea!
           — OLIVER WENDELL HOLMES

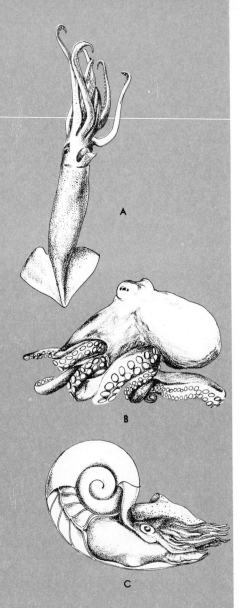

Fig. 26.10 Some kinds of cephalopods. A, Squid. B, Octopus. C, Nautilus. Part of the nautilus shell has been cut away, showing the internal chambers.

The octopus and squid resemble the nautilus but are without an external shell. The squid has an internal skeleton consisting of a stiff chitinous blade imbedded in the mantle. The octopus has an even more reduced internal skeleton of two small pieces.

The cephalopod "foot" is a number of long tentacles bearing suckers. There are eight tentacles in an octopus, ten in a squid, and about ninety in a nautilus. The posterior end of the foot is modified to form a funnel connecting the mantle cavity with the outside. Contraction of the mantle forces water out of the mantle cavity through the funnel, resulting in a sort of jet propulsion of the animal. By turning the funnel in different directions the mollusc can steer itself.

Many cephalopods possess a pigment-secreting organ known as the **ink sac.** This produces a dense, dark substance which may be ejected into the water, clouding the water so that enemies are unable to see. This may provide cover for the escape of the animal if he is pursued. This is a sort of smoke screen, a device which, like that of jet propulsion, has been independently developed by man and adapted to his own purposes.

Cephalopods have a pair of large, efficient eyes, and a well-developed nervous system. They are by far the speediest and most active group of molluscs. Unlike clams and snails, cephalopods have a closed circulatory system.

The giant squid is the largest of invertebrates, reaching fifty feet in length. Such an animal even attacks whales.

Like other cephalopods, the squid has powerful beaklike jaws with which it can tear off pieces from the animals on which it preys. Its great speed and the reach of its long, sucker-bearing tentacles enable it to capture almost any marine animal it wishes for food. See Figure 26.10.

SUMMARY

The molluscs are a special phylum unlike most others except for the trochophore larva. Molluscs are unsegmented, and have a characteristic mantle and foot and fairly well-developed organ systems. They vary greatly in habit from the slow-moving or stationary clams without well-developed heads or nervous systems, through the slow-moving but alert snails with good heads and more highly developed nervous systems, to the extremely active squids with excellent nervous equipment.

REVIEW QUESTIONS

1. Characterize the Mollusca.
2. Differentiate among the classes of molluscs.
3. Describe the structure of a clam.
4. Explain the process of pearl formation.
5. How do clams travel?
6. How do clams obtain food?
7. Describe reproduction in clams.
8. Of what commercial importance are pelecypods?
9. Describe the Gastropoda.
10. Describe the Cephalopoda.

GENERAL QUESTIONS

1. Describe the changes in mantle and shell as a clam grows.
2. Describe the nerve impulses and muscular responses involved in clam locomotion.
3. The way to a clam's heart is through its stomach and intestine. Is there any advantage in having the intestine pass through the heart?
4. Of what advantage is the gill as a brood pouch for clam embryos?
5. Trace the pathway of water into and out of a clam.
6. What is the significance, if any, of the similarity of the larvae of aquatic snails and of polychetes?
7. What characteristics of snails predispose them to act as intermediate hosts for parasitic flatworms?
8. The nautilus inhabits the ocean surface, the squid the intermediate levels, and the octopus the ocean bottom. Is there any correlation between habitat and structure in these three cephalopods?
9. What causal relationships, if any, exist between the speed of cephalopods and their highly developed nervous system and eyes?
10. Is the absence of segmentation in molluscs a beneficial or detrimental feature?

CHAPTER 27

Echinodermata

The echinoderms are all marine animals which pass through bilaterally symmetrical stages during their embryonic development, but assume radial symmetry in the adult. Characteristically parts are repeated in fives or multiples of five. This is a serial repetition of parts such as occurs in segmented worms and arthropods, except that the echinoderms repeat in a circle instead of a straight line.

The name *echinoderm* comes from the Greek for "spiny skin." Limy plates are imbedded in the skin, and often these bear spines which project through the skin and protect the animal from some enemies.

Five classes of living echinoderms are recognized:

I. The Asteroidea, including the starfishes. These have a central disc from which radiate five arms, or in some cases more than five. There is no sharp boundary between disc and arms. Limy plates are loosely imbedded in the skin.

II. The Ophiuroidea, or brittle stars. These are somewhat like starfishes, except that the disc is sharply marked off from the arms, and the skin plates are more closely knit together.

III. The Echinoidea, or sea urchins. These have the five arms pulled up over the disc and fused to each other along their edges, so that the whole animal is enclosed in a box made of the joined plates in the skin.

IV. The Holothurioidea, or sea cucumbers. These have five arms incorporated into the body, but their skin plates are very few, and the skin is soft and fleshy.

V. The Crinoidea, or sea lilies. These have five arms which are much branched, producing the appearance of long, coarse feathers projecting from a small central disc. They have closely joined plates in the skin.

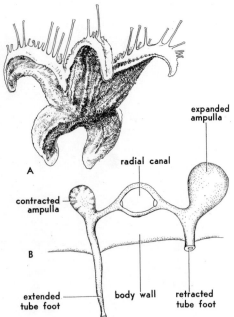

A

expanded ampulla

radial canal

contracted ampulla

B

extended tube foot

body wall

retracted tube foot

Fig. 27.1 Starfish tube feet. **A,** Starfish moving. **B,** Detail of one pair of tube feet. When the ampulla contracts, water is forced into the tube foot, making that foot longer and stiffer. Contractions of muscles in the tip of the foot draw back the center of the foot, forming a suction cup. When the ampulla relaxes, water flows back into it, and the tube foot collapses.

ASTEROIDEA

The Starfish

The starfish is the most generally known echinoderm, and its anatomy and physiology will be described as representative of the phylum. *Asterias forbesi* is common along the Atlantic coast of the United States south of Cape Cod.

External Anatomy

The <u>mouth</u> of the starfish is in the center of the ventral side of the disc. The ventral side of the arms is provided with a large number of short, tentaclelike projections, the **tube feet.** See Figure 27.1. These tube feet are important in locomotion. Each tube foot is a cylindrical tube projecting through the skin and connected on the inside of the animal with a bulb, the **ampulla.** The tube foot is full of water. When the ampulla contracts, more water is forced into the tube foot, which is extended. If the extended tip of the foot makes contact with some solid object such as a stone, the ampulla may relax slightly, and the flat, circular tip of the tube foot becomes concave, acting as a sucker to grip the stone. Then longitudinal muscles in the wall of the tube foot contract, pulling the body of the starfish toward the stone. When the tube foot is shortened by this contraction, the ampulla may again force water into the tube foot. This releases the suckerlike tip and extends the tube foot again.

One tube foot alone is quite weak, but many collaborate in moving the starfish from place to place. This movement is relatively quite slow.

The dorsal surface of the starfish has no tube feet, but is provided with spines, gills, and **pedicellariae.** The <u>spines</u> are projections from the skeletal plates imbedded in the skin. The spines project through the skin, and contribute to the pebbly, rough external appearance characteristic of the starfish.

The <u>gills</u> are tiny outpouchings of thin places in the skin. Through these gills carbon dioxide diffuses out of the animal and oxygen diffuses in.

The **pedicellariae** are tiny, pincerlike structures with which the animal protects itself against some attackers. They also serve to keep debris from accumulating by picking up solid particles and moving them from one to another pedicellaria until they are dropped over the edge of the starfish. They are especially active in keeping the surface of the gills clean. See Figure 27.2.

Digestive Tract

The mouth opens into a very short, narrow <u>esophagus</u>, which expands into the large <u>stomach</u>. Dorsal to the stomach is a somewhat <u>smaller intestine</u>. Emptying into the intestine are the <u>ducts</u> of two digestive glands in each arm. From the intestine a very narrow <u>rectum</u> leads to the <u>anus</u> on the dorsal side of the disc. Two small pouches, the **rectal ceca,** open into the <u>rectum</u>. See Figure 27.3.

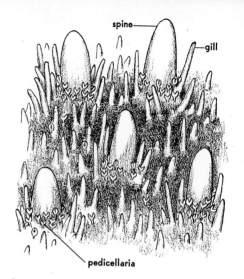

Fig. 27.2 Detail of starfish skin. Note the large spines, the pincerlike pedicellariae, and the fingerlike gills.

The food of the starfish consists of marine molluscs, arthropods, worms, or other animals. Clams and oysters are especially common victims and starfish cause much damage in commercial oyster beds. When the slow starfish overtakes the slower clam, the clam closes its shell. The starfish fastens onto one valve of the clam shell with many tube feet from one arm, and onto the other valve with tube feet from another arm. Then the starfish pulls at the clam shell. If the clam is small, the shell may open soon. If the clam is large, it may resist the pull for some time. When the tube feet of the starfish tire, other tube feet are used, and the starfish may shift to another two arms. The clam has no second team to send into the game, however, and eventually its muscles become fatigued and the shell opens.

The starfish then everts its stomach through its mouth and into the mantle cavity surrounding the body of the clam. Enzymes from the starfish's digestive glands and intestine digest the clam in its own shell, and then the stomach is withdrawn into the starfish, bringing the digested food with it.

Very little waste is brought back into the starfish. Indigestible materials usually drop out of the mouth. The food is absorbed through the walls of the digestive tract. The rectal ceca contribute excretory products to the rectum, and these are passed out through the anus.

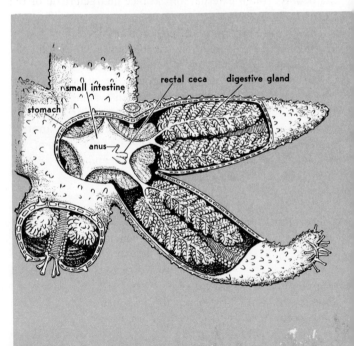

Fig. 27.3 Starfish digestive system. How can the starfish get along with such a tiny anus?

Celom

Surrounding the digestive tract and penetrating the arms is the celom. Waste materials from the organs and tissues of the body diffuse into the celom. Liquids and dissolved gases may diffuse out of the celom through the gills. Solid wastes are picked up by amebalike cells wandering through the celomic fluid. These cells, when they are filled with wastes, crawl out through the gills and are lost in the ocean. They resemble somewhat the white blood corpuscles of humans.

Circulatory Systems

The blood circulatory system consists of a ring around the esophagus from which one branched vessel extends into each arm and a ring near the dorsal surface from which vessels extend to the reproductive organs. The two rings are connected with each other by a vertical vessel. The blood has white corpuscles only.

Paralleling the ventral part of the blood circulatory system is a water circulatory system. This, too, has a **ring canal** around the esophagus, and a branched vessel, the **radial canal,** in each arm just dorsal to the corresponding blood vessels. The branches are short, perpendicular tubes leading to the tube feet just below the ampullae. The branches alternate long and short as illustrated in Figure 27.4.

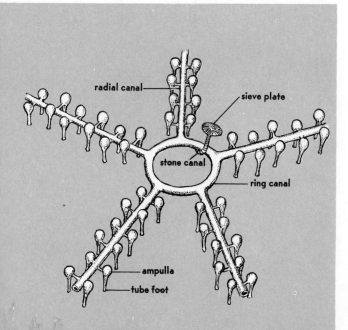

Fig. 27.4 Water vascular system of a starfish. Water enters at the sieve plate and diffuses out through the tube feet.

Paralleling the vertical vessel of the blood system is a vertical **stone canal** of the water system. This canal opens through the dorsal surface by means of a **sieve plate** through which sea water is filtered and drawn into the system. Cilia keep up the pressure in the water tubes by replacing water diffused out from the tube feet.

Nervous System

The nervous system follows a pattern similar to the blood system, and external to it. The nerve ring around the mouth is connected to a nerve trunk in each arm. A dorsal ring around the anus has branches supplying the dorsal surface of the body. The tips of the ventral nerve trunks end in a pigmented, light-sensitive eyespot at the end of each arm.

Reproduction

Sexes are separate in starfishes. In the angle between each two arms are the openings of reproductive organs. Each arm contains two of these organs. See Figure 27.5. The testes produce sperm cells and empty them into the ocean. The ovaries of a female starfish produce egg cells which are also shed into the ocean. Here fertilization may occur. The fertilized eggs become larvae, bilateral in symmetry, and having bands of cilia and internal structures much like those of the annelid and mollusc trochophore

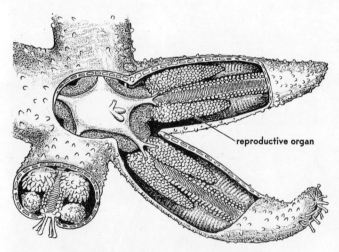

Fig. 27.5   Reproductive system of the starfish.

larvae. After these larvae swim about for a time, they metamorphose into the adult, changing from bilateral to radial symmetry.

Regeneration

Starfishes have considerable powers of regeneration. An arm and part of the disc are able to regenerate an entire animal. Since the starfish is such a menace to clams and oysters, the oyster fishermen attempt to get rid of them. By sweeping across an oyster bed with a long mop, the fishermen dredge up the starfishes. When a fiber of the mop is drawn across a starfish, the pedicellariae close over it and hang on. When the mop is pulled out of the water, the starfish are taken off. Formerly the fishermen simply tore the starfishes in two and threw them back. Some of them were eaten by other animals, and some became infected and died. But some regenerated. When this was discovered, the starfishes were no longer thrown back, but were hauled to the land and used as fertilizer.

If a live starfish is held by an arm, or if the arm is injured, the starfish may break off its own arm, a process known as **autotomy**. This ability is present in many animals, such as most of the arthropods. The lost arm may then be regenerated.

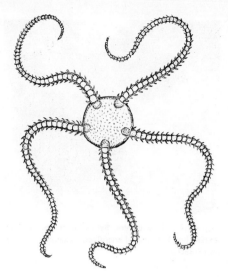

OPHIUROIDEA

Brittle stars (Fig. 27.6) are much like starfishes in general, although their tube feet are not very effective as locomotor organs. The brittle star tube feet are chiefly sensory organs, although some respiratory and excretory activities may also be carried on here. They travel by means of muscular movements of their slender arms pushing against the ocean bottom and make much more speed than do the starfishes. Their ready autotomy gives the name "brittle star" to these animals.

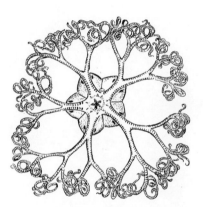

Fig. 27.6   Brittle stars.

The arms do not contain any of the viscera, but consist of muscles and skeleton, plus branches of the circulatory and nervous systems and celom. The nerve cords in the arms have ganglia along them. The nervous equipment of the brittle star seems to be better than that of a starfish, correlated with the more rapid movement, although brittle stars have no eyespots.

The digestive system is reduced to a small mouth, an esophagus, and a large stomach. Small pieces of food are taken in, and undigested material is dropped from the mouth.

Reproduction, embryology, and metamorphosis resemble those of the starfish.

ECHINOIDEA

In the sea urchin (Fig. 27.7) the skeleton is fused to form a rigid box through which protrude the tube feet and the spines. The spines are movably jointed to the box and can be operated by muscles so that a traveling sea urchin looks as if it were walking on stilts. The ventral tube feet are long enough to extend beyond the spines and may be used in locomotion as in the starfish. The dorsal tube feet are sensory.

The sea urchin has a set of five powerful teeth with which it can pick off pieces of food from the animals it eats or scrape algae from rocks. The internal systems are not greatly different from those of other echinoderms. The sea urchin eggs and embryos have been studied extensively in an effort to understand the process of embryonic development.

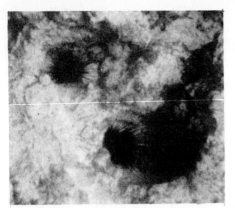

Fig. 27.7 Sea urchins. Below, close-up. To what extent has this animal sacrificed locomotor powers to protection?

HOLOTHURIOIDEA

Sea cucumbers (Fig. 27.8) live mostly buried in the sand or mud at the bottom of the ocean near the shore. They are soft bodied with a very muscular body wall. Around the mouth is a circle of tentacles. Two internal gill-like respiratory organs connect with the anus and water is pumped into these, aiding in gaseous exchange.

When the sea cucumber is molested by an enemy, such as a lobster, it may contract its body wall so forcibly that its internal organs are squeezed out of and broken away from its body in the face of the attacker. Some of the secretions accompanying these viscera are very sticky, and while the surprised enemy is untangling himself from the viscera, the body wall wriggles down into the sea floor out of reach. In a few weeks a new set of organs is regenerated, although the sea cucumber is now smaller than it was. If not irritated further, it will grow, however.

CRINOIDEA

Most of the adult sea lilies (Fig. 27.9) are attached to rocks or other solid objects by stalks. The arms are highly branched, and ciliated grooves on them bring food particles to the mouth. The tube feet are sensory and not locomotor organs. The internal structures are like those of other echinoderms. Sea lilies live in deeper water than most other echinoderms, and are not so commonly found along the seashore as the members of the other four classes.

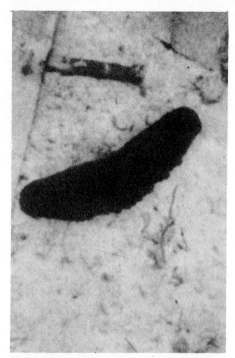

Fig. 27.8 Sea cucumbers. Lower, photograph of a glass model. How would you recognize that this is an echinoderm?

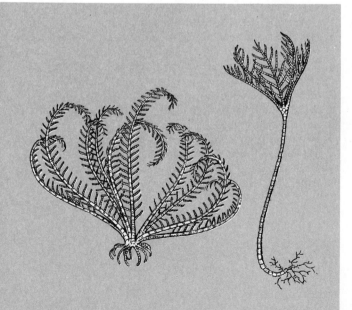

Fig. 27.9 Sea lilies.

SUMMARY

The Echinoderms are all marine animals which metamorphose from bilateral, free-swimming larvae to radial,
stationary or slow-moving adults. No parasitic echinoderms
are known. A water-circulatory system in addition to the
blood system is peculiar to and characteristic of echinoderms. The digestive and nervous systems are simpler
than those of arthropods, but more complex than those of
flatworms. In general, though, they resemble other more
complex animals in their bodily organization.

REVIEW QUESTIONS

1. Characterize the Echinodermata.
2. Differentiate among the classes of echinoderms.
3. Describe the structure of a starfish.
4. Describe locomotion in a starfish.
5. Describe the activity of pedicellariae.
6. Describe reproduction and regeneration in the starfish.
7. Describe a brittle star.
8. Describe a sea urchin.
9. Describe a sea cucumber.
10. Describe a sea lily.

GENERAL QUESTIONS

1. Why do you suppose there are no fresh-water echinoderms?
2. Describe the nervous and muscular actions involved in the
   removal of a piece of debris from a starfish by the bucket
   brigade of pedicellariae.
3. Write a journalistic play-by-play account of a battle between
   a large starfish and a large clam.
4. Describe in detail the regeneration of an arm in a starfish.
5. Describe the appearance of the cut surface of a starfish disc
   bisected dorsoventrally through the madreporite.
6. Is the relative speediness of brittle stars correlated with
   structural peculiarities?
7. Describe locomotion in sea urchins.
8. Write a journalistic account of a battle between a lobster
   and a sea cucumber.
9. Is there a causal correlation between the deeper habitat of
   sea lilies and their habit of attachment by stalks?
10. What is the significance, if any, of the change of symmetry
    from larva to adult in echinoderms?

CHAPTER 28

Chordata

CLASSIFICATION OF CHORDATES

The chordates include the most familiar of all animals, including man. The phylum name is derived from one constant characteristic, the possession of a **notochord** at some stage in the animal's life. The notochord is a stiff rod passing longitudinally along the animal. It serves as a support, or internal skeleton, during early development, and in some of the chordates it is present throughout life.

Chordates have their central nervous system on the dorsal, rather than the ventral side. It consists of a hollow tube enlarged at the anterior end rather than a ventral chain of ganglia such as is found in annelids or arthropods. The chordate heart is ventral to the digestive tract, in contrast again to annelids and arthropods. The circulatory system is closed. The respiratory system of chordates, unlike that of other animals, is derived from the pharynx. Chordates are bilaterally symmetrical.

There are four subphyla of Chordata, but only one, the **Vertebrata,** will be described in detail. The other three — **Hemichordata** (acorn worms), **Urochordata** (sea squirts), and **Cephalochordata** (lancelets) — are relatively inconspicuous and few in number of species. They are all marine. See Figure 28.1.

VERTEBRATES

The Subphylum Vertebrata includes those animals in which the supporting action of the notochord is partly or wholly taken over in the adult by a vertebral column. The vertebrate embryo always develops a notochord, and this may remain throughout life in some vertebrates, but is lost during later development in others.

The structure and physiology of one vertebrate, the human, was described in Part I of this book. Compare the structure of man with the characteristics of chordates and of vertebrates as given in the preceding paragraphs.

The seven classes of living vertebrates are:

I. Cyclostomata: with cartilage skeletons, no jaws, no scales, no paired appendages, and with a persistent notochord.

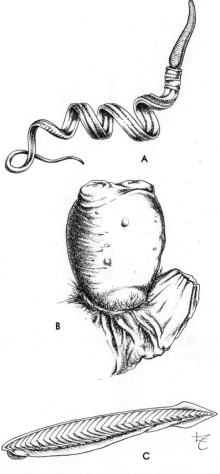

Fig. 28.1 Some nonvertebrate chordates. **A,** Hemichordate — acorn worm. **B,** Urochordate — sea squirt. **C,** Cephalochordate — amphioxus, or lancelet.

II. Elasmobranchii: with cartilage skeletons, jaws, scales, paired fins, and a persistent notochord.

III. Pisces: with bony skeletons, jaws, scales, and paired fins, but with the notochord disappearing in the adult.

IV. Amphibia: with bony skeletons, jaws, no scales, paired legs, disappearing notochord, and no neck.

V. Reptilia: with bony skeletons, jaws, scales, paired legs, neck, and notochord disappearing in the adult.

VI. Mammalia: with bony skeletons, jaws, hair, paired legs, neck, and no notochord in the adults.

VII. Aves: with bony skeletons, jaws, feathers, paired wings and legs, neck, and no notochord in the adult.

Cyclostomata

The **Cyclostomata** include hagfishes and lampreys. These animals are aquatic, and get their food by attacking living fishes and sucking blood or tearing off pieces of flesh. See Figure 28.2.

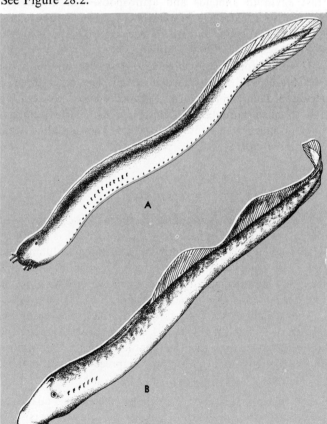

Fig. 28.2 Kinds of cyclostomes. A, Hagfish. B, Lamprey.

The notochord of the cyclostome remains throughout life, and the vertebral column is represented by a series of neural arches perched like chevrons along the notochord.

The term *cyclostome* means round mouth. The animal has no jaws, but the suckerlike mouth is provided with a tongue which bears horny projections. When a lamprey or hagfish fastens its mouth to the side of a fish, its tongue rasps off the skin, exposing the soft tissues below.

Cyclostomes have no paired lateral appendages, but do have median fins, and a long, muscular body, which equips them for powerful swimming. As in all vertebrates, the internal structure shows segmentation. The vertebrae, the muscles, the peripheral nerves, the blood vessels, the developing kidneys — all show serial arrangement.

The skin is smooth, covered by an epidermis, and somewhat protected from friction with the water by a coat of mucus secreted by the skin.

Seven pairs of openings, called gill slits, open from the pharynx through the sides of the body wall. Water comes in the mouth, through the pharynx, and out these gill slits. Blood vessels in the walls of the passageways from pharynx to the openings through the skin permit the exchange of carbon dioxide and oxygen.

No differentiated stomach occurs. The esophagus is rather long and leads to the still longer intestine.

The destructiveness of cyclostomes to fish constitutes a problem of some economic importance to humans. Within recent years the marine lamprey has invaded the Great Lakes and has reduced the supply of commercially important food fish there to an alarming degree. State and national government agencies are working on methods of combating this menace.

Elasmobranchii

The Class **Elasmobranchii** includes the sharks and skates, all marine animals. These have paired lateral appendages in the form of fins. They also have jaws. The skin is supplied with spiny scales. Some of these scales also occur in the lining of the mouth and are there enlarged and are called teeth. The teeth of sharks are sharp, with cutting edges, whereas the teeth of skates are flattened, grinding structures. Sharks are fast swimmers and overtake fishes, squids, crustacea, and other marine animals on which they prey. Skates usually crawl on the ocean floor and capture worms, clams, and similar animals which they crush with their teeth and use for food. See Figure 28.3.

The notochord is somewhat reduced from the embryonic condition in adult elasmobranchs, and is surrounded by vertebrae with centra as well as neural arches. The internal skeleton is made of cartilage and never develops bone.

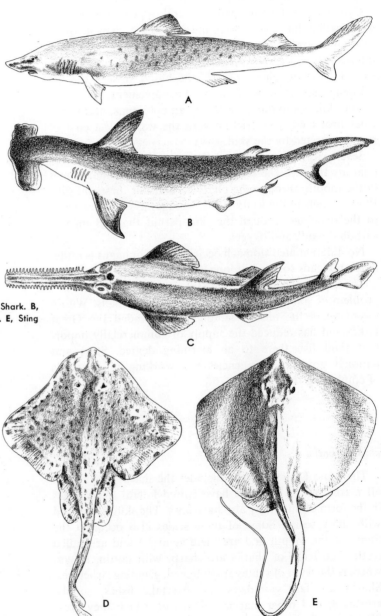

Fig. 28.3 Kinds of elasmobranchs. **A,** Shark. **B,** Hammerhead shark. **C,** Sawfish. **D,** Skate. **E,** Sting ray.

The respiratory system is similar to that of the lamprey. The digestive tract has a stomach. The other systems are not fundamentally different from those of humans or other vertebrates.

The elasmobranch egg usually has a great deal of yolk. Some members of this class, like the skate, lay their eggs in protective capsules, and the young develop in the ocean. Others, like the dogfish shark, have the young developing in the uterus of the mother.

Sharks are not quite the man hunters they are reputed to be. Many of the accounts of sharks attacking or eating humans are cases of mistaken identity involving other fishes, such as the barracuda.

The electric ray has a specialized back muscle which acts as a condenser and stores an electric charge of twenty to thirty volts. This may be discharged on an enemy. The electric eel, a bony fish, can develop a charge ten times as great.

Pisces

The Class **Pisces** includes the bony fishes, marine and fresh-water. The skeleton contains bone as well as cartilage. The mouth is usually at the anterior end of the head, instead of on the ventral side as in elasmobranchs. The scales are horny and larger and more flexible than those of the shark. The notochord may disappear completely in the adult fish. The gills are collected into a pair of common chambers, each partly covered by a flap of skin supported by skeletal plates. See Figure 28.4.

Fig. 28.4 Some kinds of Pisces. **A,** Herring. **B,** Salmon. **C,** Codfish. **D,** Eel. **E,** Mudskipper. **F,** Sunfish. **G,** Climbing perch. **H,** Three kinds of lungfishes.

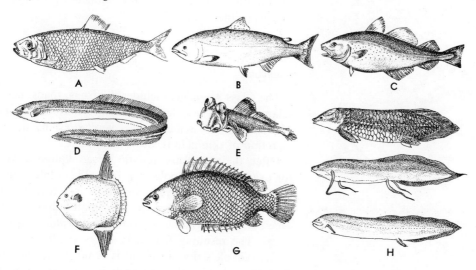

Bony fish are important commercially as food, and for some other purposes, such as the vitamins concentrated in fish liver oils. About ten billion herrings are caught annually. The young herrings are packed as sardines. The wealth of Holland, particularly of Amsterdam, was built on herring fisheries two or three centuries ago, and then some of this wealth was reinvested in the diamond industry and other enterprises. The salmon is another food fish of great economic importance. Salmon live in the oceans, but go far up rivers to spawn. After the eggs and sperm cells are released, the parent fishes die, and the fertilized eggs develop into young salmon, which eventually find their way to the ocean. In their turn, these salmon will later find their way up the same stream from which they came.

The fresh-water eel reverses this process, going to the sea to spawn. A region southwest of Bermuda seems to be a center for eels from both North American and European rivers. Here the eggs and sperm are released. One female may produce as many as ten million eggs. The young eels are transparent except for the pigment in the eyes. They find their way to fresh-water streams and grow to adulthood there, and then return to the breeding area.

A few bony fish can live out of water for a short time. The mudskippers may paddle about on mud flats. Climbing perch can even scramble up a slanting tree trunk after insects. The lungfishes have lungs in addition to gills and may hole up in a clay burrow when the river is low, leaving the mouth at the opening of the burrow so that air gets into the lung. Thus they can live even if the river bed is dry for months, becoming active swimmers again when water returns to the river.

Amphibia

The Class **Amphibia** includes the frogs, toads, newts, and salamanders. These have two pairs of legs but no fins. The skin has no scales, but is kept moist by the mucous secretion of skin glands. See Figure 28.5.

Often the young are aquatic larvae equipped with gills, for example, the tadpole of a frog. The adult is the result of metamorphosis. Metamorphosis is under the regulation of the thyroid hormone. If a small tadpole is given an excess of the hormone, it will metamorphose earlier than usual. The resulting frog may be as small as a housefly. If the tadpole's thyroid gland is removed, it will not metamorphose but continue to grow into a giant tadpole.

Fig. 28.5 Some kinds of Amphibia. **A,** Mudpuppy. **B,** Salamander. **C,** Frog. **D,** Toad.

The tails of frogs and toads are absorbed during metamorphosis, and lungs replace gills as the active breathing organs. The hind legs are long and strong, and are used for leaping. The toes of the hind legs are webbed, and make good swimming appendages.

Amphibian eggs are usually laid in water, and protected by a thick, gelatinous envelope. A few, like the European salamander, have the young developing within the mother.

Amphibia are insect-eating animals. Some live in the water all their lives, as the mudpuppies and the hellbenders; some vary between water and land, as the frogs and the newts; some live most or all of their adult lives on land, as the toads and woodland salamanders. But none of them can live for an extended time in a dry environment, since the skin is not scaly and is used in part as a respiratory organ. No amphibia live in salt water.

Reptilia

The Class **Reptilia** includes crocodiles, turtles, lizards, and snakes. The skin has horny scales. Eggs are laid on land, or the young are carried by the mother for a time before they are born.

The crocodiles and alligators (Fig. 28.6) are the largest of the living reptiles, some crocodiles being over thirty feet long. They are carnivorous animals with short, thick legs and heavy, powerful tails. Their walk on land is somewhat clumsy, but they can travel at a fair rate of speed. In the water, the tail is a strong swimming organ, and they overtake prey readily.

Fig. 28.6   Kinds of Crocodilia. **A,** American alligator. **B,** Nile crocodile.

The turtles (Fig. 28.7) are both plant- and animal-eaters, but they have no teeth. The rims of the jaws have horny coverings with which they can bite. The ribs enlarge and lock together, forming a protective box around the trunk of the turtle, which is in turn covered by the large, fused scales on the surface of the body. The head, tail, and feet may be partly withdrawn into this box. This heavy, cumbersome shell is a hindrance to fast travel not only because of its weight, but because the legs must operate at a straddling angle. But the gain in protection seems to compensate for the loss of speed.

Lizards (Fig. 28.8) are the swiftest travelers of the class. They are insect-eaters, and live on the ground or on trees. The chameleon is renowned for its color-changing ability, which is sometimes exaggerated. They are normally gray-green, turning gray in low temperatures, and green in high temperatures. In bright sunlight, they become darker; in darkness or in times of stress they are lighter in color. However, if you put one on a Scotch plaid and expect an exact match, you will be disappointed.

Some lizards have a degree of autotomy, being able to break off the tail if it is seized. Thus they may escape being eaten by birds or other enemies. The "glass snake" is really a lizard with remarkable powers of self-fragmentation and regeneration.

Of the lizards in the United States, only one is poisonous — the Gila monster of the Arizona desert regions. The skin of the Gila lizard is brightly colored red, yellow, and brown, and looks like beadwork. The poison fangs are in the lower jaw, and when it attacks another animal, it bites, and then throws itself over on its back, thus tearing the wound open and allowing poison to drain down out of the fangs into the wound.

Among the largest living lizards are the South American iguana, which may be six feet long and is used as food, and the Southeast Asian Komodo dragon, a nine-foot animal weighing as much as 250 pounds. The Komodo dragon eats wild pigs. It is an active and ferocious animal, but lives in dense jungles, seldom crossing the path of humans.

Snakes (Fig. 28.9) show little or no external evidence of paired limbs, although portions of the shoulder and hip girdles may still be present. Scales on the ventral side aid in locomotion. The body is long and slender, and very muscular, with the internal organs arranged along the narrow, cylindrical trunk. The tongue is long and slender, and is sensitive both to odors and to vibrations, so that a snake runs its tongue out of its mouth as a sense organ.

Fig. 28.7   Kinds of turtles. **A,** Leathery turtle. **B,** Snapping turtle. **C,** Snake-necked turtle. **D,** Tortoise.

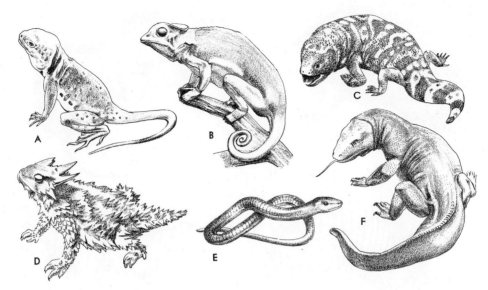

Fig. 28.8 Some kinds of lizards. **A**, Collared lizard, or mountain boomer. **B**, Chameleon. **C**, Gila monster. **D**, Horned toad. **E**, Glass snake. **F**, Komodo dragon.

Fig. 28.9 Kinds of snakes. **A**, Garter snake. **B**, Chain snake. **C**, Rattlesnake. **D**, Copperhead. **E**, Water moccasin. **F**, Coral snake.

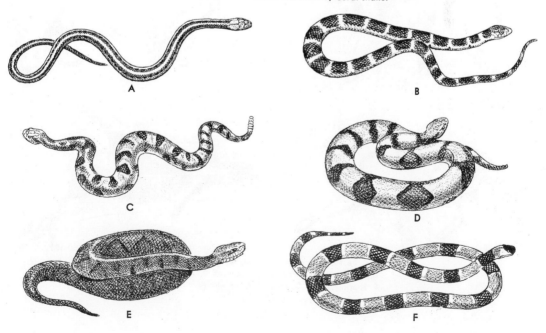

Fig. 28.10   Kinds of mammals. **A**, Spiny anteater.
B, Opossum. **C**, Armadillo. **D**, Squirrel. **E**, Baboon.
F, Hippopotamus. **G**, Dog. **H**, Killer whale.

Fig. 28.11   Kinds of birds. A, Ostrich. **B,** Goose.
C, Kite. **D,** Woodcock. **E,** Dove. **F,** Chicken. **G,** Great
horned owl. **H,** Barn swallow.

Snakes have sharp teeth, but no grinding teeth. Like amphibia and most reptiles, snakes swallow their food whole. The digestive enzymes are powerful. A snake may completely disintegrate a swallowed rat, even though the snake's stomach has no hydrochloric acid. The jaws may separate from each other at the hinge, so that a snake may swallow an animal of greater diameter than the snake itself. A python, for example, may swallow a calf.

Among the deadly poisonous snakes in this country are the rattlesnakes, copperheads, water moccasins, and coral snakes. Most snakes are not poisonous to humans, but are of definite value as destroyers of harmful rodents, insects, and so forth. The fear of harmless snakes unfortunately trained into people by their parents and associates is unjustified. There are many misconceptions such as those of the hoopsnake or whipsnake, which is supposed to take its tail in its mouth and roll after a man and stab him in the back. Another snake is reputed to milk cattle. Some snakes are supposed to hypnotize birds. Even the notion that snakes are slimy is baseless, as the skin of a snake, like that of other land reptiles, is dry. The snake sheds its scales all at one time, turning the "skin" inside out as it crawls out of the shed outer layer.

Mammalia

The Class **Mammalia** includes the mammals (Fig. 28.10), in which the scales characteristic of many vertebrates are modified into hairs, except for a few cases. In the armadillo, the scaly anteater, and the tail of rats some scales remain among the hairs. Mammals maintain a constant body temperature regardless of the environmental temperature, a characteristic peculiar to mammals and birds. Mammals have a muscular partition, the diaphragm, between the chest and abdomen. Their red blood corpuscles do not have nuclei; those of other vertebrates do. With the exception of one small order, the **Monotremata,** which lay eggs, all mammals carry their young in the uterus of the mother for some time during early development. Furthermore, the females have mammary glands which secrete a nourishing milk on which the newborn young feed.

Mammals are primarily land animals, although bats have wings and can fly, and whales and manatees live entirely in the ocean. Some other animals such as beavers, otters, seals, and hippopotami live much of the time in water. Yet all of these breathe by means of lungs and must come to the air for oxygen.

Among the most familiar orders of mammals are the following arranged in the order of increasing specialization of structure:

The **Marsupials,** or pouched mammals, include the opossums and the kangaroos. The young are relatively immature when born, and are carried in the external abdominal pouch of the mother where the mammary glands open. Young opossums are born after 13 days' development in the mother's uterus. They may spend two months in the pouch before becoming independent.

The **Rodents,** or gnawing mammals, include rabbits, squirrels, rats, mice, beavers, and porcupines. They have long, constantly growing incisor teeth, and no canine teeth.

The **Primates** are the monkeys, apes, and humans, which are relatively primitive mammals except for the great development of the brain. One of these primates — man — was described at some length in Part I of this book, so that a detailed account of mammalian anatomy and physiology is not presented here.

The **Ungulates,** or hoofed animals, include the pigs, hippopotami, deer, sheep, goats, camels, llamas, giraffes, horses, and rhinoceroses. They are all vegetarian, and usually much larger than most other animals except the elephants and whales.

The **Carnivores,** or clawed mammals, include the dog, cat, bear, weasel, and seal families. They attack other animals for food, and depend upon their strength and sharp claws and teeth for destroying their prey.

The **Cetacea,** or whales, are large, exclusively marine animals which have reduced limbs. The sulfur-bottom, or blue, whale is the largest of all animals, present or past, some being over 100 feet long and weighing nearly 150 tons.

Aves

The last class of vertebrates to appear in the fossil record of the earth's history is the **Aves,** or birds (Fig. 28.11). Birds have the front pair of limbs modified into wings, and most of them are able to fly. Their bones are hollowed out, providing air sacs which increase the respiratory surface and lighten the animal's weight. The birds maintain a body temperature a few degrees higher than that of mammals. The mouth is extended into a bill and contains no teeth. The scales covering the body are in the form of feathers except for those on the feet.

The song of birds is produced by a voice box with a flap of tissue, the **syrinx,** at the lower end of the trachea just as it forks into the two bronchi. Air passing this flap.

forcibly causes it to vibrate, and the shape and size of the flap help determine the quality of the song. The hoarse caw of the crow is made by vibrating a short, stubby flap, while the thrushes and warblers have a longer, more slender syrinx.

Birds lay relatively few but comparatively large eggs with abundant yolk and albumen and a protective limy shell. Ordinarily the eggs develop in a nest warmed by the body of the mother, and the embryo hatches in an advanced stage, ready to eat and move about.

Some species of birds spend their whole lives within a few miles of the nest where they were hatched. They exhibit a sense of private ownership of an area; their calls appear to warn other birds to stay away. Other species of birds migrate twice annually. They move to a warmer climate in the fall and to a cooler climate in the spring, along rather well-defined flyways. Much evidence supports the idea that the quantity of sex hormones in the bird's blood is the stimulus for migration. The concentration of sex hormones in at least some birds varies with the length of the day.

Some kinds of birds and mammals have been domesticated for man's use. Through careful selection of the characteristics of animals he breeds, man has developed genetic varieties of such organisms which he especially desires.

SUMMARY

The Phylum Chordata includes the animals with a dorsal skeletal rod, the notochord, which is supplemented or replaced by a vertebral column in the subphylum of vertebrates. One vertebrate, man, was described in Part I of this book, and serves as an example of a vertebrate.

The vertebrates occupy the sea, fresh waters, land, and air. Most vertebrates are larger than animals of other groups. The internal skeleton, the pharyngeal respiratory organs, and the efficient circulatory system make this enlargement possible. At the same time, greater size means a demand for much greater quantities of food, and many of the specializations of vertebrates are directly correlated with food-getting. The nervous system and sense organs of vertebrates are highly developed. Two pairs of lateral appendages are characteristic of most vertebrates except cyclostomes, snakes, and whales.

Sexes are separate. Except for some fishes, relatively few young are produced by any pair of vertebrates, and some form of care and protection of the young is common. Specialization of tissues is at a high level, and regenerative ability is very little compared to that of the simpler animals such as coelenterates or flatworms.

Although variation and numbers of individuals are not as great among vertebrates as among insects, the greater size of body and increased development of the nervous system make the vertebrates contenders with the arthropods for supremacy and dominance of the earth.

REVIEW QUESTIONS

1. Characterize the Chordata; the Vertebrata.
2. Describe a cyclostome.
3. Of what economic importance are cyclostomes?
4. Describe the elasmobranchs.
5. Describe the bony fishes.
6. Describe the amphibia.
7. What changes take place in the metamorphosis of a frog?
8. Describe the reptiles.
9. Describe the mammals.
10. Describe the birds.

GENERAL QUESTIONS

1. Which of the other phyla do chordates most closely resemble?
2. Does segmentation confer any advantages on vertebrates?
3. How could you demonstrate that humans are segmented animals?
4. Propose a practical scheme for protecting Great Lakes fishes from lampreys.
5. How does an electric eel produce electric shocks?
6. Would it be justifiable to include lungfishes with the amphibia?
7. Which reptiles are most like the amphibia? Which reptiles are most like the mammals?
8. What brings about the color changes of chameleons in different environments?
9. Are metamorphosis and regeneration primitive characteristics?
10. Which are more specialized vertebrates: mammals or birds?

EVOLUTION

EVOLUTION THEORY

Part I of this book describes many of the biological factors involved in the life of one species of organism, man. Parts II and III show by examples some of the diversity among living organisms and emphasize the similarities in fundamental biological phenomena running through variety in form and behavior. Part IV will discuss some of the attempts of biologists to account for this warp of similarity in the woof of diversity.

As long as there have been humans to compare with each other, it has been obvious that any two humans are similar but never exactly identical. Yet, the two most unlike humans are still more similar to each other than either is to a tiger or a horse. Tigers, horses, and humans share some characteristics not possessed by birds or alligators. And all these have in common some attributes not found in insects and worms. Animals have long been recognized as different from plants, and both are certainly distinct from rocks.

The awareness of the degree of similarity is reflected in many folklores. The elephant-headed god, Ganesha, of India; the cat-goddess, Bubastis, of Egypt; the centaurs of ancient Greece; and the werewolves of northern Europe all testify to the recognition of similarity in diversity. Not quite as common are the combination of nonmammalian vertebrates with humans, for example, the ibis-headed god Thoth, Medusa with snaky hair, the mermaids, and the boaster of last century's American frontier who claimed to be "half man, half alligator." There are even degrees of epithets, passing from "dog" and "snake" to "insect" and "worm."

In addition to this popular thought about the relationships among living organisms, there have been philosophical and scientific hypotheses dealing with the same problem. The gathering of factual information about organisms is necessary to the understanding of their relationships, but to most scientists a catalog of facts is not satisfying. It is to be supplemented by a general theory explaining as many as possible of the facts, and corresponding as nearly as possible to reality as the scientist sees it. Then this theory is to be subjected to as vigorous testing as human minds can conceive, altered and adapted to newly discovered facts wherever possible, and discarded when it fails to explain better than any alternative hypothesis.

The theory currently most widely accepted among biologists as an explanation of the similarities in the various kinds of living organisms is the Evolution Theory. This states that organisms of different species are genetically related. That is to say, the similarities to be found in cats, leopards, tigers, and lions are the result of inheritance of these qualities from a common distant ancestor. The differences are due to changes which have occurred in the generations since that remote ancestor.

The story of the development of this theory will be given briefly in Chapter 29, and then evidence bearing on the theory will be discussed in Chapter 30. Chapter 31 will outline the degrees of relationship postulated among living organisms by contemporary students of evolution.

REVIEW QUESTIONS

1. What type of observations led to the Evolution Theory?
2. How ancient are these observations?
3. State the Evolution Theory.

GENERAL QUESTIONS

1. Is any part of the Evolution Theory included in ancient mythology?
2. Is the desire for theoretical explanation of observed facts justifiable?
3. Could a science be constructed without theories?

CHAPTER 29

History of the Theory of Evolution

EARLY SPECULATIONS

Our knowledge of the early speculations of an evolutionary nature is based on written accounts available for our study. Undoubtedly many thinkers produced theories to satisfy their own curiosity, but did not write them down for other people to read. Also, many written accounts have been lost. From those that remain we may select the ones most directly bearing on evolution theory. And these we must interpret as well as we can, without reading into them meanings the author did not intend.

Anaximander

The foundation of European philosophy and culture is to be found in the writings of ancient Greece. The poem *On Nature* by Anaximander (*c.* 611–547 B.C.) is said to be the first book on natural science. It has come down to us only in the form of quotations by later authors. But in it there was an account of the origin of living organisms from mud when the earth solidified out of a fluid condition. According to Anaximander, the first humans lived in the ocean and resembled fishes. After land was formed, men came ashore, shed their fishlike skins, and lived a terrestrial life. He supports his view of change of form with change of environment by arguing that the helplessness and gradual adjustment of a newborn baby are indications that humans were not primarily intended for life on land and altered their characteristics to adapt themselves.

Xenophanes

Anaximander's pupil Xenophanes (*c.* 570–480 B.C.) agreed with his master's idea of the emergence of land and land animals from the sea and marine animals. He referred to fossil shells and fish and seaweed found in the rocks in quarries and on mountains as proof that the sea and its inhabitants once covered what is now land. This is the first recorded appeal to paleontology as evidence to support the idea of change in the structure and environment of organisms in times past.

Empedocles

Empedocles (*c.* 490–430 B.C.) put the origin of variation in organisms on a strictly naturalistic or mechanistic basis. All things, including living organisms, are made of certain combinations of four fundamental elements — earth, water, air, and fire. The combinations of these, formed deep underground under the influence of heat, were cast up to the surface in shapeless lumps. These lumps became parts of bodies — isolated legs, heads, eyes, organs. A force of affinity drew groups of these together. Some assemblies proved quite unworkable, and these perished. Others were somewhat better, and survived awhile, but could not reproduce, and so their kind was not perpetuated. Still others were so well assorted and united that they could not only flourish but could, in Lucretius' words, "do the work of Venus," and produce other organisms like themselves. These successful species survived. At first it was the simplest forms which attained this degree of perfection — the plants. Then came the lower animals, the higher animals, and finally man. There was no change from one species to another, but rather a closer approach to perfection in the parts formed by the earth, and in the workings of the affinity which united these parts into complete organisms. No directing hand was guiding this approach to perfection, but chance, through a long period of time, produced combinations able to perpetuate themselves.

Plato

This notion of the approach to perfection was reversed by Plato (*c.* 427–347 B.C.). Plato conceived of reality and perfection as residing in ideas. The trees visible on the landscape were only imperfect representatives of the ideal tree. Man was the most nearly perfect form, but even living humans were incomplete samples of the ideal man.

Further, the variations in the animal kingdom could be said to represent degeneration, rather than progress. Women were men with cowardly characteristics. Birds and mammals were men who had degenerated in intelligence. Fishes were men who had departed so far from their ideal goals that they could not even breathe pure air. Plato rejected scientific observation, and devoted himself to reasoning and speculating about the ideal truths.

Aristotle

Plato's greatest student and successor as a philosopher was Aristotle (384–322 B.C.). Aristotle, however, disagreed with his teacher at many points. He made a thorough investigation of many kinds of living organisms, and the conclusions he drew about them were more like those of Empedocles than like those of Plato.

Aristotle elaborated the idea of a sequence of living forms gradually increasing in perfection, from inanimate objects through plants and lower and higher animals to man. He also pointed out that it was impossible to draw sharp lines. For example, many organisms in the ocean possess characteristics of both plants and animals.

Plato's concept of an ideal object being the reality of which visible examples were only images was modified in Aristotle's mind to a concept of form as a guiding principle. To him the form of a human was not only the goal toward which an embryo worked, but also the motivating force of development. Adaptations in structure, physiology, and behavior were brought about by an active purpose to achieve a definite result. This is diametrically opposed to Empedocles' idea that the structure of organisms was a matter of pure chance and the survival of lucky combinations. But in tracing the purpose and ideal forms exhibited in nature, Aristotle usually pursued the path of direct observation of living organisms. Where this was impossible, he accepted the testimony of others, sometimes unwisely. He dissected animals and followed embryonic development in as many forms as possible.

Epicurus

Epicurus (*c.* 342–270 B.C.) opposed Aristotle's view of form as a purposive force directing natural events and taught that every phenomenon had mechanical causes inherent in matter itself. He was not concerned with the investigation of the mechanical causes, but was more interested in maintaining that man should be an opportunist in adapting his behavior to the laws of nature in his search for happiness.

DECLINE OF SCIENCE

About this time, philosophic and scientific inquiry went into a decline. The students of philosophy for nearly the next two thousand years followed either Aristotle's ideas of a progressively more nearly perfect series of organisms motivated by a purposive force, or Epicurus' idea of natural law as opposed to any extra-material forces. The Roman Empire became the dominant political force, and practical affairs received men's attention largely to the exclusion of intellectual pursuits.

With the coming into prominence of the Christian Church in Europe, the outstanding thinkers were theologians. In the conflict between the followers of Aristotle and those of Epicurus, the theologians sided with Aristotle. The philosophy of Epicurus had degenerated in later centuries into pursuit of momentary pleasures, and this in addition to the denial of supernatural forces brought the vigorous denunciation of the leaders of the church. On the other hand, by referring to the purposive force of Aristotle as God, Christian theology was able to accept Aristotle's views, although the churchmen did not follow his example of active investigation of nature. When they discussed the number of teeth in a horse's mouth, they debated long and loud about how to interpret Aristotle's statements on the subject, but no one thought of looking in a horse's mouth to see.

Augustine

The great theologian Augustine (354–430 A.D.) reconciled Aristotle's concept of the gradual development of complex organisms from simple ones to the Genesis account of creation by suggesting that creation was potential and not actual. That is, the possibility of the development of complex animals was established when the universe began, but the realization of this potentiality followed only much later, after plants and simpler animals had gradually developed. In this view he was supported by a later scholar, Thomas Aquinas (1225–1274).

With such authority behind Aristotle's views, and the much more highly valued considerations of salvation to be pursued, thinkers spent little time in the study of living organisms until the sixteenth and seventeenth centuries brought a revival of scientific investigation.

Suarez

Francisco Suarez (1548–1617) took issue with the liberal interpretations of Augustine and Thomas Aquinas. Suarez maintained that when the account in Genesis described the six days of creation it was not speaking allegorically. Each species of living organism was created full-blown on one of those six consecutive 24-hour days. This account was the inspired Word of God, and was not to be tortured

Fig. 29.1   Georges Cuvier.

into any figurative agreement with the ignorant ideas of a heathen philosopher. Suarez' views became accepted by the contemporary authorities of the Roman Catholic Church and were popular also with the Protestant leaders.

The supremacy of man among organisms was a standard belief. Other organisms were placed on earth for the benefit of man, so that the study of plants and animals became a search for the uses for which they were intended, and not an investigation of their relationships with each other.

TOWARD MODERN THEORY

Linnaeus

During the eighteenth and nineteenth centuries there was a great resurgence of the scientific investigation of living organisms. The work of Linnaeus (1707–1778) has already been described. In his earlier publications on classification, Linnaeus maintained stoutly that the species he described had remained unchanged from the time of their creation. In his later years, however, he found so much variation and such intergrading of specimens that he postulated the production of forms intermediate between species by the crossing of individuals from different species.

Cuvier

Georges Cuvier (1769–1832) agreed with Linnaeus' earlier views, and established an international reputation as an anatomist and paleontologist. See Figure 29.1. It was his claim that species were so completely distinct from each other that if he were given any one bone of any animal, he could in his mind reconstruct and identify the entire animal.

Buffon

Georges de Buffon (1707–1788) opposed Linnaeus' views of the fixity of species. See Figure 29.2. He found, for example, that pigs have toes which do not reach the ground, and can be of no use in walking, but which yet are supported by distinct bones like those of other animals all of whose toes are useful in walking. He concluded that pigs of today have changed from the condition of their remote forebears, which had all toes reaching the ground.

Fig. 29.2   Georges de Buffon.

Lamarck

This idea was elaborated by Jean de Lamarck (1744–1829). See Figure 29.3. Lamarck thought that environmental forces altered the characteristics of living organisms, and the changes thus brought about were perpetuated in later generations. For example: the breeding of greyhounds for speed changed the inheritance of these animals permanently. An ungulate feeding on the leaves of trees developed a very long neck by continual stretching and became a giraffe. Lamarck believed that whenever the environment changes, plant and animal characteristics cnange in adaptation. Hence, living organisms today are different from those of another time and place.

And so, by the nineteenth century, the argument among the followers of Empedocles, Aristotle, and Epicurus as to whether organisms progressively improved by the weeding out of unlucky chance combinations from more successful ones, or by definite supernatural purpose, or by the operation of purely mechanical forces had become something quite different. The special creationists held that species were and are permanently fixed, formed at the beginning with the characteristics they now possess and will retain so long as the species lives. The evolutionists believed that species are not fixed, but subject to change, even to new species, due to changes in environmental opportunities for new adaptations.

Fig. 29.3   Jean de Lamarck.

Darwin

Into this controversy came Charles Darwin (1809–1882), who attempted to account for evolutionary changes by discovering the motivating forces in the realm of natural law. See Figure 29.4. Darwin, after an unsuccessful attempt at the study of medicine, trained for service in the Church of England. He was much interested in natural history, and was recommended by one of his botanical friends for a position as naturalist on the British ship *Beagle*, which was about to sail around the world to take soundings and study coastlines in the interests of the British Navy. Darwin's father disapproved of the idea, but to settle his son's insistent entreaty said that if Charles could find any man of common sense to recommend his going, permission would be granted. Charles had been a frequent visitor to the home of his cousin, Emma Wedgwood, a vivacious young lady with whom he was falling in love. Emma's father quickly recommended that Charles be sent off on the voyage, thus fulfilling the necessary condition, and Darwin spent almost five years on the trip. During this time he collected an immense amount of data on the kinds and geographic distribution of living organisms.

Fig. 29.4   Charles Darwin.

Fig. 29.5   Alfred Wallace.

After he returned, married his cousin Emma, and began to work up this material, he became more convinced than ever of the validity of the evolutionary hypothesis, and in 1842 drew up an account of his explanation of it. From then on he devoted his time to working out the details and corollaries of this theory. He discussed it with some of the scientific leaders of his country, who urged him to publish his ideas. But Darwin insisted on waiting until he had accumulated enough evidence to convince even the most skeptical opponent.

In 1856, however, he was finally persuaded to start work on what was planned to be a monumental volume. While he was still writing on this project, one day in June, 1858, he received a letter from a young naturalist, Alfred Wallace (1823–1913), who was exploring the East Indies. See Figure 29.5. Wallace had been taken ill with a tropical fever, and while he was recovering, he had been thinking over the distribution of various species, and had a flash of insight which explained some of his discoveries. This flash was a duplicate of the theory Darwin had been working on for some years. Entirely unaware of Darwin's ideas, Wallace wrote to Darwin a brief summary of his notions, and suggested that if Darwin thought well of them, they might be published.

Although somewhat stunned by this turn of events, Darwin felt honor-bound to publish Wallace's paper first, and then corroborate it with his own work. His friends would not hear of this arrangement. They felt it deprived Darwin of the priority which was his due. The dilemma was settled by the simultaneous publication of Wallace's paper and Darwin's 1842 outline. Then, the following year, Darwin published an abridged version of the book he had been working on. This volume summarized its message in its title: *On the Origin of Species by Means of Natural Selection, or the Preservation of Favored Races in the Struggle for Life*. The book aroused a furore of controversy. Wallace generously gave full credit for originating the theory to Darwin, and supported it faithfully by continued researches in biogeography — the distribution of plants and animals.

Darwin's Theory of Evolution

The substance of the Darwin-Wallace theory is as follows: The characteristics of living organisms change over long periods of time so that a present-day species may be descended from ancestors whose characteristics

were so different that they would be classified in quite
another species. The variations need not be great at any
one time, but the accumulation of variations over thousands
of generations may produce pronounced differences. The
variations more suited to the environment in which the
animal lived were preserved and the disadvantageous ones
lost. Thus the environment did not bring about variations,
but it sorted them out after they appeared. In other words,
nature selected the most favorable variations, just as men,
breeding domestic animals and cultivated plants, select the
variations they prefer and perpetuate these while discarding
others. Darwin didn't know what brought about these
variations in the first place. But that variations do occur
is obvious to anyone who seeks to find two identical
organisms.

The natural laws which Darwin and Wallace postulated
to account for evolution by natural selection may be summarized as follows:

1. Variation. No two organisms are alike.
2. Overproduction. Plants and animals are capable of
reproducing many more offspring than can be provided
for on this earth.
3. Struggle for existence. With more organisms than there
is space or food for, competition will be keen for what
supplies are available.
4. Survival of the fittest. In the competition, those
organisms which vary in the direction of favorably adapted
characteristics will survive.
5. Inheritance of adaptive characteristics. The surviving
forms will be the ones to reproduce and hand on to their
successors these especially fit characteristics.
6. Development of new species as environments change.
If there are changes in environments, then the criteria of
selection change. A characteristic which was favorable in
the older environment might be unfavorable in the new,
and hence be a detriment to its possessor. Other neutral
or disadvantageous attributes might now become advantageous. Thus, a changed environment will select a different
kind of organism, and the characteristics which define the
species will likewise change.

This may be illustrated by an example. Among the
sandworms similar to the species described on pages 404–
405 some have short nephridia and some have long nephridia. The longer nephridia are able to secrete more
salt out of the excretory solution into the worm's blood.

In sea water, this is of no particular advantage, since the worm's blood contains about the same concentration of salt as the surrounding water. In fact, a longer nephridium requires more energy to build and maintain, and keeps wastes in the body for a longer time than a short nephridium does.

However, in those animals which get into brackish water, at the mouths of rivers, the longer nephridia are a definite asset. The more dilute habitat would wash salts out of the worm unless the nephridial cells secreted salt back into the worm's body from the excretory fluid. Worms with short nephridia do not establish themselves in brackish water. Worms with long nephridia flourish here, free from the competition of other sandworms. Any tendency for the worms with long nephridia to develop short ones would result in their disappearance from this habitat.

Similar hereditary changes in other animals may have made them capable of surviving in fresh waters or even on land, as is the case in such crustacea as crayfish and land crabs. Animals which inherit genes for adaptive characteristics thrive and pass on to their progeny these genes. Forms not adapted do not survive, and their characteristics disappear from the species in that habitat.

Now, given a mechanism for altering species characters, Darwin could look back into the past and suggest that over a period of millions of generations, with the changes in environment established by geologists, it is possible that the huge number of species found today may have come from a very few, or perhaps but one, original species. The method of origin of these first few or one species Darwin did not attempt to explain. This is another problem, falling outside the theory of evolution.

But the grandeur of this concept of genetic relationship of all living organisms, with changes arising from causes unknown, and selected by the weeding-out process of the environment, brings to a focus the great mass of hitherto unrelated facts accumulated by biologists over hundreds of years. Here may be united under the shelter of one great generalization the millions of species of living organisms. Here may be found a rational, natural explanation of the similarity in diversity that is so evident among plants and animals.

But it is one thing — and a great one — to propose such a theory. It is another thing to accumulate sufficient evidence to affirm or deny the validity of the theory. It is to this phase of the work of Darwin and Wallace and their successors that the next two chapters will be devoted.

REVIEW QUESTIONS

1. Explain the evolutionary concepts of Anaximander, Xenophanes, and Empedocles.
2. Contrast the views of Plato and Aristotle on the scale of living organisms.
3. Discuss the attitude of Christian philosophers toward the ideas of Aristotle and Epicurus.
4. Contrast the views of Augustine and Suarez on evolution.
5. Explain the views of Linnaeus and Cuvier on species.
6. Explain the views of Buffon and Lamarck on species.
7. Describe Darwin's life.
8. What did Wallace contribute to the Evolution Theory?
9. Explain the Darwin-Wallace Theory.
10. What could Darwin not explain?

GENERAL QUESTIONS

1. Of the views held by Empedocles, Aristotle, and Epicurus, which seems most like the view of present-day scientists?
2. Why did interest in science decline after the time of Epicurus?
3. Why did Suarez' views gain acceptance in the Roman Catholic and Protestant Churches of his time?
4. Suggest specific examples which might have affected Linnaeus' views on the fixity of species.
5. Is Cuvier's claim of ability to reconstruct an animal from a single bone justifiable?
6. How might Cuvier have answered Buffon's evidence from the pig?
7. How would Darwin have believed about Lamarck's view of environmental influence on heredity?
8. Why do some sandworms have longer nephridia than others?
9. Would Darwin's theory have been more acceptable if he had left humans out of it?
10. From the material discussed in the first three parts of this book, can you find any evidence for or against Darwin's theory?

CHAPTER 30

Evidence for the Evolution Theory

VALUES OF EVOLUTION THEORY

The particular value of the evolution theory lies in its tying together into a connected story so many previously unrelated facts. It not only offers an explanation for these many facts, but also enables biologists to make successful predictions of observations yet to come. The facts explained better by the evolution theory than by any other and the ones which support that theory are to be found in the fields of comparative anatomy, comparative embryology, comparative physiology, taxonomy, biogeography, genetics, and paleontology.

COMPARATIVE ANATOMY

Comparative anatomy deals with the similarities in structure among different species of living organisms.

All living organisms are built of protoplasm. Protoplasm is a colloidal substance having both watery and fatty phases intimately mixed together. Each phase contains in solution many other substances. Protoplasm maintains some uniformity and stability amid continuous changes of materials.

In most organisms protoplasm is organized into one or more cells. Cells have definite characteristics — a semipermeable cell membrane, fluid cytoplasm, and nearly always a somewhat less fluid nucleus, containing chromatin granules. Special structures such as mitochondria and vacuoles occur very widely distributed among plant and animal cells. The cellular and protoplasmic characteristics common to algae, angiosperms, protozoa, and vertebrates make reasonable the theory that these all came from some primordial ancestor of a cellular nature.

In plants other than Schizomycetes and blue-green algae, there are gamete-forming cells and sporangia which form spores.

In bryophytes and in pteridophytes which have independent gametophyte stages, the gametophyte is a green, branched filament, a flattened plate, or a leafy structure, with rhizoids that project into the ground. Antheridia and archegonia are imbedded in or extend from the green tissue. The antheridium is composed of a stalked capsule made of sterile cells, but containing sperm-forming cells within the capsule. The archegonium is made of a swollen venter containing the egg and ventral canal cells, and a neck containing neck canal cells.

In *Selaginella* and in the Spermatophyta the gametophytes are parasitic on the sporophytes. The male gametophyte is represented in *Selaginella* by one vegetative cell and an antheridium consisting of a jacket of sterile cells and a few hundred flagellated sperm cells. In the pine the male gametophyte is a tiny mass of protoplasm with no antheridia and with only six nuclei at the most — two vegetative, one tube, one stalk, and two sperm nuclei. In the angiosperms the male gametophyte has only three nuclei — the tube and two sperm nuclei.

The female gametophyte of *Selaginella* has a mass of cells, some green, within the cracked megaspore wall, and develops one or more archegonia, each with an egg, a ventral canal cell, and a neck canal cell. In the pine the female gametophyte forms within the megaspore, imbedded in the nucellus, and is composed of a mass of cells without chlorophyll; usually two archegonia appear in the gametophyte, each with an egg and a ventral canal cell. In the angiosperms the female gametophyte is a small bit of colorless cytoplasm in the megasporangium or ovule; it contains no archegonia and as a rule only eight nuclei — an egg, two synergid, two polar, and three antipodal nuclei.

The sporophyte generation in all plants having one consists of the zygote and its derivatives up to the formation of spores by meiosis. In *Ricciocarpus* the mature sporophyte is a simple capsule containing spore-forming cells. In *Anthoceros* the capsule is an elongated structure having a foot buried in the old archegonium. In land ferns, elongation of the foot pushes the sporophyte out of the archegonium, and the sporophyte establishes contact with the soil and becomes an independent plant with roots, stems, and leaves. The roots and stems form epidermis, cortex, and stele. Xylem and phloem tissues develop. The leaves bear the spore-making capsules or sporangia.

The sporophytes of *Selaginella*, gymnosperms, and angiosperms also have roots, stems, and leaves; epidermis, cortex, and stele; xylem and phloem tissues; and sporangia on modified leaves. Botanists are not all in agreement that angiosperm flower parts represent modified leaves, however.

If we go into the details of structures, we find in the

angiosperms, for example, flowers bearing some or all of the following: sepals, petals, stamens, and pistils. The stamens usually will have anthers (sporangia) borne on stalks. The pistils will ordinarily have ovules (sporangia), within an ovary, and a stigma borne on a stalk arising from the ovary.

In the monocotyledons, the flower parts are generally in threes or multiples of three. In species having flower parts in numbers less than three, as in the two sepals of the flower of a corn tassel, there is often an indication that the third one is suppressed. There is a vein for each of the two sepals, and a third vein which now has no corresponding sepal. Such an indication of a structure supposedly present in the ancestors of the organism is called a **vestige.** This third vein is a vestige in the corn plant, as are the vegetative cell of the *Selaginella* male gametophyte and the two vegetative nuclei of the pine male gametophyte, the abortive pistil in the corn tassel flowers, the suppressed stamens in the corn ear flowers, and many other structures, some of which will be mentioned later.

The presence of vestiges, which seem to take no active part in the life of the organism, is readily explained on the basis of the evolution theory. They are characteristics, the genes for which were inherited from ancestors which used them in some phase of their life history, but which, due to the change in characteristics over a long period of time, are of no apparent use, and are in the process of being lost by natural selection.

When we turn to the animal kingdom, we find a similar story. The Protozoa have many cellular structures in common. The many-celled animals have their cells specialized into tissues — epithelial, connective, muscular, nervous, and vascular. These tissues are commonly combined into organ systems. Most animals have an epidermis of some sort. The nervous system is made of nerve cells in synapses with each other. The digestive tract is lined with epithelium. Excretory systems show a gradual increase in complexity from the flame cells of flatworms through the nephridia of earthworms and clams to the kidneys of vertebrates. Ovaries and testes are fundamentally similar in all many-celled animals. Muscle cells in the earthworm intestine are much like those of the human intestine. Gills are built along the same pattern in crayfishes, starfishes, and bony fishes. The walking leg of a spider is comparable in many respects to the walking leg of a bumblebee or a crayfish.

In the vertebrates, we find a remarkable similarity in the components of the skeletal system, for example. A fish, a frog, an alligator, a chicken, and a human all have skulls, vertebral columns, ribs, shoulder and hip girdles, and bones which support the appendages. In the skulls, furthermore, you will find in all five of the animals just listed many of the same bones: frontals, parietals, occipitals, components of the temporals, nasals, vomers, lacrimals, maxillae, palatines, and dentaries. Other elements like the ethmoids, sphenoids, and turbinals are present in all forms, but as cartilage rather than bone in some.

The forelimbs of frogs, birds, horses, and humans are somewhat dissimilar in their actions, yet each contains a humerus, a radius and an ulna, a set of carpals, some metacarpals, and phalanges. Each has extensor and flexor muscles operating each joint. Each has a nerve supply which passes through a plexus. Each has blood vessels of similar distribution. Each has skin and connective tissue.

Any of the organ systems may be traced in considerable detail in these animals comparatively. The cranial and spinal nerves correspond very closely. The blood vessel pattern is comparable in all vertebrates.

In fishes, the heart has four chambers, a sinus venosus, an atrium, a ventricle, and a conus arteriosus. From the conus arteriosus the ventral aorta carries blood to the branchial arteries which divide into numerous capillaries, supplying the gills. Blood from these capillaries is brought together into the dorsal aorta, which gives off subclavian arteries to the forelimbs, esophageal, celiac, and mesenteric arteries to the digestive tract, lumbar arteries to the body wall, renal arteries to the kidneys, and iliac arteries to the hind limbs. Hepatic portal veins gather blood from the walls of the digestive tract and carry it to the liver. Iliac, renal, lumbar, and subclavian veins unite into common channels carrying blood back to the heart. Carotid arteries lead from the branchial arteries to the head, and jugular veins return blood from the head to the heart.

In amphibia, the heart is like that of fishes, but the atrium is divided into two chambers, the right and left auricles. Branchial arteries are fewer in number than in the fishes, but still give off carotid arteries. The dorsal aorta has branches like those of the fish, and venous return to the heart is similar in fishes and amphibia.

In the reptile heart there are two auricles, and in some reptiles the ventricle is partially divided into two; the conus arteriosus is divided into two channels, the aorta and the pulmonary trunk. The aorta divides into right and left arches, representing one pair of branchial arteries, each giving off carotid arteries. The two arches unite into a

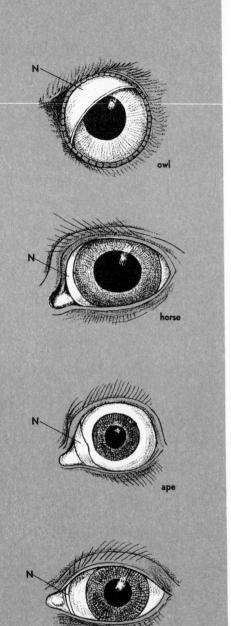

dorsal aorta, which has branches like those of fishes. Again the venous drainage is like that of fishes.

In mammals and birds the ventricle is divided into right and left chambers, but the sinus venosus consists of separate venae cavae and pulmonary trunks. In mammals the right aortic arch is not present in the adult, the left arch being the sole route from the heart to the dorsal aorta. In birds the left arch is not present in the adult, the right being the pathway of blood from the heart to the dorsal aorta. In both birds and mammals, the arterial and venous branches described for the fishes are present. Hence, the circulatory system in vertebrates follows a common pattern in considerable detail. The minor variations in blood vessel pattern only point up the gradual transition from fish to mammal and bird postulated on the basis of other studies.

. Any one of these similarities by itself is not a very strong argument for the descent of different species from a common ancestor. But the impressive number and extent of these similarities is overwhelming. Coupled with the huge number is the relative degree of similarity. Birds and reptiles are more nearly alike in *all* of these characteristics than birds and fishes. Birds and fishes are more nearly alike in *all* of their structural similarities than birds and earthworms. Birds and earthworms are more nearly alike in *all* their structural similarities than birds and protozoa. It is not that birds are more like alligators in their skull bones, more like earthworms in heir blood vessels, and more like protozoa in their excretory systems. A closeness of relationship established by a study of, say, the skull bones is confirmed by the study of muscles, digestive organs, respiratory system, nervous structures, excretory, circulatory, reproductive, and endocrine systems. A detailed elaboration of this point could run into many volumes. The theory of common ancestors explains this mass of information readily.

In animals, too, vestigial organs may be found. The human has, in the inner corner of each eye, a fold of flesh which seems to have no useful action. In many reptiles and birds there is a comparable structure, the third eyelid, or nictitating membrane, which periodically sweeps across the eye, removing dust which has accumulated there. See Figure 30.1.

The cecum of the rabbit intestine is a large sac about the size of the rabbit's stomach. In the rabbit and several other mammals, the cecum is very active in the digestion of vegetable foods. In man and many other mammals the cecum is much reduced. In humans, the appendix of the

Fig. 30.1   Nictitating membrane of birds and of mammals. It sweeps across the eye of birds, but in humans it is reduced to an inactive fold at the inner corner of the eye. N = nictitating membrane.

cecum may even be a liability, for it may become diseased and require surgical removal. An occasional human will be born with a tail several inches in length. See Figure 30.2. Some snakes and whales, neither of which have hind legs, may possess pelvic girdles and other reduced remnants of appendages. See Figure 30.3.

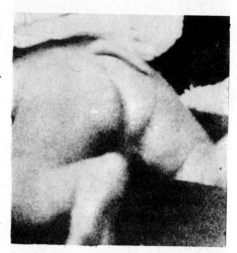

Fig. 30.2 Human tail.

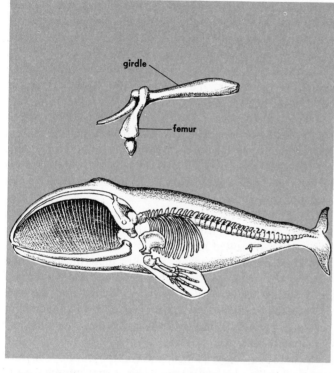

Fig. 30.3 Pelvic girdle of a whale. The girdle is shown in place in the lower sketch and enlarged in the upper one.

The muscles which erect the hair and those which move the external ears are much reduced in humans. The wisdom teeth (see pages 56–57) seem to be on their way out, evolutionarily speaking. The little toe seems to be becoming less and less prominent. These evidences of change in anatomical characteristics support the evolution theory.

In summary, the argument from comparative anatomy rests on three generalizations:

1. Organisms seemingly diverse in form and nature have fundamentally similar structural organization.

2. The degree of similarity between any two kinds of organisms is much the same no matter what structures or systems are considered.

3. Vestigial structures are reasonably explained by the theory of common descent and gradual elimination by natural selection.

COMPARATIVE EMBRYOLOGY

Fig. 30.4   A seedling cactus. Note the two cotyledons.

In comparative embryology we find examples corroborating the same type of argument presented by comparative anatomy. In plants, for example, a spore will develop into a protoplasmic filament in many molds, algae, and bryophytes. In some forms such as *Ulva* and *Coleochaete scutata* among the green algae, *Laminaria* among the brown algae, and *Ricciocarpus* among the bryophytes, this filament grows into a flat plate. In most of the larger plants, growth occurs by the repeated division of one cell, the apical cell, or one or more small groups of cells, the meristem. In cactus plants, in which the leaves are reduced to needlelike spines in the adult, the young plant possesses leaflike cotyledons. See Figure 30.4.

The process of cell division by mitosis is a rather complicated method of producing two cells from one. This process is similar throughout both the plant and animal kingdoms. Likewise the process of meiosis, by which haploid gametes are formed from diploid cells, is common to most species of plants and animals.

If one compares the development of zygotes of the hydra, earthworm, crayfish, fish, reptile, and human, he finds many similarities. Repeated mitoses produce first two, then four, then eight nuclei, and so on. Some of these nuclei migrate close to the surface of the embryo and become marked off in ectoderm cells. Others turn internally and become contained in endoderm cells. At this point the hydra embryo cells are specialized into epithelial, secretory, nervous, and nematocyst cells.

In the other forms named, the embryo develops a third layer of cells, the mesoderm. This forms muscles, connective tissue, excretory, reproductive, and circulatory organs. The ectoderm, meanwhile, forms epidermis, exoskeletal, and nervous structures, and the endoderm becomes the lining of the digestive tract. The earthworm organs are elaborated from these tissues.

In crayfish, fish, reptile, and human embryos the nerve cells are concentrated in ganglionic masses including a prominent brain. A conspicuous heart is developed. Gills appear. Jointed appendages are produced. A head is specialized. The crayfish organ systems are then completed.

The fish, reptile, and human embryos each form an internal skeleton, including vertebral column, skull, ribs, limb girdles, and limb cartilages. The gills open through from the pharynx to the outside. The brain develops into a cerebrum, diencephalon, midbrain, cerebellum and pons, and medulla. Cranial nerves appear. The spinal cord, ganglia, and nerves develop. Eyes, ears, and nose are formed. The digestive tract differentiates into mouth, pharynx, esophagus, stomach, intestine, liver, pancreas, rectum, and anus. Kidneys form in the anterior and middle parts of the trunk. Head, trunk, and limb muscles are similar. Blood vessels run from the heart, through the gills, to a dorsal aorta. This supplies the trunk with blood, and cardinal veins return the blood to the heart. The fish then hatches into a young fry, with structures ready to carry on adult functions.

In the reptile and the human embryos, the pharyngeal gills are closed up, and lungs develop. The limb skeletons differentiate into humerus, radius and ulna, carpals, meta-carpals, and phalanges in the forelimb; and femur, tibia and fibula, tarsals, metatarsals, and phalanges in the hind limb. Specialized muscles operate the joints of the limb. The cerebrum of the brain develops further. The pineal body becomes quite conspicuous, and in a few reptiles, espe-cially the New Zealand *Sphenodon*, it develops into a third eye. The kidneys first formed degenerate, and a new pair develop farther posterior in the body. The blood vessels running through the gills disappear except for a few which are modified, becoming the carotid arteries, the two aortae, and the pulmonary arteries. The cardinal veins are replaced by two anterior venae cavae and one posterior vena cava. Then the reptile hatches into an active young animal.

In the human embryo, the cerebrum elaborates further, the pineal body is reduced to a glandular structure, and the right aorta and part of the left anterior vena cava are lost. A short tail develops, a thick coat of hair covers the body, and the embryo's arms are as long as its legs. The tail and the fur coat normally are gone before birth, and the legs grow much longer than the arms. The newborn baby is recognizably human, but alters its proportions for some years after birth.

The point demonstrated here is that the relative simi-larity established by studies of comparative anatomy is corroborated by studies of comparative embryology. Not only do animals of different species develop similarly, but the more similar the adult animals are, the more fully do their embryonic developments resemble each other.

The idea that the embryo of a complex animal goes through stages resembling the embryos of its ancestors is called the **Biogenetic Theory.** This theory is sometimes misunderstood to mean that the embryo of a complex animal resembles the adult of a simpler contemporary animal. Such an interpretation is obviously false, for the

gastrula stage of a human is not like an adult hydra —
it has no tentacles, no nematocysts, no nerve network. The
resemblance is closer between the human gastrula and the
two-layered hydra embryo before the hydra cells are
specialized. But the Biogenetic Theory does not claim that
the human embryo is descended from hydra embryos.
It says, rather, that the human gastrula and the hydra two-
layered embryo both descend from the embryo of a common but remote ancestor, from which the human has
changed more than the hydra.

The appearance in the human embryo, for example, of
pharyngeal gills equipped with blood vessels; of anterior
kidneys which disappear before birth; of an eyelike pineal
body; of cardinal veins which are modified and lost before
birth; of jaw bones which become the bones of the middle
ear; of a heavy coat of hair; and of a tail — all these are
readily explained by the evolution theory as hereditary
characters handed down from previous generations, but
modified by changes which have occurred since these were
retained in adults.

The similarity of the larvae of some annelids, molluscs,
and echinoderms was mentioned in Part III. This ciliated
larva represents to the evolutionist an indication of relationship, a common descent from some primitive, ciliated
animal larva whose characteristics changed in diverse ways
during thousands of generations. Some such primitive organisms developed linear segmentation, some varied toward
absence of segmentation, and some formed radially symmetrical adults. The nauplius larvae of the crustaceans, pictured
in Figure 25.11, is another case in point.

The evidence from comparative embryology corroborates
that from comparative anatomy in support of the evolution
theory.

COMPARATIVE PHYSIOLOGY

This, too, represents a field from which similar support
for the evolution theory may be drawn. The process of
photosynthesis is common to all the species of plants
which possess chlorophyll. A student investigating photosynthesis may expect to find the fundamentals and many
of the details of the process alike whether he studies a green
alga, a moss, or an apple tree.

Similarly, the process of oxidation by which food is
broken into carbon dioxide and water with the release of
energy is common to almost every species of organism,
whether mold, moss, or monocotyledon; malaria organism,

mollusc, or man. The synthesis of protoplasm follows much the same route in all organisms studied, although the specific proteins involved vary in some degree. Most plants and animals store carbohydrates as starch, or make fats from them, or both.

Pteridophytes and spermatophytes have vascular tissues which are able to transport materials from one part of the plant to another by processes described in Part II. The processes are common to all members of these two phyla.

Growth and reproduction are characteristic of all living organisms. In considering any one group, such as the bryophytes or the tapeworms, the details of the reproductive process are remarkably similar within the group.

In plants and animals, the enzyme method of digestion is universal, and the enzyme which acts in one organism may produce the same result in another. Secretion is common to all living organisms.

Among animals, locomotion, sensation, coordination, and excretion are common activities, provided for by some modification of similar processes. As in the case of comparative anatomy and comparative embryology, not only do remarkable similarities exist, but the closer the evolutionary relationships suggested by some physiological processes the more nearly alike are the others. For example, a shark and a bony fish are more alike in their physiology than either is like a frog. The shark and the bony fish swim by trunk movements. The frog swims by kicking the hind legs. Sharks and bony fishes breathe through the gills; frogs breathe through the skin and lungs. Sharks and bony fish deposit fats in liquid form (oil) in the liver. Frogs deposit fats in solid form in a fat body near the kidney. Sharks and bony fish are normally active throughout their adult lives; frogs often hibernate during the winter. Turtles are more like frogs than like fish. They swim by leg movements. They breathe through lungs. Fat is stored in solid form in diffuse masses about the trunk. Turtles also hibernate.

One of the more recent developments in comparative physiology concerns serology, a field unknown to Darwin. If, for example, human blood is injected into a rabbit, the rabbit produces antibodies against the foreign proteins in the human blood. Then, after a time, if more human blood is injected into the rabbit, a vigorous antibody reaction takes place, precipitating out some of the foreign protein just introduced. If, instead of human blood, ape blood is used in the second injection, the reaction will be nearly as vigorous. If monkey blood is used the second time instead

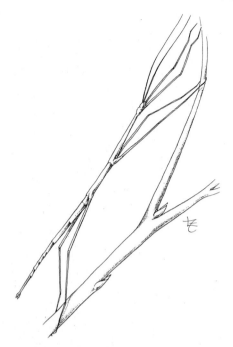

Fig. 30.5 Walking stick insect. The shape resembles closely that of a twig. What advantage might this give the animal?

Fig. 30.6 Monarch (above) and viceroy butterflies. Although these belong to quite different families, they have a great resemblance to each other in pattern. Their colors are also nearly identical. What advantage does this bestow on the viceroy?

of human blood, the reaction is not as great. Marmoset blood stimulates an even smaller reaction, and lemur blood practically none at all. The proteins in lemur blood must be so different from those in human blood that the rabbit antibodies do not react with them.

Similar tests have been tried on other mammals, birds, amphibia, molluscs, echinoderms, worms, crustacea, and many species of plants, and in almost every case the serological results correspond exactly to the evolutionary relationships postulated on the basis of comparative anatomy. In the few exceptions, the relationships postulated from anatomical studies were considered doubtful before the serological tests were tried.

The evidence from comparative physiology adds to the immense weight of support for the evolution theory.

One further type of phenomenon, both structural and physiological, is explained easily on the basis of evolution, but is more difficult to account for otherwise. This is protective resemblance.

The walking stick, an insect belonging to the Order Orthoptera, is long, narrow, and cylindrical, with very long, slender legs. See Figure 30.5. It is a leaf-eating insect living in trees. In the spring it is greenish in color, turning brown later in the year. When the insect is motionless, its position and appearance in a tree strongly resemble those of a twig. This similarity to a tree twig is thought to be an advantage in concealing it from birds and lizards and other predatory enemies.

Another famous example of protective resemblance is that of monarch and viceroy butterflies. See Figure 30.6. The monarch is a butterfly with bright and colorful wing colors in a standard pattern. It is distasteful to birds, who soon learn by experience to avoid eating monarchs. The viceroy butterfly belongs to quite a different family, and is not at all distasteful. But the wing colors and pattern of the viceroy butterfly closely resemble those of the monarch. Birds which associate the evil taste of monarch butterflies with the appearance of the wings avoid the viceroy as well. According to the evolution theory, those viceroys which most closely resembled the monarchs were the ones which survived the predation of birds, and perpetuated their characteristics.

An animal appearing like its environment is less readily seen and less likely to be attacked than a more conspicuous prey. Examples of such protective coloration are common in the animal world. Some moths resemble the bark of trees. See Figure 30.7. The Australian sea horse, a bony fish, lives

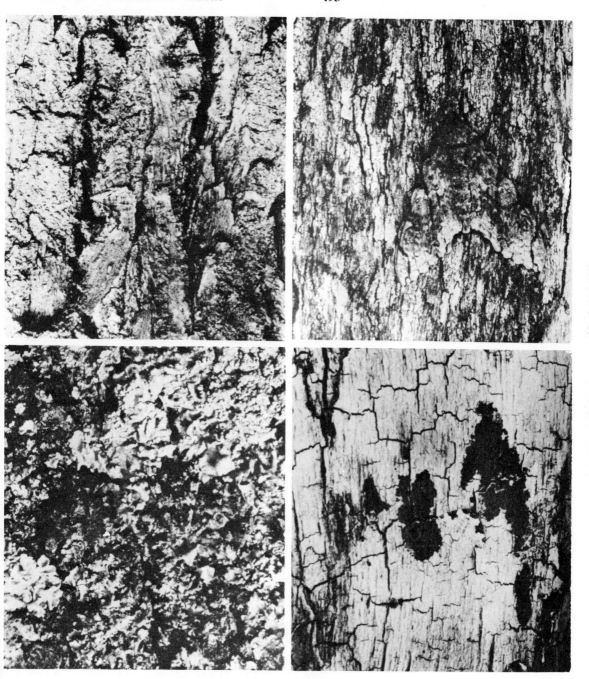

Fig. 30.7 Examples of protective coloration among moths. Can you find the moths near the center of each picture?

Fig. 30.8 Australian sea horse. How do you account for the strange form of the branches from his body and tail?

in mats of seaweed, which it closely resembles. See Figure 30.8. Frogs, lizards, birds, giraffes, zebras, leopards, and tigers are often striped or spotted, resembling the pattern of lights and shadows cast by the sun shining through grass blades or leaves of trees and shrubs. Female birds are often dun-colored, like the surroundings in which they build their nests. Snowshoe rabbits are white in winter.

Sometimes conspicuous color patterns seem to be advantageous. The brightly colored male birds may be more attractive to female birds, and therefore beget offspring more frequently than their less gaudy fellows. In Chapter 26 was recounted the story of a fluke which parasitizes the tentacle of a snail. The fluke acquires a brightly colored striping which, in addition to the twitching of the tentacle, calls the attention of birds. Those flukes which because of this characteristic were eaten by birds were the ones that survived and passed on their characteristics to the next generation.

Types of behavior may be advantageous in preserving animals, too. The opossum and the hog-nosed snake, when disturbed, may appear as if dead, and may thus seem undesirable to a predator. The startling movements and hissing of a snake, the arched back and erected hair of a cornered cat, and the barking of a dog may be effective in frightening away an enemy. This is not to say that the animals concerned affect the behavior for the purpose of frightening away intruders, but that those animals which have inherited these reaction patterns to threatening encounters have survived more often than those of their kind which did not have such behavior patterns.

Protective resemblance and warning behavior are explained as hereditary advantages of organisms preferentially selected by the weeding out of less fortunate organisms by the environment.

TAXONOMY

The classification of plants and animals is based chiefly on their anatomical characteristics and secondarily on their physiological and embryological characteristics. If each species were distinct and endowed with a set of characteristics different from those of any other species, the taxonomist would by diligent study be able to define and enumerate the species now in existence without too much difficulty and confusion. If, however, species have changed considerably in the past, and are even now in flux, gradually changing their characteristics in response to natural selection, the problems of the taxonomist would be much more difficult.

In actual practice, the taxonomist finds classification filled with practically insuperable difficulties. To begin with, it seems to be impossible to get a widely accepted working definition of "species." The present schemes of classification generally accepted by biologists are admittedly arbitrary. A student selects a group of organisms, works on them for a long time, studying a large number of characteristics, and erects a classification which seems to him most reasonable. Another investigator going over the same material evaluates the relative importance of the same characteristics differently, and comes up with a somewhat different scheme. New specimens will be discovered, showing, perhaps, that some sample used as a basis before was aberrant, and should not be considered typical, or some varieties may be found exactly intermediate between two closely related species. What is to be done, then? Each expert must decide for himself how much of the previous work he is willing to accept, and what revisions seem to him to be indicated by the specimens available to him. The result is that there is little hope of getting universal agreement in taxonomy in the foreseeable future. This is just what would be expected on the basis of the evolution theory.

Collections like those of snails along the eastern border of North America point up this issue very clearly. If one arranges on a table members of a certain group of snails gathered from Labrador to Florida, he may pick out from the collection a half dozen or so which seem by ordinary

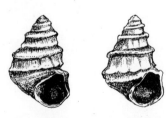

Fig. 30.9 Similarity in snail shells, from Puget Sound, Washington.

criteria to represent quite distinct species. But by looking elsewhere on the table he will find, between any two of these, examples showing a very gradual transition from one to the other. Nowhere along the line is it reasonable to separate one species from another. See Figure 30.9. This intergrading of forms contributes to the difficulties of the taxonomist and necessitates an undesirable arbitrariness in his results. But it also lends strong support to the theory of evolution.

BIOGEOGRAPHY

The example of the intergrading snails also illustrates one of the lines of evidence from a study of biogeography, or the geographical distribution of plants and animals. The slight variations to be found in the same species inhabiting neighboring but different areas are accentuated as the areas get farther and farther from each other and the environments become more and more different. If a species is spread over a wide area, but its members do not travel very far in one lifetime, the more primitive, original varieties tend to occur near the center of the area, and the more specialized, divergent varieties at the periphery.

A certain genus of sparrows, *Zonotrichia*, has five recognized species. One lives in Alaska, one in northern Canada, one in eastern Canada, and one over most of Canada and down into California. The fifth has spread into Central and South America. This fifth species, *Zonotrichia capensis*, has varied so greatly in different parts of its wide range that twenty-two subspecies are recognized. The northernmost four of these subspecies are the only ones with yellow bands on the bend of the wings, and the marking is apt to be faint in these. In the four species in North America the yellow marking is always present. Furthermore, as the investigator proceeds south in South America, the various subspecies of *Zonotrichia capensis* have longer and longer wings. The very southernmost subspecies, on Cape Horn, are the only ones which migrate regularly, and undoubtedly find this longer wing an advantage. Thus, the farther one gets from the main center of this particular genus (Canada), the greater is the variation detected (loss of yellow band, longer wings).

It is also true that those species of living organisms which are widely distributed over the earth are just the ones which have good powers of locomotion and against which geographical barriers are ineffective. On the other hand, those forms which are restricted to relatively small areas are the ones which do not travel widely, and against which geographical barriers are effective. For example, some species of mackerel, which swim in the surface waters of the open ocean, are present in most of the temperate ocean regions of the world. In contrast, the rainbow trout of the western part of the United States are differentiated into numerous subspecies, even species, being distinguishable from lake to lake or river to river.

The nature of the land plants and animals found on islands furnishes evidence for evolution. Indeed, it was Darwin's investigation of the organisms on the Galapagos Islands which so much stimulated his thought along the lines of descent with change.

The Galapagos Islands are located in the Pacific Ocean about six hundred miles west of Ecuador in South America. The Cape Verde Islands are in the Atlantic Ocean about three hundred and fifty miles west of French West Africa. Both sets of islands are of volcanic origin, tropical, and of similar environmental characteristics. The plants and animals of the Galapagos are closely related to but are different from those of neighboring western South America. The species of the Cape Verde Islands bear the same relationship to species of West Africa. But the West African species are much different from those of South America.

There may be distinctive species for each of some of the islands. As Darwin pointed out, a naturalist familiar with African and American species would unhesitatingly declare those of the Cape Verde Islands African and those of the Galapagos Islands South American in type. The evolutionist would explain this by saying that when the volcanic islands were formed, no land organisms were there. Such forms as are now found there must have descended from those which migrated in or were carried in from the nearer land masses.

The explanation of the biogeographer, then, is that the present-day distribution of living organisms is reasonably accounted for on the theory that each species evolved in one place and spread from there to all favorable environments from which it was not separated by impassable barriers. Descendants' characteristics were changed as different environments selected this or that feature and weeded out others. When the characteristics of the descendants in one area become enough different from the characteristics of descendants in another area, distinct species are recognized.

GENETICS

So far in our discussions in this chapter we have dealt with assemblies of facts which can be explained by the

Fig. 30.10   Varieties of dogs. A, Bulldog. B, Toy terrier. C, St. Bernard. D, Great Dane. E, Chihuahua. F, Greyhound. G, Mexican hairless. H, Sheep dog.

evolution theory. But what about direct evidence of the formation of new species? Is there any evidence that new species are now being developed, or have developed in the past?

Darwin suggested that the development of new species is a very slow process, occupying thousands of generations. Therefore, time prevents us from getting a speedy answer to these questions. But there is some evidence to be considered.

Darwin knew nothing of Mendel's work. The development of genetics into the large body of information and substantiated theory that it is today has occurred within the twentieth century. But the practical aspects of plant and animal breeding have been pursued for thousands of years. By choosing for breeding those organisms which had characteristics he especially prized, man has selected certain types and facilitated their increase.

Darwin interested himself in pigeon-raising and found a wide variety of forms originally derived from the wild rockdove. Dogs vary from the tiny chihuahua and toy terrier to the huge Great Dane and St. Bernard; from the massive bulldog to the graceful greyhound; from the shaggy sheep dog to the Mexican hairless. See Figure 30.10. The wide variety of present-day roses, wheat, and apples is a testimony to selection as carried on by humans. If humans, in a few thousand years, can bring about such changes, it is reasonable to suppose that changing environments over millions of years can do much more.

The detailed studies of the genetics of the fruit fly, *Drosophila*, have shown that hereditary variations occur with measurable frequency, and some of these variations may be advantageous in certain environments, some disadvantageous, and some neutral.

It has been estimated that any one gene in *Drosophila* is apt to undergo mutation about once in a million generations. This is quite infrequent, of course, and it might seem that the opportunity to observe such changes would be very slight. But we believe that there are about ten thousand genes in *Drosophila*. It is only about ten days between generations. Therefore, if we kept a thousand flies in the laboratory, we might anticipate one mutation a day on the average. Since there are billions of fruit flies in the world, the number of mutations per day must be tremendous.

Although most of the changes that have been observed are detrimental, there may be a few mutations of a nature which would enable the fly to live in a place its ancestors were unable to colonize.

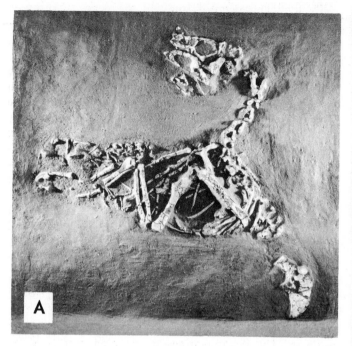

So, genetics provides us with evidence that hereditary changes do actually occur, and these changes provide the material on which environmental selection may operate.

What brings about these mutations is not completely known. The rate of mutation may be very greatly increased in *Drosophila* by exposing the flies or their eggs to X-rays. It has been reasoned from this that cosmic rays constantly reaching the earth from outer space may bring about at least some of the spontaneous mutations observed in living organisms.

PALEONTOLOGY

If, then, all the conditions necessary for evolution are available, can we show that progressive change in plant and animal characteristics has actually occurred in the past? Our knowledge of past life on the earth is based on the study of fossils, the relics of plants and animals long since dead. These fossils may be made of preserved hard parts of the organisms, such as shells, bones, or teeth. They may be films of carbon left when the volatile protoplasmic materials were forced out of plant or animal bodies by rock pressures. Or they may be casts or molds of part or all of the organism, as of footprints, or clam shells, or the trunk of a tree fallen in mud. See Figure 30.11.

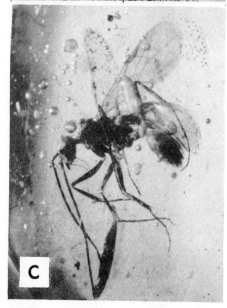

Fig. 30.11   Types of fossils. A represents bones left in the rocks. B shows the cast of the shell of an animal. C is an insect trapped in amber. D (on next page) shows footprints preserved in rock.

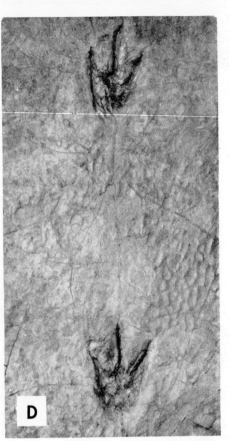

D

By long and detailed study of the deposits in which such fossils are found, their relative ages as shown by their positions on top of each other, and comparison of deposits from different parts of the earth, geologists have been able to construct a timetable of past ages and to correlate with this timetable the types of organisms existing during those ages. It should be emphasized that this information is very incomplete. Many organisms are of such a nature that they rarely if ever leave fossil impressions. Others live in environments, such as forests, which are not conducive to fossil formations. Still other organisms may have left excellent fossil records of themselves in places not yet accessible to study. Geologists have not explored every cubic foot of rock in the earth's crust. We have literally just scratched the surface in some places. But the information already obtained is valuable evidence and gives promise of much more in the future.

The timetable, shown in Table 30.1, includes five great eras, each of the last four shorter than its predecessor. The last three eras are divided into periods. The duration of each era and period shown in the table is a very rough estimate. The determinations of duration are based on sedimentation rates and thickness of strata, radioactivity

TABLE 30.1

GEOLOGIC TIME SCALE

(*Approximate time in millions of years*)

ERA	DURATION FROM	DURATION TO	TOTAL	PERIOD	DURATION FROM	DURATION TO	TOTAL
Cenozoic	60	Now	60	Pleistocene	1	Now	1
				Pliocene	11	1	10
				Miocene	20	11	9
				Oligocene	35	20	15
				Eocene	60	35	25
Mesozoic	180	60	120	Cretaceous	120	60	60
				Jurassic	150	120	30
				Triassic	180	150	30
Paleozoic	550	180	370	Permian	210	180	30
				Pennsylvanian	250	210	40
				Mississippian	290	250	40
				Devonian	340	290	50
				Silurian	380	340	40
				Ordovician	460	380	80
				Cambrian	550	460	90
Proterozoic	1100	550	550				
Archeozoic	2000	1100	900				

of elements in the rocks, and chemical content. Measurements vary and their interpretations vary even more, so that the figures given are general approximations.

Archeozoic

The Archeozoic Era occupies about the first half of the earth's past. No fossils from this era are generally recognized. In rocks deposited late in the Archeozoic there have been found a few markings which some paleontologists interpret as indications of sponges. Others interpret these as inorganic formations.

Proterozoic

The Proterozoic Era fills approximately the third quarter of the earth's history to date. In Proterozoic rocks are to be found remnants of the limy secretions of certain algae, a few Radiolarian and sponge skeletons, and some markings interpreted as worm trails in mud which later hardened into rock. See Figure 30.12. A large amount of carbon is found in Proterozoic rocks, and this is thought to be evidence of life in the era, but what kinds of organisms gave rise to the carbon deposits is still unknown.

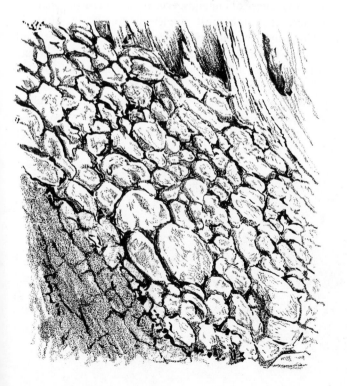

Fig. 30.12   Fossil algae from the Proterozoic Era.

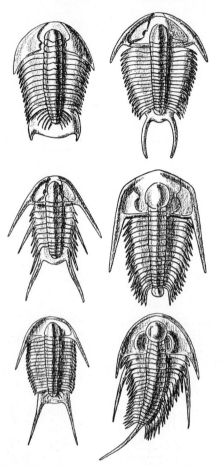

Fig. 30.13 Forms of trilobites from the Cambrian Period. What present-day animals do these most nearly represent?

Fig. 30.14 Brachiopods from the Cambrian Period. Although superficially resembling clams, they belong to a quite different phylum, having much simpler internal anatomy.

There are several reasons for the dearth of recognizable fossils in rocks of the first two long eras. The organisms that lived during the earlier times were small, soft-bodied forms, such as algae and protozoa, most of which had no hard parts. Bacterial decay destroyed their bodies before they could be preserved in sediments. The older rocks have undergone great stresses and deformations, and what few fossils may have been formed were subject to grinding and distortion until they are no longer identifiable. Also, Archeozoic and Proterozoic rocks are for the most part buried deep under later deposits or have been melted by volcanic activity.

Paleozoic

Fossils are very abundant in the rocks of the Paleozoic Era. At the very beginning of the Paleozoic Era, the Cambrian Period shows an abundance of algae, and marine animals of most of the phyla of animals except chordates. No fresh-water or land forms are known to occur in Cambrian rocks.

A few protozoa are present; sponges and coelenterates occur. An extinct class of echinoderms, the **cystoids,** is represented. Some tiny snails and cephalopods are to be found. Evidences of annelids, crustacea, and onychophorans are there. But the most numerous fossils are those of **trilobites** and **brachiopods.** The trilobites are arthropods somewhat like primitive crustaceans. They walked around on the ocean floor and were the dominant animals of their time. See Figure 30.13. The brachiopods were shell-bearing forms with internal anatomy much simpler than the clams of today. See Figure 30.14. The trilobites have long since died out, but we still have a few living brachiopods, descendants of those that lived 500,000,000 years ago.

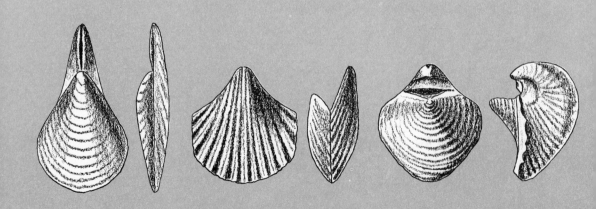

In the Ordovician Period trilobites and brachiopods were still abundant. Algae, snails, and cephalopods were also numerous. One of the cephalopods, *Endoceras*, developed a long conical shell which reached fifteen feet in length and about ten inches in its largest diameter. See Figure 30.15.

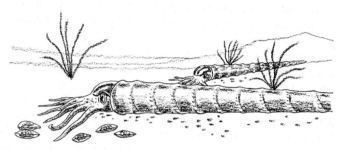

Fig. 30.15   Ordovician cephalopods. They resemble a nautilus which has a straight instead of a coiled shell.

Protozoa and sponges also were found. Among the groups found first in Ordovician rocks are corals, crinoids, clams, and another group of marine animals, the **Bryozoa,** which reached great prominence in the Paleozoic Era, but have diminished to a very minor position today. See Figure 30.16. The **graptolites,** a group of animals thought by some to be coelenterates, and by others to be primitive chordates, appeared in the Ordovician rocks and faded away in the next period, the Silurian. See Figure 30.17. The first signs of other chordates occurred in the Ordovician. A primitive fishlike animal, the **ostracoderm,** was represented here by

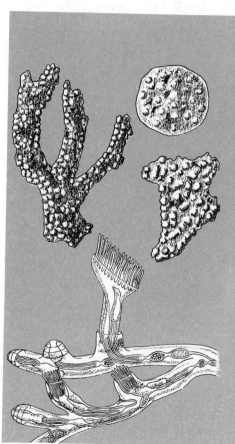

Fig. 30.16   Bryozoa. **Above,** Skeletal remains of Ordovician bryozoa. **Below,** Structure of living bryozoa growing on a rocky surface.

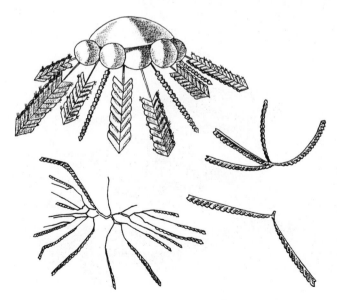

Fig. 30.17   Graptolites. Can you suggest possible reasons why these animals became extinct?

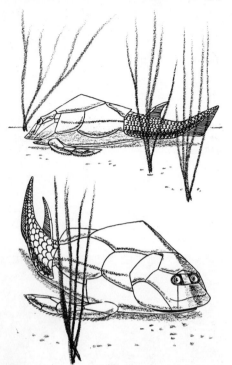

several species. These had no jaws, and only one nostril, but seem to have had a pineal eye and an electric organ. See Figure 30.18.

Studies of the Silurian rocks demonstrate the diminution of the graptolites and the trilobites. Ostracoderms, clams, and cephalopods were relatively rare. More common were algae and fungi, cystoids, snails, and crustacea. On the increase and quite numerous were corals, crinoids, brachiopods, and bryozoa. Appearing for the first time were starfishes, sea urchins, and aquatic millipedes and arachnids. There came into prominence also a type of arthropod somewhat like giant scorpions, the **eurypterids.** Some of these were nine feet long. See Figure 30.19. A few small eurypterids had appeared in the late Ordovician. From the Silurian Period also comes the first meager evidence of land plants.

The Devonian Period showed a continuation of marine animal development and a remarkably full colonizing of the land. In the ocean, trilobites were disappearing, molluscs and echinoderms were relatively rare except for clams and crinoids, which were abundant. Sponges, corals, bryozoa, and ostracoderms were numerous. The brachiopods were reaching their heyday and formed the most numerous fossils of all in this period. Fishes had become diversified, with sharks and bony fish represented. One of these fishes, *Dinichthys*, reached a length of thirty feet. See Figure 30.20. Some lungfishes occurred. Forms resembling fishes but associated with land deposits indicate the early appearance of land vertebrates, the primitive amphibia. When these vertebrates arrived on land, they found millipedes and spiders, huge ferns and fern allies, and some very early gymnosperms already there.

Fig. 30.18   Devonian ostracoderm, *Pterichthys milleri.*

Fig. 30.19   Types of eurypterids. What modern animals do these most nearly resemble?

Fig. 30.20 The huge Devonian fish *Dinichthys* was about thirty feet long in life.

In the Mississippian Period the trilobites had about disappeared. Corals were declining. But bryozoa, brachiopods, echinoderms, molluscs, and sharks were common in the seas. Land plants had increased tremendously, and amphibia and primitive reptiles crawled about the swamps in which pteridophytes and gymnosperms grew. See Figure 30.21.

Fig. 30.21 Reconstruction of a Mississippian landscape. Note the pteridophytes in the swampy background, the arthropods and amphibia in the foreground.

In the Pennsylvanian Period the situation was much the same as in the Mississippian, although marine forms were not so common. On the land, centipedes and insects appeared. See Figure 30.22. The abundant growth of swamp plants produced great masses of organic material, much of which was buried in the swamps and over the succeeding millions of years has been transformed into coal. Because most of our present-day coal beds are remains of Mississippian and Pennsylvanian plants, these two periods are sometimes referred to as Carboniferous time.

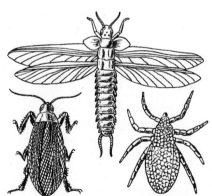

Fig. 30.22 Arthropods from the Pennsylvanian Period. The upper figure is an insect of an order no longer represented among living animals. The lower left figure is a primitive cockroach. The lower right figure is a spider.

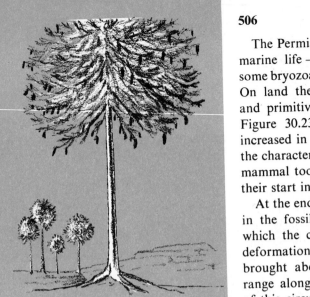

Fig. 30.23 Cone-bearing gymnosperm from the Permian Period. What modern plants does this most nearly resemble?

Fig. 30.24 Animals in transition from reptiles to mammals found in Permian rocks. These illustrations were reconstructed from fossils found in South Africa. They are, from top to bottom, *Cynognathus, Kannemeyeria,* and *Lycaenops.*

The Permian Period saw the extinction of many forms of marine life — many kinds of corals, most crinoids, and some bryozoa. Brachiopods and molluscs were still common. On land the cone-bearing trees replaced the large ferns and primitive gymnosperms over much of the earth. See Figure 30.23. Insects became more diversified. Reptiles increased in number and variety. In a few of these reptiles the characters of the teeth show changes in the direction of mammal tooth structure. The first mammals probably got their start in the Permian. See Figure 30.24.

At the end of the Permian Period occurred a sharp break in the fossil record. A time of upheaval ensued, during which the crust of the earth underwent movements and deformations of great magnitude. One of the changes brought about was the formation of a great mountain range along the eastern part of North America. Because of this circumstance, the time of turmoil is known as the Appalachian Revolution.

Mesozoic

After the Appalachian Revolution came the Mesozoic Era. Conditions in the oceans changed only slowly, since the environment was not pronouncedly different from one era to the next. On land, however, the continents were upraised, drier climates prevailed, and new plants found an opportunity to thrive. The dominant animals of this era were reptiles, some attaining sizes not since found in land animals. The amphibia and the newly developed mammals could not contend successfully with this great increase of reptiles and played an inconspicuous role during the Mesozoic Era.

In the Triassic Period, some of the cone-bearing gymnosperms were trees two hundred feet high. Reptiles reinvaded the water from the land, for example, the fishlike ichthyosaurs and the long-necked plesiosaurs. See Figure 30.25. In the sea the brachiopods diminished strikingly, and the corals, molluscs, and echinoderms became much more like the modern forms than were their Paleozoic forerunners.

The Jurassic Period saw a continuation of the modernization of marine animals and land gymnosperms. The insects became more numerous and more varied, the butterflies, flies, and social ants appearing for the first time. But the most spectacular development was again in the reptiles. The dinosaurs had arrived in full force. The huge *Brontosaurus,* a vegetarian monster over sixty feet long and weighing nearly forty tons, waded through swamps and

Fig. 30.25 Ichthyosaurs and plesiosaurs. The ichthyosaurs were more fishlike in form, with rounded bodies and no necks. The plesiosaurs had very long necks and long paddlelike appendages.

Fig. 30.26 *Brontosaurus.* Its huge weight suited it to living in water most of the time. Why would that be better than land living?

Fig. 30.27 *Diplodocus,* a Jurassic dinosaur nearly ninety feet long.

small streams with the water buoying up some of his great weight. His long neck enabled him to reach for the leaves and branches which constituted his diet. See Figure 30.26. The ninety-foot *Diplodocus* was more slender and graceful. See Figure 30.27. Preying on these animals were carnivorous dinosaurs like the thirty-foot *Allosaurus.* See Figure 30.28. Turtles and crocodiles developed at this

Fig. 30.28 *Allosaurus,* a carnivorous dinosaur of the Jurassic Period.

time, too. Two branches of the reptile class were modified in the direction of flight organs. The **pterodactyls** developed a leathery web of skin running from the greatly elongated little finger of the forelimb to the trunk and thigh on each side. See Figure 30.29. The *Archeopteryx* developed a pair of wings much like those of the pterodactyls, but in addition modified its reptilian scales into feathers. See Figure 30.30.

Fig. 30.29   Jurassic pterodactyl, or flying dinosaur.

Fig. 30.30   *Archeopteryx.* Can you recognize the similarity of this animal to the reptiles?

It retained the teeth, long tail, and free claws on the forelimbs that characterize reptiles, but the appearance of feathers is a landmark on the road to the development of present-day birds. Mammals had by this time diversified into four orders, none of which is recognized among living mammals. One of the four, however, is thought to be the ancestor of the marsupials. See Figure 30.31.

In the Cretaceous Period the most conspicuous changes again were those on land. The angiosperms arrived in considerable numbers and diversified quickly into many of the groups recognizable today. The reptiles continued to be the dominant animals, producing forms like the herbivorous *Triceratops* with its prominent head shield and protective spines, and the carnivorous *Tyrannosaurus*,

Fig. 30.31   Head of a Jurassic mammal, *Ctenacodon.*

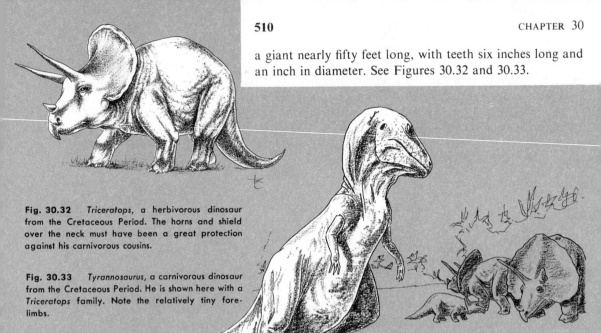

a giant nearly fifty feet long, with teeth six inches long and an inch in diameter. See Figures 30.32 and 30.33.

Fig. 30.32 *Triceratops,* a herbivorous dinosaur from the Cretaceous Period. The horns and shield over the neck must have been a great protection against his carnivorous cousins.

Fig. 30.33 *Tyrannosaurus,* a carnivorous dinosaur from the Cretaceous Period. He is shown here with a *Triceratops* family. Note the relatively tiny fore-limbs.

Fig. 30.34   Heads of Cretaceous mammals.

The coming of the flowering plants is associated with a new surge of differentiation in insects and mammals. Some insects and flowers became adapted to each other with the result that insects found sugar solutions in the flowers and carried pollen from one flower to the next. Many mammals found the succulent leaves and fruits of angiosperms very suitable for food. Among the kinds of mammals appearing in the Cretaceous Period are the marsupials and the **insectivores.** The insectivores are a group including the moles, shrews, and hedgehogs. See Figure 30.34. Toothed birds, probably descendants of *Archeopteryx* or something like it, occurred in the Cretaceous. See Figure 30.35.

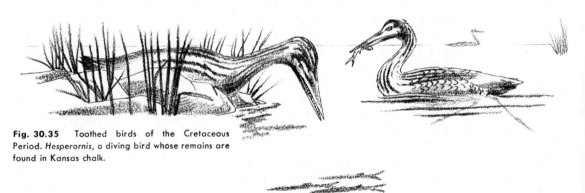

Fig. 30.35   Toothed birds of the Cretaceous Period. *Hesperornis,* a diving bird whose remains are found in Kansas chalk.

At the end of the Cretaceous Period occurred another great upheaval, the Rocky Mountain Revolution. As its name suggests, this was the time of formation of the mountain chain in western North America, and of the Andes in South America as well. This disturbance produced climatic changes resulting in the disappearance of the great dinosaurs. The birds and mammals, being warm-blooded, could survive periods of cold, whereas the cold-blooded reptiles would become sluggish, and unable to get enough food to supply their vast bulk. The development of angiosperms provided lush vegetation suited to the birds and mammals, and the mammals especially became the dominant forms in the Cenozoic Era, competing for this dominance with the insects.

Cenozoic

The Eocene Period saw the rapid diversification of mammals into types which would not be recognized today. The **titanotheres, creodonts, amblypods,** and **condylarths** are all now extinct. See Figure 30.36. But smaller forms like the present-day rodents, primates, and ungulates were beginning to appear. See Figure 30.37. Reptiles were restricted to turtles, crocodiles, lizards, and the newly developed snakes which appeared in the late Cretaceous Period. The first toothless birds were developed.

Fig. 30.36 Early Cenozoic mammals. **A**, Eocene titanothere. **B**, Eocene condylarth. **C**, Eocene amblypod. **D**, Oligocene oreodont.

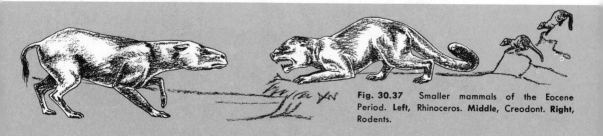

Fig. 30.37 Smaller mammals of the Eocene Period. **Left**, Rhinoceros. **Middle**, Creodont. **Right**, Rodents.

In the Oligocene Period giant pigs and some of the early carnivores occurred. The remains of a small ape have been found. See Figure 30.38.

In the Miocene Period occur the first grasses. This gave a boost to the ungulates; and the horses, camels, rhinoceroses, and elephants underwent remarkable changes, increasing in size and in certain specializations such as loss of toes and increase in the grinding surfaces of the teeth. See Figure 30.39. Rodents and carnivores increased and became more like their present-day representatives. In the Miocene Period a primate, *Dryopithecus*, appeared, which may have been the ancestor or very much like the ancestor of present-day apes and humans. See Figure 30.40.

In the Pliocene Period the mammals were not greatly different from those living today. See Figure 30.41. The human genus differentiated during this time, probably late in the period.

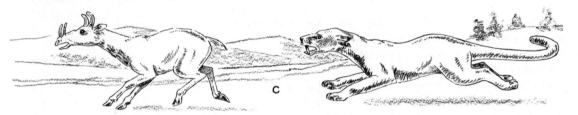

Fig. 30.38   Oligocene mammals. **A**, Giant pig. **B**, Foxlike dog. **C**, Carnivore chasing an ungulate.

Fig. 30.39   Miocene mammals. **A**, Dog. **B**, Forerunner of the elephant. **C**, Forerunner of the horse. **D**, Forerunner of the camels and giraffes.

Fig. 30.40 Jaw of *Dryopithecus* with teeth. Portions not shaded are reconstructions based on a knowledge of comparative anatomy.

Fig. 30.41 Pliocene mammals. **A**, Mastodon. **B**, Rhinoceros. **C**, Saber-toothed tiger. **D**, Bear. **E**, Horse. **F**, Deer.

The Pleistocene Period brings us down to the present day. That the appearance of new forms and the extinction of old ones is not a finished story may be shown by the disappearance during recorded history of the Irish elk, the passenger pigeon, the dodo, the moa, and the heath hen; the near extinction of the bison, the milu or Father David's deer of China, and the maidenhair tree (*Ginkgo*) of the Orient; and the disappearance from certain regions of formerly abundant organisms, such as the marsupial "wolf" in Australia, trees on the island of St. Helena, and wild turkeys and wildcats from many parts of the United States. See Figure 30.42.

Man's introduction of organisms into new areas, such as the English sparrow and starling into the United States, the rabbit into Australia, and the rubber tree into the East Indies, promotes the possibilities of the formation of new species by the selective action of a different environment on an organism adapted to a previous habitat.

Fig. 30.42 **A**, Passenger pigeon. **B**, *Ginkgo* tree and leaf. **C**, Emu. **D**, Whooping crane. **E**, Irish elk. **F**, Bison. **G**, Dodo. **H**, Marsupial wolf.

The argument from paleontology shows not only that plants and animals have clearly changed their characteristics in times past, but that these changes follow trends, and that these trends are the ones which might be expected if evolution by natural selection had been in operation throughout the history of the earth. At first the organisms were simple — algae, protozoa, and sponges seem to have been the first to leave fossil records. Then marine forms of a wide variety of classes appeared. Later the marine chordates developed. When the colonizing of the land began, first plants, then arthropods, and then amphibia appeared. The plants were able to manufacture their own food. The arthropods could live on plants. The amphibia could eat both plants and arthropods. Still later, reptiles developed, while ferns and gymnosperms were abundant. Then mammals, birds, and angiosperms came along. The direction is from the simple toward the more complex; new species retained some characteristics of their ancestors and developed new ones. It would seem that this continual change of living forms associated with changing environments would be conclusive evidence that evolution has gone on in the past.

PRESENT–DAY STUDIES

Work is continuing in the fields of comparative biology, taxonomy, biogeography, genetics, and paleontology to secure further information bearing on the evolution theory. In comparative biology the threads of similarity woven through series of organisms are being sought. For example, the structural relations, developmental differentiation, and action of the muscles of vertebrates have been studied in an effort to trace hereditary likenesses from primitive to more complex conditions.

In taxonomy, efforts are being made to produce a more definite concept of species, and to analyze organisms not on the basis of isolated characteristics, but on the basis of the product of many characteristics considered as an interacting pattern. For example, spiders are being classified not only on a basis of the arrangement of hairs on the leg, but also on more fundamental structural features such as the type and anatomy of the respiratory systems, the openings in the wall of the heart, and the relations of the legs to the body.

In biogeography, the geographical distribution of organisms is correlated with variations in characteristics to determine the relations between different environmental factors and the variations on the one hand, and the effect of geographical separation and isolation upon perpetuation or change of hereditary characters on the other. Isolation in some cases, not in all, seems to enhance the formation of new subspecies and species.

Correlated with this study of the effects of geographic isolation are the studies of ecological and of physiological isolation. Within an area, if two groups of the same species are found in different habitats and do not invade each other's territory extensively, ecological isolation occurs. For example, one species of field mouse lives chiefly in open grasslands, and feeds on insects and some vegetation. Another species of field mouse lives mainly in woods, and eats more vegetation and less insects. At the borderline between the two, they intergrade.

If some physiological changes in one group make it incompatible with the other, physiological isolation is said to take place. Certain Iowa crickets seem to have no constant anatomical differences by which they may be divided into distinct species. The male crickets make a vibrating noise by rubbing the wing rapidly on the back of the thorax. The frequency of the vibration varies from one group of males to another. If, as is sometimes suggested, this noise attracts females, the females may be attracted by certain definite pitches or vibration frequencies, and hence the purity of the group is maintained, and no natural crosses occur between a male calling in one pitch and a female attuned to another. Human intervention has brought about crosses of different types, however, and they prove to be fertile. The characteristic seems to be controlled by the interaction of several genes. These studies of the factors which isolate potentially or actually different species permit a further insight into the methods of natural selection.

In genetics, the nature of mutations is being carefully investigated. By experimentation, various factors have been shown to affect the rate of mutations — exposure to different kinds of radiation, temperature changes, and various chemicals. The effect of these on the proteins in the chromosomes is being studied in an effort to find out how they bring about hereditary changes. Genes are studied not only individually but also in groups to find out what effects they have on each other.

Statistical analyses of characteristics in large populations help to determine whether these characteristics are increasing or decreasing in frequency, and hence what evolutionary changes are actually taking place in groups of organisms. Various crosses are investigated to see what the possibilities of hybridization are. One investigator, Karpechenko, has succeeded in obtaining fertile offspring from a cross between a radish and a cabbage. Their germ cells each contain a complete haploid set of the chromosomes of a radish and of a cabbage, so that the zygote has a diploid set of the chromosomes of both species of plants. The radish and the cabbage belong to two different genera in the same family of angiosperms.

In paleontology, the trends of structural changes in organisms from one period to the next are being investigated. This is being correlated with structural changes in living species in an effort to build up a connected story of the possible directions of evolutionary development in the past. For example, in some cephalopod molluscs, from the Mesozoic Era, the shells enlarged as the body grew and moved forward in the shell. The floors laid down by the animal in its successive positions intercept the walls of the shell in lines called **sutures.** These sutures became more and more intricately folded in later periods, as is shown in Figure 30.43. Comparisons of this trend with the structure of living cephalopods enable scientists to understand better the mode of life of long-extinct animals.

SUMMARY

The evidence for the theory of evolution is of two sorts:

1. The ability of the theory to furnish an explanation for great accumulations of factual data from the fields of comparative anatomy, comparative embryology, comparative physiology, taxonomy, and biogeography.

2. The observations of changing characteristics provided by studies in genetics and paleontology. Here direct evidence of evolutionary changes is available: the changed characteristics of domesticated forms, the appearance of mutations, and the fossil record of a billion years, showing profound changes in the structure of plants and animals, and recognizable trends, adaptations, and extinctions correlated with changes in environment.

At the present time, the theory of evolution is almost universally accepted by biologists as a working theory. Its ability to explain factual observations is so great that it is considered a basic assumption of contemporary biology. The meaning evolution gives to comparative anatomy, embryology, and physiology, and to taxonomy and biogeography is a great advance over a mere catalog of unrelated facts. The investigation of the factors of evolution by the study of variation and inheritance, and the account of evolutionary changes in the past by the study of paleon-

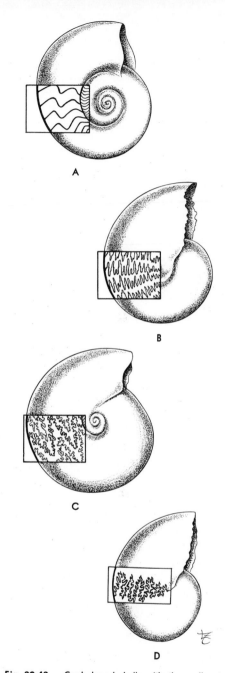

A

B

C

D

Fig. 30.43   Cephalopod shells with the wall cut away to show the increase in folding of the sutures from one genus to another. Each suture represents the intersection of the floor with the wall at one stage of the animal's life. In **D**, only one suture is shown. **A,** *Gastrioceras.* **B,** *Medlicottia.* **C,** *Perrinites.* **D,** *Phylloceras.*

tology have gained point and direction by the evolution theory. Furthermore, new discoveries in all of these fields tend to confirm the theory.

REVIEW QUESTIONS

1. Describe the kind of evidence on evolution found in studies of comparative anatomy.
2. Describe the kind of evidence on evolution found in studies of comparative embryology.
3. State the Biogenetic Theory.
4. Describe the kind of evidence on evolution found in studies of comparative physiology.
5. Describe the kind of evidence on evolution found in studies of taxonomy.
6. Describe the kind of evidence on evolution found in studies of biogeography.
7. Describe the kind of evidence on evolution found in studies of genetics.
8. Describe the kind of evidence on evolution found in studies of paleontology.
9. Describe the kinds of organisms to be found fossil in the eras and periods of geologic history.
10. What kinds of studies now going on bear on evolution?

GENERAL QUESTIONS

1. Is all protoplasm alike? Does your answer affect the validity of the evidence for evolution from the study of protoplasm?
2. Are all living organisms cellular?
3. Some people believe the structural similarities of organisms indicate that they were all made by one Creator. Is this a more reasonable explanation than the Evolution Theory?
4. Compare the circulatory system of a fish with that of a human.
5. Is the human appendix useful to the human?
6. How would a believer in special creation explain the pharyngeal gills of human embryos?
7. Sharks and humans have paired forelimbs and hindlimbs. Snakes and earthworms do not. What does this indicate about evolutionary relationships?
8. Some domestic cats are striped, as are tigers. Some are tawny, as are lions. Does this have a bearing on their evolutionary relationships?
9. Is the argument for evolution from protective resemblance valid?
10. Are taxonomic schemes based on objective observation or subjective opinion?
11. Why does Australia have so many more native kinds of marsupials than other parts of the world?
12. How can a geneticist determine what constitutes a species?

13. How do you account for the great abundance of fossils in the earliest Paleozoic rocks, when the late Proterozoic rocks have so few?

14. Can the evidence from paleontology be explained reasonably on a basis other than that of the Evolution Theory?

15. Estimate the relative value of the scientific studies now in progress as to the possibilities of their producing pertinent evidence on evolution.

CHAPTER 31

The Evolution Story

EVOLUTION STORY

If evolution has taken place, it is a natural and fascinating quest to search out the story of development of the great variety of living organisms from the one or more simple forms which gave them rise. Since we cannot return to the past eras and make direct observations of evolutionary changes, we must attack the problem indirectly, by induction and deduction from the incomplete evidence at our disposal. This means that the results of our study will be uncertain and speculative, but the more abundant our observations and experiments and the keener our analysis, the more reasonable and convincing will be our conclusions.

PLANT ORIGINS

Although the origin of the first living organism is not within the scope of the evolution theory, yet speculation on this point has occupied some evolutionists. One idea is that bacterial spores or virus molecules may have drifted through space and landed on the earth. This is difficult to test. If such an event accounts for the beginnings of life on this planet, it does not solve the problem of the origin of life, but merely changes the setting. This may be important, however, because there may be other planets where origin of life from nonliving matter is more likely to have occurred than here. No convincing evidence has been brought forth that life arises on earth now from nonliving matter. But since evidence supporting this speculation of extraterrestrial origin of life is lacking, it remains only a theoretical possibility.

Another idea is that some fortuitous combination of chemical substances under suitable conditions became self-perpetuating and possessed the characteristics of life. The similarity of virus molecules to nonliving protein molecules suggests that this is the most probable realm in which such a transition may have occurred. The virus so formed may have been quite unlike any present-day viruses, and undoubtedly was free-living, for no more complex organisms existed in which it could have been parasitic. The fact that we know no free-living viruses today is not a satisfactory reason for believing they did not exist in the early days of the earth, or, indeed, that they do not exist now. Viruses are detected because of their disease-producing properties, and until we learn to find and identify viruses by some other characteristic such as their images in an electron microscope or their secretion products in a test tube, we shall not be able to investigate free-living viruses.

The similarity of viruses to protein molecules and the concept of viruses as the simplest living organisms are all we have to go on to support the idea that they represent the earliest forms of life. No fossil viruses have as yet been identified, although it is conceivable that the effects of virus diseases may show up on fossil organisms.

Thallophytes

Whatever may have been their origin, viruses seem to be structurally the simplest living organisms. Most closely allied to the viruses among other living organisms are the bacteria. These have diversified considerably, but retain a relative simplicity. Organized nuclei are not differentiated from the cytoplasm in most bacteria. Cell walls vary in size and constitution. Reproduction is by simple fission as is the case in viruses. Some bacteria adhere in clusters or chains, hinting at colony formation as in plants like *Gonium* or the filamentous algae.

The blue-green algae are like the bacteria in that the protoplasm is not divided into cytoplasm and nucleus. Some blue-green algae are single cells, some are filamentous. They possess cell walls and, unlike bacteria, have chlorophyll. A few bacteria have photosynthetic pigments related to chlorophyll, however, and the circumstantial evidence for the origin of blue-green algae from bacteria is very attractive.

It is not too difficult to imagine the green algae evolving from blue-green algae. Green algae may appear as single cells, as filaments, as flat plates, or as hollow spheres. Nuclei and chloroplasts are differentiated in the cytoplasm. Cell walls are present in many, although there are exceptions, such as *Euglena*. (See p. 351.) This absence of a cell wall in *Euglena*, and the similarity between *Euglena* and *Astasia* suggest that flagellate Protozoa could have been derived from flagellate green algae.

The other groups of Algae, the golden algae, brown algae, and red algae are all at present rather specialized forms giving no certain indication of their origin. Whether they were derived from blue-green algae directly, or through green algae, or even by some other route from the earliest organisms will be difficult to establish. The intermediate forms have undoubtedly failed to survive into the present time, perhaps because of the gradually increasing concentration of salt in the ocean during past geologic eras, or because of some other environmental factor like competition with more efficient specialized forms.

The Actinomycetales are not greatly different from some of the other bacteria and, on the other hand, show characteristics resembling the Myxomycetes and Phycomycetes. From the Phycomycetes to the Ascomycetes and Basidiomycetes is not an impossible series of jumps, and the evolution of the fungi could conceivably have occurred by the gradual development of the hyphae and increase in complexity of spore formation and life cycle.

Another possibility is the derivation of these mycelial fungi from filamentous algae which lost their chlorophyll. A few green algae, like *Vaucheria*, are filamentous forms without partitions dividing the filament into cells. See Figure 31.1. On the whole, though, derivation of filamentous fungi from bacteria through the Actinomycetales seems more probable.

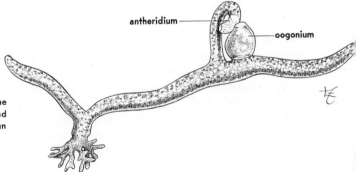

Fig. 31.1 *Vaucheria.* No cell walls interrupt the continuity of the protoplasmic mass. At the left end is a modified portion of the plant which serves as an anchor, fastening the plant to some solid surface.

Bryophytes

The bryophytes most probably arose from green algae. One genus of green algae, *Coleochaete*, has a body of branched filaments radiating from a common center, or a flat, disclike plate. See Figure 31.2. Antheridia produce swimming sperm, and the egg-producing structure develops a long neck somewhat like the trichogyne of a fungus or the archegonial neck of a bryophyte. The sperm swims to this neck and fertilizes the egg. The zygote is surrounded by a thick wall and may rest during the winter or some other period unfavorable for development. Eventually the zygote divides by meiosis, forming a group of cells from which motile spores are developed. This life cycle seems like a precursor of the alternation of generations to be found in a bryophyte such as *Ricciocarpus.*

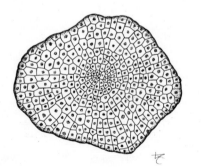

Fig. 31.2 Form of *Coleochaete.* How is this like *Ricciocarpus?*

In *Ricciocarpus* the gametophyte stage is a flat plate, and the sporophyte is nothing more than a sporangium. In *Anthoceros* and *Funaria*, the sporophyte develops a foot and a stalk, in addition to the sporangium, now called a capsule. In the moss, the gametophyte plant is more than just a flat plate, differentiating into a leafy stalk with rhizoids.

Vascular Plants

The origin of vascular plants is at present the subject of some disagreement. The older view is that the earliest pteridophytes were derived from some form such as *Anthoceros* in which the sporophyte, already supplied with stomata, chlorophyll, and spore-making cells, achieved independence of the gametophyte by establishing contact with the ground and developing xylem and phloem tissues which transport substances throughout the plant. The gametophyte of a fern is not greatly different from the gametophyte of a liverwort, except that the antheridia and archegonia of the fern are located on the underside of the gametophyte, facilitating the contact of the embryonic sporophyte with the soil.

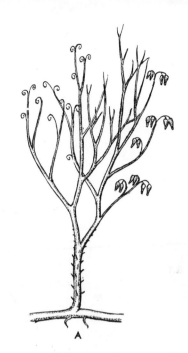

A more recent view holds that the pteridophytes are derived directly from green algae. One group of fern allies, the **Psilopsida,** is represented by a few fossil forms from the Silurian and Devonian Periods and by two living genera. See Figure 31.3. The plants have horizontal, creeping stems like the ferns, slender rhizoids projecting into the soil, upright branches bearing diminutive leaves, and small sporangia at the tips of the upright branches in fossil forms, and in the leaf axils in present-day forms. The theory maintains that some filamentous alga in the middle Paleozoic or before varied in the direction of resistance to drying, strengthening of the stem, development of vascular tissues, formation of terminal sporangia, and differentiation of rhizoids and leaves. At the same time, the gametophyte generation must have developed specializations that enabled it to live in moist soil instead of water. This series of variations would have made it possible for the new kind of plant to live in a land habitat. This is a rather extensive series of changes, and from the standpoint of comparative anatomy the idea has been criticized. However, the fact that these Psilopsida are found in middle Paleozoic time, whereas the oldest fossil bryophytes date from the Pennsylvanian rocks, has led many botanists to follow the newer concept. The absence of Psilopsida from the fossil record between the Devonian Period and the

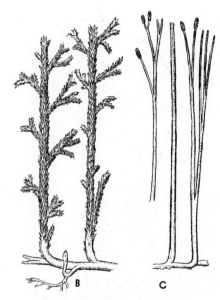

Fig. 31.3   Psilopsida. A, *Psilophyton*. B, *Asteroxylon*. C, *Rhynia*. These are all Devonian pteridophytes.

present and the possibility that bryophytes may have occurred during the periods before the appearance of Psilopsida, but whose fossil remains, if any, have not yet been discovered make the newer idea uncertain. There still remains a good deal of circumstantial evidence for the theory that bryophytes are intermediate between algae and pteridophytes.

Certainly if the bryophytes gave rise to pteridophytes, it was the liverworts which did so. The mosses have specialized and seem to lead into a blind alley with the gametophyte reaching about the limits of development which will still allow the sperm cells to swim to eggs in a drop of water.

Like the Psilopsida, the other fern allies have small leaves and possibly gave rise to the ferns on one hand and to the gymnosperms on the other. Some gymnosperms, such as the pine, have relatively small leaves, whereas others, like the cycads or sago palms, have large, fernlike leaves.

The closest approach to pine reproductive structures among the living pteridophytes seems to be found in *Selaginella*. This does not, of course, mean that *Selaginella* is the direct ancestor of the pine, but rather that both are descended from some remote common ancestor from which the fern ally has deviated less than the gymnosperm. It should be remembered throughout this discussion that present-day forms are not ancestor and progeny, but rather cousins, some having changed their characteristics more than others since their branches first separated off the common trunk. Thus, if the story so far is to be accepted, the pine trees of today may have descended from the same Archeozoic virus as the present-day nitrogen-fixing bacteria, but the bacteria have changed relatively little during the billion or two years, and the pine trees have evolved very much.

From the gymnosperms, perhaps through the late Jurassic ancestors of the Gnetales, the angiosperms developed, first the dicotyledons, and later, from these, the monocotyledons.

Animal Origins

In the plant kingdom, although this story is largely speculation, the line of probable relationships is easier to trace than in the animal kingdom. The key structures which establish the classification of plants are more apt to be preserved in fossil form than is the case with animals. And among living forms, plant structures are not quite as diverse as animal structures. A moss, a fern, and an apple

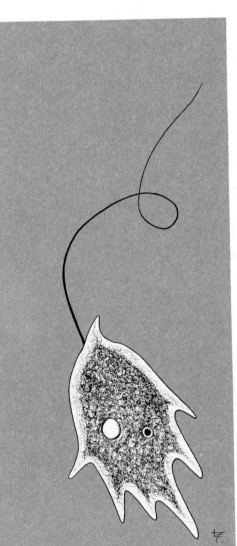

Fig. 31.4 *Mastigameba.* This animal seems to be intermediate between *Sarcodina* and the flagellates in its structural characteristics.

tree have readily recognizable similarities. A clam, a honey-bee, and an alligator are so different, however, that one is hard put to it to find similarities. So, even more doubt and disagreement will be found in tracing the evolution of animal phyla and classes than in that of plant phyla and classes.

Protozoa

The similarity of flagellate protozoa to flagellate algae has already been mentioned. One of the flagellate protozoa, *Mastigameba*, has an amebalike body with a flagellum protruding from one edge. See Figure 31.4. It is conceivable that some ancient form like the present-day *Mastigameba* may have given rise to the Sarcodina.

Another branch of the flagellates may have developed more numerous locomotor extensions and a coordinating device like the neuromotor system of *Paramecium*, and thus produced the ciliates.

Many biologists consider that, in general, parasites evolved from nonparasitic forms. If this assumption is correct, the evolution of parasitism in animals, as in plants, is usually accompanied by degeneration of many of the vegetative organs and accentuation of the development of reproductive structures. The sporozoa are all parasitic protozoa which possess no locomotor appendages, food vacuoles, mouths, and so forth, but which have developed efficient means of reproducing themselves in considerable numbers. Most likely the sporozoa evolved from flagellates, too.

Metazoa

Some flagellates have a little collar about the flagellum. These collared flagellates resemble the gastrodermal cells of sponges so closely that support is given to the idea of the origin of sponges from flagellate protozoa. The discovery of a small colony of collared flagellates, *Proterospongia*, fitted so well into the story that its name is an outgrowth of this circumstance. See Figure 31.5.

The Volvocine Series described in Chapter 15 serves as an example of the way many-celled animals may have arisen from the flagellate protozoa. In a spherical colony of cells in which some form of coordination and cooperation in locomotion and food-getting had developed, some cells may have become specialized as reproductive cells, and others as digestive cells. These reproductive and digestive cells may then have sunk into the interior of the sphere.

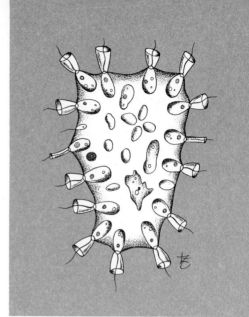

Fig. 31.5   *Proterospongia, a flagellate colony somewhat resembling a simple sponge.*

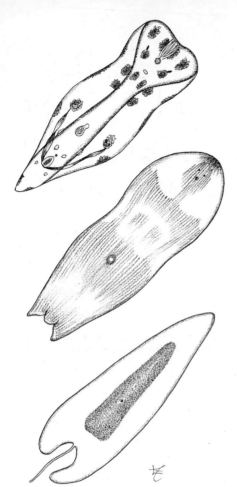

Fig. 31.6 Forms of the simple flatworms, called Acoela. This group of animals has an outer form like planarias, but the internal anatomy is somewhat simpler.

Food could be captured by surface cells, passed to the interior cells, and there digested. The digested food then diffused throughout the colony, supplying all of its cells. Thus the two-layered organisms such as hydras may have had their origin. Progressive specialization of the outer layer resulted in an epidermis with protective cells, muscular structures, a nerve net, and nematocysts. The inner cells formed a gastrodermis with gland cells and phagocytic cells, and also some muscular and nervous elements. From the early, primitive coelenterates developed the polyps, jellyfish, corals, and others still represented today.

The jellyfish, sea anemones, and corals possess between the epidermis and gastrodermis layers some scattered cells and fibers forming a primitive sort of connective tissue. The mesenchyme cells in this connective tissue are little changed from the embryonic condition and often wander about in ameboid fashion.

The simplest flatworms have a ciliated epidermis surrounding a mass of digestive and reproductive cells and a mouth in the middle of the ventral surface, but not much of a digestive cavity. The animals are flattened, bilaterally symmetrical organisms with a slight concentration of nervous tissue at the anterior end and a nerve net through the rest of the body. See Figure 31.6. Thus they are not greatly advanced over the hypothetical primitive coelenterates except for the flattening, the bilateral symmetry, and the beginnings of a central nervous system. *Planaria* develops a more prominent gastrovascular cavity, differentiates muscles from the connective tissue, and adds a distinct excretory system.

Some few Turbellaria are parasitic, and it is from these that the flukes and tapeworms may have evolved along two separate lines.

The roundworms may have been derived from primitive flatworms. Roundworms have an anus, a body cavity (not a true celom) between the digestive tract and the epidermis, and long, tubular reproductive organs. They do not have flame cells as do the more advanced Turbellaria, indicating that they may have diverged from the flatworm line before the flame cells were developed.

The trochophore larva was described in Chapter 17. It is a ciliated larva with a simple bent tube for a digestive tract, a cavity between this and the epidermis, and a few mesoderm cells in the cavity. It is not unreasonable to think of this animal as arising from the primitive flatworms by the completion of the digestive tract and the appearance of the body cavity. The great similarity of the trochophore larvae of marine molluscs and of marine annelids supports the idea that molluscs and annelids came from a common ancestor related to the flatworms.

The molluscs developed the characteristic mantle, body mass, foot, and gills. The six present-day classes of molluscs diverged from some primitive form resembling the chitons more than any of the other groups.

The annelids developed a true celom, an elongated cylindrical body, and the habit of segmentation. From the more primitive marine polychetes were probably derived the oligochetes, like the earthworm. The leeches seem to be modified annelids derived from oligochetes.

The similarity of *Peripatus* to polychetes on the one hand and to arthropods on the other suggests one possibility for the derivation of the arthropods. Certainly the annelids seem the most likely group of animals from which arthropods might have arisen. However, *Peripatus* is a land form, and the paleontological record shows no evidence of life on land until the Silurian Period, whereas the trilobites were conspicuous throughout the Cambrian and Ordovician Periods. It is conceivable, of course, that some marine onychophore like those found in Cambrian rocks may have occurred in the Proterozoic and have given rise to the ancestors of the trilobites, but that due to thinner chitin, or none at all, and to changes in Proterozoic rocks, the fossils have been destroyed or have not yet been discovered.

At any rate, the trilobites have much in common with the present-day crustacea and very likely gave rise to the crustacea. From either the trilobites or the crustacea may have come the eurypterids.

In the middle Paleozoic Era arthropods began colonizing the land. Examples of arachnids and millipedes occur in Devonian rocks, and insects and centipedes are found fossil in Pennsylvanian deposits. Their relationships are quite uncertain, but perhaps the arachnids were derived from eurypterids, which seem to resemble scorpions somewhat, and scorpions are the oldest known fossil arachnids. The millipedes may have evolved from crustacea. The centipedes and insects are more like each other than like any other arthropods, and may have had a common ancestor derived from another branch of the crustacea.

The echinoderms and chordates are left to be accounted for, among the prominent modern phyla of animals. Just as the annelids and molluscs are thought to be related because of a common type of larva, the trochophore, so the echinoderms and chordates have in common the **dipleurula** type of larva, suggesting a relationship. The

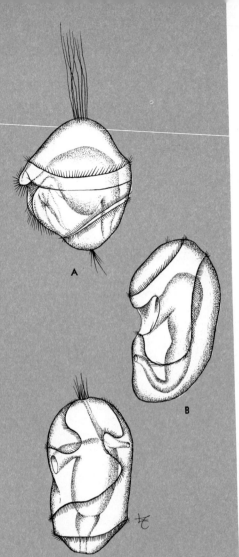

A

B

C

Fig. 31.7 Trochophore and dipleurula larvae. **A,**
Trochophore of an annelid. **B,** Dipleurula of an
echinoderm. **C,** Dipleurula of a hemichordate. In
what ways are these alike? What is the significance
of this likeness?

trochophore larva forms its mouth from the blastopore
and develops a new opening for the anus. The dipleurula
forms its anus from the blastopore and has a new opening
for the mouth. In the development of a trochophore larva,
the cells formed during early cleavage are determined as
to their destiny quite early. That is to say, in the 32-cell
stage it is already established which cells will give rise to
ectodermal structures, which endodermal, and which
mesodermal. The mesoderm develops separately, not from
the endoderm, and the celom develops as a gap forming in
mesodermal tissue. In the development of the dipleurula
larva, the determination of individual cells occurs much
later in development, often under the influence of changes
in neighboring cells. The mesoderm arises by outpouching
of the endodermal tract wall, and the celom is simply part
of the former endodermal cavity.

Although these developmental characteristics distinguish
between trochophore and dipleurula larvae, these forms
have quite a bit in common. Both bear ciliated bands; and
both have an epidermis, a digestive tract with mouth and
anus, and mesoderm cells in the space between gastrodermis
and epidermis. See Figure 31.7.

The echinoderms all have dipleurula larvae, and in all of
them further development shows a transition from the
larval bilateral symmetry to an adult radial symmetry.
The earliest fossil echinoderms found were sessile, stalked
forms, like the crinoids of today. The starfish embryo goes
through a stalked stage in passing from larva to adult, and
it is possible that the starfish was derived from one of the
early attached echinoderms. The brittle stars, sea urchins,
and sea cucumbers are all more specialized and modified
forms resembling the starfish, and perhaps derived from
starfishes or their immediate ancestors.

Chordates

Among the chordates, the hemichordates have a larval
stage which resembles the echinoderm dipleurula very
closely. The adult hemichordate has a structure resembling
a notochord, and a ventral heart, a pharynx with openings
to the outside, and a dorsal nerve cord in addition to the
ventral nerve cord. See Figure 31.8. The structure resembling
a notochord is not as similar to the vertebrate notochord
as those of the other subphyla of chordates, but taken with
the other typically chordate characteristics it contributes to
the justification of classifying hemichordates with the other
chordates. The chordates other than hemichordates do not
have a dipleurula larva, so the relation between echinoderms

and chordates is a bit tenuous. The fact that some physiological similarities are found between echinoderms and chordates gives support to the idea of their close kinship, but anatomical considerations cast doubt on the idea. The segmented character of the vertebrates has led to speculation about their derivation from annelids or arthropods, and these theories have some supporting evidence. The consensus at present seems to be that the relations of vertebrates to invertebrate phyla are highly uncertain, with the echinoderm hypothesis a little more likely than the others.

The larvae of the urochordates resemble tadpoles somewhat and are like the vertebrates much more than are the adult urochordates. See Figure 31.9.

The cephalochordates seem like aberrant, highly modified, or degenerate relatives of the simplest vertebrates. The larvae of cyclostomes have many features in common with the adult cephalochordates. See Figure 31.10.

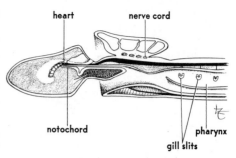

Fig. 31.8 Longitudinal section of a hemichordate adult. Which characteristics convince taxonomists that this animal is a chordate?

larva

adults

Fig. 31.9 Urochordate larva and adults. The larva resembles somewhat the larva of an amphibian.

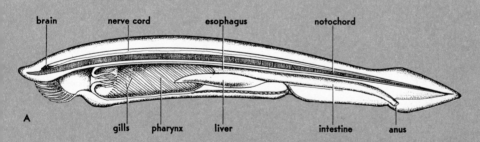

A

brain   nerve cord   esophagus   notochord

gills   pharynx   liver   intestine   anus

Fig. 31.10 Cephalochordate adult and cyclostome larva. A, Amphioxus. B, Ammocoetes larva of a cyclostome.

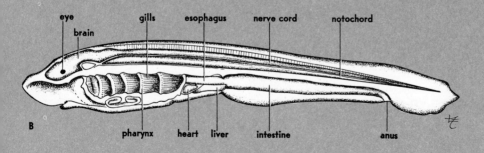

B

eye   gills   esophagus   nerve cord   notochord

brain

pharynx   heart   liver   intestine   anus

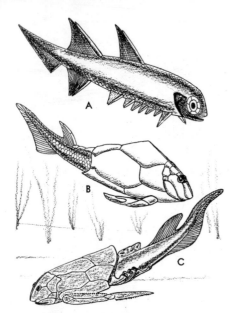

Fig. 31.11   Devonian placoderms. **A,** *Climatius* from the early Devonian. **B,** *Pterichthyodes* from the middle Devonian. **C,** *Bothriolepis* from the late Devonian.

Among the vertebrates, the most primitive types of which we have evidence seem to be the ostracoderms of the early and middle Paleozoic Era. These gave rise to two groups, one of which is represented today by the cyclostomes. Both the ostracoderms and the cyclostomes lack jaws.

The other branch of the ostracoderm stem is the **placoderms,** another group now extinct. See Figure 31.11. The placoderms, however, gave rise to both the elasmobranchs and the bony fish.

Among the early kinds of bony fish are members of a group called the **Crossopterygii.** See Figure 31.12. These developed lungs, paddlelike appendages, and bony skulls containing fewer separate elements than most other fishes. From these Crossopterygii were developed the first land vertebrates, a group of amphibia called from the winding enamel ridges on their teeth the **labyrinthodonts.** See Figure 31.13. Fossil remains of the Crossopterygii disappear after the Mesozoic Era. Until comparatively recently the group has been considered quite extinct. Then, in 1939, a commercial fisherman brought into a South African port a specimen of a crossopterygian caught in the ocean off the coast of Africa. The specimen was not in the best of condition when scientists received it, but they were able to identify it, and the find stimulated an ardent desire for more and fresher specimens for further study. Some other specimens have been captured since.

The labyrinthodont amphibia are now extinct (although such statements are subject to correction by discoveries like that of the African fish). They gave rise to the present-day newts, salamanders, frogs, and toads, and to the **cotylosaurs,** a reptile group from which the other kinds of reptiles — turtles, lizards, snakes, crocodiles and alligators, and dinosaurs — were derived. See Figure 31.14.

Fig. 31.12   Crossopterygian fishes from the Devonian Period. **Above,** *Holoptychius.* **Below,** *Osteolepis.*

Fig. 31.13   Late Paleozoic labyrinthodonts. These were somewhat fishlike forms with legs, apparently capable of coming out of the water and crawling about on land. They were the early amphibians.

From the late Paleozoic reptiles arose the first primitive mammals, and from Mesozoic reptiles came the early birds.

All of this tracing of the descent and relationships of the classes of plants and animals is, of course, speculative. Since the separation of one class from another is supposed to have taken place in periods millions of years before there were human beings to observe and record the events, our evidence is indirect. But if one accepts the arguments for the theory of evolution at all, he will find the same sorts of arguments used in support of the evolution story here recounted. The details of the story are much more doubtful than the evolution theory itself, but continued investigation of the fields from which evidence is derived and fresh consideration and interpretation of the evidence may be expected to confirm or modify the story as given. The pursuit of this confirmation or emendation of the evolution story is one of the most fascinating activities of the mind of man, and draws on not only all branches of biology, but also other sciences for information and helpful concepts.

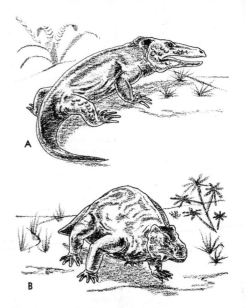

Fig. 31.14   Cotylosaurs. A, *Seymouria*. B, *Bradysaurus*. In what ways do these seem to be intermediate between amphibia and reptiles?

SUMMARY

The piecing together of the evolution story is comparable to the reconstruction of an atom-bombed metropolitan telephone exchange by a child who has only seen a few telephone receivers. We know something about living plants and animals, and we have some fossil remnants to go on. Extensive study of the evidence available plus ingenious hypotheses, most of which cannot be adequately tested, have given us a sort of trial schedule of the possible directions of evolution of living organisms. This trial schedule is illustrated in Figure 31.15, which should be taken as the product of many informed guesses, rather than a permanently established scheme.

REVIEW QUESTIONS

1. How might life have originated?
2. Describe the postulated relationships among plants.
3. How might animals have arisen from plants?
4. Describe the postulated relationships among animals.
5. How valid are these postulated relationships?

GENERAL QUESTIONS

1. Evaluate various theories of the origin of life.
2. Is the Phylum Thallophyta a valid taxonomic group?
3. How do you think vascular plants first arose?
4. What do a clam, a honeybee, and an alligator have in common?
5. Could Sporozoa have arisen from Sarcodina?

6. What are the chief differences between flatworms and coelenterates?
7. How much alike are trochophore and dipleurula larvae?
8. How might scientists go about determining the closest relatives of the chordates?
9. In what parts is the scheme shown in Figure 31.15 weakest?
10. In what parts is the scheme shown in Figure 31.15 strongest?

Fig. 31.15 A trial schedule showing possible directions of evolution of living organisms.

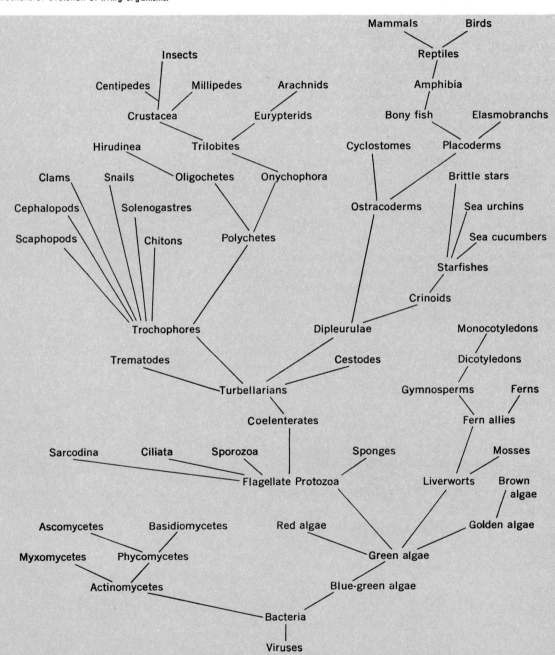

PART V

LIVING TOGETHER

ASSOCIATION OF ORGANISMS

Living together in a world of limited extent forces plants and animals to be in competition with each other for space, for the raw materials of protoplasm, and for environmental conditions favorable to their growth and reproduction. Living organisms vary greatly in their methods of food getting. Green plants make food, starting with photosynthesis. Other organisms devour these plants or their products or other living organisms or dead bodies of organisms.

Living organisms are usually found in associations of one sort or another. The association in many instances is necessary to their survival as individuals and as species. The differences and resemblances of organisms in respect to the environments in which they can grow and reproduce result in groupings of organisms based primarily upon environmental factors. Knowledge of the relationship of plants and animals is important to humans because humans are completely dependent upon other organisms for food and to a great extent dependent upon other organisms for clothing and shelter.

In Part V will be considered the variety of ways in which organisms get food, the types of societies they form, the biogeography of the United States as an example of the grouping of organisms based upon environment, and the importance to humans of the practical applications of biological knowledge.

CHAPTER 32

Food Getting

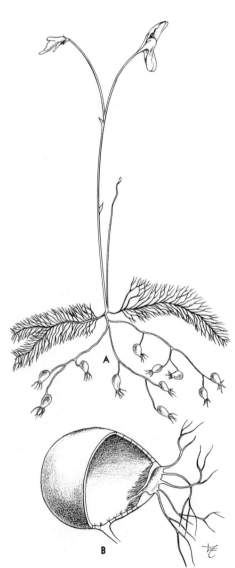

Fig. 32.1 Bladderwort. **A,** Entire plant. **B,** One of the bladders.

TYPES OF NUTRITION

Living organisms may get their food in several ways. If an organism possesses chlorophyll, it may manufacture its own food from water, carbon dioxide, and other inorganic materials in the presence of sunlight. This process is called photosynthesis, and is confined to plants with chlorophyll and other pigments. Such plants are said to have a **holophytic** type of nutrition. Other organisms may eat the plants, and still others may eat the organisms which eat plants, and so on. This is a common method among animals, which are said to have a **holozoic** type of nutrition. Still other organisms live on or in another organism, and depend upon their host for food. This method of nutrition is called **parasitic.** A fourth type of nutrition is the breakdown of the products and dead bodies of organisms and absorption of the resulting substances. If a plant does this, it is said to be **saprophytic.** If an animal does it, it is said to be **saprozoic.** For convenience in discussion these two types may be considered under the term **saprotrophic.**

There are some difficulties in the application of these terms. There are degrees of parasitic association, which will be discussed later in this chapter. The terms *holozoic* and *saprozoic* are not completely mutually exclusive. If a lion kills an antelope and eats the flesh, the lion is holozoic. If a hyena comes along later and cleans up the remains, it is devouring parts of a dead and decaying organism, yet the hyena is said to be holozoic, too. Saprotrophic organisms are said to absorb food substances in solution, as do fungi and some flagellate protozoa.

A spider catches its prey, kills it, and injects into it digestive enzymes. When the flesh of the prey has been liquefied by the enzymes, the spider sucks up the dissolved substances from the dead organism. Is the spider holozoic or saprozoic? The female mosquito which sucks living blood is another problem in definition. Is it holozoic, parasitic, or saprotrophic?

In spite of these semantic difficulties, the terms are helpful in a discussion of nutrition. Most plants other than Fungi are holophytic. The Fungi and a few other plants, such as the Indian pipe and the pinesap, are saprophytic or parasitic.

Carnivorous Plants

A few plants, such as the bladderwort, sundew, Venus' flytrap, and pitcher plant, not only are photosynthetic but are carnivorous — they trap and digest insects and other animals which come within reach. The bladderwort has a sort of trapdoor which, when sprung by a small aquatic animal, ensnares the animal and holds the prey until the plant may digest it. See Figure 32.1.

The sundew has on its leaves processes with sticky, rounded tips. These may capture and hold insects while they are digested and absorbed. See Figure 32.2.

The Venus' flytrap has hinged leaves, each leaf with a hinge down the middle like the back of an open book. Projecting from the surface of the leaf are long spines. If a fly should light on such a leaf, the two halves of the leaf close together, trapping the prey. See Figure 32.3.

The pitcher plant has a rolled, tubular leaf with a sticky secretion at the bottom, and downward-angled spines on the inner walls of the leaf. An insect getting into this leaf will find that it is easy to coast down the spines, but is difficult or impossible to climb out. The unfortunate insect mires down in the sticky concoction in the base of the leaf and is digested.

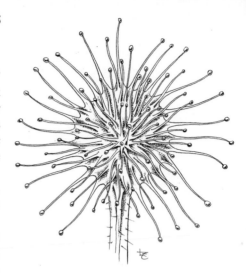

Fig. 32.2 Sundew. The modified leaves of this plant bear numerous hairlike projections which have sticky droplets at their tips. If an insect alights on one, he sticks to it, and the hairs nearby bend over and entrap the insect further. The secretions of the plant contain enzymes which help digest the insect. The leaf absorbs the digested products.

CYCLES

The elements of which all organisms are made include carbon, hydrogen, oxygen, and nitrogen. Other elements used by some or all organisms include sulfur, phosphorus, magnesium, iron, chlorine, sodium, and potassium, but these are not used in as many compounds as the first four mentioned. Though some of these elements are more abundant than others, all are limited in supply. One set of processes incorporates the elements into living protoplasm, and another set frees them from the bodies of organisms, making them available to other organisms. On a world-wide basis these two sets of processes have apparently been going on at approximately the same rate for millions of years. They will, to the best of man's ability to predict, continue at approximately the same rate for many more millions of years. Perhaps tracing carbon, hydrogen, oxygen, and nitrogen through different kinds of organisms will make this point clear, as well as show some of the nutritional relationships of organisms.

Carbon Cycle

The carbon available to green plants is part of the carbon

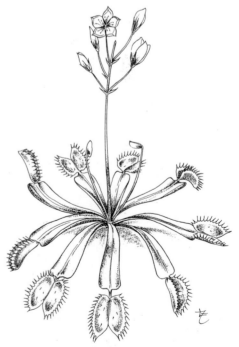

Fig. 32.3 Venus' flytrap. The leaves of this plant capture and digest insects.

dioxide molecule. Carbon dioxide comprises less than one half of one per cent of the atmosphere. It is quite soluble in water, however, so great quantities of carbon dioxide are dissolved in the oceans and lakes of the earth. Limestone, principally calcium carbonate, and other carbonate rocks constitute a tremendous storehouse of carbon, which, as carbon dioxide, is slowly released to the water or air by chemical processes, leaching by ground water, and in volcanic gases. Coal, petroleum, and natural gas constitute another large store of carbon. Burning these fuels adds carbon dioxide to the air. Of course, both the limestone and the carbon-containing fuels are the result of processes that took place in plants and animals in past ages. But even today plant deposits (peat, for example) and animal deposits (coral rock, which is calcium carbonate, for example) continue to remove carbon from ready availability.

Carbon is obtained by green plants from the carbon dioxide absorbed from the air or water in the process called photosynthesis, as described in Chapter 15. One product of this process is sugar. From the sugar other compounds may be made — cellulose, starch, fats, proteins — and used or stored in the plant. The foods used by the plant in the release of energy are broken down into carbon dioxide and water. The carbon dioxide may be re-used or it may diffuse out of the plant and be restored to the air or water.

If the carbon-containing compound made by the plant is not used by the plant for energy, it may be ingested with the plant by some animal. Leaves, seeds, and fruits are frequently devoured. Stems and roots also furnish nourishment to some animals. Algae, lichens, liverworts, and mosses are eaten by other animals. In the animal many carbon compounds are converted to sugars. The sugar may be recombined into starches, fats, or other substances, or oxidized into carbon dioxide and water. In the latter case, the carbon dioxide diffuses out of the animal and returns to the atmosphere or hydrosphere.

If the animal does not oxidize the carbon compound, another animal may ingest it; it may be passed from one animal to another indefinitely. If an animal, or even the plant which first synthesized the sugar, dies, the body may be eaten or it may be attacked by saprotrophic organisms, such as fungi. The bacteria are especially active saprotrophs. The carbon compounds are broken down by extracellular enzymes, and the resulting sugars are used by the saprotrophs with the release of energy. In any case, the carbon returns to the air or water in carbon dioxide and is again available to photosynthesizing organisms.

Hydrogen Cycle

The hydrogen cycle is somewhat simpler than the carbon cycle. Hydrogen is obtained from water. Water is the normal habitat of many of the living organisms of the earth, and is furnished by rainfall and normal soil water to many of the others. Plants obtain water by its diffusion in through the body surface in aquatic plants or through the roots or other organs of land plants. The hydrogen is separated off and combined with carbon dioxide during photosynthesis. Much of the resulting sugar is converted by plants into such compounds as other carbohydrates, fats, proteins, cellulose, and lignin. When these compounds or the sugar itself are oxidized either in the plant which first made them or in the animals or saprotrophs which destroy the plant, water is one of the products. The water may diffuse away or be excreted, being restored to the natural bodies of water on the earth, to the soil, or to the atmosphere.

Oxygen Cycle

The oxygen that is part of the water molecules involved in photosynthesis is released as free oxygen. The oxygen of the carbon dioxide molecule becomes incorporated into carbohydrate molecules during photosynthesis. Like carbon and hydrogen, it may pass through many organisms. When the oxygen-containing organic compound finally breaks down with the release of energy, it does so by combining with free oxygen, producing carbon dioxide and water. The atmosphere of the earth contains about one fifth free oxygen, in addition to the oxygen combined in water vapor, carbon dioxide, and other compounds. The rivers, lakes, and oceans contain some dissolved oxygen. So there is in most habitats of living organisms enough free oxygen for the organisms to obtain the element with which to oxidize their food. A few anaerobic organisms obtain energy by methods which do not require free oxygen.

Nitrogen Cycle

Free nitrogen makes up almost four fifths of the earth's atmosphere. Most plants are unable to use this as a source of the nitrogen used in making proteins. However, a few species of nitrogen-fixing bacteria, present in great numbers, are able to transform dissolved atmospheric nitrogen into nitrates. Some of these nitrogen-fixing bacteria are free in the soil, and some form associations with other plants, as in the case of the root nodules of legumes.

Green plants absorb fixed nitrogen, mostly in nitrates, dissolved in the water in which they live, or in the ground water in the soil to which their roots have access. In the plant nitrogen is combined with carbohydrates, forming amino acids, which are in turn built into proteins. The proteins may be eaten by animals, broken down into amino acids, and reassembled into animal proteins. This process may be repeated as one animal eats another. Finally, when a plant or animal dies, the proteins are broken down by saprotrophs. Or the organism containing the protein may break it down itself. In either case, ammonia, carbon dioxide, and water are the usual end products of protein breakdown. In many animals, such as humans, most of the ammonia is changed into urea or some related compound before it is released. Bacteria may form ammonia from the urea. The ammonia restored to the water or land is changed by still other kinds of bacteria into nitrates. Nitrates may then be used by green plants, or may be changed by bacterial action into free nitrogen.

FOOD CHAINS

Although we are not so familiar with life in the oceans as we are with life on land, it will be remembered from the account of paleontology that the earliest fossil records show that land plants and animals are newcomers. The ocean seems to have been the primeval home of living organisms. It is still the home of the vast majority of organisms. Algae are very abundant in the ocean, especially the diatoms. Protozoa find the diatoms and other small algae especially suitable sources of food. Many worms, molluscs, and smaller arthropods also devour algae and protozoa which eat algae. Sponges, coelenterates, and echinoderms may also eat these smaller forms. Larger arthropods, some worms, cephalopods, and echinoderms eat these moderate-sized invertebrates. Fishes eat the larger forms. The largest fishes, arthropods, and cephalopods may eat fishes. Whales may eat diatoms, protozoa, smaller and larger invertebrates, and fishes. The giant squid may attack whales. Thus, there is no organism in the ocean safe from attack by some other organism seeking its dinner. Bacteria and other fungi in the ocean break down excretion products, fragments, and dead bodies, and are in turn eaten by protozoa and other animals. Thus, there is a cycle of food organisms, each link depending on preceding ones and being essential to the survival of succeeding ones.

The same sort of cycle occurs on land and in fresh waters. Land plants manufacture food. Some are devoured by vegetarian animals. These in turn are eaten by carnivorous forms, and these by still others, until some forms die and decay. This releases their elements to the environment, from which they may be recombined by other plants into living protoplasm.

If any one of these links in the chain is broken, another link must be put in its place or the entire cycle will fail. If all decay organisms should be destroyed, plant and animal bodies would accumulate and retain the elements necessary for further life, so that living organisms would starve. If the small crustacea in the ocean died, many fish would find it difficult to locate and ingest enough diatoms or protozoa to supply their needs. If green plants disappeared from the face of the earth, animals could eat each other for a while, but the source of new food would be gone. Any event which changes the balance of living organisms on a large scale will have a profound effect on all life.

PARASITISM

Parasitism may have arisen by evolutionary specialization of some predatory organisms. It apparently developed many times in evolutionary history, for it occurs in quite a number of classes of living organisms. There are various degrees of parasitism and similar relationships. In the restricted sense, the relationship is called **parasitism** when the association is advantageous or necessary for the life of one member, the parasite, and when for the other member of the association, the host, the relationship is detrimental. If one member finds the association advantageous, and the other nearly or quite neutral, the relationship is called **commensalism.** If both associates benefit from the relationship, it is called **symbiosis.**

Symbiosis

Examples of symbiosis include lichens (p. 273), mycorrhiza (p. 273), and the relation between Hypermastigina and termites (p. 356). Some crabs and hermit crabs carry coelenterate polyps such as sea anemones perched on their bodies (Fig. 32.4). The coelenterate drives off some potential enemies of the crustacean with its nematocysts. The arthropods are not very neat eaters, tearing their food apart and scattering the fragments in the water. The polyps feed on some of these crumbs.

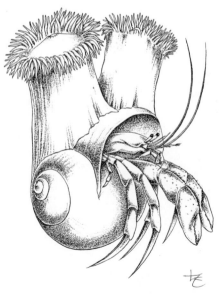

Fig. 32.4 An example of animal symbiosis. A hermit crab, an arthropod, inhabits the discarded shell of a snail, a mollusc, on the back of which ride two sea anemones, coelenterates.

Commensalism

Examples of commensalism include the shark sucker, *Remora*, a fish with an adhesive plate on the dorsal side of the head. The shark sucker attaches itself to the body of a shark, and is carried through the ocean as a hitchhiker. It does no harm to its host, but when the shark overtakes food, the *Remora* helps eat it. Some other fishes hide themselves in coral colonies, swimming deftly in and out without touching the polyps. Enemies of the fish are kept away by the nematocysts of the coelenterates. Bacteria living in the human intestine may be commensals, getting their living from the materials in the intestine without doing any damage to the human. Some may even contribute to the host's welfare by secreting vitamins; such organisms are then called symbiotic.

Parasites

As was pointed out in Chapter 31, considerable differences in the relative development of the systems of the body often distinguish parasites from their nearest free-living relatives. Some of these differences have been described earlier in this book. Lack of locomotor and digestive systems, great reproductive ability, and very complex life cycles have been described, especially in the flatworms.

Examples of many-storied parasitism are known. The rat flea is parasitized by the bacterium which causes bubonic plague. The ciliate protozoan, *Opaiina*, lives in the rectum of frogs, and is itself parasitized by an ameba, which in turn harbors a bacterium. It is quite conceivable that there are bacteriophagic viruses on the prowl which might attack this bacterium. The famous lines of Augustus de Morgan are well put:

"Great fleas have little fleas upon their backs to bite 'em,
And little fleas have lesser fleas, and so *ad infinitum*.
And the great fleas themselves, in turn, have greater fleas
    to go on;
While these again have greater still, and greater still, and
    so on."

Among viruses and bacteria many parasites are known. Examples of these were given in Chapter 13. The viruses on which studies have been made are all parasitic; whether nonparasitic ones exist now has not yet been established for lack of certain means of identification other than their parasitic effects. Only a small minority of known bacterial species are parasitic on humans, some are parasitic on other animals or plants, many are saprophytic, a few are free-living.

Several of the species of fungi are parasitic. The wheat rust was described in detail in Chapter 14. Other parasitic fungi were mentioned briefly.

Among the bryophytes and pteridophytes parasites are unknown, except for one stage of development of a species being parasitic or partially so on the other generation of the same species. Members of one genus of liverworts, *Riccardia*, lack chlorophyll, but they live as saprophytes.

Among the seed plants only a few parasites are found. Examples are dodder, mistletoe, beechdrops, and *Rafflesia* (Fig. 32.5). Dodder is a true parasite of other seed plants. It is not green, obtains all its nourishment from its host, and frequently damages the host severely. Outgrowths from the dodder stem, called **haustoria,** penetrate the stem and other organs of the host; through the haustoria, food manufactured by the host and water and minerals absorbed from the soil by the host enter the dodder plant. Mistletoe possesses green leaves and presumably is dependent upon its host, a tree, only for water and minerals. Beechdrops and the spectacular *Rafflesia* are not green. Though once thought to be true parasites, these are now considered to be at least partially saprotrophic. Their haustoria penetrate the roots of their seed plant hosts, but also gain some or most of their nourishment from dead tissues, some of which may not be attached to the host. *Rafflesia* is a Malaysian genus. One of its species produces the largest flower known, three feet in diameter; its very short stem and single flower are the only parts that appear above ground. *Rafflesia* is an extreme example of specialization characteristic of parasites.

In the Phylum Protozoa there are many parasitic forms. The entire class of Sporozoa is made up of parasitic organisms. Many flagellates, such as trypanosomes; some sarcodinans, such as *Endameba;* and a few ciliates, such as *Opalina*, are parasitic.

Sponges and coelenterates are free-living forms in general. A very few coelenterates show evidences of parasitic habits.

The flatworms have two classes, Trematoda and Cestoda, composed entirely of parasitic forms. A few Turbellaria are also parasitic.

Many roundworms are also parasites.

Among the annelids, the leeches may be parasitic in that they withdraw blood or other substances from living hosts for food. The associations are usually temporary, however; a leech will leave its host when it has secured its food. A few other annelids are parasitic.

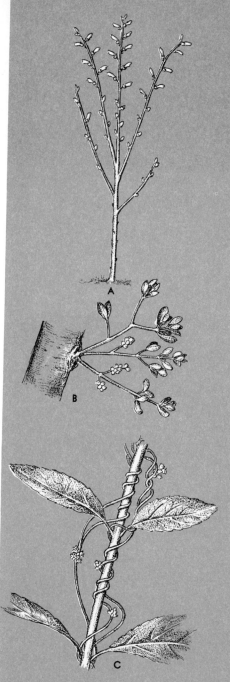

Fig. 32.5 Parasitism among plants. **A,** Beechdrops. **B,** Mistletoe. **C,** Dodder.

Among the arthropods are to be found many parasitic forms. *Sacculina* has already been described (pp. 418–419). Several other kinds of crustacea are parasitic. Mites and ticks are parasitic arachnids. Many kinds of parasitic insects are known, such as mosquitoes, fleas, lice, and bedbugs. Ichneumon flies lay their eggs on the bodies of living caterpillars or among the eggs of spiders, and the ichneumon fly larvae, hatching quickly, devour the host or hosts.

The parasitic larvae of fresh-water clams, the glochidia, were mentioned in Chapter 26.

No parasitic echinoderms are known.

Among the vertebrates the parasitic habits of cyclostomes were described in Chapter 28. Almost all other vertebrates are free-living, except in the sense of the embryos of mammals being parasitic on their mothers.

SUMMARY

The green plants and a few kinds of bacteria manufacture their own food from inorganic ingredients, a type of nutrition called holophytic. Other plants are saprophytic or parasitic. Animals secure their food by holozoic methods (eating other organisms, living or dead), or by saprozoic or parasitic methods. Chains of food organisms may be traced in various habitats, small animals eating small plants, and being in turn eaten by larger animals, and so on. All forms are subject to decay after death, and their elements are restored to accessibility to green plants by the action of bacteria and other fungi.

REVIEW QUESTIONS

1. Describe the types of food getting characteristic of living organisms.
2. Describe the food-getting methods of carnivorous plants.
3. Describe the cycles of carbon, hydrogen, oxygen, and nitrogen.
4. Describe a food chain.
5. Describe and give examples of symbiosis.
6. Describe and give examples of commensalism.
7. Describe and give examples of parasitism.
8. What are the effects of parasitism on the parasite?
9. How is the habit of parasitism distributed among the phyla and classes of organisms?
10. Give examples of animals whose larvae are parasitic, but whose adults are free-living; and vice versa.

GENERAL QUESTIONS

1. What type of food getting would you call that of mildew? yeast? sundew? *Astasia? Plasmodium?* earthworm? hyena?
2. What happens to the parts of captured insects a pitcher plant does not digest?
3. Describe the cycle of sulfur through living organisms.
4. Would the human species die out sooner if all green plants were suddenly destroyed or if all bacteria were suddenly destroyed?
5. What would be the effect on humans of the sudden permanent disappearance from the earth of all annelids? of all crustacea? of all reptiles?
6. Is symbiosis ever intentional?
7. How could a commensal relationship have evolved?
8. How could a parasitic relationship have evolved?
9. Is a cow parasitic on grass?
10. Is a mammal embryo parasitic on its mother?

CHAPTER 33

Societies of Organisms

Living organisms commonly lead lives of independence from others of the same species, except as members of opposite sexes are associated in reproduction. However, it is a characteristic of many species that individuals live together in groups or societies. If the structural, physiological, or behavioral characteristics of individuals are modified by association in groups, we may speak of the group as a **society.** Varying degrees of modification are observed, from the loosely organized society represented by a school of fish to the necessary association of the social insects in which individuals are structurally adapted to one or another type of activity to the exclusion of other activities. A few examples of plant and animal societies will demonstrate the variety of societies.

Plant Societies

In the Myxomycetes, as in *Ceratiomyxa*, described in Chapter 14, several ameboid cells coalesce to form one large, multinucleate protoplasmic mass, and this mass thereafter acts as a single individual. This is a sort of association in which individuality is lost in the composite society.

In the algae there are examples of single-celled forms dividing and forming chains or clusters of cells which remain together as a filament or a colony. Similar events occur among the bacteria and among the protozoa. The Volvocine Series demonstrates this cooperation among cells associated together in a common mass.

It was postulated in Chapter 31 that many-celled plants and animals may have evolved from single-celled organisms along this general pathway. After cells became associated in colonies, a differentiation among cells in a colony permitted specializations in the direction of particular activities such as food getting, digestion, reproduction, defense, or impulse conduction.

Coelenterate Societies

The next level of society formation is shown by some of the coelenterates. Coral polyps, for example, collaborate in building a platform out of their exoskeletons, the secretion of each being fastened to the exoskeleton of ones next to it, forming a solid, rocklike base. In many cases among the coelenterates, even the individual polyps may be different from each other. In *Obelia*, mentioned in Chapter 22, some polyps in the colony are specialized as food-getting polyps, and others as reproductive individuals. In other forms, as the Portuguese man-of-war, there are in addition individuals specialized as protective devices. These have effective nematocysts, but no mouths. The top of the Portuguese man-of-war colony is modified into a gas-filled float.

Sex Differentiation

In the molluscs there are some cases of association related to reproduction. In the marine snail, *Crepidula*, for example, one may occasionally find a stack of individuals, one perched upon another to the height of several snails. The lowermost one is a female, and the others are males. The *Crepidula* larva which settles down on a bare rock usually becomes a female. If another larva settles down on the top of this *Crepidula*, the newcomer becomes a male. Any later arrivals settling down on this growing column will be males. If the column is broken in two, the bottom individual of the upper part of the column usually becomes transformed from a male to a female.

This change of sex is not peculiar to *Crepidula*. Many animals normally change sex, or are able to do so in certain conditions. Oysters may reverse their sexes every several months. Some amphibia possess latent tissues in the gonads which, if the active reproductive tissues are destroyed, will develop into gonads of the other sex. Hens in which the single, left ovary is damaged may become cocks by the development of a testis on the right side.

Insect Societies

It is in the insects that we find the societal organizations most highly developed. They have the structural differentiation and physiological specialization characteristic of coelenterate colonies, and the separateness of body and interdependence of behavior of human societies. The structural modifications and behavioral specializations in a termite colony were described in Chapter 25.

In a bee colony, the sole reproductive female is the queen. The other females are sexually immature and are called workers. They provide the food, build the honeycomb, and care for the larvae. The males are drones. Their sole contribution to the colony is that of providing sperm cells, and only one of their number may mate with the queen during her nuptial flight.

Among the workers, a rather remarkable degree of cooperative activity is to be noted. Bees collect the sugar secretions of various flowering plants and process this material into honey, which is stored in the honeycomb the workers build from the wax they secrete. The details of the honey collecting activity have been studied by many workers, particularly in recent years by the German investigator Karl von Frisch. A worker bee which has left the hive in search of food seems to be able to retain a knowledge of the direction in which it has gone by means of sensing the direction from which polarized light from the sky strikes its eyes. When the bee, in its meanderings, comes upon a field of flowers producing a desirable kind of nectar, the bee draws the fluid into a special enlargement of the esophagus, the honey sac. Then the bee flies back to its hive. Here it is able to communicate to the other bees not only that it has discovered a good source of nectar, but also the direction and approximate distance from the hive to the flowers.

The direction is conveyed to other bees by communicating the angle of the line of flight to the direction of polarized light waves from the sky. This is done by the bee walking on the vertical wall of a honeycomb inside the hive at a comparable angle to the vertical. For example, if the polarized light rays make an angle of thirty degrees with the line of flight required to reach the flowers, the bee walks at a thirty-degree angle with the vertical — circles around, and walks the thirty-degree angle path again — and repeats this dance many times.

The distance from the hive to the flowers seems to be indicated by the speed with which the circuit is executed. The closer to the hive the flowers are, the faster the bee goes along its pathway, curves around, and begins again.

Some species of ants form societies of thousands of individuals. Army ants may form societies of over one hundred thousand individuals. They have alternating periods of temporary camps and marches. The temporary camp is built around the queen; when she is ready to lay eggs, the ant colony clusters about her, with occasional forays for food by some of the workers. After egg-laying is completed, the entire colony starts off across country, marching by night and stopping by day, until such time as the queen is ready for egg-laying again.

On the march the army ants proceed in a column, the front ones being pushed along by the oncoming followers, and the followers tracing the path of the leaders by the sense of smell in their antennae. The chemical secretions of ants have much to do with the coordination of their activities. Several kinds of worker ants are differentiable by size, structure, and behavior when they come across prey. The larger ones attack the prey, tear it apart, and distribute it among the others. Even large vertebrates may be destroyed by the overwhelming numbers of ants, each taking a bite. Accounts have been written of the army ants invading houses in the tropics and driving before them all other insects, rats, reptiles, and so forth, completely ridding the place of pests.

The harvester ants collect seeds and store them in chambers in their underground burrows. These may later be eaten. Some investigators have found that the ants bite off the radicle of seeds, thus preventing sprouting. If the seeds are dampened by seepage from a heavy rain, the ants may bring the seeds to the surface of the ground and spread them out after the rain is over. This facilitates drying, although the ants probably act in response to the odor of the wet seeds, not in anticipation of the drying effect of exposure.

The gardening ants bite off pieces of leaves and carry these into their underground chambers. The leaf pieces are then bitten into tiny fragments. On these fragments grow fungi, upon which the ants feed.

There are even slaveholding ants, which invade the habitations of other species of ants and carry off the larvae and pupae. When these larvae and pupae mature into adult workers, they secure food, and care for the young of their captors. In some species of slaveholding ants, the securing of workers of other species seems to be essential to continuation of the colony, for they do not possess in their own species forms which carry on all the duties necessary to preservation of the society.

These social organizations of arthropods do not show the characteristics of forethought, planning, or reasoned behavior that we associate with human society. They are rather inherited capacities for reacting to certain stimuli in certain set ways. If the front of a column of marching ants happens to circle about and overtake the rear of the column, a circle of marching ants may continue until the ants die of exhaustion. There is no set leader, and each ant follows the trail of its predecessors. A fatal circle rarely occurs, however. A column advances because the oncoming ants push each other along. One ant pushed ahead of the advancing front of the column will run forward a few steps and stop. Another ant will follow it, and bumping into it run past on one side or the other, and then stop, having lost the scent it was tracing. Other ants will push past this one, and stop. This gradual inching forward will continue until pathways are established. In the ant societies which have a fixed burrow, the first trails are blazed in this haphazard way, and then subsequently followed unless a rainstorm or some other event destroys the trail scent.

Vertebrate Societies

Among vertebrates, societies vary from the loose associations represented by schools of fish through flocks of birds, and herds of mammals, to the societies of humans. In all of these groups, the individuals are not structurally varied except for sexual differences. There is no anatomical distinction which predisposes one form to be a queen, one to be a soldier, one to be a food-gatherer, one to be a nursemaid. The distinctive activities of different individuals are determined by other factors. Leadership may be centered in one or a few individuals. Social hierarchies develop, for example, the **peck order** of chickens. In a flock of chickens, it has been discovered that some birds may peck at other birds without retaliation. There is one bird in the flock which is free to peck every other bird and not be pecked in return. Another bird may freely peck every bird in the flock but this first one, and so on.

Many similar hierarchies are known. In monkeys, for example, leadership is established by a dominant individual subduing all possible rivals. Deer and elephants have similar social patterns.

Prairie dogs form societies in which the dwellers at the edge of the city act as sentinels, giving a warning call at the sense of danger. Crows at the border of a flock may give a cry when a hunter approaches, after which the entire flock flies away.

The study of human societies is a branch of knowledge by itself — sociology — and would take us too far afield to develop here. Its characteristics are somewhat familiar to the reader. The versatility of individuals is apparent, for, except for sexual differences, humans are enough alike that anyone may undertake several kinds of activities which contribute to the welfare of himself and his group. In fact, humans, more than other animals, belong to a multiplicity of groups — the family, the circle of friends, the various political divisions, numerous social and religious organizations, and other groups of common intellectual or emotional interests.

SUMMARY

Living organisms may be solitary in their adult existence or may be associated in societies of less or greater degree of unity. Many-celled organisms are in one sense groups of single cells in which cooperation is mandatory. Many-celled organisms may live together in collaborating groups. In some cases, as in the colonial coelenterates and social insects, structurally different individuals are specialized, performing certain specific activities which contribute to the welfare of the whole. In other cases, division of labor is not correlated with structural variations so much as with adjustments to the social environment. In any case, social organization has proved to be, for some organisms, an advantage in the battle for survival, and is subject to natural selection.

REVIEW QUESTIONS

1. Define a society.
2. Compare colony structure in plants and in coelenterates.
3. Discuss the differentiation of sexes in animals.
4. Describe the activities of a bee colony; of ant colonies.
5. Describe types of vertebrate societies.

GENERAL QUESTIONS

1. Is a *Volvox* sphere an individual or a society?
2. Compare the organization of a Portuguese man-of-war with that of a termite colony.
3. How does association with a female bring about the differentiation of a *Crepidula* larva into a male?
4. How is a bee able to understand the significance of the direction and distance of a field of flowers from the activities of a returned scout?
5. Contrast insect and human societies.

CHAPTER 34

Biogeography of the United States

ENVIRONMENTAL ZONES

One who travels by train or auto from the east to the west coast of the United States notes great differences in the kinds of native and cultivated plants he sees along the way. In one trip he can see, for example, coniferous forests, deciduous forests, desert, grassland, cornfields, cottonfields. Moreover, on such a trip the traveler would note that all the forests in one region are of coniferous, and all those in another region are of deciduous trees. He would note that many farmers in one region were raising corn; in another region many were raising cotton. In still another region the traveler would note that the vegetation consists mainly of grasses upon which cattle were grazing and that in this region were no cultivated fields.

If the traveler were to inquire, he would learn that each of these regions differs from the others in climate. And he would learn that in the United States one can find climates ranging from subtropical to arctic, oceanic to continental, humid to very dry. Climate is composed of many factors which affect living organisms. Among these factors are temperature (extremes are of great importance), annual precipitation (rain, snow), duration and frequency of droughts, length of day during the growing season, wind.

The pattern of these climatic factors results in a corresponding pattern of vegetation because of differences in the characteristics of the plants themselves. Only some can withstand one or the other extreme of temperature. Only some can withstand drought. Some can reproduce only if summer days are as long as those in northern United States. A number of deciduous trees produce new leaves only after exposure to freezing temperatures for a period of weeks.

Animals are dependent for food upon plants or upon other animals that are dependent upon plants, and like plants in this respect, many animals are limited by physiological characteristics to a certain climatic environment. In addition, many predator and parasitic animals are adapted to specific sources of food. Some birds are found near water because they are adapted to feeding on water plants and animals. The characteristics of some animals limit them to grass as a source of food. Many reptiles cannot withstand cold winters. Some insects feed upon only one species of plant or parasitize only one kind of animal. The result of all these relationships and limitations is that animal populations and ranges make a pattern that roughly corresponds with the plant population pattern.

A plant or animal that one finds at any location either evolved there or was introduced by some means or another. The Monterey Cypress is found naturally on the coast of Monterey Bay, California, and nowhere else in the world. Presumably it evolved there. On the other hand, the English sparrow was brought to the United States only about one hundred years ago (1850), and it can now be found in almost every part of the country. Many of our cultivated plants and all of our domestic farm animals except the turkey were brought from Europe or Asia. Most of these can survive only under the care of humans. But many of man's introductions, the English sparrow, for example, are well enough adapted to the climate and conditions of the location to which they have been transported to get along on their own.

Man is only one agency of dispersal. Other animals, wind, and water are also effective in carrying seeds and spores. The process of dispersal goes on continuously. If the new arrival is at least as well adapted to conditions as the organisms already on the ground, it may become established and increase. If it is better adapted, it may take the place of some organisms already there.

Some organisms in effect eliminate themselves. Deer may eat all the available food and then starve. A parasite may kill its only available host. Water plants may fill a pond, providing a foothold for land plants which send their roots among the dead bodies of the water plants. A forest of one kind of trees may shade the ground so completely that seedlings of its own species cannot survive. The result of all these processes is that both plant and animal populations are continuously changing. Sometimes the change is rapid, as when within a few decades man replaces a vast forest or prairie with farm crop plants. Sometimes the change is gradual as in the change of a pond to a forest.

The traveler, in the United States or on the oceans off its shores, needs much specific knowledge if he is to understand what he sees — much more knowledge than can be obtained in one course in elementary biology. However, his trip can be more interesting, his idle hours less boresome if he fills those hours with speculations based on a sound knowledge of biology. The pattern of man's activities, especially those related to getting food, are closely correlated with patterns of vegetation and climate. These patterns are often referred to as **biogeographic zones.**

It is customary to describe and designate these zones by a combination of climatic and physiographic characteristics and the dominant vegetation populating each zone. The vegetation used is the so-called "original" vegetation, that is, the vegetation occurring there when the United States was settled by Europeans.

BIOGEOGRAPHIC ZONES

The environments and their living inhabitants may be divided into twelve types for convenience in description. These are the oceans bordering on the United States, the fresh-water habitats, the subtropical area of southern Florida, the southeastern evergreen forests, the chaparral areas of the southwest, the deserts of the southwest, the midwestern prairie and plain, the eastern deciduous forests, the eastern coniferous forest, the Rocky Mountain coniferous forest, the Pacific coastal coniferous forest, and the mountaintop tundras. Each of these will be briefly described in turn. Figure 34.1 shows the approximate locations of dry-land zones on a map of the United States. Of course, these areas overlap, and isolated patches of one type of environment may be found within the borders of another. But the map gives a general idea of the distribution of these areas.

Ocean

The marine environment, with its constancy of temperature, great volume, and abundance of the substances necessary for life, is especially favorable to a wide variety of living forms. The most numerous organisms are the algae and the bacteria. Some seed plants grow in the oceans, also. All of the phyla of animals described in Part III are copiously represented.

Three varieties of marine environment may be listed: the **littoral zone** along the shores, the **pelagic zone** on the surface of the open sea, and the **abyssal zone** in the darker depths of the ocean. These intergrade, and some of the plants and animals in one will be found in another, but yet these three zones possess somewhat different characteristics.

The littoral zone has the widest variety of living organisms of all. Life is more plentiful there than in any other type of

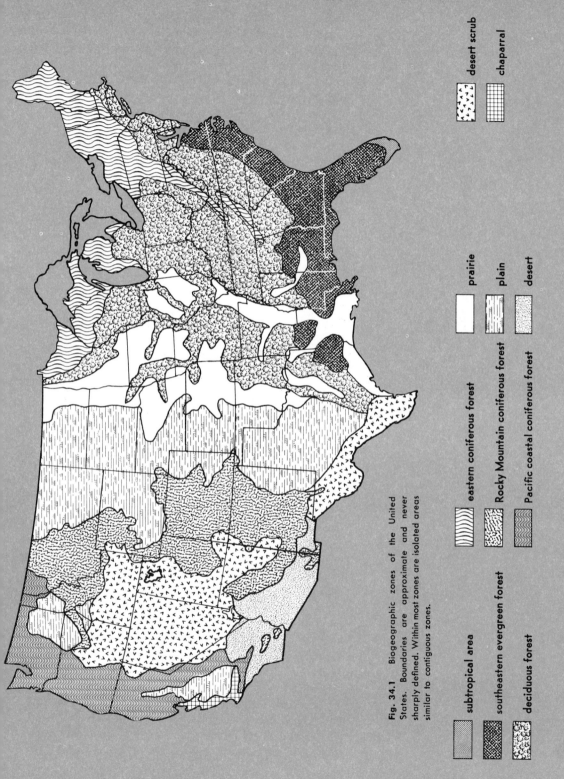

Fig. 34.1 Biogeographic zones of the United States. Boundaries are approximate and never sharply defined. Within most zones are isolated areas similar to contiguous zones.

desert scrub

chaparral

prairie

plain

desert

eastern coniferous forest

Rocky Mountain coniferous forest

Pacific coastal coniferous forest

subtropical area

southeastern evergreen forest

deciduous forest

habitat. Especially common are blue-green algae, green algae, golden algae, and brown algae. Bacteria and other fungi are abundant. A few seed plants such as eelgrass thrive along the shores.

Protozoa are common, especially flagellates. Coelenterates are well represented by hydroid individuals and colonies, sea anemones, and some corals. Some flatworms occur. Roundworms are abundant. Brachiopods and bryozoa are present. Among the annelids, the polychetes predominate, with an abundance of species. Arthropods are very numerous, especially the smaller crustacea — copepods, barnacles, and so forth. Some of the larger forms occur, too, such as crabs, lobsters, and shrimp. The horseshoe crabs appear, reminiscent of the Paleozoic armored arthropods. See Figure 34.2. Molluscs are especially numerous — a great many clams and snails, some squids and chitons. Oysters are planted and tended in Chesapeake Bay and Long Island Sound among other places. Starfishes, sea urchins, and sea cucumbers are numerous. The hemichordates and urochordates are found. And fish, both elasmobranchs and the much more abundant Pisces, are very well represented.

The pelagic flora and fauna seem to be derived by modification from the littoral. These organisms depend upon the water alone for support, and have various devices which keep them afloat without reliance upon the ocean floor. Air sacs, storage of oils, and large surface areas are all factors aiding organisms in keeping afloat. The somewhat greater rigor of life in the open ocean results in a smaller number of organisms and fewer kinds of organisms to be found in the pelagic expanses.

In the surface waters of the open sea there are numerous algae, chiefly one-celled blue-green, green, and golden algae. One very abundant plant is the brown alga, *Sargassum*. Bacteria are the most common fungi. The most common protozoa are sarcodinans such as foraminifera and radiolaria. Among the coelenterates, medusae are most prominent. These have a thick mesoglea layer, mostly water, which helps reduce their specific gravity. The Portuguese man-of-war is another pelagic coelenterate. A few flatworms and some annelids occur. Many kinds of small crustacea are common, the copepods being especially abundant. Molluscs are fewer than in the littoral zone, and more specialized — a few kinds of shell-less snails and one shell-less clam, a few cephalopods, especially nautili. Echinoderms are rare; one type of sea cucumber is represented. The larvae of many invertebrates are very numerous in the open seas, however — larvae of coelenterates, poly-

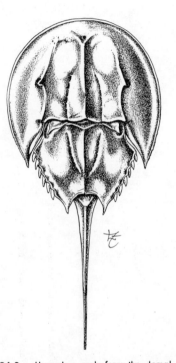

Fig. 34.2   Horseshoe crab from the dorsal side. Which Paleozoic animal does this most nearly resemble?

chetes, crustacea, molluscs, echinoderms, and invertebrate chordates. A few urochordates lead adult lives in the pelagic area. Some sharks and rays are pelagic. Many bony fish, like the mackerel, are free-swimmers. Sea turtles, seals, sirenians, and whales spend much time in the open ocean. A few birds may be found there, such as albatrosses, petrels, and shearwaters. Of course, they spend most of their time in the air above the ocean.

The living and dead organisms which sink down from the pelagic areas constitute the food of the abyssal zone forms. The darkness prevents photosynthesis in plants except for some of the red algae which can manufacture food in very dim light. Bacteria and other fungi are saprophytic, however, and carry on decay. In general, the animals in the abyssal zone resemble ancient forms found in previous geologic ages. Perhaps these forms cannot compete successfully with their more modern cousins in the surface areas, and thrive only in regions of less vigorous competition. Some rather bizarre modifications do occur, however — bizarre in the sense that they are less familiar to us than the forms we see more frequently. See Figure 34.3.

Foraminifera are represented. Sponges are common on the ocean floors in some places. A few primitive corals and other polyps occur. Bryozoa and brachiopods are abundant. A few annelids, some crustacea, and a very few clams, snails, and cephalopods may be found. Solenogastres and scaphopods are more numerous here than elsewhere. Echinoderms occur, especially abundant being brittle stars and crinoids. Some urochordates, many unusual fish, and some whales may also be found deep down.

In the ocean, then, occur the greatest variety, representing all phyla of animals, and the greatest abundance of thallophytes. Bryophytes and pteridophytes occur chiefly on land, though a few are fresh-water forms. A very few seed plants occur in the ocean. Some kinds of organisms occur only in the ocean: brown algae, corals, brachiopods, molluscs except for clams and snails, echinoderms, and invertebrate chordates. Others have only a few fresh-water representatives such as the red algae, sponges, coelenterates, bryozoa, polychetes, and elasmobranchs.

Fresh Water

The fresh waters of the United States are much more varied in some characteristics than are the oceans. Temperature varies more widely. Some rivers have swift currents, some slow; lakes may have none. Depth varies from a very shallow rill to Lake Superior, over a thousand feet at its

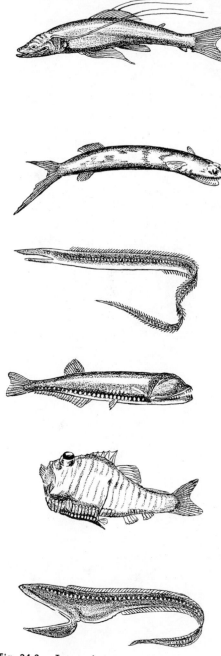

Fig. 34.3 Types of deep-sea fish. These look strange to us because we are more familiar with the surface fishes.

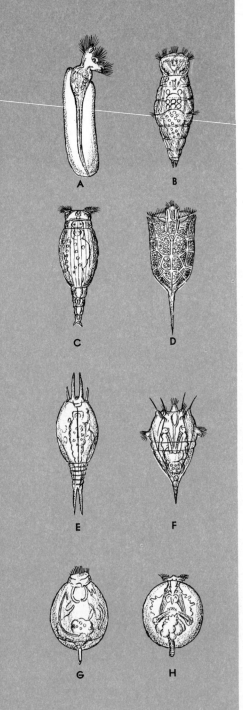

Fig. 34.4 Rotifers. **A,** *Floscularia.* **B,** *Hydatina.* **C,** *Philodina.* **D,** *Anuraea.* **E,** *Salpina.* **F,** *Synchaeta.* **G,** *Monostyla.* **H,** *Pterodina.*

greatest depth. Chemical content is different in different bodies of water, and such things as oxygen content may change from time to time and from part to part in the same body of water. Fresh waters are subject to comparatively frequent change in geologic time, and most bodies of fresh water are of quite recent origin. This, combined with the difficulties of adjusting to low salt content and wide range of environmental variation and with the restriction of migration, accounts in part at least for the smaller numbers and variety of organisms in fresh waters than in seas.

Blue-green, green, and golden algae are present in considerable numbers. Fungi, especially bacteria, are common. Some bryophytes, such as *Ricciocarpus,* are aquatic. Some pteridophytes are also, such as the water ferns. Quite a few kinds of seed plants live in rivers and lakes, such as parrot's feather, pond lilies, and rushes. Protozoa are quite common, especially ciliates, which are more abundant here than in the ocean. Many flagellates and sarcodinans occur in fresh waters, too. Some fresh-water sponges, a few coelenterates such as hydras, a few bryozoa, some flatworms, and many nematodes are fresh-water animals. Some animals found in fresh waters, like the rotifers, belong to none of the phyla described in Part III. See Figure 34.4. Among the annelids, oligochetes and leeches are found. Many crustacea occur. Insects, and especially many kinds of insect larvae, inhabit rivers and lakes. Clams and snails are numerous. Some cyclostomes, many bony fish, some amphibia such as salamanders and frogs, and some turtles and snakes live in fresh waters. Among aquatic birds are ducks, geese, gulls, terns, and herons. Some aquatic mammals occur, such as muskrats, otters, and beavers.

In a few special places the living organisms are quite limited. In hot springs a few blue-green algae may grow. In warm springs with temperatures above fifty degrees Centigrade, some protozoa are able to survive. Below that, crustacea of a few kinds live in warm springs. In general, contrasted with marine forms, fresh-water organisms are fewer in number and more limited in variety.

Subtropical Zone

The southern end of Florida is subtropical. Here the winters are somewhat cooler than the summers, but temperatures rarely if ever get down to frost level. The average annual rainfall is 50–65 inches. Extensive droughts are rare. Along the shores and in brackish swamps mangrove forms almost impenetrable thickets. The floor of the swamp, frequently under water and shaded by the leaves overhead, is not suitable for many organisms. Alligators, snakes, some amphibia, insects, and some other invertebrates grow and thrive. Birds are fairly common.

Where drainage is good, live oaks (retaining green leaves throughout the year), palms, palmettos, cypresses, magnolias, various shrubs, cane (a kind of bamboo), and some ferns occur. Partially parasitic plants growing on some of the trees include dodder and mistletoe. Spanish moss grows on other plants, too, but it is holophytic in nutrition. It is a seed plant, related to the pineapple. See Figure 34.5.

In the better drained parts one finds soil protozoa, roundworms, oligochetes, most kinds of arthropods except aquatic crustacea, snails, and many amphibia, reptiles, birds, and mammals.

Fig. 34.5 Spanish moss. This is a seed plant, growing on trees but not dependent on them for food.

Fig. 34.6   Longleaf   pine   forest,   Hattiesburg,
Mississippi.

Southeastern Evergreen Forest

The southeastern evergreen forest covers much of south eastern United States. The average annual rainfall is 45–50 inches, with more rain in summer than in the other seasons. Most of the area is subject to annual killing frosts, but the average growing season ranges from 200 to more than 320 days. The dominant trees are pines and oaks of various species. The live oak thrives in the more southerly parts. In the swamps, the characteristic tree is the cypress. Shrubs, including evergreen holly, constitute some of the under-growth; grasses and brightly flowered herbs form the flora of the forest floor. Soil bacteria, protozoa, and roundworms are abundant. Arthropods are very common, especially insects, spiders, mites, ticks, millipedes, and centipedes. Land vertebrates of many kinds are to be found — newts, toads, lizards, snakes, turtles, birds, and several species of mammals.

Deciduous Forest

Deciduous forests cover much of the eastern United States north of the southern evergreen forest area; some deciduous trees are found in every forested part of the United States. In the deciduous forest, the annual precipita-tion, some of which is snow, ranges from 35–45 inches, and as a rule temperature extremes are not so great as in the prairie to the west. The trees are chiefly dicotyledonous, broad-leaved plants which shed their leaves in the fall, remain bare in the winter, and grow new leaves in the spring. Examples of such trees are oak, maple, beech, hickory, elm, ash, poplar, birch, willow, and chestnut. The chestnut has been reduced to root sprouts in recent years because of the epidemic of chestnut blight, a disease caused by an ascomycete fungus. The Dutch elm disease, a similar fungus attack, is currently a dangerous epidemic of the elm tree.

Liverworts, mosses, ferns, and fern allies are common in deciduous forests. The moisture under the protecting shade of the trees is sufficient to supply these bryophytes and pteridophytes. Many herbaceous and shrubby seed plants live in the forests, too.

The soil is abundantly populated with fungi, a few algae, protozoa, a few flatworms, roundworms in abundance, and earthworms. Air-breathing snails are common. Arthro-pods are especially numerous, including a few land crustacea such as sowbugs, millipedes, centipedes, arachnids, and many kinds of insects, especially bugs, termites, butterflies

Fig. 34.7 Deciduous forest, Nicolet National Forest, Wisconsin. Large trees left to right are maple, elm, ash, and elm. Branches of hemlock (evergreen) show in foreground.

and moths, ants, flies, gnats, and a great variety of beetles. Amphibia are quite common. Lizards, snakes, and turtles occur in considerable numbers. Birds are widely varied and numerous. Various kinds of thrushes, warblers, vireos, flycatchers, and woodpeckers are found. Among the mammals are many kinds. Opossums, bats, moles, shrews, mice, squirrels, rabbits, and beavers are some of the smaller forms. Deer, bears, raccoons, martens, foxes, wolves, and wildcats are examples of larger mammals of the forest.

Eastern Coniferous Forest

The eastern coniferous forest includes areas in New England, the Adirondacks, and southward along the Appalachians, and parts of Michigan, Wisconsin, and Minnesota. The long, severe winters restrict the kinds of plants and animals which survive here. The growing season varies from four to five and a half months, and during much of the winter and early spring the ground is covered with snow. Rainfall is less than in deciduous forest areas. Hemlock is a common conifer here; red and white pines and red spruce are also plentiful. Some deciduous trees occur, especially birches, beeches, maples, and black cherries. Ferns, mosses, and lichens carpet the forest floor in places. Insects and spiders are present, a few frogs and toads, a few snakes and turtles, and several birds and mammals. Among the birds are owls, grouse, thrushes, wood warblers, kinglets, woodpeckers, jays, and crossbills. Mammals are represented by moles, shrews, bats, bears, foxes, martens, weasels, skunks, squirrels, chipmunks, wood mice, woodchucks, varying hares, deer, moose, and caribou. Mountain lions were formerly numerous, but have been largely exterminated by man.

Rocky Mountain Coniferous Forest

The Rocky Mountain coniferous forest stretches along the Rockies from Canada into Mexico. Rainfall here is higher than in the plains to the east or in the desert or semi-desert to the west, ranging from an annual average of 20 inches southward to more than 40 inches northward, in Idaho. Much of this falls in winter.

Many of the same genera of plants and animals found in the eastern coniferous forest are found here, but most of the species are different. Western white and yellow pines, larch, western hemlock, white and Douglas firs, red cedar, and Engelmann spruce cover the mountain slopes below the timber line. Black snakes and garter snakes are to be found,

Fig. 34.8 Eastern coniferous forest, Heart's Content, Pennsylvania. The trees here are white pine and hemlock.

Fig. 34.9 Pacific coastal coniferous forest, Soda Springs, Washington. All the large trees here are Douglas fir.

Fig. 34.10 (Above) Once covered with prairie grasses six to fourteen feet high, this portion of Clayton County, Iowa, is now farm land. Trees and shrubs have been planted near buildings and in gullies.

Fig. 34.11 (Below) Plains grasses, Weld County, Colorado. Much of the plains area is range land. The low rainfall makes agriculture hazardous here.

and many of the same families of birds and mammals as in the eastern coniferous forest, although of variant species. Eagles occur in places, and timber wolves may still be found, also badgers, lynxes, pikas, elk, mule deer, bighorn sheep, and mountain goats.

Pacific Coastal Coniferous Forest

The Pacific coastal coniferous forest covers the coastal ranges in Oregon, Washington, and northern and northeastern California. Here we find a very high annual precipitation, averaging from 40 to 146 inches. One record of 153.54 inches a year has been recorded, in northern California. More than half of this falls from November to March, a great deal of it as snow at higher altitudes. Summers are quite dry, but near the coast summer fogs are common.

Among the dominant trees of this forest are some of the largest and oldest trees of the earth. In Washington, Douglas firs may reach heights of 400 feet. In Oregon and California, redwoods grow to heights of more than 300 feet and diameters of 10 to 15 feet. Douglas fir and redwood cover enormous areas. Near the coast of northern California the big tree, or giant sequoia, which occurs in small groves, exceeds 300 feet in height; and one specimen, the General Sherman tree, is 27 feet in diameter 8 feet above the ground. The redwoods and big trees attain ages of 2000 to 3000 years.

Ferns, rhododendron, and dogwood appear in the lower layers of the forest community. Tree toads, frogs, garter snakes, and turtles are to be found. Most of the same mammals occur here as in the Rocky Mountain forests.

Prairie and Plain

The prairies and plains are grasslands covering much of the area between the Rocky Mountains and the Mississippi River. Precipitation ranges from an annual 35 inches at the eastern edge to 10 inches at the west. Extended droughts, most frequent at the west, are characteristic, as are tornadoes in the south in spring or early summer and blizzards in the north in winter. Tall grasses — 5 to 10 feet high — dominate in the east where rainfall is greatest. This is prairie. The dominant grasses of the western part, the plain, are less than one foot high. Trees are found only along streams.

Grasshoppers, small beetles, and ants are the most common insects, and spiders are very numerous. Roundworms and earthworms, protozoa and bacteria inhabit the soil. Lizards, snakes, and some kinds of turtles are abundant. The birds are chiefly runners, such as the sage cock and the

Fig. 34.12   One phase of the desert in Arizona. The largest plants are the giant cactus, *Cereus giganteus.*

prairie fowl, or predators such as hawks and owls. Rodents are the most common mammals, including gophers, prairie dogs, rabbits, and mice. Wolves, foxes, and coyotes represent the carnivores. Formerly the dominant ungulates were bison and pronghorn antelopes. All the mammals have been greatly reduced in number by conversion of the prairies into farms and ranches. Some are now found only in national parks or reservations.

Desert and Desert Scrub

The desert regions of southwestern United States are characterized by low rainfall, annually three to ten inches. In general, rain comes in short downpours during one or two rainy periods. Local areas may get no rain during a whole year. Summer temperatures reach 125° F. Except in oases, the perennial plants either accumulate water during the rainy season and lose it sparingly during the dry seasons, or they are of the type which are not killed by drying to a state of brittleness. Many of the perennials, such as the cactus, are thorny or have spiny leaves. The stems of the cactus plants are large, contain chlorophyll, and may retain great quantities of water with very little loss. A few sparse grasses and shrubs occur. Sagebrush, greasewood, mesquite, acacias, and yuccas are the more familiar perennial desert plants.

During rainy seasons, especially the winter rainy season, an enormous crop of annuals appears. These plants spring up from seeds produced in past rainy seasons, and can complete the cycle from "seed to seed" in four to six weeks.

Animals are often protectively colored, burrowing, and fast-moving. Many of the small mammals and reptiles such as the desert turtle are vegetarian. Their entire water need is supplied by plants — the water content of the plant and the water produced by the animal's metabolism of plant materials. Most desert mammals and reptiles are nocturnal. Few can survive the high daytime temperature and drying. Grasshoppers, beetles, scorpions, and spiders are among the arthropods present. Lizards, such as the horned toad and the Gila monster, and snakes, such as the sidewinder rattlesnake, represent the reptiles. Some birds occur, such as the sage grouse, the elf owl, and the cactus wren. The mammals are usually of the burrowing rodent type. There may be a few carnivores such as the desert fox.

One phase of this desert, called desert scrub, extends northward between the Coast Ranges and the Rocky Mountains almost to the Washington border. Another extension is eastward along the south border of Texas.

Fig. 34.13 Chaparral near Mt. Palomar, California.

These extensions get a little more rainfall, and temperatures are not so high. Throughout the northward extension the dominant vegetation is sagebrush and similar shrubs, although trees are found along streams, and occasionally, in the more favored locations, there are grasslands.

Chaparral

The chaparral area is sometimes considered as a phase of the desert. It includes approximately the southern two thirds of coastal California. The summers are usually long, hot, and dry. The winters are cooler and more humid. Here the plant population is composed largely of small trees, including several live oaks, and shrubs like manzanita in which the leaves are coarse and rough, with only a few stomata, restricted to the lower surface. The chaparral area is small compared with the other types of habitat, and the animal inhabitants are those which are common to surrounding territories.

Tundra

The tundra is typical of polar regions, and is found in the United States only in the higher peaks of the Rocky Mountains. Total annual precipitation is in general less than that of regions to the south, and the temperatures are lower. Lichens and mosses, with a few flowering plants such as grasses, sedges, heaths, and willows constitute the dominant green plants. Some flies, bees, moths, and spiders inhabit these areas, together with a few kinds of snails. The snowy owl, some rodents, and the bighorn sheep and Rocky Mountain goat live here. Other animals wander in and out from the surrounding areas of lower altitude. It is a more bleak and sparse habitat than the others described except for the desert.

SUMMARY

The physical features of the environment — water, temperature, light, and degree of climatic change — have much to do with the kinds of plants and animals present. Because living organisms frequently depend on other organisms for food, the presence of some is an advantage to others and a disadvantage to still others. Thus, the relationships among kinds of organisms show some degree of uniformity over wide ranges. This uniformity is of a general nature — such as the presence of salamanders in deciduous forests — and not a specific one. The species of

Fig. 34.14 Willow tundra near Jones Pass,
Arapaho National Forest, Colorado.

salamander common in an Oklahoma forest is different from the species of salamander found in North Carolina.

To summarize the information presented in this chapter in another direction, we may consider the distribution of different kinds of organisms. Fungi, especially bacteria, are found practically everywhere that life occurs at all. Algae require water or at least moisture. All classes are common in the ocean, but brown algae are not found elsewhere, and only a few kinds of red algae inhabit fresh water. Blue-green algae and a few green algae may live on land. Lichens survive on land in exposed, barren places where other plants do not compete, such as bare rocks and rocky soil in the cold regions of the tundra. Mosses and liverworts do not live in salt water, but occur in fresh waters, and especially on land in moist, shady areas. Ferns and fern allies are predominantly forest inhabitants in warm climates. Gymnosperms constitute the dominant plants in the southern and northern evergreen forests. The deciduous forests and the grasslands are the localities of the most abundant angiosperms in the United States, although they occur in all environments to some extent, except for the oceans, and even here they invade the coastal waters.

Protozoa are very common in the water, and inhabit the soil in great numbers. Sponges are chiefly deep water forms occurring in the ocean, although a few occur in fresh water. Coelenterates are primarily marine forms with a few fresh-water representatives.

Flatworms are marine, fresh-water, and land forms. Roundworms, as was pointed out in Chapter 23, are among the most widely distributed of living organisms, occurring almost everywhere that life occurs at all. Annelids are marine, principally, with oligochetes and leeches occurring in fresh water, and a few worms, such as the earthworm, widely distributed in the soil.

Among the arthropods crustacea are extremely numerous in the ocean, quite common in fresh water, and represented by a few forms on land, especially in forests. Millipedes and centipedes are land forms. Arachnids are principally land forms and are quite numerous in forests and prairies. Insects are primarily land forms and are found everywhere on land. A few live in or on the water.

Molluscs are characteristic of the ocean, although clams and snails are common in fresh waters, and some snails successfully inhabit the land, especially in forests.

Echinoderms are strictly marine forms, as are the brachiopods. Most bryozoa live in the ocean, although a few live in fresh water.

Chordates are primarily marine animals. A few lampreys and many bony fishes live in fresh water. Amphibia cannot live in the seas and are fresh-water and land forms requiring moisture. Reptiles are primarily land forms, though a few inhabit the water. These are "cold-blooded" animals and are active only when the environment is warm or hot. Those which inhabit temperate regions hibernate in cold weather. Birds and mammals live in all kinds of environments except the ocean depths, and even there the whale may spend some time. But birds and mammals are primarily land animals. Forests are their natural homes, although many have their homes in grasslands, tundra, or even deserts.

REVIEW QUESTIONS

1. Describe the factors which determine the presence of an organism in a given environment.
2. List and locate the biogeographic zones of the United States.
3. Describe the flora and fauna of each of the biogeographic zones in the United States.
4. Characterize the distribution of different classes of plants and animals in the United States.

GENERAL QUESTIONS

1. What kinds of organisms might be found in all three of the ocean zones?
2. Why do not bryophytes and pteridophytes grow in the ocean?
3. What part has *Sargassum* played in human history?
4. Why have echinoderms not invaded fresh-water habitats?
5. Describe the food chain in a mangrove swamp.
6. How could you quickly distinguish between a southern and a northern evergreen forest by their inhabitants?
7. Describe the food chain in a desert.
8. How has the advent of Europeans affected the flora and fauna of the prairies of the United States?
9. What characteristics of the deciduous forest make it favorable to the most abundant land flora and fauna in the United States?
10. What kinds of organisms may be found in any land area of the United States?

CHAPTER 35

Humans and Biology

APPLICATIONS OF BIOLOGY

The study of biology and the application of biological knowledge occupies the time and energy of a very large portion of the human race. Some of the better known examples of these pursuits will be discussed in this chapter.

Research

Professional biologists conduct much of the research along the frontiers of biology, discovering and evaluating new facts, and fitting them into contemporary theories. This enterprise may involve the revision or rejection of widely held theories and the formulation of new theories. It means repeating and confirming or rejecting the work of others, criticizing methods and results, designing new experiments, new techniques, and new apparatus, investigating organisms and problems not before studied, and devising new explanations for biological phenomena.

Usually a research biologist will specialize in some small branch of biology. He may study the genetics of corn, or the embryology of a sea urchin, or the behavior of a virus in a human. He ordinarily combines research activities with teaching, which is a stimulating and rewarding occupation in its own right. Relatively few people excel in both research and teaching, for each requires for excellence intense enthusiasm, concentration, and great amounts of time, energy, and patience. Often a biologist will be good at one job and mediocre at the other. There are notable exceptions, however, who are outstanding both as discoverers and as teachers.

Some research biologists are associated with industrial or commercial organizations, or endowed institutions, and pursue investigations full time. A few biologists have personal fortunes enabling them to devote their time to biology independently.

Applied Biology

People engaged in applying biological knowledge far outnumber those engaged in research and teaching. Farmers and ranchers raise both plants and animals in great quantities for use as food and for many other purposes.

Genetics has been of particular value in developing varieties of plants and animals with characteristics especially suitable to human needs. New strains and varieties of small grains (wheat, oats, barley, rye) are resistant to damage by parasitic fungi. Numerous hybrid corn varieties have been developed for: uniformity of size of stalk and ear, facilitating harvest operations; resistance to damage by drought, insects such as the corn borer, and fungus parasites; and for earlier maturity, thus extending the range of profitable corn raising hundreds of miles northward.

Agronomy, the study of crop production methods, has greatly increased yields by developing methods of increasing and maintaining soil fertility, and more efficient methods of fertilizing, seeding, and harvesting.

The investigation of the characteristics and life cycles of parasites has made possible the development of methods for reducing the damage done by parasitic organisms. For example, such studies have resulted in reduced stem rust damage to wheat by removal of the common barberry, which is the alternate host of the disease organism, and in reduced damage to apples by development of a spray schedule timed so that the poison is applied when the fungi are in susceptible stages.

Experiments on the physiology of plants and animals have been useful in improving agriculture. Demonstration that plants need such "trace elements" as boron, cobalt, and molybdenum, which are absent or scarce in some soils, but can be supplied in fertilizer, has saved agricultural industry in some places. Discovery of nutritional requirements of farm animals and application of this knowledge have increased yields of milk, meat, and eggs.

In these ways and many others both producers and users of agricultural products benefit from the application of biological information.

Many problems are still unsolved, and much biological science that could be applied has not yet been widely used in the production, processing, preserving, and marketing of economically valuable living organisms and their products. Among the specialists who have benefited or who can benefit from the application of biological knowledge are fishermen, clam diggers, lobstermen, oystermen, beekeepers, hunters, veterinarians, doctors; processors and packers of fish, cereals, vegetables, fruit, meat, wool, and other fibers; and marketers of every kind of product produced by living organisms.

Many large industries are dependent for success on facts discovered by biologists that can be applied to production and processing of the plants or animals which are their basic materials. Among such industries are the following: meat packing and marketing; spinning and weaving of cotton, wool, linen, and silk; woodworking, which includes cutting the trees, and processing them into such items as lumber, veneer, paper, and rayon; fermentation, which yields alcohols, acetone, and numerous drugs; and rubber, which has through its use in tires changed the habits of a nation.

Other large industries service those who raise the plants and animals. Much biological knowledge is used by and much research is engaged in by the industries which supply fertilizer, insecticides, farm feeds, and agricultural implements.

DEPENDENCE AND INTERDEPENDENCE

In many previous pages the dependence of one organism upon another has been pointed out. Parasites are dependent upon their hosts, for example. Man, certainly a biological organism, is dependent upon other organisms in many ways (food and clothing), and numerous organisms, especially domesticated plants and animals, are dependent upon man's activities for survival. The relationship between man and his domesticated organisms is an example of **interdependence.** Many other **interrelationships** could be mentioned. Darwin pointed out the relationship of cats to beef production in England. Cattle eat clover which is pollinated mostly by bumblebees. Bumblebees nest in the ground, and their nests are often destroyed by mice. Cats eat mice. Hence, the more cats, the fewer mice, the more bees, the more clover seed, the more clover, and the more beef. Interesting elaborations on this series of interrelationships have been made. For example, since old maids keep cats and British sailors eat beef, the more old maids in England, the stronger the British Navy.

By reflection the reader will be able to discern numerous other interrelationships among the activities of men. One result of our recognition of interrelationships and interdependence is the present widespread interest in conservation of our natural resources.

CONSERVATION

The invention and use of machinery for multiplying the effectiveness of man's labor in production have rapidly depleted many of our natural resources. Forests, soils, waterways are all used to a much greater degree with modern methods of production than formerly. This brings about the necessity of intensive conservation methods. A study of the supply of natural resources available for human use and the rate at which these are being exhausted is necessary to the wise use which will provide for the welfare of later generations. A well-managed forest will produce abundantly and indefinitely. A scorched-earth policy of tree harvest will destroy the productivity of the forest for generations to come. This important problem occupies the attention of many investigators, policy makers, and governmental officers. It is possibly the most important activity of government, although not often recognized as such. Certainly the abundance of materials available when the people of the world practice a wise policy of conservation will go a long way toward removing many of the economic, social, and political problems now so important.

Conservation of natural resources is an interlocking problem involving extensive knowledge of soil, water, forests, minerals, wild animals, and humans. Soil which is suitable for agricultural purposes is called topsoil, a thin layer on top of the barren rock, gravel, or sand. This layer, averaging about six inches in thickness, is the accumulation of hundreds and thousands of years of natural growth and decay of living organisms. It is possible for unwise farming to use and destroy this topsoil in one human generation. Growing one crop, such as corn or cotton, year after year and returning nothing to the soil will deplete the soil to the point at which later crops are definitely inferior. The great dust storms of the nineteen thirties and the lesser ones of the nineteen fifties in the United States were the result of use of the topsoil without adequate precautions to conserve it. A priceless heritage, built through the centuries, disappeared in a few years.

Erosion is speeded up tremendously when the natural vegetation is removed from sloping land without proper terracing and control of drainage. Examples of the ruin of valuable crop and grazing lands by erosion are numberless. Proper grading of the land, wise rotation of crops, adequate fertilization, and continual planning for the future can save the remaining topsoil and even rebuild it where it has been stripped away.

Water conservation is another concern of all people. Fishing, if uncontrolled, may decimate desirable fish and result in increase of less desirable water animals — mosquito larvae, for example. Sewage and industrial wastes poured into streams and other bodies of water may pollute them until the character of the life in them is completely changed, and the population shifts in favor of the less desirable inhab-

itants. Of more spectacular concern are the dangers of flood and drouth. To a considerable degree these dangers are the results of unwise use of land, especially forests.

Very little of the water that falls as rain on a forest runs off the soil surface. Some evaporates from the leaves of forest plants. The remainder sinks into the accumulated humus on the floor of the forest and is added to the water table. Rain falling on bare ground largely runs off, forming muddy streams and rivers. Completely stripping a forest of its trees for lumber destroys much of its value for many years to come. Selective cutting and replanting will make a forest continue to produce lumber interminably, and wise forest practice will greatly increase the long-term production.

Forest fires are among the most completely destructive catastrophes, for they not only destroy the trees and undergrowth and much of the wildlife, but they burn the humus in the soil upon which restoration of growth depends. The United States Forest Service has estimated that about a

Fig. 35.1 One way of conserving soil on slopes is to use contour cultivation, thus reducing erosion. This scene is near Spartanburg, South Carolina.

Fig. 35.2 This forest in Wyoming suffered a fire seventy-five years before the picture was taken. It is apparent that the trees have staged very little comeback as yet. Such a fire destroys the soil and the sources of seed for reforestation.

quarter of all forest fires are deliberately set by malicious humans, and about a half of all forest fires are the results of human carelessness such as discarding lighted cigarettes and neglecting campfires.

In addition to its value in water conservation and lumber resources, a forest furnishes cover for a great variety of wildlife. The food, furs, and other commercial products obtained from wild animals, the sport provided by hunting and fishing, and the other recreational opportunities are valuable. A forest with its population of many kinds of interdependent organisms is also a valuable laboratory. Studies have shown that ordinarily in forests, populations change slowly because of predator-prey and other interrelationships.

Man has often unintentionally or intentionally disregarded or acted in ignorance of such knowledge. By unrestricted killing, by conducting campaigns of extermination against some organisms, or by introducing and cultivating others, he has unwittingly harmed himself. The passenger pigeon, beautiful, edible, and a century ago present in tremendous numbers, has become extinct through unrestricted killing and destruction of the primeval forest. The orange groves of California were once threatened by a scale insect accidentally introduced from Australia. Investigation showed that in Australia one of the scale insect's natural enemies was a ladybug. This beetle was with some difficulty imported and established in California and now keeps the pest under effective control.

Such fortunate results as this last example are the outcome of careful and thorough study of the relationships of living organisms. Incomplete investigation may produce less happy results. The Asiatic mongoose was brought into Jamaica to combat the rats and snakes found there. It was very effective, soon reducing the rat population to a small number. Then, deprived of this source of food, the mongooses took to destroying birds, both the wild songbirds and the domesticated poultry. Thus the mongoose became an undesirable pest.

We are far from knowing all the possible results of destroying all of a group of living organisms or of introducing organisms into new habitats. It behooves us to make haste slowly in such activities. Yet even now we know better than we practice. If we should scrupulously apply the knowledge we have to the conservation of our natural resources, looking to the future over a long range rather than solely to the immediate exploitation of available resources, we should live in a far better and more productive world.

HEALTH

A final conservation program to be considered involves the conservation of human life and health. The absolute antithesis of such conservation is, of course, war. Control of this pattern of destruction is more of an educational and political than a biological problem, but its nature is fundamentally a biological and psychological one.

Preservation of human life and health is the goal of the many branches of medicine. Physicians, surgeons, and dentists are concerned with the prevention of defects and deficiencies, and the treatment of diseases and injuries when they do occur. Public health officers contribute to disease prevention. The prevention of injuries is the goal of safety organizations. Research in medicine has long been a vital activity, but in recent years its dimensions have vastly increased, due to public interest and the provision of funds for the advancement of knowledge of the human body and the ills to which it is subject.

The tremendous increase in medical knowledge is reflected both in the extensive training required of practitioners and in the number of specialties recognized professionally. Doctors and dentists spend four years in professional training beyond their college training, and some states require additional interneship experience for a license to practice. Many medical specialties require even further training beyond this before the candidate is recognized by the appropriate examining board as qualified to practice.

Many branches of knowledge associated with medical practice are pursued both for the practical advantages they confer and for the theoretical understanding obtained by such research. Examples are bacteriology, parasitology, anesthesiology, pediatrics (the study of the health of children), geriatrics (the study of health in old age), prosthetics (the development of mechanical substitutes for natural structures, such as artificial limbs and false teeth), and psychiatry. Veterinarians, morticians, and laboratory technicians are applied biologists. In a sense, every housewife who plans her meals with a view to providing her family with vitamins, proteins, and other requirements in adequate amounts is using biological information to promote health.

OTHER APPLICATIONS OF BIOLOGY

Psychology

The field of psychology borders on and borrows from biology quite extensively. At the same time, it is in a position to contribute to the biologist's understanding of animal and human behavior.

Sociology

Both the biologist and the psychologist are sought out by the sociologist for background information in understanding human social groups, human population problems, evaluation of human variation, human defectives, and the foundations of human social behavior.

Law

The field of law touches on biology at a few points. Legal medicine has developed into an established field in recent years.

Education

Education is paying more attention to biological problems of growth, the nature of learning, human variability, and the interest of children in the natural world. The public interest in living organisms is so vital that all branches of education — schools, books, movies, radio, television, and so on — have made special efforts to incorporate biological information in their materials for dissemination to the public.

Art

Artists have always made use of living organisms. Artists in painting, design, architecture, literature, music, dance, and the theater have all used plant and animal subjects extensively.

Recreation

Recreation involves biological activities. Hunting and fishing are well-recognized sports. Gardening, flower cultivation, and keeping animal pets are widely indulged in as hobbies. Bird watching, shell and butterfly collecting, hiking in the woods or along the seashore, nature photography, and outdoor camping are pursuits enthusiastically followed. Many amateur biologists carry on valuable and interesting scientific research as an avocation. Amateur microscopists and amateur naturalists have contributed an immeasurable amount of information to the sum incorporated in contemporary science.

Philosophy

And finally, biology contributes grist to the philosopher's mill. Many biologists become philosophers themselves, attempting from the basis of scientific knowledge to evaluate and contribute additional understanding to the philosophies of the day.

SUMMARY

Application of biological knowledge to man's own purposes has taken many forms. In addition to the satisfaction of increased knowledge and understanding of natural phenomena, biology has numberless practical applications. Agriculture and the food processing and distributing industries are of primary importance. In addition to food, varieties of uses are made of organisms cultured or collected for the purpose. Wood, textile fibers, leather, fur, buttons, medicinal drugs, and many other useful materials are obtained. Also to be included are the many materials coming from long extinct organisms, such as coal, petroleum, sulfur, iron, and chalk. Conservation of the supplies of such resources is of outstanding importance to the continued existence of civilized man. Medicine in all of its far-flung branches is of vital concern to the preservation of human life and health. Many other fields of human interest border on and interfertilize biology. Among these are psychology, sociology, law, education, the arts, recreation, and philosophy.

REVIEW QUESTIONS

1. Describe the aim and some of the active fields of biological research.
2. Describe the applications of biological knowledge to agriculture.
3. Describe the relation between old maids and the British Navy.
4. Discuss the need for and desirable methods of conservation of natural resources.
5. What part does biological knowledge play in the conservation of human life and health?
6. In what ways do biology and other fields of human activity interact with each other?

GENERAL QUESTIONS

1. What traits characterize a good research biologist?
2. What traits characterize a good biology teacher?
3. Describe five lines of biological investigation for which you can imagine no practical application.
4. How does an area recover from a large forest fire? Be detailed.
5. Describe the formation of topsoil.
6. Describe the effects of the introduction into the United States of the codling moth; the starling; beef cattle; cotton.
7. Is the lengthening of the human life span by medical developments entirely desirable?
8. Is it defensible to consider psychology and sociology as divisions of biology?
9. How do biology and religion interact with each other?
10. What is the place of biology in the whole realm of man's knowledge?

GLOSSARY

GLOSSARY

Abdomen is the posterior section of the body of certain animals.

Abducens (ab dū'senz) refers to the sixth pair of cranial nerves, which supply the external recti muscles of the eyes.

Abductor refers to a muscle which pulls a structure away from the axis of an animal. (L. that which leads away)

Abscess is a concentration of pus in a disintegrating tissue.

Absorption is the diffusion of substances into a cell or group of cells. (L. sucking in from)

Abyssal (a biss'ul) refers to the depths of the oceans. (L. too deep to be sounded with a line)

Acetylcholine (a set eel kō'leen) is a chemical substance released when a nerve impulse reaches a synapse in certain autonomic ganglia or at the end of a parasympathetic fiber. (L. vinegar and G. bile)

Acidophil (a sid'ō fill) refers to cells which are stained by acid stains. (L. sour and G. fond of)

Acromegaly (ak rō meg'al i) is the deformity brought about by disproportionate growth of bones under the influence of abnormal secretion of growth hormone. (G. large extremities)

Actinomyces (ak tin ō my'sees) is the genus of bacteria which causes lumpy jaw in cattle.

Actinomycetales (ak tin ō my see-tā'leez) is an order of Schizomycetes in which long filaments are characteristic.

Adductor refers to a muscle which pulls a structure toward the axis of an animal. (L. that which leads toward)

Adenosine (ad en'ō sin) is an organic compound used in the contraction of muscles.

Adrenal (ad ree'nul) refers to the endocrine glands located near the kidneys.

Adrenin (ad ren'in) is the hormone secreted by the medulla of the adrenal gland.

Adsorption is the attachment to the surface of a substance of molecules of another substance. (L. sucking in to)

Aeciospore (ee'see ō spōr') is a spore produced in an aecium.

Aecium (ee'see um) is a cluster of basidiomycete hyphae formed from the mycelia of two individual organisms.

Aerobic (ā'er ō'bik) refers to an organism or process which uses free oxygen in its oxidations. (G. air life)

Agglutinin (ag glū'tin in) is a secretion of white blood corpuscles which changes the surface of bacteria in such a way that the bacteria tend to clump together. (L. gluing to)

Agronomy is the study of crop production methods. (G. land management)

Albatross is a seagoing bird. (Portuguese: alcatraz, from the Arabic al qadus, from the Greek for bucket, the name given to the pelican because it carries water in its pouch.)

Albino is an organism which does not develop the pigments characteristic of its species. (L. white)

Albumin (al bū'min) is a type of protein soluble in water and coagulable by heat.

Alcohol is a type of organic compound in which carbon and hydrogen atoms make up the molecule and in which one or more hydroxyl (OH) groups is attached to one or more carbon atoms. (Arabic: powdered antimony used as a cosmetic; the fine powder was obtained by sublimation, and the term al kohl came to be applied to anything sublimed or distilled.)

Algae (al'jee) is the subphylum of Thallophyta in which the plants have chlorophyll. (L. seaweeds)

Allantois (al lan'tō iss) is a pouch extending out from the hindgut of certain embryos. (G. sausage-shaped)

Allosaurus (al'lō saw'rus) is a genus of dinosaurs. (G. another lizard)

Alpha globulin (al'fa glob'yū lin) is one of a group of substances in blood plasma associated with transportation of hormones.

Alternation of generations is the type of life cycle in which stages with diploid nuclei alternate with stages with haploid nuclei, or some similar alternation of life stages.

Alveolus (al vē'ō luss) is a small chamber or rounded cavity, as the alveolus of a lung.

Ameba is a genus of Sarcodina.

Amino acid (am'in ō) is a type of organic compound in which one carbon atom has an amino group (NH₂) and another, usually an adjacent one, has an acid group (OOH). (The name amino, derived from ammonia, comes from the Egyptian god Ammon; the decayed refuse of the animals sacrificed at his temple was the first source of ammonium compounds.)

Amnion (am'ni on) is a membrane enclosing the embryo of certain animals.

Amorphous (ā mōr'fuss) means formless, as the amorphous fraction in the secretion of the adrenal cortex whose structural formulas have not yet been determined. (G. without form)

Amphibia (am fib'i a) is the class of Vertebrata with bone, legs, and no exoskeleton. (G. both living, since amphibia live both in water and on land)

Amphineura (am fi nū'ra) is the class of Mollusca with a skeleton of eight dorsal plates. (G. both nerves — having two nerve cords)

Ampulla (am pull'la) is a bulb-like swelling, as the ampulla of a semicircular canal of the ear or of a starfish tube foot. (L. flask)

Amylase (am'i lās) is an enzyme which catalyzes the breakdown of starches into maltose. (G. starch, and the ending for an enzyme)

Anaerobic (an ā er ō'bik) refers to an organism or process which does not use free oxygen in its oxidations. (G. no air life)

Anaphase (an'a fāz) is the stage of cell division in which paired chromosomes are separated from each other.

Anaphylaxis (an af i lax'is) is the strong reaction of an organism to foreign substances such as proteins not normally present. The reaction is an abnormal metabolic process resulting in such symptoms as a rash or asthma. (G. backward protection)

Anatomy is the study of the structure of an organism. (G. cutting apart)

Androsterone (an dros'te rōn) is a hormone secreted in a testis. (G. man, solid secretion)

Anesthesiology (an ess thē zi ol'ō-ji) is the study of anesthetics and their effects on organisms. (G. no sensation study)

Angiospermae (an'ji ō spur'mi) is the subphylum of Spermatophyta in which seeds are enclosed during their formation. (G. encased seeds)

Annelida (an nell'i da) is the phylum of segmented worms having a true celom. (L. like little rings)

Annulus (an'yū luss) is the incomplete ring of fern sporangium cells, part of whose walls are much thickened. (L. little ring)

Anodonta (an ō don'ta) is a genus of fresh-water Pelecypoda. (G. toothless)

Anopheles (an of'eh leez) is a genus of mosquitoes which carry malaria. (G. hurtful)

Antenna (an ten'na) is a rodlike sensory appendage of an arthropod. (G. upstretching)

Anterior refers to the foremost end of an organism. (L. fore)

Anther is the microsporangium of a flower.

Antheridium (an thur id'i um) is a chamber in certain plants in which sperm cells develop.

Antibiotic (an'ti bī o'tik) is a substance which inhibits the growth and increase of living organisms such as bacteria. (G. against life)

Antibody is a substance produced by an organism in response to and reacting with a foreign body.

Antienzyme (an'ti en'zīm) is a substance secreted by a cell which inhibits enzyme activity.

Antigen (an'ti jen) is a foreign body which arouses antibody formation in an organism. (G. forming against)

Antipodal (an tip'ō dull) means opposite to, as the antipodal nuclei of an angiosperm female gametophyte opposite to the micropyle. (G. opposite foot)

Antithrombin (an'ti throm'bin) is a substance in blood which neutralizes thrombin, inhibiting the formation of a blood clot. (G. against clot)

Antitoxin (an'ti tox'in) is a substance secreted by a white blood corpuscle which neutralizes a toxin. (G. against poison)

Anus (ā'nus) is the posterior opening or exit of the digestive tract.

Anvil is the middle bone of the middle ear.

Aorta (ā ōr'ta) is the chief artery of an organism. (G. shoulder strap, from its form curving over and down)

Apical cell (ā'pi kull) is a cell at the tip or edge of a plant body which divides repeatedly, increasing the extent of the body.

Appalachian revolution is the geologic upheaval at the end of the Paleozoic Era.

Appendicular (ap pen dik'ū lur) refers to the appendages of an organism. (L. hanging on)

Appendix is a small structure attached to a larger one, as the vermiform (worm-shaped) appendix attached to the human cecum. (L. hanging on)

Aqueduct of Sylvius is the channel through the midbrain and pons Varolii which carries the cerebrospinal fluid. (Aqueduct from the L. for water-carrying)

Aqueous chamber is the eye cavity in front of the lens, containing the aqueous humor.

Aqueous humor is the lymphlike liquid in the aqueous chamber.

Arachnida (a rak'ni da) is the class of Arthropoda without antennae. (G. spider, from the mythological Arachne, who defeated the goddess Athena in a spinning contest, and was transformed into a spider for her presumption)

Archegonium (ar ke gō'ni um) is a many-celled chamber in certain plants in which an egg develops. (G. primitive seed)

Archeopteryx (ar kē op'te rix) is a genus of extinct birds. (G. primitive wings)

Archeozoic (ar kē ō zō'ik) is the first of the geologic eras. (G. primitive animals)

Arginase (ar'ji nās) is the enzyme which catalyzes the hydrolysis or breakdown of arginine to urea and ornithine.

Arginine (ar'jin in) is an amino acid formed during the change of ammonium carbonate into urea.

Artery (ar'tuh ri) is a vessel carrying blood from the heart to capillaries. (G. air vessel, since it was formerly thought that arteries carried air)

Arthropoda (ar throp'ō duh) is the phylum of segmented animals with a chitinous exoskeleton. (G. jointed feet)

Arytenoid (a ri'te noid) refers to one of two cartilages in the dorsal wall of the larynx anterior to the cricoid cartilage.

Ascaris (ass'ka riss) is a genus of roundworms. (G. intestinal worm)

Ascocarp (ass'kō karp) is a wall of hyphae surrounding an ascus.

Ascomycetes (ass kō mī see'teez) is a class of Fungi in which spores are formed in a sac and germinate into hyphae with cross-walls.

Ascorbic acid, or Vitamin C, is a water-soluble vitamin involved in the maintenance of the healthy condition of connective tissue ground substance. (L. against scurvy)

Ascospore (ass'kō spōr) is a spore developing in an ascus.

Ascus is a sac in which spores develop in the Ascomycetes. (G. bag)

Asexual (ā'sex yū ul, or a'sex yū-ul) refers to a type of reproduction in which a new individual is formed from one, not two, living entities.

Astasia (ass tā′zee uh) is a genus of Flagellata.

Aster is a starlike body, as the set of cytoplasmic radiations about a centriole.

Asterias (ass te′ri us) is a genus of Asteroidea, the starfish. (G. star)

Asteroidea (ass te roi′di uh) is the class of Echinodermata with unbranched arms not sharply demarcated from the central disc. (G. starlike)

Atlas is the most anterior vertebra of a vertebral column. (Named for the Greek mythological character who held the earth on his shoulders, in reference to the atlas holding the skull)

Atmosphere is the blanket of air around the earth. (G. vapor sphere)

Atrium (ā′tri um) is a chamber, as the atrium of a fish heart. (L. inner court)

Auditory refers to hearing, as the auditory canal or auditory nerve. (L. hearing)

Aureomycin (aw ree ō mī′sin) is an antibiotic manufactured by one of the Actinomycetales.

Auricle is an earlike projection, as that on the head of a planaria, or a heart chamber which receives blood from the veins. (L. little ear)

Auriculoventricular bundle (awrik′yū lō ven trik′yū lur) is a strand of muscle which carries contraction waves from auricles to ventricles in the heart.

Autocatalysis (aw tō ka tal′i sis) is the process of a substance catalyzing formation of more of itself. (G. self-dissolving)

Autonomic (aw tō nom′ik) refers to a part of the nervous system associated with visceral muscles and with glands. (G. self-managing)

Autotomy (aw tot′uh mi) is the spontaneous separation of a part of an organism from the rest. (G. self-cutting)

Autotrophic (aw tō trō′fik) refers to the ability of an organism to manufacture its own food from inorganic substances.

Aves (ā′veez) is the class of Vertebrata with bone, legs, wings, and an exoskeleton with feathers. It includes the birds.

Axial refers to the principal axis of an organism.

Axillary (ax′il lā ri) refers to the armpit, as the axillary arteries and veins. (L. armpit)

Axis is an imaginary line through an organism about which the organism is in some way symmetrical; it refers also to the second most anterior vertebra, which has a projection upon which the atlas rotates, as on an axis.

Axon is a branch of a nerve cell which carries impulses from the cell body.

Azygos (az′i guss) refers to a vein draining the dorsal wall of the chest.

Bacillariophyceae (ba sill ā′ri ō fī′si ee) is the phylum proposed to include the diatoms.

Bacillus (ba sill′luss) is a rod-shaped bacterium. (L. rod)

Bacteriology is the study of bacteria.

Bacteriophage (bak tē′ri ō fāj) is a virus which destroys bacteria.

Bacterium is a schizomycete large enough to be seen with a light microscope.

Balantidium (bal an ti′dē um) is a genus of parasitic Ciliata.

Barnacle (bar′nak ull) is a crustacean.

Basidiomycetes (ba si′dē ō mī sē′teez) is a class of Fungi in which spores are formed on stalks and germinate into hyphae with crosswalls.

Basidium is a tiny stalk bearing a spore in the Basidiomycetes.

Basophil (bā′so fil) refers to cells which are stained by alkaline stains. (G. base, fond of)

Beech is a dicot tree.

Beriberi (bā′ri bā′ri) is a wasting disease resulting from thiamin deficiency. (Term is derived from the Singhalese)

Beta globulin (bā tuh glob′yū lin) is one of a group of substances in blood plasma associated with transportation of enzymes such as thrombin and prothrombin.

Biceps (bī′seps) is a muscle with the contractile portion divided in two at one end, such as the flexor muscle of the human elbow. (L. two heads)

Bicuspid (bī cuss′pid) refers to a structure with two rounded surfaces, as a bicuspid tooth or the bicuspid valve between the left auricle and left ventricle of the human heart. (L. two points)

Bile is the secretions of the liver which are passed to the duodenum.

Biogenetic theory states that the embryo of a complex animal goes through stages resembling the embryos of its ancestors.

Biogeography is the study of the geographic distribution of living organisms. (G. life, earth, writing)

Biology is the science of living organisms. (G. study of life)

Biotin (bī′ō tin) is a water-soluble vitamin involved in oxidations in the body. (G. living substance)

Blade is the flat, expanded part of a leaf.

Blaze is a single patch of unpigmented hair occurring in a coat of pigmented hair.

Blood is a circulatory substance composed of water containing many substances in solution and colloidal suspension and many corpuscles.

Bone is a rigid, solid skeletal secretion composed of both organic and inorganic substances.

Book lung is a respiratory organ of a spider.

Botany is the study of plants.

Bowman's capsule (bō′munz capsūl) is a double-walled epithelial cup at the beginning of a kidney tubule.

Brachial (brā′ki ul) refers to arm, as the brachialis muscle of the arm. (G. arm)

Brachiopod (brak′i ō pod) is a marine animal with a shell having dorsal and ventral valves.

Brackish refers to water intermediate in salt content between fresh water and ocean water.

Brain is the enlarged portion of the central nervous system located in the head.

Branchial (bran'ki ul) refers to gill, as the branchial artery which supplies a gill. (G. gill)

Brine fly is a dipteran living in very salt water.

Bronchiole (bron'ki ōl) is a branch of the bronchus in a lung. (G. little windpipe)

Bronchus (bron'kuss) is the passageway through which air goes between the rest of the lungs and the trachea. (G. windpipe)

Brontosaurus (bron'tō saw'russ) is a genus of dinosaurs. (G. thunder lizard)

Bruise is a blood clot in a tissue.

Bryophyta (brī off'i tuh) is the phylum of plants in which differentiated vegetative tissues and organs occur, but in which there is no differentiated vascular tissue. (G. moss plants)

Bryozoa (brī ō zō'uh) is a group of aquatic animals formerly more abundant than now. (G. moss animals)

Bubastis (byū bass'tiss) is the cat-goddess of ancient Egypt.

Bud is a stem tip with a cluster of partly developed leaves.

Buffering is the balancing of acids and alkalis in a solution by groups of chemical substances which may neutralize an excess of either acid or alkali.

Bulbo-urethral (bul'bō yū ree'-thrull) refers to a gland attached to the urethra of certain male animals.

Calorie is a measure of heat energy equal to the amount used in raising a kilogram of water from 14.5 to 15.5 degrees Centigrade. A calorie, written with a small c, is a thousandth of a Calorie. (L. heat)

Calyx (kā'lix) is the lowest whorl of leaves on a flower. (G. husk)

Cambium is a cylinder of actively dividing cells in the stems and roots of certain plants, producing other cells such as vascular and cork cells. (L. changing)

Cambrian (kam'bri un) is the first period of the Paleozoic Era.

Canine (kā'nīn) refers to the eye-teeth, so named for their doglike characteristics. (L. dog)

Capillary is a small vessel through which blood or lymph passes and through which substances diffuse into and out of the vascular fluid. (L. like a little hair)

Capsule is a covering of all or part of an organism. (L. little box)

Carbohydrate is a type of organic compound composed of carbon, hydrogen, and oxygen with the latter two substances usually in the proportion of 2:1.

Carboxypeptidase (kar box i pep'-ti dās) is an enzyme which catalyzes the breakdown of certain peptide linkages in some polypeptides and dipeptides.

Cardiac refers to the heart. (G. heart)

Cardinal means principal, as the cardinal veins of certain vertebrates and vertebrate embryos. (L. important)

Carnivora (kar ni'vō ruh) is the order of Mammalia with small incisor teeth and large, fanglike canines. (L. meat-eating)

Carnivorous (kar ni'vō russ) refers to meat-eating.

Carotid (kuh rot'id) refers to arteries supplying the most anterior parts of the body. (The name comes from the Greek for stupor, because pressure on these arteries was supposed to produce stupor.)

Carpal is a bone of the wrist. (G. wrist)

Cartilage (kar'ti lij) is a flexible, solid, skeletal secretion enclosing the cells which secrete it. (L. gristle)

Casein (kā'sē in) is the protein found in milk. (L. cheese)

Catalysis (ka ta'li sis) is the alteration of the rate of a chemical reaction by some substance which does not become an integral part of the products of the reaction.

Catalyst is a substance which alters the rate of a chemical reaction without entering into the products of the reaction.

Caterpillar is the larva of a lepidopteran.

Cecum (see'kum) is a blind pouch opening from another organ, as the cecum which is connected to the beginning of the human large intestine.

Celiac (see'li ak) refers to an artery which supplies organs in the anterior part of the abdomen. (G. cavity)

Cell is a structural unit of protoplasm bounded by a membrane and containing nuclear and cytoplasmic materials.

Cell body is the central portion of a nerve cell from which its branches arise.

Cell membrane is the living boundary of a cell.

Cell theory is the idea that all living organisms are composed of cells and cell products.

Cellulose is a complex carbohydrate used by many plant cells in their cell walls.

Cell wall is a coat secreted by a cell about itself outside of the cell membrane.

Celom (see'lom) is the body cavity of an animal, enclosed in mesodermal tissue. (G. cavity)

Cenozoic (see'nō zō'ik) is the fifth of the geologic eras. (G. recent animals)

Centaur is the mythological part horse part man of ancient Greece.

Centimeter is a hundredth of a meter, or about two fifths of an inch.

Centriole is a body within a cell which acts as a center for the spindle and asters involved in cell division.

Centromere is the part of a chromonema to which a spindle fiber may attach. (G. central part)

Centrosome (sen'trō sōm) is a body within a cell which houses one or more centrioles. (G. central body)

Centrum is the main body of a vertebra.

Cephalochordata (sef'uh lō kor-dā'tuh) is the subphylum of Chordata with the notochord running nearly the length of the body, but without a vertebral column. (G. head chord)

Cephalopoda (sef uh lop'ō duh) is the class of Mollusca with the foot divided into many arms. (G. head foot)

Cephalothorax (sef uh lō thō'rax) is the fused head and thorax of some arthropods.

Ceratiomyxa (se rā'ti ō mik'suh) is a genus of Myxomycetes.

Cercaria (ser kā'ri uh) is a larval stage of a fluke. (G. tailed)

Cerebellospinal tract is a nerve tract carrying impulses from the cerebellum to the spinal cord.

Cerebellum (sār uh bell'lum) is the part of the brain dorsal and anterior to the medulla oblongata and behind the cerebrum. (L. little brain)

Cerebrospinal fluid (sār'eh brō-spī'null) is the lymphlike liquid in the central cavity of the brain and spinal cord.

Cerebrospinal tract is a nerve tract carrying impulses from the cerebrum to the spinal cord.

Cerebrum (sār'eh brum) is the large, anterior part of the brain. (L. brain)

Cervix (ser'vix) is the narrowed portion of the uterus at its posterior end. (L. neck)

Cestoda (ses tō'duh) is the class of Platyhelminthes with no cellular epidermis and no digestive tract.

Chaparral (chap uh ral') is a dense thicket of evergreen oak trees.

Chelicera (kel i'se ruh) is one of the anteriormost pair of appendages in an arachnid. (G. claw horn)

Chestnut blight is a disease of chestnut trees caused by an ascomycete.

Chiasma (kī az'muh) is a crossing of fibers, as the optic chiasma. (G. X-mark)

Chilopoda (kī lop'ō duh) is the class of Arthropoda many of whose segments have a pair of six-jointed appendages. (G. lip feet)

Chitin (kī'tin) is a nitrogen-containing carbohydrate secreted on the surface of certain organisms such as arthropods.

Chlamydomonas (klam'i dō mō'-nuss) is a genus of Chlorophyceae. (G. cloaked unit)

Chloromonadophyta (klō'rō mō'-na doff'i tuh) is the phylum proposed to include algae with yellow and green pigments and two flagella. (G. green unit plants)

Chloromycetin (klō'rō mī see'tin) is an antibiotic manufactured by one of the Actinomycetales.

Chlorophyceae (klō'rō fī'see ee) is the class of Algae having chlorophyll and some carotene pigments, but no others. (G. green algae)

Chlorophyll (klō'rō fill) is one of a group of substances found in certain plant cells, which act as a catalyst in photosynthesis. (G. green leaf)

Chlorophyta (klō'roff'i tuh) is the phylum proposed to include green-colored algae such as the Volvocine Series. (G. green plants)

Cholecystokinin (kō'le sis'tō kī'-nin) is the hormone, secreted by the duodenum, which stimulates the contraction of the gall bladder, forcing bile into the duodenum. (G. gall bladder mover)

Cholesterol (kō les'ter ol) is a lipoid substance secreted by an organ such as the liver or gall bladder.

Choline (kō'lin) is a water-soluble vitamin apparently involved in the metabolism of food products.

Chondroclast (kon'drō klast) is a cell which dissolves cartilage. (G. cartilage breaker)

Chordata (kōr dā'tuh) is the phylum of animals with a notochord at some stage of life, and a dorsal tubular central nervous system. (G. having a chord)

Choroid (kō'roid) refers to the middle coat of the eyeball, heavily pigmented so that it appears black.

Chromatin (krō'ma tin) is the substance found in the nuclear granules which are deeply colored by certain stains. It is thought that these granules carry heritable units. (G. colored)

Chromonema (krō mō nee'muh) is a thread carrying chromatin granules.

Chromophobe (krō'mō fōb) refers to cells which do not take stain well, as the chromophobe cells in the pituitary body. (G. fearing color)

Chromosome (krō'mō sōm) is a condensed chromonema during cell division.

Chrysophyceae (krī sō fī'see ee) is the class of Algae having chlorophyll and more carotene than the Chlorophyceae. (G. golden seaweed)

Chrysophyta (krī soff'i tuh) is the phylum proposed to include Chrysophyceae with brown chloroplasts and no capsule. (G. golden plants)

Chymotrypsin (kī'mō trip'sin) is an enzyme which catalyzes the breakdown of certain peptide linkages in proteins and protein products.

Chymotrypsinogen (kī mō trip sin'-ō jen) is the inactive form of chymotrypsin, which is secreted by the pancreas and activated in the small intestine.

Ciliary body (sil'i ā ri) is the thickened attachment of the lens ligament to the choroid coat of the eye.

Ciliary ganglion (sil'i ā ri gang'-gli un) is an autonomic ganglion through which pass impulses that bring about the constriction of the pupil of the eye.

Ciliata (sil'i ā'tuh) is the class of Protozoa which move by means of cilia.

Cilium (sil'i um) is a whiplike cytoplasmic process extending from a cell and capable of beating in rhythmic fashion. The plural is "cilia."

Circulatory refers to a system involved in transportation of substances throughout an organism; sometimes it is called "vascular." (L. going around)

Circumpharyngeal (sur'kum fahrin'jē ul) means around the pharynx, as the circumpharyngeal nerve trunks of an earthworm.

Cirrus (sir'rus) is a slender appendage.

Class is a taxonomic group of organisms with greater similarity than a phylum or subphylum but less than an order.

Clitellum is a swollen glandular band on such an animal as the earthworm.

Clitoris (klī'tō riss) is a small structure in certain female animals comparable in origin to the penis of a male.

Cnidocil (nī'dō sill) is the trigger associated with a nematocyst.

Coccus (kok'kuss) is a spherical bacterium. The plural is "cocci" (kok'si). (G. berry)

Cochlea (kōk'le uh) is the coiled portion of the inner ear, in which the organ of hearing occurs.

Cocoon is the woven fibrous cover surrounding developmental stages of certain arthropods.

Coelenterata (see len te rā'tuh) is a phylum of radial metazoa with gastrovascular cavities. (G. hollow intestines)

Coenzyme (kō en'zīm) is a substance which is involved in the transfer of hydrogen atoms during oxidation reactions in cells.

Coleochaete (kō'lee ō kee'te) is a genus of Chlorophyceae.

Coleoptera (kō lee op'te ruh) is an order of Insecta with stiff, hardened forewings.

Collecting tubule is a channel into which lead several kidney tubules.

Colloid is a mixture of substances in which some particles are composed of more than one molecule each and yet are invisible even with a light microscope.

Colon (kō'lun) is a portion of the large intestine, or all of it.

Colony is a group of individuals of the same species associated together. (L. settlement)

Commensalism (kom men'sul izum) is an association of two or more species of organisms in which one or more associates are benefited and one or more associates are neither benefited nor harmed. (L. table together)

Companion cell is a phloem cell adjacent to a sieve tube; unlike the sieve tube, the companion cell retains its nucleus.

Compound eye is a cluster of pyramidal eyes in some arthropods.

Concha is the part of the outer ear projecting from the head.

Condylarth (kon'di larth) is an extinct type of mammal.

Conidium (kō ni'dē um) is a fungus spore occurring at the tip of a hypha.

Conifer (kō'ni fur) is a gymnosperm which may bear cones, or strobili. (L. cone bearer)

Conjugation is the temporary cytoplasmic union associated with sexual reproduction in such animals as paramecia. (L. yoking with)

Conjunctiva (kon junk tī'vuh) is the thin, transparent epidermis over the front of an eye.

Conjunctive (kon junk'tiv) refers to a type of nerve cell which carries impulses between nerve cells. (L. joining together)

Connective refers to a tissue in animals composed of fibers, cartilage, or bone. (L. binding together)

Conservation is the saving from unwise destruction and the increase where possible of natural resources. (L. keeping together)

Contractile vacuole (kon trak'til vak'yū ōl) is a cytoplasmic body in which water accumulates and is periodically expelled.

Control is the term applied to those organisms or objects in an experiment which do not undergo all of the experimental alterations of the other organisms or objects, and with which the latter group are compared at the close of the experiment.

Conus arteriosus (kō'nuss ar tē'ri-ō'suss) is a heart chamber in such animals as a fish.

Convoluted (kon'vō lū'ted) means twisted or contorted.

Copepod (kō'peh pod) is a type of crustacean. (G. oar foot)

Coral is a type of coelenterate, or the skeletal support secreted by the coelenterate.

Cork is a layer of thick-walled cells in the outer part of the cortex of some plant stems and roots.

Cork cambium is the layer of cells which undergo repeated division, forming cork cells.

Cornea is the transparent front part of the sclera of the eye.

Corolla (kō rol'luh) is a row of flower leaves, often colored, below the reproductive parts and above the calyx. It is that part of the flower which is also called the petals. (L. little crown)

Coronary refers to the blood vessels in the wall of the heart.

Corpus allatum (kor'pus al lā'tum) is an endocrine organ found in such animals as grasshoppers.

Corpus cavernosum (kor'pus cavur nō'sum) is one of two masses of blood sinuses in a penis.

Corpuscle is a small body, such as a blood cell. (L. little body)

Corpus luteum (kor'pus lū'te um) is the body formed by the healing of a broken ovarian follicle. (L. yellow body)

Corpus spongiosum (kor'pus spunji ō'sum) is a single mass of blood sinuses in a penis. (L. spongy body)

Cortex is the outer portion of a rounded object, as the cortex of a kidney, or brain, or tree stem. (L. rind)

Corticosterone (kor'ti kos'te rōn) is a group of steroids produced in the adrenal cortex.

Corticotrophin (kor'ti kō trō'fin) is the pituitary hormone which stimulates corticosterone secretion by the adrenal cortex.

Cotyledon (kot i lē'dun) is a temporary food-storing leaf of an embryo sporophyte. (G. socket or cup)

Cotylosaur (kot'i lō sawr') is an extinct type of reptile.

Cover cell is a cell at the outer end of an archegonium, which closes the neck canal.

Cranium is the portion of the skull enclosing the brain.

Creatine (krē'uh tin) is an organic compound found in muscles.

Creatinine (krē a'tin in) is a dehydrated form of creatine.

Crepidula (kre pid'yū luh) is a genus of marine Gastropoda. (L. small sandal)

Cretaceous (krē tā'shuss) is the third period of the Mesozoic Era.

Cricoid (krī'koid) refers to the ringlike cartilage at the posterior end of the larynx. (G. ringlike)

Crinoidea (krī noi'dē uh) is the class of Echinodermata having branched arms. (G. lilylike)

Crossbill is a bird with the ends of the bill crossed when closed.

Crossopterygii (kraw'sop tuh rid'ji ī) is an order of Pisces with lobelike fins. (G. fringed fins)

Crustacea (krus tā'shuh) is a class of Arthropoda having two pairs of antennae. (L. with a shell)

Cutin (kyū'tin) is a waxy substance found on the outer surface of the epidermis of leaves. (L. skin)

Cyanophyceae (sī'an ō fī'see ee) is the class of Algae having both green and blue pigments. (G. blue seaweed)

Cyclostomata (sī'klō stō'mah tuh) is the class of Vertebrata without jaws.

Cyst is a rounded chamber, such as the dormant stage of certain protozoa. (G. bladder)

Cystic (sis'tik) refers to a bladder, as the cystic duct coming from the gall bladder. (G. bladder)

Cysticercus (sis ti sur'kuss) is the vesicle containing one or more tapeworm larvae.

Cystoid (sis'toid) is an extinct type of echinoderm.

Cytochrome (sī'tō krōm) is a type of iron-containing compound involved in the transfer of hydrogen atoms during oxidation processes in cells. (G. cell color)

Cytoplasm (sī'tō plazm) is that part of a cell surrounding the nucleus and within the cell membrane; in it most of the metabolic changes occur.

D-alanine (dē al'uh nin) is an amino acid.

Deciduous (dē sid'yū uss) refers to plants which shed all their leaves at one season of the year, and get new ones at another season. (L. falling off)

Dehydroandrosterone (dē hī'drō-an dros'te rōn) is a hormone secreted in a testis.

Dehydrogenase (dē hī'drō jen ās or dē hī droj'en ās) is an enzyme which catalyzes the transfer of hydrogen from some substance to a coenzyme.

Dendrite is a branch of a nerve cell which carries impulses to the cell body. (G. tree)

Dentine (den'tin) is the bonelike layer of a tooth.

Depressor refers to a muscle which lowers a structure.

Dermis is the inner portion of the skin, composed of connective tissue. (G. skin)

Desoxycorticosterone (dess ok'si-kōr ti kos'te rōn) is a group of steroids produced in the adrenal cortex.

Devonian is the fourth period of the Paleozoic Era. (From Devon)

Diabetes mellitus (dī'uh bē'tēz mel lī'tus) is the disease caused by insulin deficiency. (G. going through, L. sweet)

Diaphragm (dī'uh fram) is a muscular partition between the chest and the abdomen of mammals. (G. wall across)

Diastole (dī ass'tō li) is the relaxation of the muscles of a heart chamber. (G. to open)

Diatom (dī'uh tom) is an alga of the class Chrysophyceae. (G. two atoms)

Dicot is a shortened form of Dicotyledoneae.

Dicotyledoneae (dī kot'i lē dō'nee-ee) is the group of Angiospermae in which seeds have two cotyledons each.

Diencephalon (dī en sef'uh lon) is the part of the brain anterior to the midbrain and posterior and ventral to the cerebrum. (G. through the brain)

Diffusion is the penetration of molecules of a substance through a medium. (L. pouring apart)

Digastric (dī gas'trik) refers to a muscle with two bellies in series, as the muscle which lowers the mandible in the human. (G. two bellies)

Digestion is the transformation of food substances into a form in which they may be absorbed by the body. (L. carrying apart)

Di-iodo-tyrosine (dī'ī ō'dō tī'rō sin) is a substance which enters into the synthesis of the thyroid hormone.

Dinichthys (dī nik'thiss) is a genus of extinct fish. (G. terrible fish)

Dinosaur (dī'nō sawr) is an extinct kind of reptile. (G. terrible lizard)

Dipeptide (dī pep'tid) is a type of chemical compound formed by combining two amino acids.

Dipleurula (dī plūr'yū luh) is a type of larva found in certain echinoderms and chordates. (G. two little ribs)

Diplodocus (di plod'ō kuss) is a genus of dinosaurs. (G. double beam)

Diploid refers to a nucleus in which genes and chromonemata occur in pairs. (G. doubled)

Diplopoda (di plop'ō duh) is a class of Arthropoda in which many body segments are fused in pairs. (G. doubled feet)

Diptera (dip'te ruh) is the order of Insecta in which the hind wings are reduced to stalked knobs. (G. two wings)

Distal (dis'tul) refers to "away from," as the distal convoluted tubule, the part of a kidney tubule away from the Bowman's capsule. (From "toward the distance")

Dodder is a parasitic dicot.

Dodo (dō'dō) is a recently extinct bird. (Portuguese: foolish)

Dominant refers to a gene whose version of the character is expressed even in the presence of a different gene for the character.

Dorsal refers to the upper or back part of an animal. (L. back)

Dorsoventrality (dōr'sō ven tral'-i tee) [ZOOLOGY] **dorsiventrality** [BOTANY] is the differentiation of a dorsal and a ventral part of an organism.

Double sugar is a carbohydrate with the formula $C_{12}H_{22}O_{11}$.

Drosophila (drō sof'i luh) is the genus name of the fruit fly, a dipteran. (G. fond of dew)

Dryopithecus (drī'ō pi thē'kuss) is a genus of fossil Primata. (G. tree ape)

Dugesia (dū jess'i uh) is a genus of Turbellaria. (Named for Dugès)

Duodenum (dū ō dē'num) is the anterior portion of the small intestine. (L. twelve; in the human, the first twelve inches of the small intestine was included in the duodenum.)

Echinodermata (ē kī nō dur'mah-tuh) is the phylum of radial animals with parts in fives or multiples of five. (G. spiny skinned)

Echinoidea (ek in oi'dē uh) is the class of Echinodermata enclosed in a rigid skeletal box.

Ecology is the study of the relations of organisms and their environments. (G. study of dwelling places)

Ectocarpus (ek tō kar′puss) is a genus of Phaeophyceae. (G. outer fruit)

Ectoderm is the upper or outer layer of an early embryo; it gives rise to epidermis and nervous system in metazoa. (G. outer skin)

Ectoplasm is the viscous outer portion of cytoplasm in certain cells as that of an ameba. (G. outer form)

Egg is the female reproductive cell.

Ejaculation is discharge or emission, as of sperm cells.

Elasmobranchii (ē laz′mō bran′ki ī) is the class of Vertebrata with jaws and with a cartilage skeleton but no bone. (G. plate gills)

Elephantiasis (el′e fan tī′uh sis) is a swollen condition of a part of the body resulting from infection with filarias.

Elimination is the disposal of a substance, as from the digestive tract, which is not a product of cellular synthesis, and has not taken part in metabolism.

Embryo is a developing individual. (G. inner swelling)

Embryology (em′bri ol′ō ji) is the study of the development of organisms. (G. inner swelling study)

Emulsification is the separation or division of fat masses in a mixture into smaller droplets. (L. make from milk)

Enamel is the hard outer layer of a tooth.

Endameba (en′da mē′buh) is a genus of parasitic Sarcodina.

Endoceras (en dos′uh russ) is a genus of fossil Cephalopoda.

Endocrine refers to secretions (hormones) transported in the circulatory system from their tissues of origin to other tissues in which they stimulate metabolic changes. (G. inner separation)

Endoderm is the lower or inner layer of an early embryo; it gives rise to the lining of the digestive tract and its outgrowths. (G. inner skin)

Endodermis is a cylinder of cells outside of a vascular bundle or group of bundles in some plants. (G. inner skin)

Endolymph is the liquid within the membranous part of the inner ear. (L. inner water)

Endomixis (en dō mik′sis) is a type of sexual reproduction involving only one individual but the fusion of two nuclei, found in such animals as *Paramecium*. (G. inner mingling)

Endoplasm is the fluid inner portion of cytoplasm in certain cells as that of an ameba. (G. inner form)

Endosperm is the triploid tissue formed in the reproduction of angiosperms. (G. inner seed)

Enterocrinin (en′te rō krī′nin or en′te rok′ri nin) is the hormone, secreted by the small intestine, which increases the rate of secretion of intestinal glands. (G. intestinal separation)

Enterogastrone (en′te rō gas′trōn) is a hormone secreted by the intestine which inhibits the motor and secretory actions of the stomach. (G. intestinal stomach substance)

Enterokinase (en′te rō ki′nās or en′te rō ki nās′) is a substance, secreted by the small intestine, which changes trypsinogen to trypsin. (G. intestinal mover)

Enzyme is an organic catalyst secreted by a cell and used in the cell or in a cavity to which the cell has access. (G. inner leaven)

Eocene (ē′ō seen) is the first period of the Cenozoic Era. (G. dawn of the recent)

Ephemerida (e fe me′ri duh) is an order of Insecta with membranous wings and vestigial mouth parts in the adult. (G. for a day)

Epidermis is the outer portion of the skin, composed of epithelial cells. (G. on the skin)

Epithelial (e pi thē′li ul) refers to a tissue which covers a surface in or on an organism.

Equilibrium is the sense of balance. (L. equal balance)

Era is one of the five great divisions of geologic time.

Esophagus (ē sof′uh gus) is the part of the digestive tract which carries food to the stomach. (G. food carrier)

Estradiol (es′tra dī′ol) is a hormone secreted in an ovary. (L. orgasm, and G. double oil)

Estrone (es′trōn) is a hormone secreted in an ovary. (L. orgasm substance)

Ethmoid refers to the skull bone partly bounding the nose cavity.

Eudorina (yū dō rī′nuh) is a genus of Chlorophyceae. (Named for Eudora)

Eugenics (yū je′nix) is the study of hereditary improvement of humans. (G. well born)

Euglena (yū glē′nuh) is a genus of Chlorophyceae.

Euglenophyta (yū glē nof′i tuh) is the phylum proposed to include such algae as *Euglena*. (G. bright-eyed plants)

Eumycetes (yū mī see′teez) is the phylum proposed to include fungi other than Schizomycetes.

Eurypterid (yū rip′te rid) is an extinct type of arthropod.

Eustachian tube (yū stā′ki an) is the passageway connecting the middle ear cavity and the pharynx. (Named for Eustachio)

Evolution is the theory that different species of organisms are genetically related to each other. (L. unrolling)

Excretion is the preparation for disposal and the disposal from an organism of waste products of its metabolism. (L. separation out)

Exoskeleton (ek′sō ske′le tun) is a hard structure secreted on the outside of an organism. (G. outer, dried up)

Extensor (ex ten′sōr) refers to a muscle which straightens a joint. (L. stretcher)

Eyespot is a light-sensitive spot in an organism.

Factor is a term used by Mendel for a hereditary unit. (L. maker)

Falsetto is a high-pitched voice produced by the vibration of the free edges of the vocal membranes without the vibration of the remainder of the membranes.

Family is a taxonomic group of organisms with greater similarity than an order, but less than a genus.

Fat is a type of organic compounds of carbon, hydrogen, and oxygen in which the proportion of hydrogen to oxygen is much greater than 2:1; it involves union of fatty acids with alcohols.

Fatty acid is an organic compound composed of carbon and hydrogen with an acid group (COOH) attached.

Fauna is the totality of animals in an area. (From Fauna, a fertility goddess)

Femur (fē′mur) is the bone of the upper leg.

Fibril (fī′bril) is a small fiber which is a component of a larger fiber.

Fibrinogen (fī brin′o jen) is a protein in blood plasma which may be involved in the formation of a clot. (L. fiber producer)

Fibroblast (fī′brō blast) is a connective tissue cell which deposits a fiber. (G. fiber germ)

Fibula (fi′byū luh) is the bone of the leg on the little toe side.

Filament is a threadlike structure.

Filaria (fi lā′ri uh) is a parasitic roundworm found in lymph vessels. (L. thread)

Fission is a method of reproduction in which an organism divides into two or more equal or nearly equal organisms.

Flagellata (fla je lā′tuh) is the class of Protozoa which move by means of one or more flagella. (L. whips)

Flagellum (fla jel′lum) is a long, motile, whiplike extension of cytoplasm from a cell. (L. little whip)

Flame cell is an excretory cell in such animals as flatworms.

Flexor refers to a muscle which bends a joint.

Flora is the totality of plants in an area.

Flower is a cluster of reproductive structures and their associated parts in an angiosperm.

Folic acid is a water-soluble vitamin involved in maintenance of a normal supply of blood corpuscles.

Follicle is a cavity surrounded by epithelial cells, as a follicle in the thyroid gland or ovary. (L. little bag)

Foramen (fō rā′men) is a hole or opening in a structure. The plural is "foramina" (fō ra′mi nuh)

Foramen of Monro is an opening from the third ventricle of the brain into either the first or the second ventricle.

Foraminifera (fō′ra mi ni′fe ruh) is a group of shelled Sarcodina.

Foregut is the anterior floored part of an embryonic digestive tract.

Fossil is the relic of an organism long dead. (L. dug out of the earth)

Freckle is a pigmented spot in the skin.

Frenulum (fren′yū lum) is the fold of tissue connecting the tongue and the floor of the mouth. (L. small bridle)

Frequency is the rate at which waves of vibration pass a given point.

Frontal refers to the skull bone supporting the forehead.

Frontal association area is that part of the cerebral cortex in front of the premotor area.

Fructose (fruk′tōs) is a single sugar found in many fruits.

Funaria (fyū nā′ri uh) is a genus of mosses.

Fundamental tone is the one of a group of simultaneous tones produced by an instrument which has the lowest frequency, and of which the other tonal frequencies are multiples.

Fundus is the enlarged part of a hollow organ, such as the fundus of the stomach or of the urinary bladder. (L. base)

Fungi (fun′jī) is the subphylum of Thallophyta in which the plants do not have chlorophyll. (L. mushrooms)

Galactose (ga lak′tōs) is a single sugar produced in the breakdown of lactose. (G. from milk)

Gall bladder (gawl bla′dur) is a bile reservoir attached to the liver.

Gallstone is a solid body formed in the gall bladder.

Gamete (ga′mēt) is a reproductive cell, such as an egg or sperm, which normally develops into a new individual only if it unites with another gamete. (G. wife)

Gametophyte (ga mē′tō fīt) is a plant whose nuclei are haploid.

Gamma globulin (gam′muh glob′yū lin) is a type of blood protein involved in making the body immune to certain diseases.

Ganesha (ga nā′shuh) is the elephant-headed god of ancient India.

Ganglion (gang′glē on) is a group of nerve cells constituting a structural unit. (G. knot)

Gastric refers to the stomach.

Gastric mill is a grinding apparatus in the stomach of such an animal as a crayfish.

Gastrin is a hormone secreted by the stomach which stimulates hydrochloric acid secretion in the stomach.

Gastrodermis (gas trō dur′miss) is the lining of the digestive tract of an animal. (G. stomach skin)

Gastropoda (gas trop′ō duh) is the class of Mollusca with a broad, flat foot and a spiral, one-piece shell or no shell.

Gastrovascular cavity (gas trō vas′kyū lur ca′vi ti) is a cavity in a coelenterate or flatworm in which food is digested and distributed to the various parts of the body.

Gastrula (gas′trū luh) is a stage in embryonic development in which ectoderm and endoderm constitute the two layers present.

Gene is a hereditary unit.

Generative cell is the cell of a pollen grain which gives rise to sperm nuclei.

Genetics is the study of the transmission of heritable characteristics of organisms from generation to generation. (G. birth)

Genotype is the kind of genes an organism carries.

Genus (jē′nus) is a taxonomic group of organisms with greater similarity than a family, but less than a species. The plural is "genera" (jen′uh ruh). (L. race)

Geology is the study of the earth.

Geriatrics (je ri at′rix) is the study of the health of old people. (G. medicine of old age)

Germ plasm is the group of potentially reproductive cells in an organism.

Gila monster (hē′luh mon′stur) is a poisonous lizard.

Gill (gil) is a thin plate or filament of tissue, often used as a respiratory organ.

Girdle is a ring of bones supporting the skeleton of the appendages.

Gizzard (giz′zurd) is a part of a digestive tract in which food is ground.

Gland is a cell or group of cells which secrete. (L. acorn)

Glass snake is a lizard adept at autotomy.

Globulin (glob′yū lin) is a type of protein insoluble in pure water, but soluble in solutions of certain salts.

Glochidium (glō ki′di um) is a young stage in the development of fresh-water clams.

Glomerulus (glō mār′yu lus) is a tuft of blood capillary loops in a Bowman's capsule of the kidney. (L. little thicket)

Glossopharyngeal (glos′sō fa rin′jē-ul) refers to the ninth pair of cranial nerves, which supply parts of the tongue and pharynx. (G. tongue, pharynx)

Glowworm is the larva of a firefly.

Glucose (glū′kōs) is a simple sugar. (G. sweet)

Glycerol (gli′sur ōl) is an organic compound, a triple alcohol with the formula CH₂OH–CHOH–CH₂OH. (G. sweet oil)

Glycogen (glī′kō jen) is a carbohydrate synthesized by organisms from sugars. It is a form of starch. (G. sweet producer)

Gnetales (nē tā′leez) is a group of genera of Gymnospermae.

Goiter is an enlargement of the thyroid gland such as that resulting from a lack of iodine compounds in the diet.

Golgi body (gōl′ji) is a mass or network in a cell which is the center of certain cell secretions. (Named for Golgi)

Gonad (gō′nad) is a reproductive organ, as an ovary or testis. (G. seed)

Gonadotrophin (gō′na dō trō′fin) is a pituitary hormone which stimulates gonads. (G. seed nourisher)

Gonium (gō′ni um) is a genus of Chlorophyceae.

Grain is a type of fruit in which the ovary wall fuses to the seed coat.

Gramicidin (gra mi sī′din) is an antibiotic manufactured by bacteria.

Graptolite (grap′tō līt) is an extinct type of animal.

Gray matter is the portion of the central nervous system in which nerve cell bodies occur. In life it is gray.

Green gland is an excretory organ in such an animal as a crayfish.

Ground substance is a secretion found among the cells and fibers of connective tissue — in the background.

Growth hormone is a secretion of the pituitary gland which regulates the growth of long bones.

Growth ring is one of a concentric series of visibly differentiated tissue in the xylem of certain plant stems and roots.

Guard cell is a specialized cell bordering a stoma.

Gullet is a passageway through which food enters an organism.

Gymnospermae (jim′nō spur′mi) is the subphylum of Spermatophyta in which seeds are exposed during development. (G. naked seed)

Hammer is the bone of the middle ear which is attached to the eardrum.

Haploid (hap′loid) refers to a nucleus in which genes and chromonemata occur singly, not in pairs. (G. single)

Haustorium (hawss tō′ri um) is a parasitic plant structure which penetrates the tissue of another plant. (L. that which draws)

Heart is the pulsatile organ which pumps blood through blood vessels.

Heartwood is xylem which has lost the ability to conduct water readily.

Hemicellulose (he mi sel′yū lōs) is a complex carbohydrate used by many plant cells in their cell walls.

Hemichordata (he mi kōr dā′tuh) is the subphylum of Chordata with the notochord in the anterior part of the body only. (G. half chord)

Hemiptera (he mip′te ruh) is an order of Insecta with piercing and sucking mouth parts, and with overlapping forewings thickened at the base. (G. half wings)

Hemoglobin (hē′mō glō′bin) is a protein found in red blood corpuscles. (G. blood and L. balls)

Hemophilia (hē′mō fi′lē uh) is a condition in which blood does not clot normally. (G. fond of blood)

Hepatic (hē pa′tik) refers to the liver. (G. liver)

Hepatic portal vein is a vein carrying blood from the spleen and the abdominal part of the digestive tract to the liver.

Hermaphroditism (hur maf′rō di-tizm) is the possession by an individual organism of both male and female reproductive organs. (Named for Hermes and Aphrodite, Greek god and goddess)

Hermit crab is a crustacean which inhabits castoff snail shells.

Heterozygous (he te rō zī′gus) refers to an organism having two unlike genes for a certain character. (G. other mate)

Hibernation is the reduction of metabolism in an organism during a winter dormant period. (L. to spend the winter)

Hindgut (hīnd′gut) is the posterior floored part of an embryonic digestive tract.

Hippuric acid (hip yū′rik) is an excretory product derived from the breakdown of amino acids. (G. horse urine)

Hirudin (hi′rū din or hi rū′din) is a secretion of a leech which prevents blood from clotting. (L. leech)

Hirudinea (hi rū di′nē uh) is the class of Annelida which have no setae; it includes the leeches. (L. leeches)

Hirudo (hi′rū dō or hi rū′dō) is a genus of Hirudinea, the medicinal leech. (L. leech)

Histamine (hiss'ta min or hiss'ta-mēn) is a secretion which produces powerful metabolic effects, such as strong contractions of visceral muscle. (G. tissue, and amine)

Holophytic (hol'ō fi'tik) refers to the means of obtaining food by photosynthesis.

Holothurioidea (hol'ō thū'ri oi'dē-uh) is the class of Echinodermata with a soft, fleshy body having very few skeletal plates. (G. whole impetuous, referring to the sudden outrush of organs at evisceration)

Holozoic (hol'ō zō'ik) refers to the means of obtaining food by eating other organisms.

Homoptera (hō mop'te ruh) is an order of Insecta with piercing and sucking mouth parts and sloping, membranous wings of an even thickness.

Homozygous (hō mō zī'guss) refers to an organism having two like genes for a certain character. (G. same mate)

Hookworm is a parasitic roundworm found in human intestines.

Hormone (hōr'mōn) is a substance secreted by an endocrine gland and transported to another location, where it stimulates some phase of metabolism. (G. arouser)

Humerus (hyū'me russ) is the bone of the upper arm.

Hyaline (hī'uh lin) refers to a type of cartilage which is semitransparent, and which does not contain many fibers. (G. glassy)

Hydrolysis (hī drol'i sis) is the chemical combination of water with another substance, resulting in the breakdown of the other substance. (G. releasing by water)

Hydrosphere is the water on the surface of the earth.

Hymen is a membrane partially closing the vagina.

Hymenoptera (hī'me nop'te ruh) is an order of Insecta having membranous wings with reduced venation, the hindwing smaller than the forewing. (G. membrane wings)

Hyoid refers to the bone at the base of the tongue. (G. upsilon-shaped)

Hypermastigina (hī'pur mas ti'ji-nuh) is a group of flagellates symbiotic in certain insects.

Hypha is a strand of a fungus.

Hypnotoxin (hip'nō tok'sin) is the poison carried by a nematocyst. (G. sleep poison)

Hypocotyl (hī'pō kot'il) is the part of an embryo sporophyte which may form the base of a stem. (G. under the cup)

Hypoglossal (hī'pō glos'sul) refers to the twelfth pair of cranial nerves, which supply some of the tongue muscles. (G. under the tongue)

Hypothalamus (hī'pō tha'luh muss) refers to the ventralmost part of the diencephalon in the brain. (G. under chamber)

Ichthyosaur (ik'thi ō sawr') is a type of extinct aquatic reptile. (G. fish lizard)

Ileum (il'ē um) is the posterior portion of the small intestine. (L. twisting intestine)

Iliac (il'i ak) refers to the ilium.

Ilium (il'i um) is an anterior bone of the hip girdle. (L. flank)

Immunity (im myū'ni ti) is the ability to resist one or more diseases. (L. free, exempt)

Immunization (im myū ni zā'shun) is the bringing about of a state of immunity in an organism.

Incisor (in sī'zur) refers to the cutting teeth at the front of the mouth. (L. incutting)

Ink sac is a pigment-secreting organ found in many cephalopods.

Innominate (in nom'i nāt) refers to an artery branching from the aorta toward the anterior part of the body. (L. unnamed)

Inositol (in o'si tol) is a substance which seems to be involved in food metabolism as part of the Vitamin B complex.

Insecta is a class of Arthropoda having only three pairs of walking legs.

Insectivora (in sek ti'vō ruh) is an order of flat-footed, sharp-nosed Mammalia with incisor and canine teeth much alike. (L. insect-eating)

Insulin is the hormone secreted by the islands of Langerhans in the pancreas. (L. island substance)

Integument is the covering or skin of an organism or part of an organism. (L. covering on)

Intercostal (in'tur kos'tul) means between ribs.

Interneship is a period of professional practice under the guidance of experienced practitioners in such fields as medicine.

Internode is a portion of a stem between nodes.

Interphase is the stage of a cell in which cell division is not in progress.

Intersegmental tract is a bundle of axons carrying impulses from one level to another in the spinal cord.

Interstitial (in'tur sti'shul) means standing between, as the interstitial cells among the tubules in a testis.

Intestine (in tes'tin) is the part of the digestive tract in which foods undergo much of their digestion and absorption.

Iodothyroglobulin (ī ō'dō thī'rō-glob'yū lin) is the hormone of the thyroid gland.

Ion is an electrified separated portion of a molecule in a solution. (G. going)

Iris is the front portion of the choroid coat, visible from the front through the cornea; its pigment gives the eye its characteristic color — blue, brown, etc. (G. halo)

Irish elk is a recently extinct ungulate.

Ischium (iss'kē um) is a posterior, dorsal bone of the hip girdle. (G. hip)

Island of Langerhans (lang'ur-hanz) is a patch of endocrine cells in the pancreas. (Named for Langerhans)

Isoagglutinin (ī sō ag glū'ti nin) is a substance in blood plasma involved in clumping blood cells together under certain conditions. (G. like, and L. glue)

Isoptera (ī sop'te ruh) is the order of Insecta with like wings in those which have wings, gradual metamorphosis, and a complex social organization. (G. like wings)

Jejunum (jē jū′num) is the middle portion of the small intestine. (L. empty)

Jellyfish is a coelenterate medusa.

Jugular (jug′yū lur) refers to veins draining the most anterior parts of the body. (L. neck)

Jurassic (jū ra′sik) is the second period of the Mesozoic Era. (Named for the Jura Mountains)

Kelp is a type of alga belonging to the Phaeophyceae.

Kidney is the excretory organ in which waste substances from the body are separated into an excretory duct.

Kinesthetic (ki nes the′tik) refers to the sense of the degree of contraction in a muscle or tension in a tendon or ligament. (G. sense of motion)

Komodo dragon (kō mō′dō) is a large lizard. (Named for the Komodo Island in the Malay Archipelago)

Kymograph (kī′mō graf) is an instrument used in recording certain metabolic actions such as muscle contraction and nerve conduction. (G. wave writer)

Labium (lā′bē um) means lip, as the underlip of an insect or the liplike fold of skin at the opening of the vagina.

Labyrinthodont (la bi rin′thō dont) is an extinct type of amphibians. (G. labyrinthine teeth)

Lacrimal refers to tears, as the lacrimal gland which secretes tears, or the lacrimal bone through which the tear duct passes.

Lactase is an enzyme which catalyzes the separation of lactose into glucose and galactose.

Lacteal refers to the lymph vessels in intestinal villi. (L. milky, from the appearance of the emulsified fat)

Lactic acid is an organic compound formed in the metabolic breakdown of carbohydrates.

Lactose is a double sugar found in milk. (L. milk)

Lanugo (la nū′gō) is a coating of hair found on the embryo of certain animals, as the human. (L. wool)

Laryngitis is an infection of the larynx.

Larynx is the passageway from the pharynx to the trachea in certain animals. In some, as the human, it is the organ of voice production.

Lateral refers to the side, or a part away from the central plane of the body. (L. side)

Lecithin (less′i thin) is a substance found in many animal cells, composed of fat, amino acid, and phosphate. (G. egg yolk)

Leishmania (lēsh mā′nē uh) is a genus of parasitic flagellates. (Named for Leishman)

Lens is a part of the eye attached to the choroid coat; it helps focus incoming light rays on the retina. (L. lentil)

Lepidoptera (le pi dop′te ruh) is an order of Insecta with scales on the wings; it includes butterflies and moths. (G. scale wings)

Levator (lē vā′tōr) refers to a muscle which raises a structure. (L. lifter)

Lichen (lī′ken) is a symbiotic association of certain fungi with certain algae.

Ligament is a bundle of elastic connective tissue fibers. (L. binder)

Linin (lī′nin) is the kind of fibers found in a cell nucleus. These fibers carry chromatin granules, and are often arranged in a network. (L. thread)

Linkage is the occurrence of two or more genes on one chromonema.

Lipase (li′pās) is an enzyme which catalyzes the breakdown of fats. (G. fat, and enzyme ending)

Lip cell is a thin-walled cell interrupting the annulus of a fern sporangium.

Lipoid (li′poid) refers to a fatty substance. (G. fatlike)

Liter (lē′tur) is a metric measure of volume equal to 1000 cubic centimeters.

Littoral refers to the zone of oceans near their shores. (L. shore)

Liver is a large digestive gland ventral to the digestive tract in the region of the stomach and duodenum.

Liverwort (li′vur wurt) is a bryophyte with dorsiventral symmetry.

Loop of Henle (hen′li) is a hairpin-shaped portion of a kidney tubule. (Named for Henle)

Lumbar refers to the dorsal body wall in the abdominal region.

Lumbricus (lum′bri kuss) is a genus of Annelida, the earthworm.

Lycopsida (lī cop′si duh) is the phylum or subphylum proposed to include such fern allies as Selaginella.

Lymph (limf) is the watery tissue fluid, containing white corpuscles, which drains from tissues through vessels into the blood stream. (L. water)

Lymph node is an organ attached to a lymph vessel which filters lymph and adds white blood corpuscles to the lymph stream.

Lysin (lī′sin) is a secretion of a white blood corpuscle which dissolves the walls of bacteria. (G. dissolver)

Macrophage (mak′rō fāj) is a cell which ingests and destroys solid bodies such as red blood corpuscles or bacteria. (G. big eater)

Malar (mā′lar) refers to the cheek, as the malar bone of the cheek.

Malpighian corpuscle (mal pi′gi an kōr′puh sul) is the Bowman's capsule of a kidney tubule plus its contained glomerulus. (Named for Malpighi)

Malpighian tubule (mal pi′gi an tū′byūl) is an excretory tube in an arthropod. (Named for Malpighi)

Maltase (mawl′tās) is an enzyme which catalyzes the separation of maltose into two molecules of glucose.

Maltose is a double sugar produced in the breakdown of certain starches.

Mammalia (ma mā′li uh) is the class of Vertebrata with bone, legs, and an exoskeleton with hairs. (L. having breasts)

Mammary refers to the breast.

Mandible is a jaw or part of a jaw, as the mouth part of an insect or the bone of the lower jaw of a human.

Mangrove is a plant association characteristic of subtropical mud-flats, and composed of various kinds of trees and shrubs; also a genus of plants in this association.

Manometer (ma nom′e tur) is a device for measuring fluid pressure. (G. slack measurer)

Mantle is the fleshy covering of a mollusc.

Mantle cavity is the space between the mantle and the rest of the body in a mollusc.

Marrow is the central cavity of a bone, largely composed of connective and vascular tissues.

Marsupialia (mar sū pi ā′li uh) is an order of mammals in which the young are carried in an external abdominal pouch of the mother during part of their early development. (G. pouched)

Mastigameba (mass′ti ga mē′buh) is a genus of Flagellata. (G. whip ameba)

Matrix (mā′trix) is a framework or substance in which bodies are imbedded.

Maxilla (mak sill′uh) is a jaw or part of a jaw, as a mouth part of an insect, or the bone of the human upper jaw.

Maxilliped (mak sill′i ped) is an arthropod appendage combining features of jaws and legs.

Medulla (me dull′uh) is the central portion of a structure such as the kidney.

Medulla oblongata is the portion of the brain nearest the spinal cord.

Medusa is the sexually reproductive form of certain coelenterates and the mythological snake-haired woman of ancient Greece whose head the coelenterate is taken to resemble.

Megagametocyte (me′guh ga mē′-tō sīt) is a sporozoon cell which may form a female gamete. (G. large wife cell)

Megasporangium is a sporangium producing megaspores. (G. large, and sporangium)

Megaspore is a spore which may develop into a female gametophyte. (G. large, and spore)

Meiosis (mī ō′sis) is the type of cell division in which the resulting cells each have half the chromonema complement of the original cell. (G. lessening)

Membrane is a sheet of protoplasm or protoplasmic secretion bounding part of a living organism.

Menopause (men′ō pawz) is the time of stopping of menstrual cycles in an organism. (G. month stop)

Menstrual cycle is the series of changes in the ovary and uterus involving hormonal sequences and the preparation and release of an egg.

Menstruation is the shedding of parts of the lining of the uterus during the menstrual cycle.

Meristem (mer′i stem) is the actively growing tip of a plant, composed of several cells dividing repeatedly. (G. dividing)

Merozoite (mer′ō zō′īt) is the stage of a sporozoon derived from division of a trophozoite.

Mesenchyme (mess′en kīm) is the kind of relatively undifferentiated cells found in certain animals. (G. middle infusion)

Mesentery (mess′en ter i) is a double sheet of connective tissue fastening an organ to the body wall. (G. between intestines)

Mesoderm is the layer of embryonic tissue intermediate between ectoderm and endoderm. (G. middle skin)

Mesoglea (mess′ō glē′uh) is a noncellular gelatinous material found between the epidermis and gastrodermis of coelenterates. (G. middle gum)

Mesophyll is a group of internal plant cells containing chloroplasts, as the mesophyll of a leaf. (G. middle of the leaf)

Mesozoic (mess′ō zō′ik) is the fourth of the geologic eras. (G. middle animals)

Metabolism (me ta′bō lizm) sums up the activities in a living organism. (G. change)

Metacarpal (me′tuh kar′pul) is a bone of the hand. (G. beyond the wrist)

Metamorphosis (me′tuh mōr′fō sis) is a pronounced change of form during the lifetime of an individual organism. (G. change of form)

Metaphase (me′tuh fāz) is the stage of cell division during which chromosomes are arranged on the equatorial plane of the cell. (G. appearing after)

Metatarsal (me′tuh tar′sul) is a bone of the foot. (G. beyond the ankle)

Metazoon (me′tuh zō′un) is an animal composed of more than one cell.

Meter is a unit of length chosen to represent a ten-millionth of the meridional distance from the pole to the equator of the earth. It equals about 39.37 inches.

Microgametocyte (mī′krō ga mē′-tō sīt) is a sporozoon cell which may form a male gamete.

Micromonospora (mī′krō mon′ō-spō′ruh) is a genus of Actinomycetales having conidia. (G. small one-spored)

Micron is a one-thousandth of a millimeter or a millionth of a meter. (G. small)

Micropyle is the opening into a megasporangium, allowing the male gamete to enter. (G. small gate)

Microsporangium (mī′krō spō-ran′ji um) is a sporangium producing microspores. (G. small, and sporangium)

Microspore is a spore which may develop into a male gametophyte. (G. small, and spore)

Midbrain is the part of the brain anterior to the cerebellum and pons Varolii, and posterior to the diencephalon.

Midgut is the intermediate, open part of an embryonic digestive tract.

Milliliter is a unit of volume equal to one thousandth of a liter, or one cubic centimeter.

Millimeter is one thousandth of a meter.

Millipede is a diplopodan. (L. thousand feet)

Milu (mi′lū), or Father David's deer, is an ungulate nearly extinct.

Miocene (mī′ō seen) is the third period of the Cenozoic Era. (G. less recent)

Mississippian is the fifth period of the Paleozoic Era.

Mitochondrion (mī′tō kon′dri on) is a fatty-protein body in a cell which is the center of certain cell secretions. The plural is "mitochondria."

Mitosis (mī tō′sis) is the type of cell division in which the resulting cells have exactly the same chromosomal components as the original cell.

Mitral (mī′trul) refers to the valve between the left auricle and left ventricle of the heart. (Mitershaped)

Molar is a grinding tooth at the back of the mouth. (L. millstone)

Mollusca (mō luss′kuh) is the phylum of unsegmented animals covered by a fleshy mantle. (L. soft)

Monocot is a shortened form of Monocotyledoneae.

Monocotyledoneae (mon′ō kot i-lē dō′nee ee) is the group of angiosperms in which seeds have only one cotyledon each.

Monotremata (mon′ō tre′mah tuh) is the order of Mammalia which are hatched from eggs laid by the mother.

Morphology (mōr fol′ō ji) is the study of the structure of organisms. (G. study of form)

Morula (mōr′yū luh) is an embryo resembling a little ball of cells.

Moss is a bryophyte with radial symmetry.

Motor refers to movement, as a motor nerve cell, which carries impulses to a part that moves.

Motor area is that part of the cerebrum which sends impulses to skeletal muscles.

Motorium is a center involved in ciliary coordination in such animals as *Paramecium*.

Mouth part is an appendage associated with the mouth in an arthropod.

Mucus (myū′kus) is a viscous protein substance secreted by many cells, especially some in the digestive tract.

Muscle (mussl) is an organ or a tissue composed of cells especially able to contract forcibly. (L. little

mouse, because of the feel of a contracting muscle in the arm)

Muscle tone is the condition of a muscle in which a few of its fibers are contracted at any time, even though the remainder of the muscle is at rest.

Muscular refers to a tissue or system composed of contractile cells.

Muscular process is the lateral corner of the arytenoid cartilage, to which certain muscles are attached.

Mutation is a change in the nature of a gene. (L. change)

Mycelium (mī see′li um) is a network of fungus hyphae. (G. fungus meadow)

Mycobacterium is the genus of bacteria which causes tuberculosis.

Mycorhiza (mī′kō rī′zuh) is a symbiotic relationship between certain fungi and the roots of certain trees and shrubs. (G. fungus root)

Myosin (mī′ō sin) is the protein of muscle fibrils.

Myxomycetes (mik′sō mī see′teez) is a class of Fungi in which spores do not germinate into hyphae.

Nasal refers to the nose.

Nasolacrimal duct (nā′zō lak′ri-mul) is the duct which carries tears from the surface of the eye into the nose cavity.

Nauplius (naw′pli uss) is the larva of a crustacean. (L. shellfish)

Nautilus is a cephalopod with a coiled shell.

Neck canal is the cavity running through the elongated part of an archegonium.

Neck canal cell is a cell in the neck canal of an archegonium.

Nemathelminthes (ne′muh thel-min′theez) is the phylum of roundworms, bilateral animals with a body cavity not completely lined by mesoderm. (G. thread worms)

Nematocyst (ne′muh tō sist′) is a harpoonlike cell found in coelenterates.

Nephridium (ne fri′dē um) is an excretory tube in such an animal as the earthworm. (G. kidneylike)

Nerve is a cable of axons and/or dendrites connecting the central

nervous system with some other part of the organism.

Nervous refers to a tissue especially able to conduct impulses.

Neural refers to nervous structures, as the neural artery of an earthworm, which supplies the nerve cord.

Neural crest is a group of cells separated from the neural tube of certain embryos; they give rise to ganglia, nerve sheaths, and adrenal medullas.

Neuroglia (new rōg′li a) is a special type of connective tissue found in the nervous system. (G. nerve glue)

Neuromotor apparatus (new′rō-mō′tur ap puh rā′tuss) is a cytoplasmic structure which regulates ciliary beat.

Neuroptera (new rop′te ruh) is an order of Insecta with densely veined fore and hind wings. (G. nerve wings)

Niacin, or nicotinic acid, is a water-soluble vitamin concerned with carbohydrate oxidation. Its deficiency results in pellagra. (Named from *ni*cotinic *aci*d vitam*in*)

Nictitating membrane is a third eyelid found in many reptiles and birds. (L. winking web)

Nitrogen-fixing refers to the transformation of free nitrogen into a nitrogen-containing compound.

Node is a portion of a stem at which tissues are much denser than elsewhere. (L. knot)

Notochord (nō′tō kōrd) is a longitudinal skeletal rod found in chordates.

Nucellus (nū sell′us) is food-storing tissue in the reproductive stages of certain plants. (L. little nut)

Nucleolus (nū klē′ō luss) is a distinct mass within a nucleus. (L. little kernel)

Nucleus is the discrete body in a cell carrying the substances which regulate much of the cell's metabolism. (L. kernel)

Nutrition is the process of using food in the body, and the study of the foods needed and how they are used.

Occipital (ok si'pi tul) is a skull bone at the posterior end of the brain. (L. toward the head)

Oculomotor (ok yū lō mō'tur) refers to the third pair of cranial nerves, which supply certain eye muscles. (L. eye mover)

Olecranon (ō le krā'non or ō lek'-ruh non) is the projection of the ulna at the elbow. (G. ulna skull)

Olfactory refers to the sense of smell.

Oligocene (ol'i gō seen) is the second period of the Cenozoic Era. (G. slightly recent)

Oligocheta (ol'i gō kee'tuh) is the class of Annelida having only a few setae in each segment, such as the earthworm. (G. few bristles)

Onychophora (on i kof'ō ruh) is the class of Arthropoda with legs not jointed. It includes *Peripatus.*

Oogonium (ō ō gō'nē um) is a chamber of not more than one cell in certain plants in which an egg cell develops. (G. egg producer)

Opalina (ō puh lī'nuh) is a genus of parasitic Ciliata.

Ophiuroidea (ō fi yū roi'dē uh) is the class of Echinodermata with unbranched arms sharply demarcated from the disc. (G. like a serpent's tail)

Opisthorchis (ō pis thōr'kiss) is a genus of Trematoda, the human liver fluke.

Opsonin (op'sō nin) is a white blood corpuscle secretion which renders bacteria more susceptible to destruction by macrophages. (G. food preparer)

Optic refers to the eye.

Oral groove is the indentation on the side of such an animal as *Paramecium* along which food is passed toward the gullet.

Order is a taxonomic group of organisms with greater similarity than a class but less than a family.

Ordovician (ōr dō vi'shun) is the second period of the Paleozoic Era. (L. ancient Celtic tribe in Wales)

Organ is a combination of tissues into a working part of an organism. (Anglo-Saxon tool)

Organism is a complete living individual plant or animal.

Ornithine (ōr'ni thin) is an amino acid used in the formation of urea from ammonium carbonate.

Orthoptera (ōr thop'te ruh) is an order of Insecta having thickened forewings and folded hindwings.

Osmosis is the diffusion of water through a membrane. (G. push)

Osmotic pressure is that which forces water through a membrane due to differences in solution concentrations on the two sides of the membrane.

Osteoblast is a cell which deposits bone. (G. bone germ)

Osteoclast is a cell which dissolves bone. (G. bone destroyer)

Otolith is a concretion found in an organ involved in the sense of static equilibrium. (G. ear stone)

Oval window is the opening in the wall of the inner ear into which the stirrup of the middle ear fits.

Ovary is a female reproductive organ.

Overtone is one of a group of simultaneous tones, produced by an instrument, which have frequencies that are integral multiples of the fundamental tone.

Oviduct is a canal through which eggs pass. (L. egg leader)

Ovule is the megasporangium of a flower.

Oxyhemoglobin (ok'si hē'mō glō'-bin) is a combination of oxygen and hemoglobin.

Palatine refers to the roof of the mouth.

Paleontology (pā'lē on tah'lō ji) is the study of the past history of living organisms. (G. study of old beginnings)

Paleozoic (pā'lē ō zō'ik) is the third of the geologic eras. (G. old animals)

Palisade layer is a compact array of columnar mesophyll cells beneath the upper epidermis of a leaf.

Palp is a fleshy appendage.

Pancreas is a large gland near the duodenum and stomach, smaller than the liver.

Pancreozymin (pan'krē ō zī'min) is the hormone, secreted in the small intestine, which stimulates the pancreas to release its digestive enzymes. (Pancreas, and G. leaven)

Pantothenic acid (pan tō the'nik) is a water-soluble vitamin probably involved in metabolism of carbohydrates. (G. from everywhere, and acid)

Papilla (pah pi'luh) is a small projection such as those on the tongue.

Para-aminobenzoic acid (par uh a'mi nō ben zō'ik) is a water-soluble vitamin apparently essential to the metabolism of many bacteria.

Parabiotic refers to two organisms whose bodies are joined, as in Siamese twins. (G. living beside)

Paracasein is one of the products of casein digestion by rennin. (G. beside cheese)

Paramecium is a genus of ciliates.

Paramylon (par am'i lon) is a form of starch found in certain algae.

Parapodium (par uh pō'dē um) is a lateral, paddlelike appendage found on polychetes. (G. beside the foot)

Parasite is an organism which gets its food from another living organism.

Parasitology (par uh si tol'ō ji) is the study of parasites.

Parasympathetic refers to that part of the autonomic system whose ganglia occur in the head, neck, and sacral region.

Parathyrin (par uh thī'rin) is the parathyroid secretion, which regulates calcium metabolism.

Parathyroid refers to an endocrine gland whose secretion regulates calcium metabolism. (G. beside the thyroid)

Parenchyma (par en'ki muh) is a plant tissue in which the cells have thin walls and are storage depots.

Parietal (puh rī'e tul) refers to a structure placed at the border or lateral side of an object, as the parietal bone of the skull.

Parotid (puh rot'id) is a salivary gland located near the ear. (G. beside the ear)

Parthenocarpy (pahr the nō kar'pi) is the formation of fruits without seeds. (G. virgin fruit)

Parthenogenesis (pahr the nō je′ne sis) is the development of an unfertilized egg into a mature organism. (G. virgin birth)

Pasteurization is a special process of heating substances to destroy pathogenic bacteria. The temperature is carefully controlled to avoid effecting undesirable changes in the material. (Named for Pasteur)

Patella (pa tell′luh) is the bone of the knee, or the kneecap. (L. pan)

Pathogen (path′ō jen) is a disease-producing organism. (G. disease-producing)

Pearl is the material secreted by the mantle of certain molluscs onto the inner part of the shell or any intervening object.

Peck order is the organization of certain bird societies in a system of relative dominance of some individuals over others.

Pectin is a complex carbohydrate secreted by certain plants and used in their cell walls. (G. congealed)

Pediatrics (pē di a′trix) is the study of the health of children. (G. child medicine)

Pedicellaria (pe di sel lā′rē uh) is a pincerlike structure in the skin of certain echinoderms. (L. with little feet)

Pedipalp (pe′di palp) is one of the second pair of appendages in an arachnid.

Pelagic (pe la′jik) refers to the surface zone of the oceans away from their shores. (G. of the sea)

Pelecypoda (pe le si′pō duh) is the class of Mollusca with a two-piece shell. (G. hatchet foot)

Pellagra (pe lā′gruh or pe lag′ruh) is a disease of the nervous system and skin resulting from niacin deficiency. (L. rough skin)

Pellicle is an elastic membrane covering an organism such as certain protozoa. (L. little skin)

Pelmatohydra (pel ma tō hī′druh) is a genus of Coelenterata.

Penicillin (pen i sil′lin) is an antibiotic manufactured by *Penicillium*. (L. brush)

Penicillium (pen i sil′lē um) is a genus of Ascomycetes.

Penis (pē′nis) is the organ in a male animal which transfers sperm to a female.

Pennsylvanian is the sixth period of the Paleozoic Era.

Pepsin is an enzyme secreted by the stomach which catalyzes the breaking of peptide linkages in certain proteins and proteoses. (G. digestion)

Pepsinogen (pep sin′ō jen) is the inactive form of pepsin secreted by stomach cells. It is changed to pepsin in the stomach cavity by the action of hydrochloric acid. (Pepsin, and L. producer)

Peptidase is an enzyme which catalyzes the breakdown of some polypeptides and dipeptides into amino acids.

Peptide linkage (pep′tid link′āj) is the method of combining amino acids in which the amino group of one fastens to the acid group of the other with the release of a water molecule.

Peptone is a type of chemical compound formed by combining many amino acids; it is soluble in water and not precipitated by a saturated solution of ammonium sulfate.

Perichondrium (pār i kon′drē um) is the fibrous sheath encasing cartilage. (G. around cartilage)

Pericycle (pār i sī′kul) is the outermost cylinder of cells of a vascular bundle or group of bundles. (G. around the circle)

Perilymph (pār′i limf) is the liquid between the bony and membranous parts of the inner ear. (G. around, L. water)

Period is a subdivision of an era of geologic time.

Periosteum (pār i os′tē um) is the fibrous sheath encasing bone. (G. around bone)

Peripatus (pe rip′uh tuss) is a genus of Onychophora.

Peristalsis (pār i stol′sis) is the series of wavelike contractions forcing materials along a tube such as the digestive tract. (G. contraction around)

Permian (pur′mē an) is the seventh period of the Paleozoic Era. (Named for a province in Russia)

Petal is one leaf of a corolla.

Petiole is the stalk of a leaf. (L. little foot)

Petrel is a bird. (L. little Peter, because it seems to walk on the sea)

Phaeophyceae (fē ō fī′see ee) is the class of Algae having green and brown pigments. (G. dusky seaweed)

Phaeophyta (fē off′i tuh) is the phylum proposed to include Phaeophyceae. (G. dusky plants)

Phagocyte (fag′ō sīt) is a cell which ingests and destroys other cells or particles. (G. eating cell)

Phalanx is a bone of a finger, thumb, or toe. (G. row of soldiers)

Pharynx is the portion of the digestive tract immediately behind the mouth.

Phenotype is the appearance of an organism with respect to hereditary characters. (G. evident sort)

Phloem (flō′em) is a plant tissue in which food substances are transported. (G. bark)

Photosynthesis (fō tō sin′the sis) is the manufacture of food from inorganic substances, using the energy of light, in the presence of a catalyst, usually a chlorophyll. (G. putting together with light)

Phrenic (fre′nik) refers to the diaphragm.

Phycomycetes (fī′kō mī see′teez) is a class of Fungi in which spores germinate into hyphae without cross-walls. (G. seaweed fungi)

Phylum (fī′lum) is a taxonomic group of organisms differing from all other organisms in many ways. Organisms with a very few characters in common may belong to the same phylum. (G. kind)

Physiology is the study of the biological actions in living organisms. (G. study of nature)

Pineal (pin′ē ul) is an organ attached to the dorsal side of the diencephalon. (L. pine cone)

Pinus (pī′nuss) is a genus of Gymnospermae, the pine.

Pisces (pis′eez) is the class of Vertebrata with bone and paired fins. It includes the bony fish.

Pistil is the part of a flower associated with the development of ovules. (L. pestle, because of its shape)

Pith is a mass of parenchyma cells in the middle of a stele.

Pitocin (pi'tō sin or pi tō'sin) is the pituitary hormone which stimulates the contraction of muscles in the uterus. (From "pituitary" and G. birth)

Pitressin (pi tres'sin) is the pituitary hormone which raises blood pressure, stimulates intestinal peristalsis, and promotes the retention of water in the body by kidney tubules. (From "pituitary" and "pressure")

Pituitary (pi tū'i tā ri) is an endocrine gland in the head which secretes several hormones. (L. having to do with phlegm)

Placenta is the tissue composed of maternal and embryonic cells through which substances diffuse between a mother and an embryo.

Placoderm (plak'ō durm) is an extinct type of primitive vertebrate. (G. plate skin)

Plain is a treeless, flat land area characterized by short grasses.

Plasma is the fluid, noncellular part of the blood.

Plasmodium is a genus of Sporozoa, the cause of malaria.

Plastid is a body in certain plant cells associated with the formation or storage of food.

Platelet is a kind of blood corpuscle which carries thromboplastin.

Platyhelminthes (pla ti hel min'theez) is the phylum of flatworms, bilateral animals without a body cavity. (G. flat worms)

Pleistocene (plīs'tō seen) is the fifth period of the Cenozoic Era. (G. most recent)

Pleodorina (plē'ō dō rī'nuh) is a genus of Chlorophyceae.

Plesiosaur (plē sē ō sawr) is a type of extinct aquatic reptile.

Pleura (plyū'ruh) is the membrane surrounding the lung and lining the chest cavity.

Plexus is an interweaving of nerves. (L. braid)

Pliocene (plī'ō seen) is the fourth period of the Cenozoic Era. (G. more recent)

Plumule (plūm'yūl) is the part of a sporophyte embryo which may form leaves and the tip of a stem. (L. little down feather)

Polarity is the predisposition of an organism to develop certain structures at specific places. (G. axis)

Polarized light is light in which the waves vibrate in one plane only.

Polar nucleus is one of the nuclei in the middle of an angiosperm female gametophyte.

Pollen grain is the mature male gametophyte of a spermatophyte.

Pollen tube is the outgrowth of a pollen grain under the influence of the tube nucleus.

Polycheta (pol'i kē'tuh) is the class of Annelida having many setae on each segment. (G. many bristles)

Polyp (pol'ip) is the columnar form of body found in many coelenterates. (G. many feet)

Polypeptide (pol ē pep'tid) is a type of chemical compound formed by the combination of several amino acids.

Polypodium (pol ē pō'dē um) is a genus of ferns.

Polysiphonia (pol ē si fō'nē uh) is a genus of Rhodophyceae.

Pons Varolii (pōnz va rō'lē ī) is the part of the brain anterior to the medulla oblongata and ventral to the cerebellum. (L. bridge, and named for Varolio)

Porifera (pō ri'fe ruh) is the phylum of sponges. (L. pore-bearers)

Posterior (poss tē'rē ur) refers to the rear or hindmost end. (L. that which follows)

Prairie is a treeless land area characterized by tall grasses. (L. meadow)

Precipitin is a substance secreted by a white corpuscle which causes toxins to come out of solution.

Predator (pre'duh tōr) is an animal which pursues and eats other animals. (L. plunderer)

Premolar is a grinding tooth near a canine tooth. (L. before the molar)

Premotor area is that part of the cerebrum in front of the motor areas.

Primates (prī mā'teez) is the order of Mammalia with relatively large brains and with flat nails on the digits.

Primitive groove is the furrow in an embryo at which the mesoderm arises.

Progesterone (prō jes'te rōn) is a hormone secreted in an ovary. (L. for carrying)

Proglottid (prō glot'id) is a body segment of a tapeworm.

Prolactin is a pituitary secretion which stimulates the breasts. (L. before milk)

Pronator (prō nā'tur) is a muscle which turns the ventral side down, as the pronator which turns the palm of the hand down. (L. bower)

Prophase is the stage of cell division during which chromosomes are formed. (G. appearing before)

Prop root is a root arising from a stem above ground, but imbedded in the ground at its lower end.

Prostate (pross'tāt) refers to a gland at the junction of sperm ducts and urethra. (G. standing before)

Prosthetics is the development of mechanical substitutes for parts of an organism.

Prostomium is an anterior projection from the first segment of an annelid.

Protein is a type of complex organic compounds composed of amino acids combined by peptide linkages. (G. first)

Proteose (prō'tē ōs) is a type of chemical compound formed by combining many amino acids. It is soluble in water but precipitated by a saturated solution of ammonium sulfate.

Proterospongia (prot ur ō spun'jē uh) is a genus of colonial Flagellata.

Proterozoic (prot ur ō zō'ik) is the second of the geologic eras. (G. previous animals)

Prothrombin is a secretion of the liver which may take part in the clotting of blood. (G. before clot)

Protoplasm is the living substance of which organisms are made. (G. first form)

Protozoa is the phylum of one-celled animals. (G. first animals)

Proximal means near to, as the proximal convoluted tubule, the part of a kidney tubule near to the Bowman's capsule. (L. next)

Pseudomonas (sū'dō mō'nus) is a genus of bacteria.

Pseudopodium (sū'dō pō'dē um) is a temporary extension of cytoplasm by means of which certain animals move. (G. false foot)

Psilophyta (sī lof'i tuh) is the phylum or subphylum proposed to include the most primitive vascular plants.

Psilopsida (sī lop'si duh) is a group of Pteridophyta of relatively simple structure.

Psychiatry is the study of mental health. (G. mind medicine)

Psychology is the study of animal behavior. (G. study of the mind)

Pteridophyta (ter i dof'i tuh) is the phylum of plants in which occur differentiated vegetative tissues and organs, including vascular tissues, but reproduction does not normally involve seed formation. (G. fern plants)

Pteropsida (ter op'si duh) is the phylum or subphylum proposed to include ferns and spermatophytes.

Ptyalin (tī'uh lin) is a starch-digesting enzyme secreted by salivary glands. (G. saliva)

Puberty (pyū'bur ti) is the time of beginning of sexual maturity in an organism. (L. time of appearance of hair — beard, etc.)

Pubis (pyū'biss) is a posterior ventral bone of the hip girdle. (L. hair, as that at the lower part of the abdomen)

Puccinia (puk si'nē uh) is a genus of Basidiomycetes, the cause of wheat rust. (Named for Puccini)

Pulmonary (pull'mō nā ri) refers to the lung.

Pupa (pyū'puh) is a stage in the metamorphosis of a lepidopteran.

Pupil (pyū'pil) is the opening through the iris of the eye. (L. doll, from the appearance of the reflection of oneself in the pupil of another's eye)

Pus is a liquid composed of secretions and disintegration products of white blood corpuscles and bacteria.

Pylorus (pī lō'russ) is the narrower part of the stomach leading to the small intestine. (G. gatekeeper)

Pyocyanin (pī ō sī'uh nin) is an antibiotic manufactured by Pseudomonas. (G. blue pus)

Pyrenoid (pī're noid) is a starch-manufacturing body in an algal chloroplast. (G. like a fruit pit)

Pyridoxin (pi ri dok'sin), or Vitamin B_6, is a water-soluble vitamin involved in the metabolism of derivatives of fats and proteins. (G. spark for oxygen)

Pyronema (pī rō nē'muh) is a genus of Ascomycetes. (G. fire thread, so called because the hyphae appear on a burned-over area)

Pyrrhophyta (pēr of'i tuh) is the phylum proposed to include brown-colored algae which store starch. (G. flame-colored plants)

Pyrus (pī'russ) is a genus of dicots, the apple tree.

Pyruvic acid (pī rū'vik) is an organic compound with the formula CH_3–CO–COOH. It is common in the metabolism of organisms, as in tissue oxidations and in photosynthesis.

Python is a snake. (G. a mythical serpent)

Radial refers to a type of symmetry in which duplication of parts occurs on the two sides of more than one plane through the axis of a body. (L. ray)

Radial canal is part of the water circulatory system in an echinoderm.

Radicle is the part of an embryo sporophyte which may develop into a root. (L. little root)

Radiolaria (rā dē ō lā're uh) is a group of Sarcodina with internal skeletons. (L. little rays)

Radius is the bone of the forearm on the thumb side. (L. ray)

Rafflesia (ra flē'zē uh) is a genus of saprophytic dicots. (Named for Raffles)

Receptacle is the tip of a stem which bears a flower.

Recessive refers to a gene whose version of the character is not expressed in the presence of a different gene for the character. (L. going back)

Rectum is the most posterior chamber of the digestive tract.

Rectus means straight, as the rectus muscles of the eye or of the abdominal wall. (L. straight)

Redia (rē'dē uh) is a larval stage of a fluke. (Named for Redi)

Reflex refers to the passage of a nerve impulse over a simple pathway from the site of the stimulus to the site of a motor response. (L. turning back)

Regeneration is the restoration of lost or damaged tissue in an organism. (L. production again)

Remora (rem'ō ruh) is a genus of Pisces, the shark sucker.

Renal (rē'nul) refers to kidney.

Rennin (ren'in) is an enzyme, secreted by the stomach, which changes casein to paracasein.

Reproduction is the formation of one or more new individual organisms from one or two other organisms.

Reptilia is the class of Vertebrata with bone, legs, and an exoskeleton of scales. (L. crawling)

Research is an investigation for the purpose of increasing knowledge. (L. to go around again)

Resin duct is a channel carrying resin in the stem of a plant such as the pine.

Respiration is the release of energy in an organism by combining food substances with oxygen. (L. breathe back)

Respiratory refers to an organ system concerned in the exchange of oxygen and carbon dioxide between an organism and its environment. (L. breathe back)

Rete (rē'tē) is a network, as the rete testis, a network of sperm passageways. (L. net)

Retina is the coat of the eye which is sensitive to light. (L. net)

Retinene (re'ti nēn) is one of the products of the breakdown of visual purple.

Rh factor, or rhesus factor, is a substance found in the blood of certain animals which may serve as an antigen to organisms not normally having it. (Named for the rhesus monkey)

Rhizoid (rī′zoid) is a cell or filament of cells extending from a plant body into the ground or water which supports the plant. (G. rootlike)

Rhodophyceae (rō dō fī′see ee) is the class of Algae having green and red pigments. (G. red seaweed)

Rhodophyta (rō dof′i tuh) is the phylum proposed to include Rhodophyceae. (G. red plants)

Riboflavin (rī bō flā′vin), or Vitamin B$_2$, is a water-soluble vitamin involved in carbohydrate metabolism.

Riccardia (rik kar′dē uh) is a genus of saprophytic liverworts.

Ricciocarpus (rik′si ō kar′puss) is a genus of liverworts.

Rickets is a disease of the skeletal system resulting from a deficiency of Vitamin D. (Old English, twisted)

Rickettsia (ri ket′sē uh) is a type of schizomycete intermediate between viruses and bacteria. (Named for Ricketts)

Ring canal is part of the water circulatory system in an echinoderm.

Rocky mountain revolution is a geologic upheaval at the end of the Mesozoic Era.

Rodentia (rō den′shē uh) is an order of Mammalia with long, constantly growing incisor teeth and no canine teeth. (L. gnawers)

Romalea (rō mā′lē uh) is a genus of Orthoptera, a grasshopper.

Root cap is a covering of dead cells over the tip of a root.

Root hair is a cytoplasmic projection from an epidermal cell of a root.

Round window is the opening in the bone of the inner ear, closed by a membrane, which reacts, equalizing the pressure, when the stirrup of the middle ear vibrates.

Sacculina (sak yū lī′nuh) is a genus of parasitic crustacea.

Sacculus (sak′yū luss) is a pouch in the vestibule of the ear involved in the sense of static equilibrium.

Sacral (sā′krul) refers to the region of the sacrum, the base of the vertebral column. (L. secret)

Sacrum (sā′krum) is a mass of fused vertebrae at the posterior end of the trunk of certain animals. (L. secret)

Saliva is the kind of secretion of certain glands into the mouth cavity.

Salt is the product of the combination of an acid and an alkali with the release of water; for example, sodium hydroxide and hydrochloric acid combine, resulting in water and the salt sodium chloride.

Saprolegnia (sap rō leg′nē uh) is a genus of Phycomycetes. (G. putrid border)

Saprophytic (sap rō fi′tik) refers to the means of getting food by digestion and absorption of dead organic materials by plants. (G. putrid plant)

Saprotrophic (sap rō trō′fik) refers to the means of getting food by digestion and absorption of dead organic materials. (G. putrid nourishment)

Saprozoic (sap rō zō′ik) refers to the means of getting food by digestion and absorption of dead organic materials by animals. (G. putrid animal)

Sapwood is xylem which is able to transport water readily.

Sarcodina (sahr kō dī′nuh) is the class of Protozoa which move by means of pseudopodia. (G. fleshlike)

Sardine (sahr dēn′) is a young herring. (Named from Sardinia)

Scaphopoda (ska fop′ō duh) is the class of Mollusca with long, conical, one-piece shells. (G. skiff foot)

Schizomycetes (ski′zō mī see′teez) is the class of Fungi in which the plants have no more than one cell, usually have no discrete nuclei, and divide by fission. (G. splitting fungi)

Schizophyta (ski zof′i tuh) is the phylum proposed to include the Schizomycetes and the Cyanophyceae. (G. splitting plants)

Sclera (skle′ra) is the outermost coat of the eyeball, the "white" of the eye. (G. hard)

Sclerenchyma (skle ren′ki muh) is a plant tissue in which the cellulose cell walls are very thick. (G. hard infusion)

Scolex (skō′lex) is the anterior knob of a tapeworm.

Scrotum (skrō′tum) is the pouch containing the testes in some male mammals.

Scurvy is the connective tissue disease resulting from Vitamin C deficiency.

Secretin (see kree′tin) is the hormone, secreted in the small intestine, which stimulates the pancreas to release an alkaline secretion. (L. separate)

Secretion is the chemical synthesis in a cell of a substance, and its diffusion out of the cell to another place in which it is involved in metabolism. (L. separation)

Selaginella (sel′uh ji nel′luh) is a genus of fern allies. (L. little juniper)

Semicircular canal is part of the inner ear involved in the sense of dynamic equilibrium.

Semilunar means crescent-shaped, as in the valves between heart ventricles and arteries. (L. half moon)

Seminal vesicle is a pouch or swelling associated with a testis or a sperm duct. (L. seed bladder)

Semipermeability is the characteristic of a membrane allowing some substances to diffuse through while restraining others.

Sensory refers to a part of the nervous system involved in impulses from other parts of the organism going toward the central nervous system.

Sepal (see′pul) is one leaf of a calyx. (L. separate)

Septum is a partition separating two chambers or cavities in an organism.

Serology (sē rol′ō ji) is the study of serums, the nature and content of body fluids in various animals.

Serum is the liquid portion of blood remaining after clotting when the clot fibers and blood corpuscles are removed. (L. whey)

Seta (see′tah) is a bristle.

Sex chromosome is a chromosome involved in sex determination.

Sex-linkage is the occurrence of genes on sex chromosomes.

Sexual refers to a type of reproduction in which the new individual is formed by the union of two distinct living entities. (L. division)

Shank is the part of the leg between the knee and the ankle.

Sieve plate is a wall with many perforations, as the end wall of a phloem sieve tube, or the entrance to the stone canal of a starfish.

Sieve tube is a phloem cell which carries dissolved substances such as food from one part of a plant to another.

Silurian (sĭ lū′rē un) is the third period of the Paleozoic Era. (L. an ancient British tribe)

Single sugar is a carbohydrate with the formula $C_6H_{12}O_6$.

Sinuauricular node (sĭ nū aw rik′-yū lur) is the portion of the wall of the right auricle of the heart which initiates the heartbeat. (From sinus venosus, and auricle)

Sinus gland is an endocrine organ in the eyestalk of such an animal as a crayfish.

Sinus venosus (sĭ′nuss vē nō′suss) is a heart chamber in such animals as fishes. (L. vein cavity)

Siphon (sĭ′fon) is a passageway for liquids, as the ingoing and outgoing passages of a clam. (G. tube)

Sirenian (sĭ rē′nē un) is a marine mammal, such as a manatee. (G. siren, from the resemblance of the animals to human female figures in the eyes of sailors long away from home)

Skeleton is the supporting framework of an organism. (G. dried up)

Society is a group of organisms whose characteristics are modified in relation to their association together. (L. companions)

Sociology is the study of human societies, or associations of other organisms.

Solenogastres (sō lē′nō gas′treez) is the class of wormlike Mollusca with small mouths.

Somatic (sō ma′tik) refers to body, as somatic mesoderm, the outer boundary of the celom. (G. of the body)

Somatoplasm (sō ma′tō plazm) is the kind of cells of an organism which are not potentially reproductive cells. (G. body form)

Somite (sō′mĭt) is a block of mesoderm cells in certain embryos; from the somites arise vertebrae, muscles, and dermis. (G. body)

Species (spē′sheez) is a taxonomic group of one kind of organism. Species are grouped into genera. When a genus is composed of more than one species, the individuals of each species population differ from each other less than do the individuals of the genus population. (L. kind. The singular and plural of the word are alike.)

Sperm is the male reproductive cell. (G. seed)

Spermatium (spur mā′shē um) is a nonmotile gamete found in certain thallophytes. (G. seed)

Spermatophyta (spur muh tof′i tuh) is the phylum of plants in which seeds are normally found. (G. seed plants)

Sphenodon (sfē′nō don) is a reptile living in New Zealand.

Sphenoid (sfē′noid) refers to the skull bone at the floor of the brain. (G. wedgelike)

Sphenopsida (sfē nop′si duh) is the phylum or subphylum proposed to include such fern allies as the horsetail rushes.

Sphincter is a ring of muscle able to close a tube such as part of the digestive or urinary tract. (G. binder)

Spinal accessory is the eleventh pair of cranial nerves, which supply some of the muscles of the neck and shoulder.

Spinal cord is the nerve trunk passing through the vertebral column.

Spinocerebellar tract (spĭ′nō ser-uh bel′lur) is a nerve tract carrying impulses from the spinal cord to the cerebellum.

Spinodiencephalic tract (spĭ′nō dĭ′en se fa′lik) is a nerve tract carrying impulses from the spinal cord to the diencephalon.

Spinomedullary tract (spĭ′nō med′-yū lā′ri) is a nerve tract carrying impulses from the spinal cord to the medulla oblongata.

Spindle is the barrel-shaped structure formed by cytoplasmic condensations during cell division.

Spinneret is a silk-producing appendage, as those on the abdomen of a spider.

Spirillum (spī ril′lum) is a helically coiled bacterium. (L. coil)

Splanchnic (splank′nik) refers to viscera, as the splanchnic mesoderm covering the viscera in the celom. (G. visceral)

Spleen is an organ which filters blood, removing broken red corpuscles and adding new white corpuscles.

Spongy layer is a loosely packed layer of mesophyll cells between the palisade layer and lower epidermis of a leaf.

Sporangium (spō ran′ji um) is a chamber in which spores develop. (G. seed vessel)

Spore is a stage of an organism in which it is highly resistant to external forces. (G. seed)

Spore mother cell is a cell which may undergo meiosis, producing spores.

Sporophyte (spō′rō fīt) is a plant whose nuclei are diploid.

Sporozoa is the class of Protozoa which have no special locomotor structures. (G. seed animals)

Sporozoite (spō′rō zō′īt) is the stage of a sporozoon derived from division of the zygote.

Sprain is a tearing of muscle or tendon fibers.

Staircase phenomenon is the gradual increase in efficiency of a muscle with its repeated contractions.

Stamen (stā′men) is the part of a flower associated with pollen grain formation.

Starch is a carbohydrate whose formula is $(C_6H_{10}O_5)_n$ in which n is an integer larger than 4.

Statocyst (sta′tō sist) is a sense organ of equilibrium in such animals as a crayfish. (G. standing cell)

Stele (stēl) is the central part of a plant root or stem, containing the vascular tissue. (Anglo-Saxon for stalk)

Steroid (stēr′oid) is any of a class of fat-soluble organic substances.

Stethoscope is an instrument for conveying sounds from the interior of an organism to the ears of a listener. (G. chest viewer)

Stigma is the tip of a pistil. The plural is stigmata. (L. puncture mark)

Stimulus is an environmental change which brings about a metabolic change in an organism, as a touch on the skin may initiate a nerve impulse. (L. goad)

Stirrup is the bone of the middle ear attached to the inner ear.

Stoma (stō'muh) is an opening through the epidermis of a plant allowing gases to diffuse into and out of cell layers deeper than the epidermis. (G. mouth)

Stomach is an enlargement in the digestive tract in which food is temporarily lodged and in which some digestion may occur. (G. little mouth)

Stone canal is part of the water circulatory system in an echinoderm.

Strepsiptera (strep sip'te ruh) is an order of Insecta parasitic on wasps.

Streptomyces (strep tō mī'seez) is a genus of Actinomycetales which has chains of conidia.

Streptomycin (strep tō mī'sin) is an antibiotic manufactured by Streptomyces.

Strobilus (strob'i luss) is a cluster of sporangium-bearing leaves.

Stroma (strō'muh) is the connective tissue, vascular vessels, and nerves of an organ such as an ovary.

Style is a rodlike structure, as the style of a pistil between the ovules and stigma. (G. pillar)

Subclavian (sub klā'vē un) refers to blood vessels associated with the forelimb. (Named for "under the clavicle")

Suberin (sū'buh rin) is a fatty substance found in the walls of cork cells. (L. the cork-oak tree)

Sublingual is a salivary gland under the tongue. (L. under the tongue)

Submaxillary is a salivary gland near the posterior end of the lower jaw. (L. under the jawbone)

Subneural refers to a position under the nerve cord, as the subneural blood vessel of an earthworm.

Subphylum is a taxonomic group of organisms with greater similarity than a phylum, but less than a class.

Subtilin (sub'ti lin) is an antibiotic manufactured by bacteria. (Named from Bacillus subtilis)

Sucrase (sū'krās) is an enzyme which catalyzes the separation of sucrose into glucose and fructose.

Sucrose is a double sugar found in sugar cane, sugar beets, and other substances.

Supinator (sū'pi nā'tur) is a muscle which turns the ventral side up, as the supinator which rotates the palm of the hand up. (L. bending backward)

Suspensor (suss pen'sur) is a structure in a developing sporophyte which elongates, pushing the embryo into a food supply. (L. hanging under)

Suture (sū'chur) is a line of junction of two or more parts, as of skull bones. (L. seam)

Swimmeret is an abdominal appendage of such an animal as a crayfish.

Symbiosis (sim bi ō'sis) is the association of organisms of different species involving advantages for each associate. (G. living together)

Symmetry is the duplication of parts about a central plane or axis. (G. measured together)

Sympathetic refers to that part of the autonomic system whose ganglia occur in the thorax and upper abdomen. (G. feeling together)

Sympathin (sim'puh thin) is a substance secreted at the end of a sympathetic nerve fiber.

Synapse (sin'aps) is the area in which a nerve impulse may pass from the axon of one cell to the dendrite of another. (G. touch together)

Syncytium (sin sish'um) is a mass of cells not partitioned from each other by membranes; their cytoplasms are confluent. (G. cells together)

Synergid nucleus (si nur'jid nyū'klē uss) is one of the nuclei near the egg nucleus of an angiosperm female gametophyte. (G. working together, and nucleus)

Syrinx (sēr'inx) is the voice box of a bird. (G. pipe)

System is a group of organs associated in the performance of a general metabolic process. (G. stand together)

Systole (sis'tō li) is the contraction of the muscles of a heart chamber. (G. pulling together)

Tadpole is the larval stage of a chordate such as a sea squirt or a frog. (Anglo-Saxon for toad-head)

Taenia (tē'nē uh) is a genus of Cestoda. (L. tape)

Tarsal is an ankle bone. (G. ankle)

Taste bud is a sense organ on the tongue.

Taxonomy (tak son'uh mi) is the study of the classification and evolutionary relationships of organisms. (G. order of arrangement)

Teliospore (tē'lē ō spōr) is a dark-colored spore formed by a basidiomycete; it survives during the winter. (G. perfect seed)

Telophase (tell'ō fāz) is the stage of cell division in which chromosomes are reconstituted into nuclei. (G. appearing at the end)

Temporal (tem'pō rull) is a skull bone in the ear region. (L. temple)

Tendon is a bundle of white connective tissue fibers.

Teredo (tē rē'dō) is a genus of Pelecypoda, the shipworm. (L. borer)

Testis is a male reproductive organ.

Testosterone (tess tos'te rōn) is a hormone secreted in a testis.

Thallophyta (thal of'i tuh) is the phylum of plants in which the bodies of the organisms are not differentiated into vegetative tissues and organs. (G. twig plants)

Thiamin, or Vitamin B$_1$, is a water-soluble vitamin involved in the breakdown of lactic and pyruvic acids. Its deficiency results in beriberi. (From sulfur-amine)

Thigh is the part of the leg between the hip and the knee.

Thoracic duct (thō rass'ik) is the chief collecting lymph vessel.

Thorax (thō'rax) is a section of an organism between head and abdomen. (G. breastplate)

Thoth (thōth or tōt) is the ibis-headed god of ancient Egypt.

Thrombin is an enzyme which catalyzes the formation of a blood clot. (G. clot)

Thromboplastin is the substance which transforms prothrombin into thrombin, thus initiating a blood clot. (G. clot-former)

Thymus is a large lymph node located at the anterior ventral part of the chest.

Thyroid refers to the large cartilage in the ventral wall of the larynx, and to the endocrine gland near that cartilage. (G. shield-shaped)

Thyrotrophin (thī rō trō'fin) is a pituitary hormone which stimulates the secretory activity of the thyroid gland. (Thyroid, and G. nourisher)

Thyroxin (thī rok'sin) is an amino acid involved in the synthesis of thyroid hormone.

Thysanura (thī san ū'ruh) is an order of Insecta without wings. (G. bushy-tailed)

Tibia (ti'bē uh) is the bone of the lower leg on the large toe side, the shin bone in a human.

Timbre (tim'bur) is the quality of sound produced by combinations of fundamental tones and overtones. (G. kettledrum)

Tissue is a group of cells of similar type and action. (L. web)

Tissue culture is the process of growing tissues in a nutrient medium outside the body of an organism.

Titanothere (tī'ta nō thēr) is an extinct type of mammal. (Named for the Titans, mythical giants, and G. wild animal)

Tonsil is a lymph node at the border of the pharynx. (L. mooring post)

Toxin is a substance secreted by an organism, which is poisonous to another organism. (G. poison)

Trace element is a chemical element present in very small amount.

Trachea (trā'kē uh) is a passageway carrying air, as the windpipe of a human or the respiratory tube of an insect. (G. rough)

Tracheid (trā'kē id) is a xylem cell which has lost its protoplasm, leaving only the cell wall. (G. windpipelike)

Tracheophyta (trā kē of'i tuh) is the phylum proposed to include pteridophytes and spermatophytes.

Trematoda (tre muh tō'duh) is the class of Platyhelminthes with no cellular epidermis, but with a digestive tract.

Triassic (trī a'sik) is the first period of the Mesozoic Era. (G. triple)

Triceps (trī'seps) is a muscle with its contractile portion divided into three parts at one end, such as the extensor of the human elbow. (L. three heads)

Triceratops (trī sār'uh tops) is a genus of dinosaurs. (G. appearing to have three horns)

Trichina (tri kī'nuh) is a parasitic roundworm found in muscle. (G. hairlike)

Trichocyst (tri'kō sist) is a harpoonlike structure in the outer part of such an animal as *Paramecium*. (G. hair sac)

Trichodesmium (tri kō dez'mē um) is a genus of Cyanophyceae. (G. hair bundle)

Trichogyne (tri'kō jīn) is a tube growing out of an oogonium. (G. feminine hair)

Tricuspid refers to the valve between the right auricle and right ventricle of the heart. (L. three points)

Trigeminal (trī je'mi nul) refers to the fifth pair of cranial nerves, which supply parts of the face and head. (L. triplet)

Triploid refers to nuclei in which genes and chromonemata occur in threes. (G. tripled)

Troch (trōk) is a band of cilia found on trochophores. (G. wheel)

Trochlear (trōk'lē ur) refers to the fourth pair of cranial nerves, which supply the superior oblique muscles of the eyes. (L. pulley, from the pulley through which the superior oblique muscle passes)

Trochophore (trō'kō fōr) is a type of ciliated larva found among several kinds of animals. (G. wheel-bearer)

Trophoblast (trō'fō blast) is the group of embryonic cells which invade the wall of the uterus. (G. nourishing germ)

Trophozoite (trō fō zō'īt) is the stage of a sporozoon swollen with food. (G. nourishing animal)

Trypanosome (tri'pa nō sōm) is a type of parasitic flagellate. (G. body borer)

Trypsin (trip'sin) is an enzyme which catalyzes the breakdown of certain peptide linkages in proteins and protein products. (G. wearing out)

Trypsinogen (trip sin'ō jen) is the inactive form of trypsin secreted by the pancreas, and activated in the small intestine by enterokinase. (Trypsin, and L. former)

Tube cell is the cell of a pollen grain which gives rise to the pollen tube.

Tube foot is a hollow, tentaclelike projection from an echinoderm.

Tubule is a small tube.

Tundra is a land area of sparse vegetation characteristic of polar regions.

Turbellaria (tur bel lā'rē uh) is the class of Platyhelminthes with a cellular epidermis. (L. little animal which turns in a circle)

Turbinal is a bone found in the nasal cavity. (L. whirlwind)

Tympanic membrane is the eardrum, a membrane at the inner end of the auditory canal. (G. kettledrum, and membrane)

Typhlosole (tif'lō sōl) is a fold of intestinal wall projecting into the digestive cavity in such animals as earthworms. (G. blind channel)

Tyrannosaurus (ti ra'nō saw'russ) is a genus of dinosaurs. (G. master lizard)

Tyrocidin (tī rō sī'din) is an antibiotic manufactured by bacteria.

Tyrosine (tī'rō sin) is an amino acid.

Tyrothricin (tī′rō thrī′sin) is an antibiotic manufactured by bacteria.

Ulna (ul′nuh) is the bone of the forearm on the little finger side. (L. elbow)

Ulva (ul′vuh) is a genus of Chlorophyceae.

Umbilical cord is the ropelike connection between an unborn or newborn baby and its placenta.

Umbo (um′bō) is the first formed part of a valve of a pelecypod shell. (L. knob)

Ungulata (un′gyū lā′tuh) is the order of Mammalia with hoofs. (L. hoofed)

Urea is a chemical compound with the formula $CO(NH_2)_2$ found in animal excretions. (G. urine)

Uredospore (yū rē′dō spōr′) is a basidiomycete spore of a reddish color. (L. blight, and spore)

Ureter (yū rē′tur) is the duct which carries waste products away from the kidney in some animals. (G. urine duct)

Urethra (yū rē′thruh) is the duct which carries urine from the urinary bladder to the outside of the body.

Uric acid is an excretory compound found in many animals.

Urinary bladder is a temporary storehouse of urine to which the ureters lead and from which the urethra carries urine away.

Urine is the mixture of excretory products formed in the kidney.

Urochordata (yū rō kōr dā′tuh) is the subphylum of Chordata with the notochord in the posterior part of the larva only, the adult being encased in a thick tunic. (G. tail chord)

Uropod (yū′rō pod) is an enlarged swimmeret at the posterior end of such an animal as a crayfish. (G. tail foot)

Uterus is a thick-walled tube to which one or more oviducts lead.

Utriculus (yū trik′yū luss) is a pouch in the vestibule of the ear involved in the sense of static equilibrium. (L. little bag)

Vacuole is a liquid-filled cavity in a cell.

Vagina (vuh jī′nuh) is the passageway from the uterus to the outside of the organism. (L. sheath)

Vagus (vā′gus) is the tenth pair of cranial nerves, which supply several of the viscera in the trunk.

Valve is a projection, flap, or muscular ring which may close a passageway, or something of similar form as the valve of a clam shell.

Vascular refers to tissues concerned in transportation of substances through an organism. (L. little vessel)

Vascular cambium is a cylinder of actively dividing cells which produces more vascular tissues in certain plants.

Vascular ray is a sheet of parenchyma cells radially dividing vascular tissues in plant stems and roots.

Vaucheria (vaw shē′rē uh) is a genus of Chlorophyceae. (Named for Vaucher)

Vegetarian means plant-eating.

Vein is a branch of a vascular bundle in a leaf, or a blood vessel carrying blood from capillaries toward the heart.

Vena cava (vē′nuh kā′vuh) is the large vein carrying blood to the heart. (L. hollow vein)

Venation (ve nā′shun) is the pattern of veins in a leaf.

Ventral refers to the lower side of an animal, the side on which the mouth is found. (L. belly side)

Ventral canal cell is a cell at the base of the neck canal of an archegonium.

Ventricle is a hollow chamber, such as a part of the heart which forces blood into arteries, or an expansion of the cerebrospinal canal in the brain. (L. little belly)

Venus is a genus of Pelecypoda. (Named for the goddess)

Vermiform (vur′mi fōrm) means worm-shaped, as the vermiform appendix.

Vertebra is one of a series of similar elements in the dorsal axial skeleton of certain animals. (L. joint)

Vertebrata is the subphylum of Chordata with a vertebral column.

Vesicle is a bladder or pouch.

Vessel is a tube which conducts liquids, as the xylem vessel of a plant or the blood vessel of an animal.

Vestibule is an entryway, as the vestibule of the inner ear at which sound waves enter.

Vestige is an indication of a structure supposed to be formerly more conspicuous in ancestors of the organism having the indication. (L. footprint)

Villikinin (vil′i kī′nin) is a hormone, secreted by the duodenum, which stimulates increased muscular action of intestinal villi. (L. hair, and G. mover)

Villus is a finger-shaped projection of the intestinal wall into the intestinal cavity. (L. hair)

Virus is a schizomycete too small to be seen with a light microscope.

Viscera is the plural of viscus.

Viscus is one of the soft organs of the body, such as the stomach, liver, or lung. The plural is "viscera."

Visual purple is the chemical substance in the retina whose breakdown due to light stimuli is involved in the initiation of a visual nerve impulse.

Vitamin is an organic catalyst of a metabolic reaction which is supplied to the body through the digestive tract. (L. life, and amine)

Vitamin A is a fat-soluble vitamin which is concerned with maintaining the healthy condition of epithelial cells.

Vitamin B is a group of vitamins including thiamin, riboflavin, niacin, pyridoxin, pantothenic acid, folic acid, para-aminobenzoic acid, choline, inositol, and others.

Vitamin C, or ascorbic acid, is a water-soluble vitamin involved in the maintenance of the healthy condition of connective tissue ground substance.

Vitamin D is a fat-soluble vitamin involved in the combination of phosphates and calcium in the formation of bone.

Vitamin E is a fat-soluble vitamin involved in maintaining the health of the reproductive and muscular systems of some animals such as the rat.

Vitamin K is a fat-soluble vitamin involved in blood clotting.

Vitamin P is a mixture of substances supposedly involved in maintaining normal permeability of blood capillaries. Its vitamin status is uncertain.

Vitreous chamber is the cavity of the eyeball between the lens and the retina, containing the vitreous humor.

Vitreous humor is the gelatinous secretion occupying the larger part of the eyeball, between the lens and the retina. (L. glassy liquid)

Vocal cord is a ligament in the larynx connecting the arytenoid and thyroid cartilages.

Vocal membrane is a membrane in the larynx stretching from the arytenoid to the thyroid and cricoid cartilages.

Vocal process is the corner of the arytenoid cartilage to which the vocal cord is attached.

Volvocine Series (vol′vō seen) is the group of Chlorophyceae including *Chlamydomonas, Gonium, Pandorina, Eudorina, Pleodorina,* and *Volvox.*

Volvox is a genus of Chlorophyceae.

Vomer (vō′mur) is a bone separating the floor of the nasal cavity into two parts.

Wave length is the distance between two consecutive wave crests of a vibration, such as wave lengths of sound or of light.

White matter is the portion of the central nervous system in which nerve cell bodies do not occur.

Wisdom tooth is one of the most posterior molar teeth in a human.

Xanthine oxidase (zan′thin ok′si-dās) is an enzyme involved in transferring hydrogen atoms in oxidation processes in cells.

Xanthophyta (zan′thof′i tuh) is the phylum proposed to include Chrysophyceae with yellowish chloroplasts.

X-chromosome is the sex chromosome found in both sexes.

Xylem (zī′lem) is a plant tissue in which water is transported. (G. wood)

Y-chromosome is the sex chromosome found in males only.

Zea (ze′uh) is a genus of monocots, corn.

Zonotrichia (zō nō tri′kē uh) is a genus of sparrows, or birds.

Zoology is the study of animals. (G. study of animals)

Zygote (zī′gōt) is the fertilized egg, a cell formed by the union of an egg and a sperm, or of two like gametes, the beginning of a new individual organism. (G. yoked)

INDEX

INDEX

Page numbers in heavy type refer to basic or principal treatment of an item with several references. Page numbers marked with an asterisk (*) indicate illustrations.